APPLET CORRELATION

Applet	Concept Illustrated	Description	Applet Activity
Random numbers	Uses a random number generator to determine the experimental units to be included in a sample.	Generates random numbers from a range of integers specified by the user.	**1.1**, 21; **1.2**, 25; **3.6**, 175; **4.1**, 195; **4.2**, 195; **4.8**, 247
Sample from a population	Assesses how well a sample represents the population and the role that sample size plays in the process.	Produces random sample from population from specified sample size and population distribution shape. Reports mean, median, and standard deviation; applet creates plot of sample.	**4.4**, 209; **4.6**, 233; **4.7**, 247
Sampling distributions	Compares means and standard deviations of distributions; assesses effect of sample size; illustrates undbiasedness.	Simulates repeatedly choosing samples of a fixed size n from a population with specified sample size, number of samples, and shape of population distribution. Applet reports means, medians, and standard deviations; creates plots for both.	**5.1**, 283; **5.2**, 284
Long-run probability demonstrations illustrate the concept that theoretical probabilities are long-run experimental probabilities.			
Simulating probability of rolling a 6	Investigates relationship between theoretical and experimental probabilities of rolling 6 as number of die rolls increases.	Reports and creates frequency histogram for each outcome of each simulated roll of a fair die. Students specify number of rolls; applet calculates and plots proportion of 6s.	**3.1**, 140; **3.3**, 151; **3.4**, 152; **3.5**, 165
Simulating probability of rolling a 3 or 4	Investigates relationship between theoretical and experimental probabilities of rolling 3 or 4 as number of die rolls increases.	Reports outcome of each simulated roll of a fair die; creates frequency histogram for outcomes. Students specify number of rolls; applet calculates and plots proportion of 3s and 4s.	**3.3**, 151; **3.4**, 152
Simulating the probability of heads: fair coin	Investigates relationship between theoretical and experimental probabilities of getting heads as number of fair coin flips increases.	Reports outcome of each fair coin flip and creates a bar graph for outcomes. Students specify number of flips; applet calculates and plots proportion of heads.	**3.2**, 140; **4.2**, 195
Simulating probability of heads: unfair coin ($P(H) = .2$)	Investigates relationship between theoretical and experimental probabilities of getting heads as number of unfair coin flips increases.	Reports outcome of each flip for a coin where heads is less likely to occur than tails and creates a bar graph for outcomes. Students specify number of flips; applet calculates and plots the proportion of heads.	**4.3**, 209
Simulating probability of heads: unfair coin ($P(H) = .8$)	Investigates relationship between theoretical and experimental probabilities of getting heads as number of unfair coin flips increases.	Reports outcome of each flip for a coin where heads is more likely to occur than tails and creates a bar graph for outcomes. Students specify number of flips; applet calculates and plots the proportion of heads.	**4.3**, 209
Simulating the stock market	Theoretical probabilities are long run experimental probabilities.	Simulates stock market fluctuation. Students specify number of days; applet reports whether stock market goes up or down daily and creates a bar graph for outcomes. Calculates and plots proportion of simulated days stock market goes up.	**4.5**, 210
Mean versus median	Investigates how skewedness and outliers affect measures of central tendency.	Students visualize relationship between mean and median by adding and deleting data points; applet automatically updates mean and median.	**2.1**, 70; **2.2**, 70; **2.3**, 70

(*Continued*)

Applet	Concept Illustrated	Description	Applet Activity
Standard deviation	Investigates how distribution shape and spread affect standard deviation.	Students visualize relationship between mean and standard deviation by adding and deleting data points; applet updates mean and standard deviation.	**2.4**, 77; **2.5**, 78; **2.6**, 78; **2.7**, 98
Confidence intervals for a mean (the impact of confidence level)	Not all confidence intervals contain the population mean. Investigates the meaning of 95% and 99% confidence.	Simulates selecting 100 random samples from population; finds 95% and 99% confidence intervals for each. Students specify sample size, distribution shape, and population mean and standard deviation; applet plots confidence intervals and reports number and proportion containing true mean.	**6.1**, 307; **6.2**, 307
Confidence intervals for a mean (not knowing standard deviation)	Confidence intervals obtained using the sample standard deviation are different from those obtained using the population standard deviation. Investigates effect of not knowing the population standard deviation.	Simulates selecting 100 random samples from the population and finds the 95% z-interval and 95% t-interval for each. Students specify sample size, distribution shape, and population mean and standard deviation; applet plots confidence intervals and reports number and proportion containing true mean.	**6.3**, 317; **6.4**, 317
Confidence intervals for a proportion	Not all confidence intervals contain the population proportion. Investigates the meaning of 95% and 99% confidence.	Simulates selecting 100 random samples from the population and finds the 95% and 99% confidence intervals for each. Students specify population proportion and sample size; applet plots confidence intervals and reports number and proportion containing true proportion.	**6.5**, 324; **6.6**, 324
Hypothesis tests for a mean	Not all tests of hypotheses lead correctly to either rejecting or failing to reject the null hypothesis. Investigates the relationship between the level of confidence and the probabilities of making Type I and Type II errors.	Simulates selecting 100 random samples from population; calculates and plots t statistic and P-value for each. Students specify population distribution shape, mean, and standard deviation; sample size, and null and alternative hypotheses; applet reports number and proportion of times null hypothesis is rejected at both 0.05 and 0.01 levels.	**7.1**, 365; **7.2**, 376; **7.3**, 376; **7.4**, 376
Hypothesis tests for a proportion	Not all tests of hypotheses lead correctly to either rejecting or failing to reject the null hypothesis. Investigates the relationship between the level of confidence and the probabilities of making Type I and Type II errors.	Simulates selecting 100 random samples from population; calculates and plots z-statistic and P-value for each. Students specify population proportion, sample size, and null and alternative hypotheses; applet reports number and proportion of times null hypothesis is rejected at 0.05 and 0.01 levels.	**7.5**, 392; **7.6**, 392
Correlation by eye	Correlation coefficient measures strength of linear relationship between two variables. Teaches user how to assess strength of a linear relationship from a scattergram.	Computes correlation coefficient r for a set of bivariate data plotted on a scattergram. Students add or delete points and guess value of r; applet compares guess to calculated value.	**11.2**, 638
Regression by eye	The least squares regression line has a smaller SSE than any other line that might approximate a set of bivariate data. Teaches students how to approximate the location of a regression line on a scattergram.	Computes least squares regression line for a set of bivariate data plotted on a scattergram. Students add or delete points and guess location of regression line by manipulating a line provided on the scattergram; applet plots least squares line and displays the equations and the SSEs for both lines.	**11.1**, 613

PEARSON ALWAYS LEARNING

James T. McClave • P. George Benson • Terry Sincich

Statistics for Business and Economics

Second Custom Edition for Miami University

Taken from:
Statistics for Business and Economics, Twelfth Edition
by James T. McClave, P. George Benson, and Terry Sincich

Cover Art: PhotoDisc/Getty Images.

Taken from:

Statistics for Business and Economics, Twelfth Edition
by James T. McClave, P. George Benson, and Terry Sincich

This special edition published in cooperation with Pearson Learning Solutions.

Pearson Learning Solutions, 501 Boylston Street, Suite 900, Boston, MA 02116
A Pearson Education Company
www.pearsoned.com

Printed in the United States of America

6 7 8 9 10 V092 16 15

000200010271761323

RH

PEARSON

ISBN 10: 1-269-19838-6
ISBN 13: 978-1-269-19838-7

Contents

Preface

This twelfth edition of *Statistics for Business and Economics* is an introductory text emphasizing inference, with extensive coverage of data collection and analysis as needed to evaluate the reported results of statistical studies and make good decisions. As in earlier editions, the text stresses the development of statistical thinking, the assessment of credibility, and the value of the inferences made from data, both by those who consume and those who produce them. It assumes a mathematical background of basic algebra.

The text incorporates the following features, developed from the American Statistical Association (ASA)–sponsored conferences on *Making Statistics More Effective in Schools of Business* (MSMESB) and the ASA's Guidelines for Assessment and Instruction in Statistics Education (GAISE) Project:

- Emphasize statistical literacy and develop statistical thinking
- Use real data in applications
- Use technology for developing conceptual understanding and analyzing data
- Foster active learning in the classroom
- Stress conceptual understanding rather than mere knowledge of procedures
- Emphasize intuitive concepts of probability

New in the Twelfth Edition

- **More than 1,200 Exercises, with Revisions and Updates to 30 Percent of Them.** Many new and updated exercises, based on contemporary business-related studies and real data, have been added. Most of these exercises foster and promote critical thinking skills.
- **Updated Technology.** All printouts from statistical software (Excel/XLSTAT, SPSS, Minitab, and the TI-84 graphing calculator) and corresponding instructions for use have been revised to reflect the latest versions of the software.
- **New Statistics in Action Cases.** Four of the 14 Statistics in Action cases are new, each based on real data from a recent business study.
- **Continued Emphasis on Ethics.** Where appropriate, boxes have been added emphasizing the importance of ethical behavior when collecting, analyzing, and interpreting data with statistics.

Content-Specific Changes to This Edition

- **Chapter 1 (Statistics, Data, and Statistical Thinking).** Material on all basic sampling concepts (e.g., random sampling and sample survey designs) has been streamlined and moved to Section 1.6 (Collecting Data: Sampling and Related Issues).
- **Chapter 2 (Methods for Describing Sets of Data).** The section on summation notation has been moved to the appendix (Appendix A). Also, recent examples of misleading graphics have been added to Section 2.10 (Distorting the Truth with Descriptive Techniques).
- **Chapter 4 (Random Variables and Probability Distributions).** Use of technology for computing probabilities of random variables with known probability distributions (e.g., binomial, Poisson, normal, and exponential distributions) has been incorporated into the relevant sections of this chapter. Also, the section on approximating a

binomial distribution with a normal distribution has been incorporated into Section 4.6 (The Normal Distribution).

- **Chapter 5 (Sampling Distributions).** Material on the sampling distribution of the sample mean (originally in Part III of Chapter 4) has been moved to create this new chapter. Also, two new sections have been added, Section 5.2 (Properties of Sampling Distributions: Unbiasedness and Minimum Variance) and Section 5.4 (The Sampling Distribution of the Sample Proportion).
- **Chapter 6 (Inferences Based on a Single Sample: Estimation with Confidence Intervals).** An optional section (Section 6.7) on estimating a population variance has been added.
- **Chapter 7 (Inferences Based on a Single Sample: Tests of Hypotheses).** The section on *p*-values in hypothesis testing (Section 7.3) has been moved up to emphasize the importance of their use in business-related studies. Throughout the remainder of the text, conclusions from a test of hypothesis are based on *p*-values.
- **Chapter 10 (Categorical Data Analysis).** A subsection on contingency tables with fixed marginals has been added to Section 10.3.

Hallmark Strengths

We have maintained the pedagogical features of *Statistics for Business and Economics* that we believe make it unique among introductory business statistics texts. These features, which assist the student in achieving an overview of statistics and an understanding of its relevance in both the business world and everyday life, are as follows:

- **Use of Examples as a Teaching Device** Almost all new ideas are introduced and illustrated by data-based applications and examples. We believe that students better understand definitions, generalizations, and theoretical concepts *after* seeing an application. All examples have three components: (1) Problem, (2) Solution, and (3) Look Back (or Look Ahead). This step-by-step process provides students with a defined structure by which to approach problems and enhances their problem-solving skills. The Look Back/Look Ahead feature often gives helpful hints to solving the problem and/or provides a further reflection or insight into the concept or procedure that is covered.
- **Now Work Exercises** A *Now Work* exercise suggestion follows most examples. The *Now Work* exercise (marked with the NW icon in the exercise sets) is similar in style and concept to the text example. This provides the student with an opportunity to immediately test and confirm his or her understanding.
- **Real Data-Based Exercises** The text includes more than 1,200 exercises based on applications in a variety of business disciplines and research areas. All the applied exercises employ the use of current real data extracted from current publications (e.g., newspapers, magazines, journals, and the Internet). Some students have difficulty learning the mechanics of statistical techniques when all problems are couched in terms of realistic applications. For this reason, we have six types of exercises:

  Learning the Mechanics. Designed as straightforward applications of new concepts, these exercises allow students to test their ability to comprehend a mathematical concept or a definition.

  Applying the Concepts—Basic. Based on applications taken from a wide variety of business journals, newspapers, and other sources, these short exercises help students begin developing the skills necessary to diagnose and analyze real-world problems.

  Applying the Concepts—Intermediate. Based on more detailed real-world applications, these exercises require students to apply their knowledge of the technique presented in the section.

Applying the Concepts—Advanced. These more difficult real-data exercises require students to utilize their critical thinking skills.

Critical Thinking Challenges. Placed at the end of the Supplementary Exercises section only, students are presented with one or two challenging business problems.

Applet Exercises. In addition to the six types of exercises, we also have exercises based on the applets (short JAVA computer programs) included on the CD, which accompanies the text. These point-and-click applets allow students to easily run simulations that visually demonstrate some of the more difficult statistical concepts (e.g., sampling distributions and confidence intervals). Most chapters contain several optional applet exercises in the exercise sets. They are denoted with the following Applet icon.

- **Statistics in Action Cases** Each chapter begins with a case study based on an actual contemporary, controversial, or high-profile issue in business. Relevant research questions and data from the study are presented and the proper analysis demonstrated in short *Statistics in Action Revisited* sections throughout the chapter. These motivate students to critically evaluate the findings and think through the statistical issues involved.
- **Making Business Decisions Cases** Seven extensive real-world business problem-solving cases, with real data and assignments for the student, serve as a good capstone and review of the material that precedes it. Typically, these cases follow two or three chapters and require the student to apply the methods presented in these chapters.
- **Hands-On Activities** At the end of each chapter, students are provided with an opportunity to participate in hands-on classroom activities, ranging from real data collection to formal statistical analysis. These Activities are designed to be performed by students individually or as a class.
- **Biographies** Brief descriptions of famous statisticians and their achievements are presented in side boxes. With these profiles, students will develop an appreciation of the statistician's efforts and the discipline of statistics as a whole.
- **Exploring Data with Statistical Software** Each statistical analysis method presented is demonstrated using output from Excel/XLSTAT, SPSS, Minitab, and the TI-84 graphing calculator. Students are exposed early and often to computer printouts they will encounter in today's high-tech business world.
- **Using Technology Tutorials** At the end of each chapter are statistical software tutorials with point-and-click instructions (with screen shots) for Minitab, SPSS, and Excel/XLSTAT. These tutorials are easily located and show students how to best use and maximize statistical software. In addition, output and keystroke instructions for the TI-84 graphing calculator are presented.
- **Data and Applet CD** The text is accompanied by a resource CD that contains files for all of the data sets marked with a CD icon in the text. These include data sets for text examples, exercises, Statistics in Action, and Making Business Decisions. All data files are saved in multiple formats. This CD also contains the applets that are used to illustrate statistical concepts and Chapter 13 (Methods for Quality Improvement: Statistical Process Control), Chapter 14 (Descriptive Analyses, Models, and Forecasting), and Chapter 15 (Nonparametric Statistics).

Flexibility in Coverage

The text is written to allow the instructor flexibility in coverage of topics. Suggestions for two topics, probability and regression, are given below.

- **Probability and Counting Rules** One of the most troublesome aspects of an introductory statistics course is the study of probability. Probability poses a challenge for instructors because they must decide on the level of presentation, and students find it a difficult subject to comprehend. We believe that one cause for these problems is the mixture of probability and counting rules that occurs in most introductory texts. Consequently, we have included the counting rules (with examples) in an appendix (Appendix B) rather than in the body of Chapter 3. Thus, the instructor can control the level of coverage of probability covered.

- **Multiple Regression and Model Building** This topic represents one of the most useful statistical tools for the solution of applied problems. Although an entire text could be devoted to regression modeling, we believe that we have presented coverage that is understandable, usable, and much more comprehensive than the presentations in other introductory statistics texts. We devote two full chapters to discussing the major types of inferences that can be derived from a regression analysis, showing how these results appear in the output from statistical software, and, most important, selecting multiple regression models to be used in an analysis. Thus, the instructor has the choice of a one-chapter coverage of simple linear regression (Chapter 11), a two-chapter treatment of simple and multiple regression (excluding the sections on model building in Chapter 12), or complete coverage of regression analysis, including model building and regression diagnostics. This extensive coverage of such useful statistical tools will provide added evidence to the student of the relevance of statistics to real-world problems.
- **Role of Calculus in Footnotes** Although the text is designed for students with a noncalculus background, footnotes explain the role of calculus in various derivations. Footnotes are also used to inform the student about some of the theory underlying certain methods of analysis. These footnotes allow additional flexibility in the mathematical and theoretical levels at which the material is presented.

Supplements

Student Resources

Student's Solutions Manual, by Nancy Boudreau (Bowling Green State University), provides detailed, worked-out solutions to all odd-numbered text exercises. (ISBN-10: 0-321-82629-9; ISBN-13: 978-0-321-82629-9)

Excel Technology Manual, by Mark Dummeldinger (University of South Florida), provides tutorial instruction and worked-out text examples for Excel. The *Excel Technology Manual* is available for download at pearsonhighered.com/mathstatresrouces or within MyStatLab.

Business Insight Videos. This series of ten 4- to 7-minute videos, each about a well-known business and the challenges it faces, focuses on statistical concepts as they pertain to the real world. The videos can be downloaded from within MyStatLab. Assessment questions to check students' understanding of the videos and answers are available. Contact your Pearson representative for details.

Study Cards for Business Statistics Software. This series of study cards, available for Excel® with XLSTAT™, Excel® 2010, Minitab®, JMP®, SPSS®, R®, StatCrunch™, and TI-83/84 graphing calculators, provides students with easy, step-by-step guides to the most common business statistics software. Available at www.myPearsonStore.com.

For the Instructor

Annotated Instructor's Edition contains answers to text exercises. Annotated marginal notes include Teaching Tips, suggested exercises to reinforce the statistical concepts discussed in the text, and short answers to the exercises within the exercise sets. (ISBN-10:0-321-82642-6; ISBN-13: 978-0-321-82642-8)

Instructor's Solutions Manual, by Nancy Boudreau (Bowling Green State University), provides detailed, worked-out solutions to all of the book's exercises. Careful attention has been paid to ensure that all methods of solution and notation are consistent with those used in the core text. Available for download at www.pearsonhighered.com/irc.

TestGen® (www.pearsonhighered.com/testgen) enables instructors to build, edit, print, and administer tests using a computerized bank of questions developed to cover all the objectives of the text. TestGen is algorithmically based, allowing instructors to create multiple but equivalent versions of the same question or test with the click of a button. Instructors can also modify test bank questions or add new questions. Tests can be printed or administered online. The software and test bank are available for download from Pearson Education's online catalog (www.pearsonhighered.com/irc).

Technology Resources

On the Companion CD-ROM:

- Data sets in multiple formats for text examples, exercises, Statistics in Action, and Making Business Decisions
- Applets
- Chapter 13: Methods for Quality Improvement: Statistical Process Control
- Chapter 14: Descriptive Analyses, Models, and Forecasting
- Chapter 15: Nonparametric Statistics

MyStatLab™ Online Course (access code required)
MyStatLab is a course management system that delivers **proven results** in helping individual students succeed.

- MyStatLab can be successfully implemented in any environment—lab-based, hybrid, fully online, traditional—and demonstrates the quantifiable difference that integrated usage has on student retention, subsequent success, and overall achievement.
- MyStatLab's comprehensive online gradebook automatically tracks students' results on tests, quizzes, homework, and in the study plan. Instructors can use the gradebook to provide positive feedback or intervene if students have trouble. Gradebook data can be easily exported to a variety of spreadsheet programs, such as Microsoft Excel. You can determine which points of data you want to export, and then analyze the results to determine success.

MyStatLab provides **engaging experiences** that personalize, stimulate, and measure learning for each student. In addition to the resources below, each course includes a full interactive online version of the accompanying textbook.

- ***Tutorial Exercises with Multimedia Learning Aids:*** The homework and practice exercises in MyStatLab align with the exercises in the textbook, and they regenerate algorithmically to give students unlimited opportunity for practice and mastery. Exercises offer immediate helpful feedback, guided solutions, sample problems, animations, videos, and eText clips for extra help at point-of-use.
- ***StatTalk Videos:*** *24 Conceptual Videos to Help You Actually Understand Statistics.* Fun-loving statistician Andrew Vickers takes to the streets of Brooklyn, NY, to demonstrate important statistical concepts through interesting stories and real-life events. These fun and engaging videos will help students actually understand statistical concepts. Available with an instructors user guide and assessment questions.
- ***Getting Ready for Statistics:*** A library of questions now appears within each MyStatLab course to offer the developmental math topics students need for the course.

These can be assigned as a prerequisite to other assignments, if desired.

- ***Conceptual Question Library:*** In addition to algorithmically regenerated questions that are aligned with your textbook, there is a library of one thousand Conceptual Questions available in the assessment manager that require students to apply their statistical understanding.
- ***StatCrunch™:*** MyStatLab integrates the Web-based statistical software, StatCrunch, within the online assessment platform so that students can easily analyze data sets from exercises and the text. In addition, MyStatLab includes access to www.StatCrunch.com, a Web site where users can access more than 15,000 shared data sets, conduct online surveys, perform complex analyses using the powerful statistical software, and generate compelling reports.
- ***Statistical Software Support:*** Knowing that students often use external statistical software, we make it easy to copy our data sets, both from the ebook and the MyStatLab questions, into software such as StatCrunch, Minitab, Excel, and more. Students have access to a variety of support tools—Technology Tutorial Videos, Technology Study Cards, and Technology Manuals for select titles—to learn how to effectively use statistical software.
- ***Expert Tutoring:*** Although many students describe the whole of MyStatLab as "like having your own personal tutor," students also have access to live tutoring from Pearson. Qualified statistics instructors provide tutoring sessions for students via MyStatLab.

And MyStatLab comes from a **trusted partner** with educational expertise and an eye on the future.

- Knowing that you are using a Pearson product means knowing that you are using quality content. That means that our eTexts are accurate and our assessment tools work. Whether you are just getting started with MyStatLab, or have a question along the way, we're here to help you learn about our technologies and how to incorporate them into your course. To learn more about how MyStatLab combines proven learning applications with powerful assessment, visit www.mystatlab.com or contact your Pearson representative.

MyStatLab™ Ready to Go Course (access code required)

These new Ready to Go courses provide students with all the same great MyStatLab features that you're used to, but make it easier for instructors to get started. Each course includes pre-assigned homeworks and quizzes to make creating your course even simpler. Ask your Pearson representative about the details for this particular course or to see a copy of this course.

MathXL® for Statistics Online Course (access code required)

MathXL® is the homework and assessment engine that runs MyStatLab. (MyStatLab is MathXL plus a learning management system.)

With MathXL for Statistics, instructors can:

- Create, edit, and assign online homework and tests using algorithmically generated exercises correlated at the objective level to the textbook.
- Create and assign their own online exercises and import TestGen tests for added flexibility.
- Maintain records of all student work, tracked in MathXL's online gradebook.

With MathXL for Statistics, students can:

- Take chapter tests in MathXL and receive personalized study plans and/or personalized homework assignments based on their test results.
- Use the study plan and/or the homework to link directly to tutorial exercises for the objectives they need to study.
- Students can also access supplemental animations and video clips directly from selected exercises.
- Knowing that students often use external statistical software, we make it easy to copy our data sets, both from the ebook and the MyStatLab questions, into software like StatCrunch™, Minitab, Excel and more.

MathXL for Statistics is available to qualified adopters. For more information, visit our Web site at www.mathxl.com or contact your Pearson representative.

StatCrunch™

StatCrunch is powerful Web-based statistical software that allows users to perform complex analyses, share data sets, and generate compelling reports of their data. The vibrant online community offers more than 15,000 data sets for students to analyze.

- **Collect.** Users can upload their own data to StatCrunch or search a large library of publicly shared data sets, spanning almost any topic of interest. Also, an online survey tool allows users to quickly collect data via Web-based surveys.
- **Crunch.** A full range of numerical and graphical methods allows users to analyze and gain insights from any data set. Interactive graphics help users understand statistical concepts, and are available for export to enrich reports with visual representations of data.
- **Communicate.** Reporting options help users create a wide variety of visually appealing representations of their data.

Full access to StatCrunch is available with a MyStatLab kit, and StatCrunch is available by itself to qualified adopters. StatCrunch Mobile now available to access from your mobile device. For more information, visit our Web site at www.StatCrunch.com or contact your Pearson representative.

StatCrunch™ eBook

This interactive online textbook includes StatCrunch, a powerful Web-based statistical software. Embedded StatCrunch buttons allow users to open all data sets and tables from the book with the click of a button and immediately perform an analysis using StatCrunch.

PowerPoint® Lecture Slides provide an outline to use in a lecture setting, presenting definitions, key concepts, and figures from the text. These slides are available within MyStatLab or at www.pearsonhighered.com/irc.

The Student Edition of Minitab® is a condensed edition of the professional release of Minitab statistical software. It offers the full range of statistical methods and graphical capabilities, along with worksheets that can include up to 10,000 data points. Individual copies of the software can be bundled with the text. (ISBN-10: 0-321-11313-6; ISBN-13: 978-0-321-11313-9)

JMP Student Edition is an easy-to-use, streamlined version of JMP desktop statistical discovery software from AS Institute, Inc., and is available for bundling with the text. (ISBN-10: 0-321-89164-3; ISBN-13: 978-0-321-89164-8)

XLSTAT™ for Pearson. Used by leading businesses and universities, XLSTAT is an Excel® add-in that offers a wide variety of functions to enhance the analytical capabilities of Microsoft® Excel® making it the ideal tool for your everyday data analysis and statistics requirements. XLSTAT™ is compatible with all Excel versions (except Mac 2008). Available for bundling with the text. (ISBN-10: 0-321-75932-X; ISBN-13: 978-0-321-75932-0)

Acknowledgments

This book reflects the efforts of a great many people over a number of years. First, we would like to thank the following professors, whose reviews and comments on this and prior editions have contributed to the twelfth edition:

Reviewers of the Twelfth Edition of *Statistics for Business and Economics*

Christine Ebert	*University of Delaware*
Laura Reisert	*Florida International University*
Bernard Dickman	*Hofstra University*
Daniel Sirvent	*Vanguard University*
Arunas Dagys	*St. Xavier University*
Rick Gibson	*American University*
L. Douglas Smith	*University of Missouri–St. Louis*
Karen Smith	*West Georgia University*
Remus Osan	*Boston University*
Steve Huchendorf	*University of Minnesota*

Reviewers of Previous Editions

CALIFORNIA Joyce Curley-Daly, Jim Daly, Robert K. Smidt, *California Polytechnic State University* • Jim Davis, *Golden Gate University* • Carol Eger, *Stanford University* • Paul W. Guy, *California State University, Chico* • Judd Hammack, P. Kasliwal, *California State University, Los Angeles* • Mabel T. King, *California State University, Fullerton* • James Lackritz, *California State University, San Diego* • Beth Rose, *University of Southern California* COLORADO Rick L. Edgeman, Charles F. Warnock, *Colorado State University* • Eric Huggins, *Fort Lewis College* • William J. Weida, *United States Air Force Academy* CONNECTICUT Alan E. Gelfand, Joseph Glaz, Timothy J. Killeen, *University of Connecticut* DISTRICT OF COLUMBIA Phil Cross, Jose Luis Guerrero-Cusumano, *Georgetown University* • Gaminie Meepagala, *Howard University* FLORIDA John M. Charnes, *University of Miami* • C. Brad Davis, *Clearwater Christian College* • Fred Leysieffer, Pi-Erh Lin, Doug Zahn, *Florida State University* • P. V. Rao, *University of Florida* • Jeffrey W. Steagall, *University of North Florida* • Edna White, *Florida Atlantic University* GEORGIA Robert Elrod, *Georgia State University* HAWAII Steve Hora, *University of Hawaii, Hilo* ILLINOIS Edward Minieka, *University of Illinois at Chicago* • Don Robinson, *Illinois State University* • Chipei Tseng, *Northern Illinois University* • Pankaj Vaish, *Arthur Andersen & Company* IOWA Dileep Dhavale, *University of Northern Iowa* • William Duckworth II, William Q. Meeker, *Iowa State University* • Tim E. McDaniel, *Buena Vista University* KANSAS Paul I. Nelson, *Kansas State University* • Lawrence A. Sherr, *University of Kansas* KENTUCKY Richard N. McGrath, *Bowling Green State University* LOUISIANA James Willis, *Louisiana State University* MARYLAND John F. Beyers, Michael Kulansky, *University of Maryland–University College* • Glenn J. Browne, Mary C. Christman, *University of Maryland* MASSACHUSETTS Warren M. Holt, *Southeastern Massachusetts University* MICHIGAN Atul Agarwal, Petros Ioannatos, *GMI Engineering and Management Institute* • Richard W. Andrews, Peter Lenk, Benjamin Lev, *University of Michigan* • Leszek Gawarecki, *Kettering University* • Toni M. Somers, *Wayne State University* • William Welch, *Saginaw Valley State University* • T. J. Wharton, *Oakland University* MINNESOTA Gordon J. Alexander, Donald W. Bartlett, David M. Bergman, Atul Bhatia, Benny Lo, Karen Lundquist, Vijay Pisharody, Donald N. Steinnes, Robert W. Van Cleave, Steve Wickstrom, *University of Minnesota* • Daniel G. Brick, Leigh Lawton, *University of St. Thomas* • Susan Flach, *General Mills, Inc.* • David D. Krueger, Ruth K. Meyer, Jan Saraph, Gary Yoshimoto, *St. Cloud State University* • Paula M. Oas,

General Office Products • Fike Zahroom, *Moorhead State University* **MISSISSIPPI** Eddie M. Lewis, *University of Southern Mississippi* • Alireza Tahai, *Mississippi State University* **MISSOURI** James Holstein, Lawrence D. Ries, *University of Missouri, Columbia* • Marius Janson, *University of Missouri, St. Louis* • Farroll Tim Wright, *University of Missouri* **NEBRASKA** James Wright, *Chadron State College* **NEW HAMPSHIRE** Ken Constantine, *University of New Hampshire* **NEW JERSEY** Lewis Coopersmith, Cengiz Haksever, *Rider University* • Lei Lei, Xuan Li, Zina Taran, *Rutgers University* • Philip Levine, Leonard Presby, *William Paterson University* **NEW MEXICO** S. Howard Kraye, *University of New Mexico* **NEW YORK** James Czachor, *Fordham-Lincoln Center, AT&T* • Bernard Dickman, *Hofstra University* • Joshua Fogel, *Brooklyn College of City University of New York* • Martin Labbe, *State University of New York, College at New Paltz* • Kenneth Leong, *College of New Rochelle* • Mark R. Marino, *Niagara University/Erie Community College* • G. E. Martin, *Clarkson University* • Thomas J. Pfaff, *Ithaca College* • Gary Simon, *New York University, Stern School of Business* • Rungrudee Suetorsak, *SUNY-Fredonia* **NORTH CAROLINA** Golam Azam, *North Carolina Agricultural & Technical University* • Edward Carlstein, Douglas A. Elvers, *University of North Carolina at Chapel Hill* • Barry P. Cuffe, *Wingate University* • Don Holbert, *East Carolina University* • J. Morgan Jones, *University of North Carolina* • Douglas S. Shafer, *University of North Carolina, Charlotte* **OHIO** William H. Beyer, *University of Akron* • Michael Broida, Tim Krehbiel, *Miami University of Ohio* • Chih-Hsu Cheng, Douglas A. Wolfe, *Ohio State University* • Ronald L. Coccari, *Cleveland State University* • Richard W. Culp, *Wright-Patterson AFB, Air Force Institute of Technology* **OKLAHOMA** Larry Claypool, Brenda Masters, Rebecca Moore, *Oklahoma State University* • Robert Curley, *University of Central Oklahoma* **PENNSYLVANIA** Mohammed Albohali, Douglas H. Frank, *Indiana University of Pennsylvania* • Sukhwinder Bagi, *Bloomsburg University* • Carl Bedell, *Philadelphia College of Textiles and Science* • Ann Hussein, *Philadelphia University* • Behnam Nakhai, *Millersville University* • Rose Prave, *University of Scranton* • Farhad Saboori, *Albright College* • Kathryn Szabet, *LaSalle University* • Christopher J. Zappe, *Bucknell University* **SOUTH CAROLINA** Iris Fetta, Robert Ling, *Clemson University* • Kathleen M. Whitcomb, *University of South Carolina* **TENNESSEE** Francis J. Brewerton, *Middle Tennessee State University* **TEXAS** Larry M. Austin, *Texas Tech University* • Jim Branscome, Robert W. Brobst, Mark Eakin, Grace Esimai, Michael E. Hanna, Craig W. Slinkman, *University of Texas at Arlington* • Katarina Jegdic, *University of Houston–Downtown* • Virgil F. Stone, *Texas A & M University* **VIRGINIA** Edward R. Clayton, *Virginia Polytechnic Institute and State University* **WASHINGTON** June Morita, Kim Tamura, *University of Washington* **WISCONSIN** Ross H. Johnson, *Madison College* **WASHINGTON, D.C.** Keith Ord, *Georgetown University* **CANADA** Clarence Bayne, *Concordia University* • Edith Gombay, *University of Alberta* **TURKEY** Dilek Onkal, *Bilkent University, Ankara* **OTHER** Michael P. Wegmann, *Keller Graduate School of Management*

Other Contributors

Special thanks are due to our supplements authors, Nancy Boudreau and Mark Dummeldinger, who have worked with us for many years. C. Brad Davis provided the excellent student activities and applet exercises, while accuracy checkers Cathleen Zucco-Teveloff and Engin Sungur helped ensure a highly accurate, clean text. The source material for many of the interesting and updated data-based exercises was provided by student researchers Demelza Hays and Charles Favreau. Finally, the Pearson Education staff of Deirdre Lynch, Marianne Stepanian, Tracy Patruno, Chere Bemelmans, Dana Bettez, Sonia Ashraf, Erin Lane, Kathleen DeChavez, Barbara Atkinson, Marielle Guiney, Jean Choe, Linda Cox, Ginny Michaud, and Integra-Chicago's Amanda Zagnoli helped greatly with all phases of the text development, production, and marketing effort.

[illegible] • Ellen Zaborowski, [illegible] State University MISSISSIPPI Eddie [illegible], University of Southern Mississippi • [illegible], Mississippi State University MISSOURI James Holstrom, [illegible] Ross, University of Missouri, Columbia • Martin Jansen, University of Missouri, St. Louis • [illegible]. Tim Wright, University of Missouri NEBRASKA James Wright, [illegible] State College [illegible] • Constantine [illegible], University of New Hampshire • Lewis Copeland, [illegible] Holt [illegible] University • [illegible] University [illegible] • [illegible] Irving [illegible] Presley, [illegible] University NEW MEXICO [illegible] University of New Mexico NEW YORK [illegible] Community College • Bernard [illegible], [illegible] University • Joshua [illegible], Brooklyn College, City University of New York • Martin [illegible], [illegible] College • [illegible] Pattz • Kenneth Leong, College of New Rochelle • [illegible] Marino, Niagara County Community College • [illegible] Martin, [illegible] University • Timothy J. Pratt, [illegible] College • [illegible] Shupe, [illegible] University • Jim [illegible] • [illegible] SUNY-Fredonia NORTH CAROLINA Colton A. [illegible], North Carolina Agricultural & Technical University • [illegible] Carlsson, [illegible] University of North Carolina at Charlotte • [illegible], [illegible] University • Don Holler, East [illegible] University • [illegible] University of North Carolina • Donald [illegible] University of North Carolina [illegible] OHIO William [illegible], [illegible] • Michael Brooks, Tim Keller, Miami University of Ohio • [illegible] • Daniel A. Wolfe, Ohio State University • Ronald [illegible], [illegible] State University • Richard W. [illegible], Wright-Patterson AFB, Air Force Institute of Technology OKLAHOMA Larry Claypool [illegible] • [illegible], Oklahoma State University • [illegible] University • [illegible] • [illegible] PENNSYLVANIA [illegible] • Carl Bedell, Philadelphia University • [illegible], [illegible] Philadelphia University • [illegible] • [illegible], [illegible] University • Patrick [illegible] • Kathryn [illegible] • [illegible] J. [illegible], Bucknell University SOUTH CAROLINA [illegible] University • [illegible] Kathleen M. Whitcomb, University of South Carolina TENNESSEE [illegible], [illegible] State University • Larry M. [illegible] • [illegible] • Jim [illegible] • Robert W. Brown, Mark [illegible] • [illegible] Sunkara, University of Texas at Arlington • Katrina [illegible] University • [illegible] • Virgil [illegible] • Edward R. Clayton, Virginia Polytechnic Institute and State University WASHINGTON June Marina Kim [illegible], University of Washington • [illegible] WASHINGTON, D.C. Keith Ord, Georgetown University • [illegible] Lawrence Barnes, [illegible] University • [illegible] • Dick Onuf, [illegible] WISCONSIN Michael P. Wegmann, Keller Graduate School of Management

Other Contributors

Special thanks to the [illegible] supplements authors: Nancy Hood [illegible] Mark [illegible], who have worked with us for many years. [illegible] provided the excellent student solutions manual, [illegible] checked [illegible] [illegible] and [illegible] a [illegible] [illegible] for [illegible] and updated [illegible] was provided by student researchers [illegible]. Finally, the [illegible] of [illegible] Leach, [illegible] [illegible], [illegible] and [illegible] Manelle [illegible], [illegible] Jean [illegible] helped greatly in all phases of the [illegible] development [illegible] production [illegible] effort.

11

CONTENTS

Where We've Been

- Presented methods for estimating and testing population parameters
- Developed a test for relating two qualitative variables

Where We're Going

- Introduce the straight-line (*simple linear regression*) model as a means of relating one quantitative variable to another quantitative variable (11.1)
- Assess how well the simple linear regression model fits the sample data (11.2–11.4)
- Introduce the *correlation coefficient* as a means of relating one quantitative variable to another quantitative variable (11.5)
- Employ the simple linear regression model for predicting the value of one variable from a specified value of another variable (11.6–11.7)

Simple Linear Regression

STATISTICS in ACTION Legal Advertising—Does It Pay?

According to the American Bar Association, there are over 1 million lawyers competing for your business. To gain a competitive edge, these lawyers aggressively advertise their services. The advertising of legal services has long been a controversial subject, with many believing that it constitutes an unethical (and in some cases even illegal) practice. Nonetheless, legal advertisements appear in nearly all media, ranging from the covers of telephone directories to infomercials on television, as well as a significant presence on the Internet. In fact, Erickson Marketing, Inc., reports that "attorneys are the #1 category of advertising in the Yellow Pages."

For this *Statistics in Action,* we present an actual recent case involving two former law partners. One partner (A) sued the other (B) over who should pay what share of the expenses of their former partnership. Partner A handled personal injury (PI) cases, while partner B handled only worker's compensation (WC) cases. The firm's advertising was focused on personal injury only, but partner A claimed that the ads resulted in the firm getting more WC cases for partner B, and therefore partner B should share the advertising expenses.

Table SIA11.1 shows the firm's new PI and WC cases each month over a 48-month period for this partnership. Also shown is the total expenditure on advertising each month and over the previous 6 months. Do these data provide support for the hypothesis that increased advertising expenditures are associated with more PI cases? With more WC cases? If advertising expenditures have a statistically significant association with the number of cases, does this necessarily mean that there is a causal relationship, that is, that spending more on advertising causes an increase in the number of cases? Based on these data, should partner A or partner B bear the brunt of the advertising expenditures?

STATISTICS in ACTION CONTINUED

Table SIA11.1 Legal Advertising Data

Month	Advertising Expenditure ($)	New PI Cases	New WC Cases	6 Months Cumulative Adv. Exp. ($)
1	9,221.55	7	26	n/a
2	6,684.00	9	33	n/a
3	200.00	12	18	n/a
4	14,546.75	27	15	n/a
5	5,170.14	9	19	n/a
6	5,810.30	13	26	n/a
7	5,816.20	11	24	41,632.74
8	8,236.38	7	22	38,227.39
9	−2,089.55	13	12	39,779.77
10	29,282.24	7	15	37,490.22
11	9,193.58	9	21	52,225.71
12	9,499.18	8	24	56,249.15
13	11,128.76	18	25	59,938.03
14	9,057.64	9	19	65,250.59
15	13,604.54	25	12	66,071.85
16	14,411.76	26	33	81,765.94
17	13,724.28	27	32	66,895.46
18	13,419.42	12	21	71,426.16
19	17,372.33	14	18	75,346.40
20	6,296.35	5	25	81,589.97
21	13,191.59	22	12	78,828.68
22	26,798.80	15	7	78,415.73
23	18,610.95	12	22	90,802.77
24	829.53	18	27	95,689.44
25	16,976.53	20	25	83,099.55
26	14,076.98	38	26	82,703.75
27	24,791.75	13	28	90,484.38
28	9,691.25	18	31	102,084.54
29	28,948.25	21	40	84,976.99
30	21,373.52	7	39	95,314.29
31	9,675.25	16	41	115,858.28
32	33,213.55	12	48	108,557.00
33	19,859.85	15	28	127,693.57
34	10,475.25	18	29	122,761.67
35	24,790.84	30	20	123,545.67
36	36,660.94	12	27	119,388.26
37	8,812.50	30	26	134,675.68
38	41,817.75	20	45	133,812.93
39	27,399.33	19	30	142,417.13
40	25,723.10	29	33	149,956.61
41	16,312.10	58	24	165,204.46
42	26,332.78	42	40	156,725.72
43	60,207.58	24	36	146,397.56
44	42,485.39	47	29	197,792.64
45	35,601.92	24	17	198,460.28
46	72,071.50	14	13	206,662.87
47	12,797.11	31	15	253,011.27
48	12,310.50	26	16	249,496.28

Source: Info Tech, Inc.

Data Set: LEGADV

The data for the case are saved in the **LEGADV** file. In the *Statistics in Action Revisited* sections of this chapter, we examine the relationship between monthly advertising expenditure and the number of new legal cases in an attempt to answer these questions.

STATISTICS in ACTION REVISITED

- Estimating a Straight-Line Regression Model **(p. 612)**
- Assessing How Well a Straight-Line Regression Model Fits Data **(p. 627)**
- Using the Coefficient of Correlation and the Coefficient of Determination **(p. 637)**
- Prediction Using the Straight-Line Model **(p. 645)**

In Chapters 6–9, we described methods for making inferences about population means. The mean of a population was treated as a *constant*, and we showed how to use sample data to estimate or to test hypotheses about this constant mean. In many applications, the mean of a population is not viewed as a constant but rather as a variable. For example, the mean sale price of residences sold this year in a large city might be treated as a variable that depends on the square feet of living space in the residence. For example, the relationship might be

$$\text{Mean sale price} = \$30{,}000 + \$60\ (\text{square feet})$$

This formula implies that the mean sale price of 1,000-square-foot homes is \$90,000, the mean sale price of 2,000-square-foot homes is \$150,000, and the mean sale price of 3,000-square-foot homes is \$210,000.

In this chapter, we discuss situations in which the mean of the population is treated as a variable, dependent on the value of another variable. The dependence of residential sale price on the square feet of living space is one illustration. Other examples include the dependence of mean sales revenue of a firm on advertising expenditure, the dependence of mean starting salary of a college graduate on the student's GPA, and the dependence of mean monthly production of automobiles on the total number of sales in the previous month.

We begin our discussion with the simplest of all models relating a population mean to another variable—*the straight-line model.* We show how to use the sample data to estimate the straight-line relationship between the mean value of one variable, y, as it relates to a second variable, x. The methodology of estimating and using a straight-line relationship is referred to as *simple linear regression analysis.*

11.1 Probabilistic Models

An important consideration in merchandising a product is the amount of money spent on advertising. Suppose you want to model the monthly sales revenue of an appliance store as a function of the monthly advertising expenditure. The first question to be answered is this: "Do you think an exact relationship exists between these two variables?" That is, do you think it is possible to state the exact monthly sales revenue if the amount spent on advertising is known? We think you will agree with us that this is *not* possible for several reasons. Sales depend on many variables other than advertising expenditure—for example, time of year, the state of the general economy, inventory, and price structure. Even if many variables are included in a model (the topic of Chapter 12), it is still unlikely that we would be able to predict the monthly sales *exactly.* There will almost certainly be some variation in monthly sales due strictly to *random phenomena* that cannot be modeled or explained.

If we were to construct a model that hypothesized an exact relationship between variables, it would be called a **deterministic model.** For example, if we believe that y, the monthly sales revenue, will be exactly 15 times x, the monthly advertising expenditure, we write

$$y = 15x$$

This represents a *deterministic relationship* between the variables y and x. It implies that y can always be determined exactly when the value of x is known. *There is no allowance for error in this prediction.*

If, on the other hand, we believe there will be unexplained variation in monthly sales—perhaps caused by important but unincluded variables or by random phenomena—we discard the deterministic model and use a model that accounts for this **random error.** This **probabilistic model** includes both a deterministic component and a random error component. For example, if we hypothesize that the sales y are related to advertising expenditure x by

$$y = 15x + \text{Random error}$$

General Form of Probabilistic Models

$$y = \text{Deterministic component} + \text{Random error}$$

where y is the variable of interest. We always assume that the mean value of the random error equals 0. This is equivalent to assuming that the mean value of y, $E(y)$, equals the deterministic component of the model; that is,

$$E(y) = \text{Deterministic component}$$

we are hypothesizing a *probabilistic relationship* between y and x. Note that the deterministic component of this probabilistic model is $15x$.

Figure 11.1a shows the possible values of y and x for five different months, when the model is deterministic. All the pairs of (x, y) data points must fall exactly on the line because a deterministic model leaves no room for error.

Figure 11.1b shows a possible set of points for the same values of x when we are using a probabilistic model. Note that the deterministic part of the model (the straight line itself) is the same. Now, however, the inclusion of a random error component allows the monthly sales to vary from this line. Because we know that the sales revenue does vary randomly for a given value of x, the probabilistic model provides a more realistic model for y than does the deterministic model.

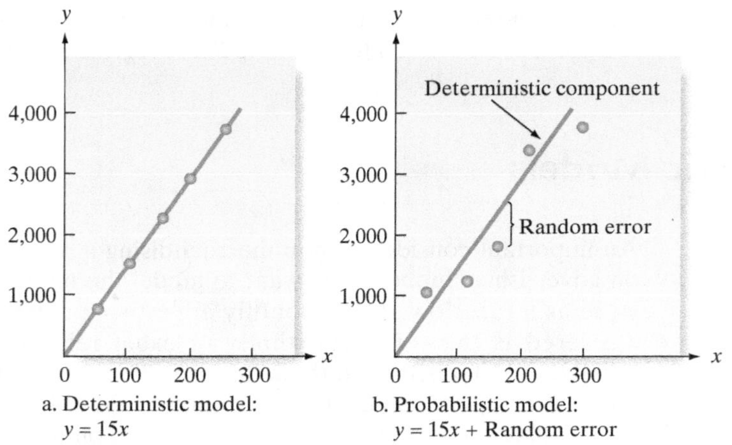

Figure 11.1
Possible sales revenues, y, for five different months, x

In this chapter, we present the simplest of probabilistic models—the **straight-line model**—which derives its name from the fact that the deterministic portion of the model graphs as a straight line. Fitting this model to a set of data is an example of **regression analysis,** or **regression modeling.** The elements of the straight-line model are summarized in the next box.

A First-Order (Straight-Line) Probabilistic Model

$$y = \beta_0 + \beta_1 x + \varepsilon$$

where

y = **Dependent** *or* **response variable** (variable to be modeled)

x = **Independent** *or* **predictor variable** (variable used as a predictor of y)*

$E(y) = \beta_0 + \beta_1 x$ = Deterministic component

ε (epsilon) = Random error component

β_0 (beta zero) = ***y*-intercept of the line,** that is, the point at which the line *intercepts or cuts through the y*-axis (see Figure 11.2)

*The word *independent* should not be interpreted in a probabilistic sense, as defined in Chapter 3. The phrase *independent variable* is used in regression analysis to refer to a predictor variable for the response y.

β_1 (beta one) = **Slope of the line,** that is, the change (amount of increase or decrease) in the deterministic component of y for every 1-unit increase in x

[*Note:* A *positive* slope implies that $E(y)$ *increases* by the amount β_1 for each unit increase in x (see Figure 11.2). A *negative* slope implies that $E(y)$ *decreases* by the amount β_1.]

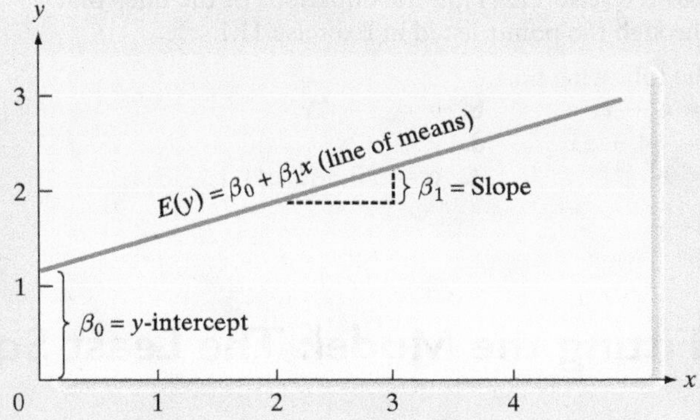

Figure 11.2
The straight-line model

BIOGRAPHY

FRANCIS GALTON (1822–1911)
The Law of Universal Regression

Francis Galton was the youngest of seven children born to a middle-class English family of Quaker faith. A cousin of Charles Darwin, Galton attended Trinity College (Cambridge, England) to study medicine. Due to the death of his father, Galton was unable to obtain his degree. His competence in both medicine and mathematics, however, led Galton to pursue a career as a scientist. Galton made major contributions to the fields of genetics, psychology, meteorology, and anthropology. Some consider Galton to be the first social scientist for his applications of the novel statistical concepts of the time—in particular, regression and correlation. While studying natural inheritance in 1886, Galton collected data on the heights of parents and adult children. He noticed the tendency for tall (or short) parents to have tall (or short) children, but the children were not as tall (or short), on average, as their parents. Galton called this phenomenon the "law of universal regression," for the average heights of adult children tend to "regress" to the mean of the population. Galton, with the help of his friend and disciple, Karl Pearson, applied the straight-line model to the height data, and the term *regression* model was coined.

In the probabilistic model, the deterministic component is referred to as the **line of means** because the mean of y, $E(y)$, is equal to the straight-line component of the model—that is,

$$E(y) = \beta_0 + \beta_1 x$$

Note that the Greek symbols β_0 and β_1, respectively, represent the y-intercept and slope of the model. They are population parameters that will be known only if we have access to the entire population of (x, y) measurements. Together with a specific value of the independent variable x, they determine the mean value of y, which is a specific point on the line of means (Figure 11.2).

The values of β_0 and β_1 will be unknown in almost all practical applications of regression analysis. The process of developing a model, estimating the unknown parameters, and using the model can be viewed as the five-step procedure shown in the next box.

Step 1: Hypothesize the deterministic component of the model that relates the mean, $E(y)$, to the independent variable x (Section 11.1).

Step 2: Use the sample data to estimate unknown parameters in the model (Section 11.2).

Step 3: Specify the probability distribution of the random error term and estimate the standard deviation of this distribution (Section 11.3).

Step 4: Statistically evaluate the usefulness of the model (Sections 11.4 and 11.5).

Step 5: When satisfied that the model is useful, use it for prediction, estimation, and other purposes (Section 11.6).

Exercises 11.1–11.9

Learning the Mechanics

11.1 In each case, graph the line that passes through the given points.

a. (1, 1) and (5, 5) **b.** (0, 3) and (3, 0)
c. (−1, 1) and (4, 2) **d.** (−6, −3) and (2, 6)

11.2 Give the slope and y-intercept for each of the lines graphed in Exercise 11.1.

11.3 The equation for a straight line (deterministic model) is

$$y = \beta_0 + \beta_1 x$$

If the line passes through the point (−2, 4), then $x = -2$, $y = 4$ must satisfy the equation; that is,

$$4 = \beta_0 + \beta_1(-2)$$

Similarly, if the line passes through the point (4, 6), then $x = 4, y = 6$ must satisfy the equation; that is,

$$6 = \beta_0 + \beta_1(4)$$

Use these two equations to solve for β_0 and β_1; then find the equation of the line that passes through the points (−2, 4) and (4, 6).

11.4 Refer to Exercise 11.3. Find the equations of the lines that pass through the points listed in Exercise 11.1.

11.5 Plot the following lines:

a. $y = 4 + x$ **b.** $y = 5 - 2x$
c. $y = -4 + 3x$ **d.** $y = -2x$
e. $y = x$ **f.** $y = .50 + 1.5x$

11.6 Give the slope and y-intercept for each of the lines graphed in Exercise 11.5.

11.7 Why do we generally prefer a probabilistic model to a deterministic model? Give examples for when the two types of models might be appropriate.

11.8 What is the line of means?

11.9 If a straight-line probabilistic relationship relates the mean $E(y)$ to an independent variable x, does it imply that every value of the variable y will always fall exactly on the line of means? Why or why not?

11.2 Fitting the Model: The Least Squares Approach

After the straight-line model has been hypothesized to relate the mean $E(y)$ to the independent variable x, the next step is to collect data and to estimate the (unknown) population parameters, the y-intercept β_0 and the slope β_1.

To begin with a simple example, suppose an appliance store conducts a 5-month experiment to determine the effect of advertising on sales revenue. The results are shown in Table 11.1. (The number of measurements and the measurements themselves are unrealistically simple to avoid arithmetic confusion in this introductory example.) This set of data will be used to demonstrate the five-step procedure of regression modeling given in Section 11.1. In this section, we hypothesize the deterministic component of the model and estimate its unknown parameters (steps 1 and 2). The model assumptions and the random error component (step 3) are the subjects of Section 11.3, whereas Sections 11.4 and 11.5 assess the utility of the model (step 4). Finally, we use the model for prediction and estimation (step 5) in Section 11.6.

Step 1: *Hypothesize the deterministic component of the probabilistic model.* As stated before, we will consider only straight-line models in this chapter. Thus, the complete model to relate mean sales revenue $E(y)$ to advertising expenditure x is given by

$$E(y) = \beta_0 + \beta_1 x$$

Step 2: *Use sample data to estimate unknown parameters in the model.* This step is the subject of this section—namely, how can we best use the information in the sample of five observations in Table 11.1 to estimate the unknown y-intercept β_0 and slope β_1?

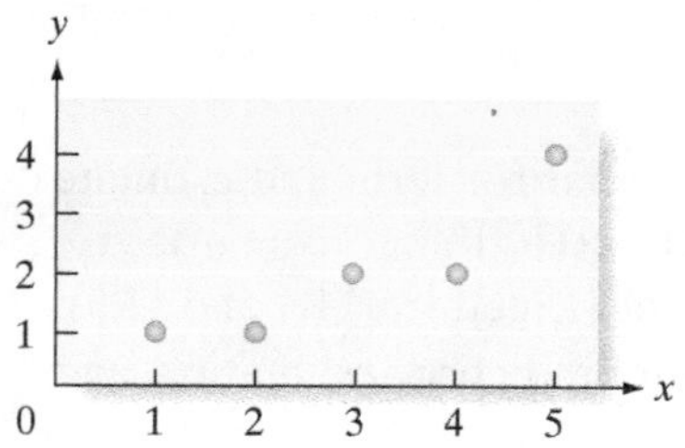

Figure 11.3
Scatterplot for data in Table 11.1

To determine whether a linear relationship between y and x is plausible, it is helpful to plot the sample data in a **scatterplot** (or **scattergram**). Recall (Section 2.9) that a scatterplot locates each of the five data points on a graph, as shown in Figure 11.3. Note that the scatterplot suggests a general tendency for y to increase as x increases. If you

Table 11.1 Advertising-Sales Data

Month	Advertising Expenditure, x ($100s)	Sales Revenue, y ($1,000s)
1	1	1
2	2	1
3	3	2
4	4	2
5	5	4

Data Set: ADSALE

place a ruler on the scatterplot, you will see that a line may be drawn through three of the five points, as shown in Figure 11.4. To obtain the equation of this visually fitted line, note that the line intersects the y-axis at $y = -1$, so the y-intercept is -1. Also, y increases exactly 1 unit for every 1-unit increase in x, indicating that the slope is $+1$. Therefore, the equation is

$$\tilde{y} = -1 + 1(x) = -1 + x$$

where $\tilde{y}$ is used to denote the predicted y from the visual model.

One way to decide quantitatively how well a straight line fits a set of data is to note the extent to which the data points deviate from the line. For example, to evaluate the model in Figure 11.4, we calculate the magnitude of the *deviations* (i.e., the differences between the observed and the predicted values of y). These deviations, or **errors of prediction,** are the vertical distances between observed and predicted values (see Figure 11.4).* The observed and predicted values of y, their differences, and their squared differences are shown in Table 11.2. Note that the *sum of errors* equals 0 and the *sum of squares of the errors* (SSE), which gives greater emphasis to large deviations of the points from the line, is equal to 2.

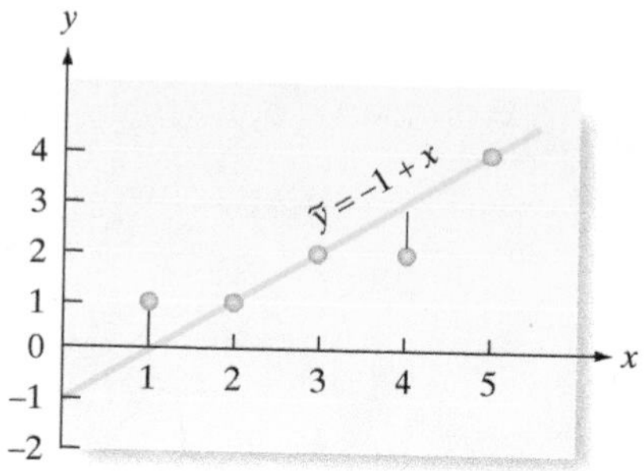

Figure 11.4
Visual straight line fitted to the data in Figure 11.3

Table 11.2 Comparing Observed and Predicted Values for the Visual Model

x	y	$\tilde{y} = -1 + x$	$(y - \tilde{y})$	$(y - \tilde{y})^2$
1	1	0	$(1 - 0) = 1$	1
2	1	1	$(1 - 1) = 0$	0
3	2	2	$(2 - 2) = 0$	0
4	2	3	$(2 - 3) = -1$	1
5	4	4	$(4 - 4) = 0$	0
			Sum of errors = 0	Sum of squared errors (SSE) = 2

You can see by shifting the ruler around the graph that it is possible to find many lines for which the sum of errors is equal to 0, but it can be shown that there is one (and only one) line for which the SSE is a *minimum.* This line is called the **least squares line,** the **regression line,** or the **least squares prediction equation.** The methodology used to obtain this line is called the **method of least squares.**

Now Work Exercise 11.12a, b, c, d

To find the least squares prediction equation for a set of data, assume that we have a sample of n data points consisting of pairs of values of x and y, say (x_1, y_1), $(x_2, y_2), \ldots, (x_n, y_n)$. For example, the $n = 5$ data points shown in Table 11.2 are (1, 1), (2, 1), (3, 2), (4, 2), and (5, 4). The fitted line, which we will calculate based on the five data points, is written as

$$\hat{y} = \hat{\beta}_0 + \hat{\beta}_1 x$$

The "hats" indicate that the symbols below them are estimates: $\hat{y}$ (y-hat) is an estimator of the mean value of y, $E(y)$, and a predictor of some future value of y; and $\hat{\beta}_0$ and $\hat{\beta}_1$ are estimators of β_0 and β_1, respectively.

For a given data point, say the point (x_i, y_i), the observed value of y is y_i, and the predicted value of y would be obtained by substituting x_i into the prediction equation:

$$\hat{y}_i = \hat{\beta}_0 + \hat{\beta}_1 x_i$$

*In Chapter 12, we refer to these errors of prediction as **regression residuals.** There, we learn that an analysis of residuals is essential in estabilishing a useful regression model.

And the deviation of the ith value of y from its predicted value is

$$(y_i - \hat{y}_i) = [y_i - (\hat{\beta}_0 + \hat{\beta}_1 x_i)]$$

Then the sum of squares of the deviations of the y-values about their predicted values for all the n points is

$$\text{SSE} = \sum [y_i - (\hat{\beta}_0 + \hat{\beta}_1 x_i)]^2$$

The quantities $\hat{\beta}_0$ and $\hat{\beta}_1$ that make the SSE a minimum are called the **least squares estimates** of the population parameters β_0 and β_1, and the prediction equation $\hat{y} = \hat{\beta}_0 + \hat{\beta}_1 x$ is called the *least squares line.*

The **least squares line** $\hat{y} = \hat{\beta}_0 + \hat{\beta}_1 x$ is one that has the following two properties:

1. The sum of the errors equals 0, i.e., mean error = 0.
2. The sum of squared errors (SSE) is smaller than for any other straight-line model, i.e., the error variance is minimum.

The values of $\hat{\beta}_0$ and $\hat{\beta}_1$ that minimize the SSE are (proof omitted) given by the formulas in the box.*

Formulas for the Least Squares Estimates

$$\textit{Slope: } \hat{\beta}_1 = \frac{\text{SS}_{xy}}{\text{SS}_{xx}}$$

$$\textit{y-intercept: } \hat{\beta}_0 = \bar{y} - \hat{\beta}_1 \bar{x}$$

where[†] $\text{SS}_{xy} = \Sigma(x_i - \bar{x})(y_i - \bar{y})$

$\text{SS}_{xx} = \Sigma(x_i - \bar{x})^2$

n = Sample size

Example 11.1

Applying the Method of Least Squares—Advertising–Sales Data

Problem Refer to the advertising–monthly–sales data presented in Table 11.1. Consider the straight-line model, $E(y) = \beta_0 + \beta_1 x$, where y = sales revenue (thousands of dollars) and x = advertising expenditure (hundreds of dollars).

a. Use the method of least squares to estimate the values of β_0 and β_1.

b. Predict the sales revenue when advertising expenditure is \$200 (i.e., when $x = 2$).

c. Find SSE for the analysis.

d. Give practical interpretations to β_0 and β_1.

Solution

a. We used Excel to make the preliminary computations for finding the least squares line. The Excel spreadsheet is shown in Figure 11.5. Using the values on the spreadsheet, we find

*Students who are familiar with calculus should note that the values of β_0 and β_1 that minimize $\text{SSE} = \Sigma(y_i - \hat{y}_i)^2$ are obtained by setting the two partial derivatives $\partial\text{SSE}/\partial\beta_0$ and $\partial\text{SSE}/\partial\beta_1$ equal to 0. The solutions to these two equations yield the formulas shown in the box. Furthermore, we denote the *sample* solutions to the equations by $\hat{\beta}_0$ and $\hat{\beta}_1$, where the "hat" denotes that these are sample estimates of the true population intercept β_0 and true population slope β_1.

†Alternatively, you can use the following "shortcut" formulas:

$$\text{SS}_{xy} = \Sigma x_i y_i - \frac{(\Sigma x_i)(\Sigma y_i)}{n}; \quad \text{SS}_{xx} = \Sigma x_i^2 - \frac{(\Sigma x_i)^2}{n}$$

	A	B	C	D	E	F	G	H
1		AdvExp (X)	SalesRev (Y)	(X - 3)	(Y - 2)	(X-3)(Y-2)	(X-3)(X-3)	(Y-2)(Y-2)
2		1	1	-2	-1	2	4	1
3		2	1	-1	-1	1	1	1
4		3	2	0	0	0	0	0
5		4	2	1	0	0	1	0
6		5	4	2	2	4	4	4
7								
8	Totals	15	10	0	0	7	10	6
9	Mean	3	2					

Figure 11.5
Excel spreadsheet showing calculations for advertising-sales example

$$\bar{x} = \frac{\Sigma x}{5} = \frac{15}{5} = 3$$

$$\bar{y} = \frac{\Sigma y}{5} = \frac{10}{5} = 2$$

$$SS_{xy} = \Sigma(x - \bar{x})(y - \bar{y}) = \Sigma(x - 3)(y - 2) = 7$$

$$SS_{xx} = \Sigma(x - \bar{x})^2 = \Sigma(x - 3)^2 = 10$$

Then the slope of the least squares line is

$$\hat{\beta}_1 = \frac{SS_{xy}}{SS_{xx}} = \frac{7}{10} = .7$$

and the y-intercept is

$$\hat{\beta}_0 = \bar{y} - \hat{\beta}_1\bar{x} = 2 - (.7)(3) = 2 - 2.1 = -.1$$

The least squares line is thus

$$\hat{y} = \hat{\beta}_0 + \hat{\beta}_1 x = -.1 + .7x$$

The graph of this line is shown in Figure 11.6.

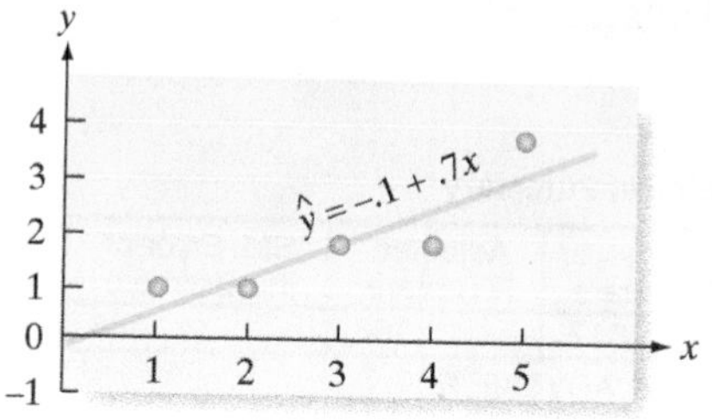

Figure 11.6
The line $\hat{y} = -.1 + .7x$ fitted to the data

b. The predicted value of y for a given value of x can be obtained by substituting into the formula for the least squares line. Substituting $x = 2$ into the least squares equation yields

$$\hat{y} = -.1 + .7x = -.1 + .7(2) = 1.3$$

Thus, when advertising expenditure is \$200, we predict monthly sales revenue to be \$1,300. We show how to find a prediction interval for y in Section 11.6.

c. The observed and predicted values of y, the deviations of the y values about their predicted values, and the squares of these deviations are shown in the Excel spreadsheet, Figure 11.7. Note that SSE = 1.10, and (as we would expect) this is less than the SSE = 2.0 obtained in Table 11.2 for the visually fitted line.

d. The estimated y-intercept, $\hat{\beta}_0 = -.1$, appears to imply that the estimated mean sales revenue is equal to $-.1$, or $-\$100$, when the advertising expenditure, x, is equal to \$0. Because negative sales revenues are not possible, this seems to make the model nonsensical. However, *the model parameters should be interpreted only within the*

	A	B	C	D	E	F
1	AdvExp (X)	SalesRev (Y)	Predicted Y=-.1+.7X	(Y-Yhat)	(Y-Yhat)(Y-Yhat)	
2	1	1	0.6	0.4	0.16	
3	2	1	1.3	-0.3	0.09	
4	3	2	2	0	0	
5	4	2	2.7	-0.7	0.49	
6	5	4	3.4	0.6	0.36	
7						
8			Sum	0	1.1	
9						
10						

Figure 11.7
Excel spreadsheet comparing observed and predicted values for advertising-sales example

sampled range of the independent variable—in this case, for advertising expenditures between \$100 and \$500. Thus, the y-intercept—which is, by definition, at $x = 0$ (\$0 advertising expenditure)—is not within the range of the sampled values of x and is not subject to meaningful interpretation.

The slope of the least squares line, $\hat{\beta}_1 = .7$, implies that for every unit increase of x, the mean value of y is estimated to increase by .7 unit. In terms of this example, for every \$100 increase in advertising, the mean sales revenue is estimated to increase by \$700 *over the sampled range of advertising expenditures from \$100 to \$500.* Thus, the model does not imply that increasing the advertising expenditures from \$500 to \$1,000 will result in an increase in mean sales of \$3,500, because the range of x in the sample does not extend to \$1,000 ($x = 10$). Be careful to interpret the estimated parameters only within the sampled range of x.

Look Back The calculations required to obtain $\hat{\beta}_0$, $\hat{\beta}_1$, and SSE in simple linear regression, although straightforward, can become rather tedious. Even with the use of an Excel spreadsheet, the process is laborious, especially when the sample size is large. Fortunately, a statistical software package can significantly reduce the labor involved in regression calculations. The SPSS, Minitab, and Excel/XLSTAT outputs for the simple linear regression of the data in Table 11.1 are displayed in Figures 11.8a–c. The values of $\hat{\beta}_0$ and $\hat{\beta}_1$ are highlighted on the printouts. These values, $\hat{\beta}_0 = -.1$ and $\hat{\beta}_1 = .7$, agree exactly with our calculated values. The value of SSE = 1.10 is also highlighted on the printouts.

Model Summary

Model	R	R Square	Adjusted R Square	Std. Error of the Estimate
1	.904[a]	.817	.756	.606

a. Predictors: (Constant), ADVEXP_X

ANOVA[b]

Model		Sum of Squares	df	Mean Square	F	Sig.
1	Regression	4.900	1	4.900	13.364	.035[a]
	Residual	1.100	3	.367		
	Total	6.000	4			

a. Predictors: (Constant), ADVEXP_X
b. Dependent Variable: SALES_Y

Coefficients[a]

Model		Unstandardized Coefficients		Standardized Coefficients	t	Sig.
		B	Std. Error	Beta		
1	(Constant)	−.100	.635		−.157	.885
	ADVEXP_X	.700	.191	.904	3.656	.035

a. Dependent Variable: SALES_Y

Figure 11.8a
SPSS printout for the advertising-sales regression

Regression Analysis: SALES_Y versus ADVEXP_X

```
The regression equation is
SALES_Y = - 0.100 + 0.700 ADVEXP_X

Predictor     Coef  SE Coef      T      P
Constant   -0.1000   0.6351  -0.16  0.885
ADVEXP_X    0.7000   0.1915   3.66  0.035

S = 0.605530   R-Sq = 81.7%   R-Sq(adj) = 75.6%

Analysis of Variance

Source          DF      SS      MS      F      P
Regression       1  4.9000  4.9000  13.36  0.035
Residual Error   3  1.1000  0.3667
Total            4  6.0000
```

Figure 11.8b
Minitab printout for the advertising-sales regression

Regression of variable SALES_Y:

Goodness of fit statistics:

Observations	5.0000
Sum of weights	5.0000
DF	3.0000
R²	0.8167
Adjusted R²	0.7556
MSE	0.3667
RMSE	0.6055
DW	2.5091

Analysis of variance:

Source	DF	Sum of squares	Mean squares	F	Pr > F
Model	1	4.9000	4.9000	13.3636	0.0354
Error	3	1.1000	0.3667		
Corrected Total	4	6.0000			

Computed against model Y=Mean(Y)

Model parameters:

Source	Value	Standard error	t	Pr > |t|	Lower bound (95%)	Upper bound (95%)
Intercept	-0.1000	0.6351	-0.1575	0.8849	-2.1211	1.9211
ADVEXP_X	0.7000	0.1915	3.6556	0.0354	0.0906	1.3094

Equation of the model:

SALES_Y=-0.10000+0.70000*ADVEXP_X

Figure 11.8c
XLSTAT printout of sales-advertising regression model

■ Now Work Exercise 11.15

Interpreting the Estimates of β_0 and β_1 in Simple Linear Regression

y-intercept: $\hat{\beta}_0$ represents the predicted value of y when $x = 0$ (*Caution:* This value will not be meaningful if the value $x = 0$ is nonsensical or outside the range of the sample data.)

slope: $\hat{\beta}_1$ represents the increase (or decrease) in y for every 1-unit increase in x (*Caution:* This interpretation is valid only for x-values within the range of the sample data.)

Even when the interpretations of the estimated parameters in a simple linear regression are meaningful, we need to remember that they are only estimates based on the sample. As such, their values will typically change in repeated sampling. How much confidence do we have that the estimated slope, $\hat{\beta}_1$, accurately approximates the true slope, β_1? This requires statistical inference, in the form of confidence intervals and tests of hypotheses, which we address in Section 11.4.

To summarize, we defined the best-fitting straight line to be the one that minimizes the sum of squared errors around the line, and we called it the *least squares line.* We should interpret the least squares line only within the sampled range of the independent variable. In subsequent sections, we show how to make statistical inferences about the model.

Estimating a Straight-Line Regression Model

We return to the legal advertising case involving two former law partners (p. 601). Recall that partner A (who handled PI cases) sued partner B (who handled WC cases) over who should pay what share of the advertising expenses of their former partnership. Monthly data were collected on the number of new PI cases, number of new WC cases, and the total amount spent (in thousands of dollars) on advertising over the previous 6 months. These data (shown in Table SIA11.1, p. 602) are saved in the **LEGADV** file. Do these data provide support for the hypothesis that increased advertising expenditures are associated with more PI cases? Define y as the number of new PI cases per month and x as the cumulative 6-month advertising expenditures (in thousands of dollars). One way to investigate the link between these two variables is to fit the straight-line model, $E(y) = \beta_0 + \beta_1 x$, to the data in Table SIA11.1.

A Minitab scatterplot of the data and a simple linear regression printout are shown in Figure SIA11.1. Note that the least squares line is also displayed on the scatterplot. You can see that the line has a positive slope and, although there is some variation of the data points around the line, it appears that advertising expenditure (x) is fairly strongly related to the number of new PI cases (y). The estimated slope of the line (highlighted on Figure SIA11.1) is $\hat{\beta}_1 = .113$. Thus, we estimate a .113 increase in the number of new PI cases for every $1,000 increase in cumulative advertising expenditures.

Does such a relationship also exist between number of new WC cases and advertising expenditure? Now let y = number of new WC cases per month and x = cumulative

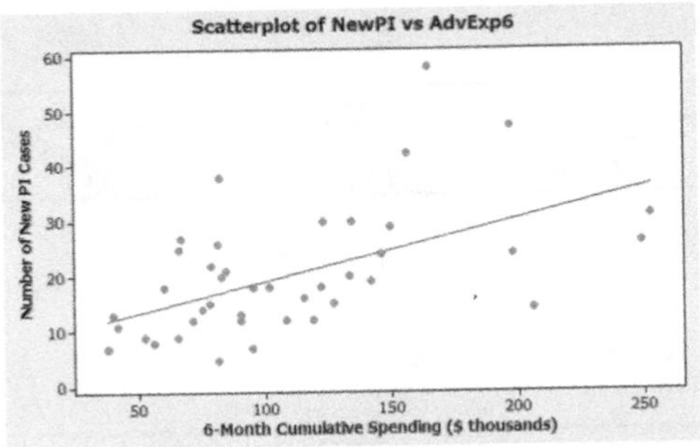

Regression Analysis: NewPI versus AdvExp6

```
The regression equation is
NewPI = 7.77 + 0.113 AdvExp6

Predictor      Coef   SE Coef     T      P
Constant      7.767     3.385  2.29  0.027
AdvExp6     0.11289   0.02793  4.04  0.000

S = 9.67521   R-Sq = 29.0%   R-Sq(adj) = 27.2%

Analysis of Variance

Source          DF      SS      MS      F      P
Regression       1  1529.5  1529.5  16.34  0.000
Residual Error  40  3744.4    93.6
Total           41  5273.9
```

Figure SIA11.1

Minitab analysis of new PI cases vs. 6-month cumulative advertising expenditure

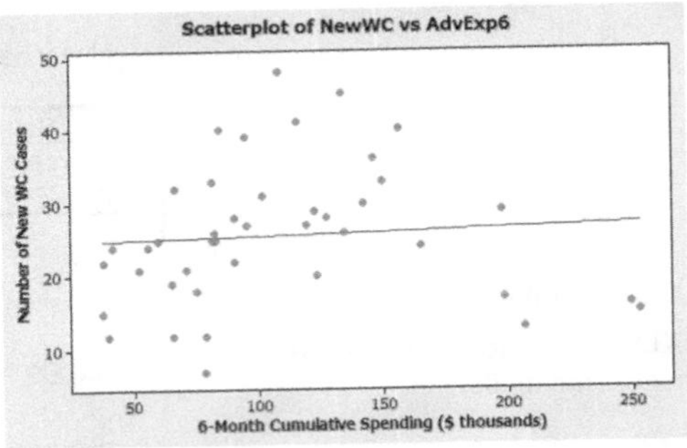

Regression Analysis: NewWC versus AdvExp6

```
The regression equation is
NewWC = 24.6 + 0.0098 AdvExp6

Predictor      Coef   SE Coef     T      P
Constant     24.574     3.367  7.30  0.000
AdvExp6     0.00982   0.02778  0.35  0.725

S = 9.62296   R-Sq = 0.3%   R-Sq(adj) = 0.0%

Analysis of Variance

Source          DF       SS     MS     F      P
Regression       1    11.58  11.58  0.13  0.725
Residual Error  40  3704.06  92.60
Total           41  3715.64
```

Figure SIA11.2

Minitab analysis of new WC cases vs. 6-month cumulative advertising expenditure

6-month advertising expenditures. A Minitab scatterplot and simple linear regression analysis for these two variables are shown in Figure SIA11.2. Compared to the previous scatterplot, the slope of the least squares line shown in Figure SIA11.2 is much flatter, and the variation of the data points around the line is much larger. Consequently, it does not appear that number of new WC cases is very strongly related to advertising expenditure. In fact, the estimated slope (highlighted in Figure SIA11.2) implies that a $1,000 increase in cumulative advertising expenditures will lead to only a $\hat{\beta}_1 = .0098$ increase in the number of new WC cases per month.

Based on these descriptive statistics (scatterplots and least squares lines), it appears that partner A's argument that partner B should share the advertising expenses is weak, at best. In the *Statistics in Action Revisited* sections that follow, we will provide a measure of reliability to this inference and investigate the legal advertising data further.

Exercises 11.10–11.26

Learning the Mechanics

11.10 The following table is similar to Table 11.2. It is used for making the preliminary computations for finding the least squares line for the given pairs of x and y values.

	x_i	y_i	x_i^2	$x_i y_i$
	7	2		
	4	4		
	6	2		
	2	5		
	1	7		
	1	6		
	3	5		
Totals	$\sum x_i =$	$\sum y_i =$	$\sum x_i^2 =$	$\sum x_i y_i =$

a. Complete the table.
b. Find SS_{xy}.
c. Find SS_{xx}.
d. Find $\hat{\beta}_1$.
e. Find $\bar{x}$ and $\bar{y}$.
f. Find $\hat{\beta}_0$.
g. Find the least squares line.

11.11 Refer to Exercise 11.10. After the least squares line has been obtained, the table below (which is similar to Table 11.2) can be used for (1) comparing the observed and the predicted values of y and (2) computing SSE.

x	y	$\hat{y}$	$(y - \hat{y})$	$(y - \hat{y})^2$
7	2			
4	4			
6	2			
2	5			
1	7			
1	6			
3	5			
			$\sum(y - \hat{y}) =$	$SSE = \sum(y - \hat{y})^2 =$

a. Complete the table.
b. Plot the least squares line on a scatterplot of the data. Plot the following line on the same graph: $\hat{y} = 14 - 2.5x$.
c. Show that SSE is larger for the line in part **b** than it is for the least squares line.

11.12 Construct a scatterplot for the data in the following table.
NW

x	.5	1	1.5
y	2	1	3

a. Plot the following two lines on your scatterplot:

$$y = 3 - x \quad \text{and} \quad y = 1 + x$$

b. Which of these lines would you choose to characterize the relationship between x and y? Explain.
c. Show that the sum of the errors of prediction for both of these lines equals 0.
d. Which of these lines has the smaller SSE?
e. Find the least squares line for the data and compare it to the two lines described in part **a**.

11.13 Consider the following pairs of measurements:
L11013

x	8	5	4	6	2	5	3
y	1	3	6	3	7	2	5

a. Construct a scatterplot for these data.
b. What does the scatterplot suggest about the relationship between x and y?
c. Find the least squares estimates of β_0 and β_1.
d. Plot the least squares line on your scatterplot. Does the line appear to fit the data well? Explain.

Applet Exercise 11.1

Use the applet *Regression by Eye* to explore the relationship between the pattern of data in a scatterplot and the corresponding least squares model.

a. Run the applet several times. For each time, attempt to move the green line into a position that appears to minimize the vertical distances of the points from the line. Then click *Show regression line* to see the actual regression line. How close is your line to the actual line? Click *New data* to reset the applet.
b. Click the trash can to clear the graph. Use the mouse to place five points on the scatterplot that are approximately in a straight line. Then move the green line to approximate the regression line. Click *Show regression line* to see the actual regression line. How close were you this time?

c. Continue to clear the graph and plot sets of five points with different patterns among the points. Use the green line to approximate the regression line. How close do you come to the actual regression line each time?

d. Based on your experiences with the applet, explain why we need to use more reliable methods of finding the regression line than just "eyeing" it.

Applying the Concepts—Basic

11.14 In business, do nice guys finish first or last? Refer to the *Nature* (March 20, 2008) study of whether "nice guys finish last" in the business world, Exercise 2.123 (p. 104). Recall that college students repeatedly played a version of the game "prisoner's dilemma," where competitors choose cooperation, defection, or costly punishment. (Cooperation meant paying 1 unit for the opponent to receive 2 units, defection meant gaining 1 unit at a cost of 1 unit for the opponent, and punishment meant paying 1 unit for the opponent to lose 4 units.) At the conclusion of the games, the researchers recorded the average payoff and the number of times cooperation, defection, and punishment were used for each player. The scatterplots below plot average payoff (y) against level of cooperation use, defection use, and punishment use, respectively.

a. Consider cooperation use (x) as a predictor of average payoff (y). Based on the scatterplot, is there evidence of a linear trend?

b. Consider defection use (x) as a predictor of average payoff (y). Based on the scatterplot, is there evidence of a linear trend?

c. Consider punishment use (x) as a predictor of average payoff (y). Based on the scatterplot (reproduced from Exercise 2.123), is there evidence of a linear trend?

d. Refer to part **c.** Is the slope of the line relating punishment use (x) to average payoff (y) positive or negative?

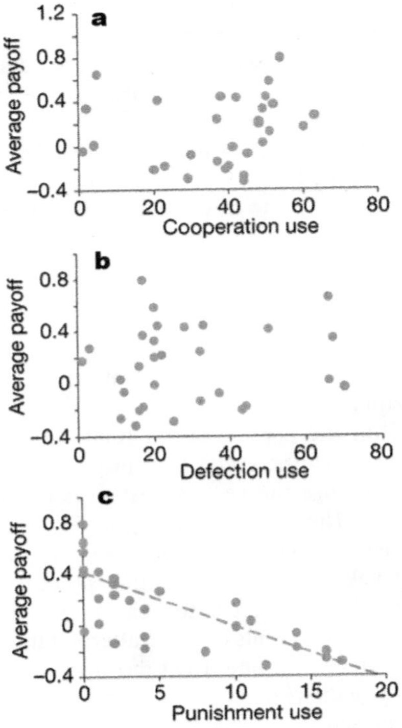

11.15 State Math SAT scores. Refer to the data on average state Math SAT scores for 2001 and 2011, Exercise 2.27 (p. 60). The first five observations and last two observations in the file are reproduced in the next table. In Exercise 2.126 (p. 105), you examined the relationship between the 2001 Math SAT scores and the 2011 Math SAT scores with a scatterplot.

NW SATMAT

State	2001	2011
Alabama	554	541
Alaska	510	511
Arizona	525	523
Arkansas	550	570
California	517	515
⋮	⋮	⋮
Wisconsin	596	602
Wyoming	545	569

Source: Based on "SAT Trends: Background on the SAT Takers in the Class of 2011." The College Board.

a. Write the equation of a straight-line model relating 2011 Math SAT score (y) to 2001 Math SAT score (x).

b. An SPSS simple linear regression printout for the data is shown on the next page. Find the least squares prediction equation.

c. Give a practical interpretation of the y-intercept of the least squares line. If a practical interpretation is not possible, explain why.

d. Give a practical interpretation of the slope of the least squares line. Over what range of x is the interpretation meaningful?

11.16 Lobster fishing study. Refer to the *Bulletin of Marine Science* (April 2010) study of teams of fishermen fishing for the red spiny lobster in Baja California Sur, Mexico, Exercise 2.124 (p. 104). Two variables measured for each of 15 teams from two fishing cooperatives were y = total catch of lobsters (in kilograms) during the season and x = average percentage of traps allocated per day to exploring areas of unknown catch (called *search frequency*). These data are listed in the table.

TRAPS

Total Catch	Search Frequency	Total Catch	Search Frequency
9,998	18	6,535	21
7,767	14	6,695	26
8,764	4	4,891	29
9,077	18	4,937	23
8,343	9	5,727	17
9,222	5	7,019	21
6,827	8	5,735	20
2,785	35		

Source: Based on Shester, G. G. "Explaining catch variation among Baja California lobster fishers through spatial analysis of trap-placement decisions," *Bulletin of Marine Science*, Vol. 86, No. 2, April 2010 (Table 1).

a. Graph the data in a scatterplot. What type of trend, if any, do you observe?

b. A simple linear regression analysis was conducted using XLSTAT. A portion of the regression printout is shown on the next page. Find the estimates of β_0 and β_1 on the printout.

SPSS Output for Exercise 11.15

Coefficients[a]

Model		Unstandardized Coefficients B	Unstandardized Coefficients Std. Error	Standardized Coefficients Beta	t	Sig.
1	(Constant)	-97.414	26.668		-3.653	.001
	MATH2001	1.188	.050	.959	23.830	.000

a. Dependent Variable: MATH2011

XLSTAT output for Exercise 11.16

Model parameters:

Source	Value	Standard error	t	Pr > |t|	Lower bound (95%)	Upper bound (95%)
Intercept	9877.8300	829.0411	11.9148	< 0.0001	8086.7957	11668.8643
SEARCHFR	-163.6024	41.9014	-3.9045	0.0018	-254.1249	-73.0799

Equation of the model:

CATCH = 9877.82997-163.60242*SEARCHFREQ

c. If possible, give a practical interpretation of the estimate of β_0. If no practical interpretation is possible, explain why.

d. If possible, give a practical interpretation of the estimate of β_1. If no practical interpretation is possible, explain why.

11.17 Drug controlled-release rate study. Researchers at Dow Chemical Co. investigated the effect of tablet surface area and volume on the rate at which a drug is released in a controlled-release dosage (*Drug Development and Industrial Pharmacy,* Vol. 28, 2002). Six similarly shaped tablets were prepared with different weights and thicknesses, and the ratio of surface area to volume was measured for each. Using a dissolution apparatus, each tablet was placed in 900 milliliters of deionized water, and the diffusional drug release rate (percentage of drug released divided by the square root of time) was determined. The experimental data are listed in the table below.

DOW

Drug Release Rate (% released/$\sqrt{\text{time}}$)	Surface Area to Volume (mm^2/mm^3)
60	1.50
48	1.05
39	.90
33	.75
30	.60
29	.65

Source: Reynolds, T., Mitchell, S., & Balwinski, K.M. "Investigation of the effect of table surface area/volume on drug release from hydroxypropyl-methylcellulose controlled-release matrix tablets," *Drug Development and Industrial Pharmacy,* Vol. 28, No. 4, 2002, pp. 457–466 (Figure 3). Reprinted by permission of the publisher (Taylor & Francis Group, www.informaworld.com).

a. Fit the simple linear model, $E(y) = \beta_0 + \beta_1 x$, where y = release rate and x = surface-area-to-volume ratio.

b. Interpret the estimates of β_0 and β_1.

c. Predict the drug release rate for a tablet that has a surface area/volume ratio of .50.

d. Comment on the reliability of the prediction in part **c.**

11.18 Extending the life of an aluminum smelter pot. An investigation of the properties of bricks used to line aluminum smelter pots was published in *The American Ceramic Society Bulletin* (Feb. 2005). Six different commercial bricks were evaluated. The life length of a smelter pot depends on the porosity of the brick lining (the less porosity, the longer the life); consequently, the researchers measured the apparent porosity of each brick specimen, as well as the mean pore diameter of each brick. The data are given in the accompanying table.

SMELTR

Brick	Apparent Porosity (%)	Mean Pore Diameter (micrometers)
A	18.8	12.0
B	18.3	9.7
C	16.3	7.3
D	6.9	5.3
E	17.1	10.9
F	20.4	16.8

Source: Based on Bonadia, P., et al. "Aluminosilicate refractories for aluminum cell linings," *The American Ceramic Society Bulletin,* Vol. 84, No. 2, Feb. 2005, pp. 26–31 (Table II).

a. Find the least squares line relating porosity (y) to mean pore diameter (x).

b. Interpret the y-intercept of the line.

c. Interpret the slope of the line.

d. Predict the apparent porosity percentage for a brick with a mean pore diameter of 10 micrometers.

11.19 Software millionaires and birthdays. In *Outliers: The Story of Success* (Little, Brown, 2008), the author notes that a disproportionate number of software millionaires were born around the year 1955. Is this a coincidence, or does birth year matter when gauging whether a software founder will be successful? On his Web blog (www.measuringusability.com), statistical consultant Jeff Sauro investigated this question by analyzing the data shown in the table on the next page.

BDAYS

Data for Exercise 11.19

Decade	Total U.S. Births (millions)	Number of Software Millionaire Birthdays	Number of CEO Birthdays (in a random sample of 70 companies from the *Fortune* 500 list)
1920	28.582	3	2
1930	24.374	1	2
1940	31.666	10	23
1950	40.530	14	38
1960	38.808	7	9
1970	33.309	4	0

Source: Sauro, J. "Were most software millionaires born around 1955?" *Measuring Usability*, November 17, 2010. Copyright © 2010 by Measuring Usability LLC. Reprinted with permission.

a. Fit a simple linear regression model relating number (y) of software millionaire birthdays in a decade to total number (x) of U.S. births. Give the least squares prediction equation.

b. Practically interpret the estimated y-intercept and slope of the model, part **a.**

c. Predict the number of software millionaire birthdays that will occur in a decade where the total number of U.S. births is 35 million.

d. Fit a simple linear regression model relating number (y) of software millionaire birthdays in a decade to number (x) of CEO birthdays. Give the least squares prediction equation.

e. Practically interpret the estimated y-intercept and slope of the model, part **d.**

f. Predict the number of software millionaire birthdays that will occur in a decade where the number of CEO birthdays (from a random sample of 70 companies) is 10.

Applying the Concepts—Intermediate

11.20 Public corruption and bad weather. The Federal Emergency Management Agency (FEMA) provides disaster relief for states impacted by natural disasters (e.g., hurricanes, tornados, floods). Do these bad weather windfalls lead to public corruption? This was the research question of interest in an article published in the *Journal of Law and Economics* (Nov. 2008). Data on y = average annual number of public corruption convictions (per 100,000 residents) and x = average annual FEMA relief (in dollars) per capita for each of the 50 states were used in the investigation.

FEMA

a. Access the data, saved in the file, and construct a scatterplot. Do you observe a trend?

b. Fit the simple linear regression model, $E(y) = \beta_0 + \beta_1 x$, to the data and obtain estimates of the y-intercept and slope.

c. Practically interpret the estimated y-intercept and estimated slope.

11.21 Ranking driving performance of professional golfers. Refer to *The Sport Journal* (Winter 2007) study of a new method for ranking the total driving performance of golfers on the Professional Golf Association (PGA) tour, Exercise 2.50 (p. 72). Recall that the method computes a driving performance index based on a golfer's average driving distance (yards) and driving accuracy (percent of drives that land in the fairway). Data for the top 40 PGA golfers (as ranked by the new method) are saved in the file. (The first five and last five observations are listed in the table.)

PGA

Rank	Player	Driving Distance (yards)	Driving Accuracy (%)	Driving Performance Index
1	Woods	316.1	54.6	3.58
2	Perry	304.7	63.4	3.48
3	Gutschewski	310.5	57.9	3.27
4	Wetterich	311.7	56.6	3.18
5	Hearn	295.2	68.5	2.82
⋮	⋮	⋮	⋮	⋮
36	Senden	291	66	1.31
37	Mickelson	300	58.7	1.30
38	Watney	298.9	59.4	1.26
39	Trahan	295.8	61.8	1.23
40	Pappas	309.4	50.6	1.17

Source: Wiseman, F., et al. "A new method for ranking total driving performance on the PGA Tour," *The Sport Journal*, Vol. 10, No. 1, Winter 2007 (Table 2).

a. Write the equation of a straight-line model relating driving accuracy (y) to driving distance (x).

b. Fit the model, part **a,** to the data using simple linear regression. Give the least squares prediction equation.

c. Interpret the estimated y-intercept of the line.

d. Interpret the estimated slope of the line.

e. In Exercise 2.132 (p. 106), you were informed that a professional golfer, practicing a new swing to increase his average driving distance, is concerned that his driving accuracy will be lower. Which of the two estimates, y-intercept or slope, will help you determine if the golfer's concern is a valid one? Explain.

11.22 Sweetness of orange juice. The quality of the orange juice produced by a manufacturer (e.g., Minute Maid, Tropicana) is constantly monitored. There are numerous sensory and chemical components that combine to make the best-tasting orange juice. For example, one manufacturer has developed a quantitative index of the "sweetness" of orange juice. (The higher the index, the sweeter the juice.) Is there a relationship between the sweetness index and a chemical measure such as the amount of water-soluble pectin (parts per million) in the orange juice? Data collected on these two variables for 24 production runs at a juice manufacturing plant are shown in the table on the next page. Suppose a manufacturer wants to use simple linear regression to predict the sweetness (y) from the amount of pectin (x).

OJUICE

Data for Exercise 11.22

Run	Sweetness Index	Pectin (ppm)
1	5.2	220
2	5.5	227
3	6.0	259
4	5.9	210
5	5.8	224
6	6.0	215
7	5.8	231
8	5.6	268
9	5.6	239
10	5.9	212
11	5.4	410
12	5.6	256
13	5.8	306
14	5.5	259
15	5.3	284
16	5.3	383
17	5.7	271
18	5.5	264
19	5.7	227
20	5.3	263
21	5.9	232
22	5.8	220
23	5.8	246
24	5.9	241

Note: The data in the table are authentic. For confidentiality reasons, the manufacturer cannot be disclosed.

a. Find the least squares line for the data.
b. Interpret $\hat{\beta}_0$ and $\hat{\beta}_1$ in the words of the problem.
c. Predict the sweetness index if amount of pectin in the orange juice is 300 ppm. [*Note:* A measure of reliability of such a prediction is discussed in Section 11.6]

11.23 Forecasting movie revenues with Twitter. Marketers are keenly interested in how social media (e.g., Facebook, Twitter) may influence consumers who buy their products. Researchers at HP Labs (Palo Alto, CA) investigated whether the volume of chatter on Twitter.com could be used to forecast the box office revenues of movies (*IEEE International Conference on Web Intelligence and Intelligent Agent Technology,* 2010). Opening weekend box office revenue data (in smillions of dollars) were collected for a sample of 23 recent movies. In addition, the researchers computed each movie's *tweet rate,* i.e., the average number of tweets (at Twitter.com) referring to the movie per hour 1 week prior to the movie's release. The data (simulated based on information provided in the study) are listed in the accompanying table. Assuming that movie revenue and tweet rate are linearly related, how much do you estimate a movie's opening weekend revenue to change as the tweet rate for the movie increases by an average of 100 tweets per hour?

TWEETS

Tweet Rate	Revenue (millions)
1365.8	142
1212.8	77
581.5	61
310.1	32
455	31
290	30
250	21
680.5	18
150	18
164.5	17
113.9	16
144.5	15
418	14
98	14
100.8	12
115.4	11
74.4	10
87.5	9
127.6	9
52.2	9
144.1	8
41.3	2
2.75	0.3

11.24 FCAT scores and poverty. In the state of Florida, elementary school performance is based on the average score obtained by students on a standardized exam, called the Florida Comprehensive Assessment Test (FCAT). An analysis of the link between FCAT scores and sociodemographic factors was published in the *Journal of Educational and Behavioral Statistics* (Spring 2004). Data on average math and reading FCAT scores of third graders, as well as the percentage of students below the poverty level, for a sample of 22 Florida elementary schools are listed in the table below.

FCAT

a. Propose a straight-line model relating math score (y) to percentage (x) of students below the poverty level.
b. Fit the model to the data using the method of least squares.
c. Graph the least squares line on a scatterplot of the data. Is there visual evidence of a relationship between the two variables? Is the relationship positive or negative?
d. Interpret the estimates of the y-intercept and slope in the words of the problem.
e. Now consider a model relating reading score (y) to percentage (x) of students below the poverty level. Repeat parts **a–d** for this model.

Elementary School	FCAT-Math	FCAT-Reading	% Below Poverty
1	166.4	165.0	91.7
2	159.6	157.2	90.2
3	159.1	164.4	86.0
4	155.5	162.4	83.9
5	164.3	162.5	80.4
6	169.8	164.9	76.5
7	155.7	162.0	76.0
8	165.2	165.0	75.8
9	175.4	173.7	75.6
10	178.1	171.0	75.0
11	167.1	169.4	74.7
12	177.0	172.9	63.2
13	174.2	172.7	52.9
14	175.6	174.9	48.5
15	170.8	174.8	39.1
16	175.1	170.1	38.4
17	182.8	181.4	34.3
18	180.3	180.6	30.3
19	178.8	178.0	30.3
20	181.4	175.9	29.6
21	182.8	181.6	26.5
22	186.1	183.8	13.8

Source: Based on Tekwe, C. D., et al. "An empirical comparison of statistical models for value-added assessment of school performance," *Journal of Educational and Behavioral Statistics,* Vol. 29, No. 1, Spring 2004, pp. 11–36 (Table 2).

Data for Exercise 11.25

School	Enrollment (# full-time students)	Annual Tuition ($)	Mean GMAT	% with Job Offer	Avg. Salary ($)
Dartmouth	503	38,400	704	—	119,800
Michigan	1,873	33,076	690	91	105,986
Carnegie Mellon	661	38,800	691	93	95,531
Northwestern	2,650	38,844	700	94	117,060
Yale	468	36,800	696	86	104,018
Pennsylvania	1,840	40,458	716	92	117,471
Cal., Berkeley	1,281	21,512	701	92	112,699
Columbia	1,796	38,290	709	95	126,319
North Carolina	855	16,375	652	86	92,565
Southern Cal.	1,588	37,558	685	82	88,839

Source: "Wall Street Journal's annual rankings of business schools," *The Wall Street Journal,* Sep. 25, 2005. Copyright 2005 by Dow Jones & Company, Inc. Reproduced with permission.

11.25 Survey of the top business schools. Each year, the *Wall Street Journal* and *Harris Interactive* track the opinions and experiences of college recruiters for large corporations and summarize the results in the Business School Survey. One of these surveys included rankings of 76 business schools. Survey data for the top 10 business schools are given in the table above. All the data are saved in the file.

TOPBUS

a. Select one of the variables as the dependent variable, y, and another as the independent variable, x. Use your knowledge of the subject area and common sense to help you select the variables.

b. Fit the simple linear model, $E(y) = \beta_0 + \beta_1 x$, to the data for all 76 business schools. Interpret the estimates of the slope and y-intercept.

Applying the Concepts—Advanced

11.26 Spreading rate of spilled liquid. Refer to the *Chemical Engineering Progress* (Jan. 2005) study of the rate at which a spilled volatile liquid will spread across a surface, Exercise 2.128 (p. 105). Recall that a DuPont Corp. engineer calculated the mass (in pounds) of a 50-gallon methanol spill after a period of time ranging from 0 to 60 minutes. Do the data in the table below indicate that the mass of the spill tends to diminish as time increases? If so, how much will the mass diminish each minute?

LSPILL

Time (minutes)	Mass (pounds)	Time (minutes)	Mass (pounds)
0	6.64	22	1.86
1	6.34	24	1.60
2	6.04	26	1.37
4	5.47	28	1.17
6	4.94	30	0.98
8	4.44	35	0.60
10	3.98	40	0.34
12	3.55	45	0.17
14	3.15	50	0.06
16	2.79	55	0.02
18	2.45	60	0.00
20	2.14		

Source: Barry, J. "Estimating rates of spreading and evaporation of volatile liquids," *Chemical Engineering Progress,* Vol. 101, No. 1, Jan. 2005. Reproduced with permission. Copyright © 2005 AICHE.

11.3 Model Assumptions

In Section 11.2, we assumed that the probabilistic model relating the firm's sales revenue y to the advertising dollars is

$$y = \beta_0 + \beta_1 x + \varepsilon$$

We also recall that the least squares estimate of the deterministic component of the model, $\beta_0 + \beta_1 x$, is

$$\hat{y} = \hat{\beta}_0 + \hat{\beta}_1 x = -.1 + .7x$$

Now we turn our attention to the random component ε of the probabilistic model and its relation to the errors in estimating β_0 and β_1. We will use a probability distribution to characterize the behavior of ε. We will see how the probability distribution of ε determines how well the model describes the relationship between the dependent variable y and the independent variable x.

Step 3 in a regression analysis requires us to specify the probability distribution of the random error ε. We will make four basic assumptions about the general form of this probability distribution:

Assumption 1: The mean of the probability distribution of ε is 0—that is, the average of the values of ε over an infinitely long series of experiments is 0 for each setting of the independent variable x. This assumption implies that the mean value of y, $E(y)$, for a given value of x is $E(y) = \beta_0 + \beta_1 x$.

Assumption 2: The variance of the probability distribution of ε is constant for all settings of the independent variable x. For our straight-line model, this assumption means that the variance of ε is equal to a constant, say σ^2, for all values of x.

Assumption 3: The probability distribution of ε is normal.

Assumption 4: The values of ε associated with any two observed values of y are independent—that is, the value of ε associated with one value of y has no effect on the values of ε associated with other y values.

The implications of the first three assumptions can be seen in Figure 11.9, which shows distributions of errors for three values of x, namely, x_1, x_2, and x_3. Note that the relative frequency distributions of the errors are normal with a mean of 0 and a constant variance σ^2. (All the distributions shown have the same amount of spread or variability.) The straight line shown in Figure 11.9 is the line of means. It indicates the mean value of y for a given value of x. We denote this mean value as $E(y)$. Then, the line of means is given by the equation

$$E(y) = \beta_0 + \beta_1 x$$

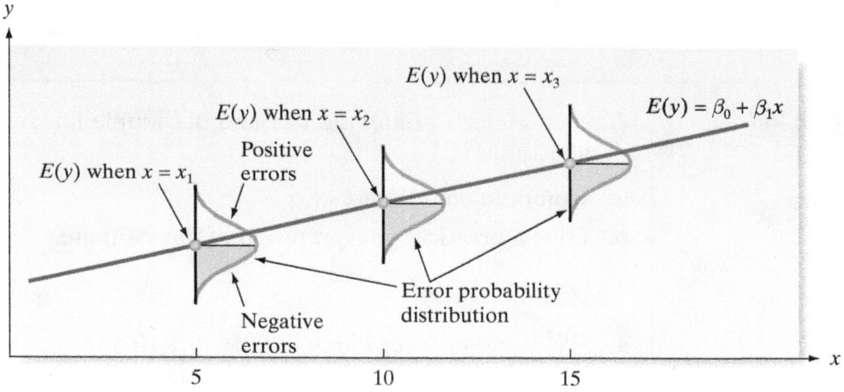

Figure 11.9
The probability distribution of ε

These assumptions make it possible for us to develop measures of reliability for the least squares estimators and to develop hypothesis tests for examining the usefulness of the least squares line. We have various techniques for checking the validity of these assumptions, and we have remedies to apply when they appear to be invalid. Several of these remedies are discussed in Chapter 12. Fortunately, the assumptions need not hold exactly in order for least squares estimators to be useful. The assumptions will be satisfied adequately for many applications encountered in practice.

It seems reasonable to assume that the greater the variability of the random error ε (which is measured by its variance σ^2), the greater will be the errors in the estimation of the model parameters β_0 and β_1 and in the error of prediction when $\hat{y}$ is used to predict y for some value of x. Consequently, you should not be surprised, as we proceed through this chapter, to find that σ^2 appears in the formulas for all confidence intervals and test statistics that we will be using.

In most practical situations, σ^2 is unknown, and we must use our data to estimate its value. The best estimate of σ^2, denoted by s^2, is obtained by dividing the sum of squares of the deviations of the y values from the prediction line,

$$\text{SSE} = \sum (y_i - \hat{y}_i)^2$$

by the number of degrees of freedom associated with this quantity. We use 2 df to estimate the two parameters β_0 and β_1 in the straight-line model, leaving $(n - 2)$ df for the error variance estimation.

Estimation of σ^2 for a (First-Order) Straight-Line Model

$$s^2 = \frac{\text{SSE}}{\text{Degrees of freedom for error}} = \frac{\text{SSE}}{n-2}$$

where $\text{SSE} = \Sigma(y_i - \hat{y}_i)^2 = \text{SS}_{yy} - \hat{\beta}_1 \text{SS}_{xy}$

$$\text{SS}_{yy} = \Sigma(y_i - \bar{y})^2 *$$

To estimate the standard deviation σ of ε, we calculate

$$s = \sqrt{s^2} = \sqrt{\frac{\text{SSE}}{n-2}}$$

We will refer to s as the **estimated standard error of the regression model.**

CAUTION When performing these calculations, you may be tempted to round the calculated values of SS_{yy}, $\hat{\beta}_1$, and SS_{xy}. Be certain to carry at least six significant figures for each of these quantities to avoid substantial errors in calculation of the SSE.

Example 11.2

Estimating σ—Advertising-Sales Regression

Problem Refer to Example 11.1 and the simple linear regression of the advertising-sales data in Table 11.1.

a. Compute an estimate of σ.

b. Give a practical interpretation of the estimate.

Solution

a. We previously calculated SSE = 1.10 for the least squares line $\hat{y} = -.1 + .7x$. Recalling that there were $n = 5$ data points, we have $n - 2 = 5 - 2 = 3$ df for estimating σ^2. Thus,

$$s^2 = \frac{\text{SSE}}{n-2} = \frac{1.10}{3} = .367$$

is the estimated variance, and

$$s = \sqrt{.367} = .61$$

is the standard error of the regression model.

b. You may be able to grasp s intuitively by recalling the interpretation of a standard deviation given in Chapter 2 and remembering that the least squares line estimates the mean value of y for a given value of x. Because s measures the spread of the distribution of y values about the least squares line, we should not be surprised to find that most of the observations lie within $2s$, or $2(.61) = 1.22$, of the least squares line. For this simple example (only five data points), all five sales revenue values fall within $2s$ (or \$1,220) of the least squares line. In Section 11.6, we use s to evaluate the error of prediction when the least squares line is used to predict a value of y to be observed for a given value of x.

Look Back The values of s^2 and s can also be obtained from a simple linear regression printout. The Minitab printout for the advertising-sales example is reproduced in Figure 11.10. The value of s^2 is highlighted at the bottom of the printout in the

*Alternatively, you can use the following "shortcut" formula:

$$\text{SS}_{yy} = \Sigma y^2 - \frac{(\Sigma y)^2}{n}$$

Regression Analysis: SALES_Y versus ADVEXP_X

```
The regression equation is
SALES_Y = - 0.100 + 0.700 ADVEXP_X


Predictor      Coef   SE Coef      T      P
Constant    -0.1000    0.6351  -0.16  0.885
ADVEXP_X     0.7000    0.1915   3.66  0.035


S = 0.605530    R-Sq = 81.7%    R-Sq(adj) = 75.6%


Analysis of Variance

Source          DF      SS      MS      F      P
Regression       1  4.9000  4.9000  13.36  0.035
Residual Error   3  1.1000  0.3667
Total            4  6.0000
```

Figure 11.10
Minitab printout for the advertising-sales regression

MS (Mean Square) column in the row labeled **Residual Error.** (In regression, the estimate of σ^2 is called Mean Square for Error, or MSE.) The value, $s^2 = .3667$, agrees with the one calculated by hand. The value of s is also highlighted in Figure 11.10. This value, $s = .60553$, agrees (except for rounding) with our hand-calculated value.

Now Work Exercise 11.32

Interpretation of s, the Estimated Standard Deviation of ε

We expect most ($\approx$95%) of the observed y values to lie within $2s$ of their respective least squares predicted values, $\hat{y}$.

Exercises 11.27–11.40

Learning the Mechanics

11.27 Visually compare the scatterplots shown below. If a least squares line were determined for each data set, which do you think would have the smallest variance, s^2? Explain.

11.28 Calculate SSE and s^2 for each of the following cases:

a. $n = 20$, $SS_{yy} = 95$, $SS_{xy} = 50$, $\hat{\beta}_1 = .75$

b. $n = 40$, $\sum y^2 = 860$, $\sum y = 50$, $SS_{xy} = 2{,}700$, $\hat{\beta}_1 = .2$

c. $n = 10$, $\sum (y_i - \bar{y})^2 = 58$, $SS_{xy} = 91$, $SS_{xx} = 170$

11.29 Suppose you fit a least squares line to 26 data points and the calculated value of SSE is 8.34.

a. Find s^2, the estimator of σ^2 (the variance of the random error term ε).

b. What is the largest deviation that you might expect between any one of the 26 points and the least squares line?

11.30 Refer to Exercise 11.10 (p. 613). Calculate SSE, s^2, and s for the least squares line. Use the value of s to determine where most of the errors of prediction lie.

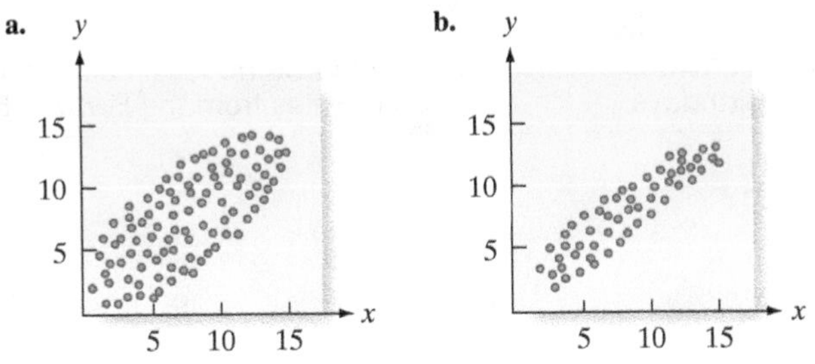

Scatterplots for Exercise 11.27

Applying the Concepts—Basic

11.31 Do nice guys really finish last in business? Refer to the *Nature* (March 20, 2008) study of whether "nice guys finish last" in business, Exercise 11.14 (p. 614). Recall that college students repeatedly played a version of the game "prisoner's dilemma," where competitors choose cooperation, defection, or costly punishment. At the conclusion of the games, the researchers recorded the average payoff and the number of times punishment was used for each player. Based on a scatterplot of the data, the simple linear regression relating average payoff (y) to punishment use (x) resulted in SSE = 1.04.

a. Assuming a sample size of $n = 28$, compute the estimated standard deviation of the error distribution, s.

b. Give a practical interpretation of s.

11.32 State Math SAT scores. Refer to the simple linear regression relating y = 2011 Math SAT scores to x = 2001 Math SAT scores, Exercise 11.15 (p. 614). A portion of the SPSS printout of the analysis is shown below.

NW

SATMAT

Model Summary

Model	R	R Square	Adjusted R Square	Std. Error of the Estimate
1	.959[a]	.921	.919	11.912

a. Predictors: (Constant), MATH2001

ANOVA[a]

Model		Sum of Squares	df	Mean Square	F	Sig.
1	Regression	80575.988	1	80575.988	567.864	.000[b]
	Residual	6952.757	49	141.893		
	Total	87528.745	50			

a. Dependent Variable: MATH2011

b. Predictors: (Constant), MATH2001

a. Locate the values of SSE, s^2, and s on the SPSS printout.

b. Give a practical interpretation of the value of s.

11.33 Drug controlled-release rate study. Refer to the simple linear regression relating the drug release rate (y) to surface area-to-volume ratio (x), Exercise 11.17 (p. 615).

DOW

a. Find the value of s for the straight-line model fit in Exercise 11.17a.

b. Give a practical interpretation of the value of s.

11.34 Structurally deficient highway bridges. Refer to Exercise 1.28 (p. 27) and the data on structurally deficient highway bridges compiled by the Federal Highway Administration (FHWA) into the National Bridge Inventory (NBI). For each state, the NBI lists the number of structurally deficient bridges and the total area (thousands of square feet) of the deficient bridges. The data for the 50 states (plus the District of Columbia and Puerto Rico) are saved in the file. (The first five and last five observations are listed in the table in the next column.) For future planning and budgeting, the FHWA wants to estimate the total area of structurally deficient bridges in a state based on the number of deficient bridges.

BRIDGE

State	Number	Area (thousands of sq. ft.)
Alabama	1,899	432.7
Alaska	155	60.9
Arizona	181	110.5
Arkansas	997	347.3
California	3,140	5,177.9
⋮	⋮	⋮
Washington	400	502.0
West Virginia	1,058	331.5
Wisconsin	1,302	399.8
Wyoming	389	143.4
Puerto Rico	241	195.4

a. Write the equation of a straight-line model relating total area (y) to number of structurally deficient bridges (x).

b. The model, part **a,** was fit to the data using Minitab, as shown below. Find the least squares prediction equation on the printout.

c. List the assumptions required for the regression analysis.

d. Locate the estimated standard error of the regression model, s, on the printout.

e. Use the value of s to find a range where most (about 95%) of the errors of prediction will fall.

Regression Analysis: SDArea versus NumberSD

```
The regression equation is
SDArea = 120 + 0.346 NumberSD

Predictor     Coef   SE Coef     T      P
Constant     119.9     123.0  0.97  0.335
NumberSD   0.34560   0.06158  5.61  0.000

S = 635.187   R-Sq = 38.7%   R-Sq(adj) = 37.4%

Analysis of Variance

Source          DF        SS        MS      F      P
Regression       1  12710141  12710141  31.50  0.000
Residual Error  50  20173111    403462
Total           51  32883252
```

11.35 Software millionaires and birthdays. Refer to Exercise 11.19 (p. 615) and the study of software millionaires and their birthdays. The data are reproduced below.

BDAYS

a. Find SSE, s^2, and s for the simple linear regression model relating number (y) of software millionaire birthdays in a decade to total number (x) of U.S. births.

Data for Exercise 11.35

Decade	Total U.S. Births (millions)	Number of Software Millionaire Birthdays	Number of CEO Birthdays (in a random sample of 70 companies from the *Fortune* 500 list)
1920	28.582	3	2
1930	24.374	1	2
1940	31.666	10	23
1950	40.530	14	38
1960	38.808	7	9
1970	33.309	4	0

Source: Sauro, J. "Were most software millionaires born around 1955?" *Measuring Usability,* November 17, 2010. Copyright © 2010 by Measuring Usability LLC. Reprinted with permission.

b. Find SSE, s^2, and s for the simple linear regression model relating number (y) of software millionaire birthdays in a decade to number (x) of CEO birthdays.

c. Which of the two models' fit will have smaller errors of prediction? Why?

Applying the Concepts—Intermediate

11.36 Public corruption and bad weather. Refer to the *Journal of Law and Economics* (Nov. 2008) study of the link between Federal Emergency Management Agency (FEMA) disaster relief and public corruption, Exercise 11.20 (p. 616). You used the data in the file to fit a straight-line model relating a state's average annual number of public corruption convictions (y) to the state's average annual FEMA relief (x).

FEMA

a. Estimate σ^2, the variance of the random error term in the model.

b. Estimate σ, the standard deviation of the random error term in the model.

c. Which of the estimates, part **a** or **b**, can be interpreted practically? Why?

d. Make a statement about how accurate the model is in predicting a state's average annual number of public corruption convictions.

11.37 Sweetness of orange juice. Refer to the study of the quality of orange juice produced at a juice manufacturing plant, Exercise 11.22 (p. 616). Recall that simple linear regression was used to predict the sweetness index (y) from the amount of pectin (x) in the orange juice.

OJUICE

a. Find the values of SSE, s^2, and s for this regression.

b. Explain why it is difficult to give a practical interpretation to s^2.

c. Give a practical interpretation of the value of s.

11.38 Are geography journals worth their cost? Refer to the *Geoforum* (Vol. 37, 2006) study of whether the price of a geography journal is correlated with quality, Exercise 2.127 (p. 105). Several quantitative variables were recorded for each in a sample of 28 geography journals: cost of a 1-year subscription (dollars); Journal Impact Factor (JIF)—the average number of times articles from the journal have been cited; number of citations for the journal over the past 5 years; and Relative Price Index (RPI). The data for the 28 journals are saved in the file. (Selected observations are listed below.)

GEOJRN

Journal	Cost ($)	JIF	Cites	RPI
J. Econ. Geogr.	468	3.139	207	1.16
Prog. Hum. Geog.	624	2.943	544	0.77
T. I. Brit. Geogr.	499	2.388	249	1.11
Econ. Geogr.	90	2.325	173	0.30
A. A. A. Geogr.	698	2.115	377	0.93
Geogr. Anal.	213	0.902	106	0.88
Geogr. J.	223	0.857	81	0.94
Appl. Geogr.	646	0.853	74	3.38

Source: Based on Blomley, N. "Is this journal worth US$1118?" *Geoforum*, Vol. 37, 2006.

a. Fit a straight-line model relating cost (y) to JIF (x). Find an estimate of σ, the standard deviation of the error term, and interpret its value.

b. Fit a straight-line model relating cost (y) to number of citations (x). Find an estimate of σ, the standard deviation of the error term, and interpret its value.

c. Fit a straight-line model relating cost (y) to RPI (x). Find an estimate of σ, the standard deviation of the error term, and interpret its value.

d. Which predictor of cost—JIF, number of citations, or RPI—leads to a regression line with the smallest errors of prediction?

11.39 FCAT scores and poverty. Refer to the *Journal of Educational and Behavioral Statistics* (Spring 2004) study of scores on the Florida Comprehensive Assessment Test (FCAT), Exercise 11.24 (p. 617).

FCAT

a. Consider the simple linear regression relating math score (y) to percentage (x) of students below the poverty level. Find and interpret the value of s for this regression.

b. Consider the simple linear regression relating reading score (y) to percentage (x) of students below the poverty level. Find and interpret the value of s for this regression.

c. Which dependent variable, math score or reading score, can be more accurately predicted by percentage (x) of students below the poverty level? Explain.

Applying the Concepts—Advanced

11.40 Life tests of cutting tools. To improve the quality of the output of any production process, it is necessary first to understand the capabilities of the process (Gitlow, et al., *Quality Management: Tools and Methods for Improvement,* 1995). In a particular manufacturing process, the useful life of a cutting tool is related to the speed at which the tool is operated. The data in the table below were derived from life tests for the two different brands of cutting tools currently used in the production process. For which brand would you feel more confident in using the least squares line to predict useful life for a given cutting speed? Explain.

TOOLS

Cutting Speed (meters per minute)	Useful Life (Hours) Brand A	Brand B
30	4.5	6.0
30	3.5	6.5
30	5.2	5.0
40	5.2	6.0
40	4.0	4.5
40	2.5	5.0
50	4.4	4.5
50	2.8	4.0
50	1.0	3.7
60	4.0	3.8
60	2.0	3.0
60	1.1	2.4
70	1.1	1.5
70	.5	2.0
70	3.0	1.0

11.4 Assessing the Utility of the Model: Making Inferences about the Slope β_1

Now that we have specified the probability distribution of ε and found an estimate of the variance σ^2, we are ready to make statistical inferences about the model's usefulness for predicting the response y. This is step 4 in our regression modeling procedure.

Refer again to the data of Table 11.1 and suppose the appliance store's sales revenue is *completely unrelated* to the advertising expenditure. What could be said about the values of β_0 and β_1 in the hypothesized probabilistic model

$$y = \beta_0 + \beta_1 x + \varepsilon$$

if x contributes no information for the prediction of y? The implication is that the mean of y—that is, the deterministic part of the model $E(y) = \beta_0 + \beta_1 x$—does not change as x changes. In the straight-line model, this means that the true slope, β_1, is equal to 0 (see Figure 11.11). Therefore, to test the null hypothesis that the linear model contributes no information for the prediction of y against the alternative hypothesis that the linear model is useful in predicting y, we test

$$H_0: \beta_1 = 0 \text{ against } H_a: \beta_1 \neq 0$$

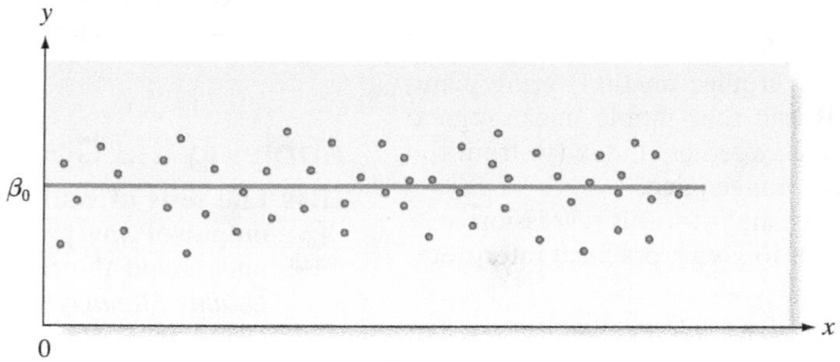

Figure 11.11
Graph of the straight-line model when slope is zero, i.e., $y = \beta_0 + \varepsilon$

If the data support the alternative hypothesis, we will conclude that x does contribute information for the prediction of y using the straight-line model (although the true relationship between $E[y]$ and x could be more complex than a straight line). Thus, in effect, this is a test of the usefulness of the hypothesized model.

The appropriate test statistic is found by considering the sampling distribution of $\hat{\beta}_1$, the least squares estimator of the slope β_1, as shown in the following box.

Sampling Distribution of $\hat{\beta}_1$

If we make the four assumptions about ε (see Section 11.3), the sampling distribution of the least squares estimator $\hat{\beta}_1$ of the slope will be normal with mean β_1 (the true slope) and standard deviation

$$\sigma_{\hat{\beta}_1} = \frac{\sigma}{\sqrt{SS_{xx}}} \quad \text{(see Figure 11.12)}$$

We estimate $\sigma_{\hat{\beta}_1}$ by $s_{\hat{\beta}_1} = \frac{s}{\sqrt{SS_{xx}}}$ and refer to this quantity as the **estimated standard error of the least squares slope $\hat{\beta}_1$.**

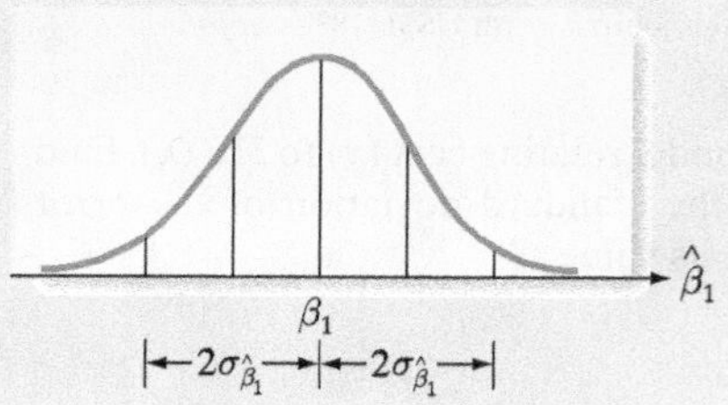

Figure 11.12
Sampling distribution of $\hat{\beta}_1$

Because σ is usually unknown, the appropriate test statistic is a t-statistic, formed as follows:

$$t = \frac{\hat{\beta}_1 - \text{Hypothesized value of } \beta_1}{s_{\hat{\beta}_1}} \qquad \text{where } s_{\hat{\beta}} = \frac{s}{\sqrt{SS_{xx}}}$$

Thus,

$$t = \frac{\hat{\beta}_1 - 0}{s/\sqrt{SS_{xx}}}$$

Note that we have substituted the estimator s for σ and then formed the estimated standard error $s_{\hat{\beta}_1}$ by dividing s by $\sqrt{SS_{xx}}$. The number of degrees of freedom associated with this t-statistic is the same as the number of degrees of freedom associated with s. Recall that this number is $(n - 2)$ df when the hypothesized model is a straight line (see Section 11.3). The setup of our test of the usefulness of the straight-line model is summarized in the following boxes.

A Test of Model Utility: Simple Linear Regression

One-Tailed Test	Two-Tailed Test
$H_0: \beta_1 = 0$ $H_a: \beta_1 < 0$ (or $H_a: \beta_1 > 0$)	$H_0: \beta_1 = 0$ $H_a: \beta_1 \neq 0$
	Test statistic: $t = \frac{\hat{\beta}_1}{s_{\hat{\beta}_1}} = \frac{\hat{\beta}_1}{s/\sqrt{SS_{xx}}}$
Rejection region: $t < -t_\alpha$ (or $t > t_\alpha$ when $H_a: \beta_1 > 0$)	*Rejection region:* $\lvert t\rvert > t_{\alpha/2}$

where t_α and $t_{\alpha/2}$ are based on $(n - 2)$ degrees of freedom

Conditions Required for a Valid Test: Simple Linear Regression

Refer to the four assumptions about ε listed in Section 11.3.

Example 11.3

Testing the Regression Slope, β_1—Sales Revenue Model

Problem Refer to the simple linear regression analysis of the advertising-sales data, Examples 11.1 and 11.2. Conduct a test (at $\alpha = .05$) to determine if sales revenue (y) is linearly related to advertising expenditure (x).

Solution As stated previously, we want to test $H_0: \beta_1 = 0$ against $H_a: \beta_1 \neq 0$. For this example, $n = 5$. Thus t will be based on $n - 2 = 3$ df, and the rejection region (at $\alpha = .05$) will be

$$|t| > t_{.025} = 3.182$$

We previously calculated $\hat{\beta}_1 = .7$, $s = .61$, and $SS_{xx} = 10$. Thus, the test statistic is

$$t = \frac{\hat{\beta}_1}{s/\sqrt{SS_{xx}}} = \frac{.7}{.61/\sqrt{10}} = \frac{.7}{.19} = 3.7$$

Because this calculated t-value falls into the upper-tail rejection region (see Figure 11.13), we reject the null hypothesis and conclude that the slope β_1 is not 0. The sample evidence indicates that advertising expenditure x contributes information for the production of sales revenue y when a linear model is used.

[*Note:* We can reach the same conclusion by using the observed significance level (p-value) of the test from a computer printout. The Minitab printout for the advertising-sales example is reproduced in Figure 11.14. The test statistic and *two-tailed* p-value are highlighted on the printout. Because the p-value is smaller than $\alpha = .05$, we will reject H_0.]

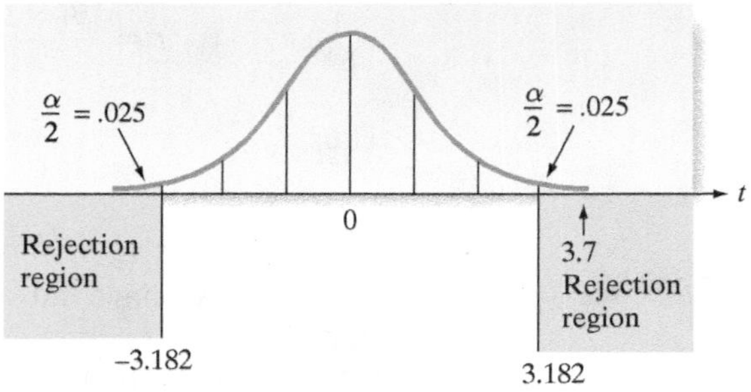

Figure 11.13
Rejection region and calculated t-value for testing H_0: $\beta_1 = 0$ versus H_a: $\beta_1 \neq 0$

Regression Analysis: SALES_Y versus ADVEXP_X

```
The regression equation is
SALES_Y = - 0.100 + 0.700 ADVEXP_X

Predictor      Coef   SE Coef      T      P
Constant    -0.1000    0.6351  -0.16  0.885
ADVEXP_X     0.7000    0.1915   3.66  0.035

S = 0.605530    R-Sq = 81.7%    R-Sq(adj) = 75.6%

Analysis of Variance

Source          DF      SS      MS      F      P
Regression       1  4.9000  4.9000  13.36  0.035
Residual Error   3  1.1000  0.3667
Total            4  6.0000
```

Figure 11.14
Minitab printout for the advertising-sales regression

Look Back What conclusion can be drawn if the calculated t-value does not fall in the rejection region or if the observed significance level of the test exceeds α? We know from previous discussions of the philosophy of hypothesis testing that such a t-value does *not* lead us to accept the null hypothesis—that is, we do not conclude that $\beta_1 = 0$. Additional data might indicate that β_1 differs from 0, or a more complex relationship may exist between x and y, requiring the fitting of a model other than the straight-line model. We discuss several such models in Chapter 12.

■ **Now Work Exercise 11.46**

Interpreting p-Values for β Coefficients in Regression

Almost all statistical computer software packages report a *two-tailed* p-value for each of the β parameters in the regression model. For example, in simple linear regression, the p-value for the two-tailed test H_0: $\beta_1 = 0$ versus H_a: $\beta_1 \neq 0$ is given on the printout. If you want to conduct a *one-tailed* test of hypothesis, you will need to adjust the p-value reported on the printout as follows:

$$\textit{Upper-tailed test } (H_a\text{: } \beta_1 > 0)\text{:} \quad p\text{-value} = \begin{cases} p/2 & \text{if } t > 0 \\ 1 - p/2 & \text{if } t < 0 \end{cases}$$

$$\textit{Lower-tailed test } (H_a\text{: } \beta_1 < 0)\text{:} \quad p\text{-value} = \begin{cases} p/2 & \text{if } t < 0 \\ 1 - p/2 & \text{if } t > 0 \end{cases}$$

where p is the p-value reported on the printout and t is the value of the test statistic.

Another way to make inferences about the slope β_1 is to estimate it using a confidence interval. This interval is formed as shown in the next box.

A 100(1 − α)% Confidence Interval for the Simple Linear Regression Slope β_1

$$\hat{\beta}_1 \pm t_{\alpha/2} s_{\hat{\beta}_1}$$

where the estimated standard error $\hat{\beta}_1$ is calculated by

$$s_{\hat{\beta}_1} = \frac{s}{\sqrt{SS_{xx}}}$$

and $t_{\alpha/2}$ is based on $(n - 2)$ degrees of freedom.

Conditions Required for a Valid Confidence Interval: Simple Linear Regression

Refer to the four assumptions about ϵ listed in Section 11.3.

For the simple linear regression of sales revenue (Examples 11.1–11.3), $t_{\alpha/2}$ is based on $(n - 2) = 3$ degrees of freedom, and, for $\alpha = .05$, $t_{.025} = 3.182$. Therefore, a 95% confidence interval for the slope β_1, the expected change in sales revenue for a \$100 increase in advertising expenditure, is

$$\hat{\beta}_1 \pm (t_{.025})s_{\hat{\beta}_1} = .7 \pm 3.182\left(\frac{s}{\sqrt{SS_{xx}}}\right) = .7 \pm 3.182\left(\frac{.61}{\sqrt{10}}\right) = .7 \pm .61$$

Thus, the interval estimate of the slope parameter β_1 is .09 to 1.31. [*Note:* This interval can also be obtained using statistical software and is highlighted on the SPSS printout, Figure 11.15.] In terms of this example, the implication is that we can be 95% confident that the *true* mean increase in monthly sales revenue per additional \$100 of advertising expenditure is between \$90 and \$1,310. This inference is meaningful only over the sampled range of x—that is, from \$100 to \$500 of advertising expenditures.

Coefficients[a]

Model		Unstandardized Coefficients B	Unstandardized Coefficients Std. Error	Standardized Coefficients Beta	t	Sig.	95% Confidence Interval for B Lower Bound	95% Confidence Interval for B Upper Bound
1	(Constant)	-.100	.635		-.157	.885	-2.121	1.921
	ADVEXP_X	.700	.191	.904	3.656	.035	.091	1.309

a. Dependent Variable: SALES_Y

Figure 11.15
SPSS printout with 95% confidence intervals for the advertising-sales regression β's

Because all the values in this interval are positive, it appears that β_1 is positive and that the mean of y, $E(y)$, increases as x increases. However, the rather large width of the confidence interval reflects the small number of data points (and, consequently, a lack of information) in the experiment. Particularly bothersome is the fact that the lower end of the confidence interval implies that we are not even recovering our additional expenditure because a \$100 increase in advertising may produce as little as a \$90 increase in mean sales. If we wish to tighten this interval, we need to increase the sample size.

Assessing How Well a Straight-Line Regression Model Fits Data

In the previous *Statistics in Action Revisited,* we fit the straight-line model, $E(y) = \beta_0 + \beta_1 x$, where x = cumulative 6-month advertising expenditures and y represents either the number of new PI cases or the number of new WC cases per month. The SPSS regression printouts for the two analyses are shown in Figure SIA11.3. (The regression for y = number of new PI cases is shown at the top, and the regression for y = number of new WC cases is shown at the bottom of the printout.) The objective is to determine whether one or both of the dependent variables are statistically linearly related to cumulative 6-month advertising expenditures.

The two-tailed p-values for testing the null hypothesis, H_0: $\beta_1 = 0$ (highlighted on the printouts), are p-value $\approx$ 0 for number of new PI cases and p-value = .725 for number

STATISTICS in ACTION REVISITED CONTINUED

Coefficients[a]

Model		Unstandardized Coefficients B	Std. Error	Standardized Coefficients Beta	t	Sig.	95% Confidence Interval for B Lower Bound	Upper Bound
1	(Constant)	7.767	3.385		2.295	.027	.926	14.609
	CUM. ADV (thous)	.113	.028	.539	4.042	.000	.056	.169

a. Dependent Variable: New PI Cases

Coefficients[a]

Model		Unstandardized Coefficients B	Std. Error	Standardized Coefficients Beta	t	Sig.	95% Confidence Interval for B Lower Bound	Upper Bound
1	(Constant)	24.574	3.367		7.299	.000	17.770	31.379
	CUM. ADV (thous)	.010	.028	.056	.354	.725	−.046	.066

a. Dependent Variable: New WC Cases

Figure SIA11.3
SPSS simple linear regressions for legal advertising data

of new WC cases. For y = number of new PI cases, there is sufficient evidence to reject H_0 (at $\alpha = .01$) and conclude that number of new PI cases is linearly related to cumulative 6-month advertising expenditures. In contrast, for y = number of WC cases, there is insufficient evidence to reject H_0 (at $\alpha = .01$); thus, there is no evidence of a linear relationship between the number of new WC cases and cumulative 6-month advertising expenditures.

We can gain further insight into this phenomenon by examining a 95% confidence interval for the slope, β_1. For y = number of new PI cases, the interval (highlighted on the SPSS printout) is (.056, .169). With 95% confidence, we can state that for every $1,000 increase in monthly advertising expenditures, the number of new PI cases each month will increase between .056 and .169. Now, a more realistic increase in cumulative 6-month advertising expenditures is, say, $20,000. Multiplying the endpoints of the interval by 20, we see that this increase in advertising spending leads to an increase of anywhere between 1 and 3 new PI cases.

Now, for y = number of new WC cases, the 95% confidence interval for the slope (also highlighted on the SPSS printout) is (−.046, .066). Because the interval spans the value 0, we draw the same conclusion as we did with the hypothesis test—there is no statistical evidence of a linear relationship between the number of new WC cases and cumulative 6-month advertising expenditures.

Recall that partner A (who handled the PI cases) sued partner B (who handled the WC cases) for not paying a fair share of the advertising expenses. These results do not support partner A's argument because there is no evidence that partner B benefitted from advertising.

Exercises 11.41–11.58

Learning the Mechanics

11.41 Construct both a 95% and a 90% confidence interval for β_1 for each of the following cases:

a. $\hat{\beta}_1 = 31, s = 3, \text{SS}_{xx} = 35, n = 10$
b. $\hat{\beta}_1 = 64, \text{SSE} = 1{,}960, \text{SS}_{xx} = 30, n = 14$
c. $\hat{\beta}_1 = -8.4, \text{SSE} = 146, \text{SS}_{xx} = 64, n = 20$

11.42 Consider the following pairs of observations:

L11042

x	1	4	3	2	5	6	0
y	1	3	3	1	4	7	2

a. Construct a scatterplot for the data.
b. Use the method of least squares to fit a straight line to the seven data points in the table.
c. Plot the least squares line on your scatterplot of part **a.**
d. Specify the null and alternative hypotheses you would use to test whether the data provide sufficient evidence to indicate that x contributes information for the (linear) prediction of y.
e. What is the test statistic that should be used in conducting the hypothesis test of part **d?** Specify the degrees of freedom associated with the test statistic.
f. Conduct the hypothesis test of part **d** using $\alpha = .05$.

11.43 Refer to Exercise 11.42. Construct an 80% and a 98% confidence interval for β_1.

11.44 Do the accompanying data provide sufficient evidence to conclude that a straight line is useful for characterizing the relationship between x and y?

L11044

x	4	2	4	3	2	4
y	1	6	5	3	2	4

Applying the Concepts—Basic

11.45 State Math SAT Scores. Refer to the SPSS simple linear regression relating y = average state SAT Math score in 2011 with x = average state SAT Math score in 2001, Exercise 11.15 (p. 614).
SATMAT

a. Give the null and alternative hypotheses for determining whether a positive linear relationship exists between y and x.

b. Locate the p-value of the test on the SPSS printout. Interpret the result if $\alpha = .05$.

c. Find a 95% confidence interval for the slope, β_1. Interpret the result.

11.46 Lobster fishing study. Refer to the *Bulletin of Marine Science* (April 2010) study of teams of fishermen fishing for the red spiny lobster in Baja California Sur, Mexico, Exercise 11.16 (p. 614). A simple linear regression model relating y = total catch of lobsters (in kilograms) and x = average percentage of traps allocated per day to exploring areas of unknown catch (called *search frequency*) was fit to the data in the file. A portion of the XLSTAT printout is reproduced at the bottom of the page.
NW TRAPS

a. Give the null and alternative hypotheses for testing whether total catch (y) is negatively linearly related to search frequency (x).

b. Find the p-value of the test on the XLSTAT printout.

c. Give the appropriate conclusion of the test, part **c**, using $\alpha = .05$.

11.47 Congress voting on women's issues. The *American Economic Review* (March 2008) published research on how the gender mix of a U.S. legislator's children can influence the legislator's votes in Congress. Specifically, the researcher investigated how having daughters influences voting on women's issues. The American Association of University Women (AAUW) uses voting records of each member of Congress to compute an AAUW score, where higher scores indicate more favorable voting for women's rights. The researcher modeled AAUW score (y) as a function of the number of daughters (x) a legislator has. Data collected for the 434 members of the 107th Congress were used to fit the straight-line model, $E(y) = \beta_0 + \beta_1 x$.

a. If it is true that having daughters influences voting on women's issues, will the sign of β_1 be positive or negative? Explain.

b. The following statistics were reported in the article: $\hat{\beta}_1 = .27$ and $s_{\hat{\beta}_1} = .74$. Find a 95% confidence interval for β_1.

c. Use the result, part **b**, to make an inference about the model. [*Note:* We will return to this problem in Chapter 12 and consider a more complex model for AAUW score.]

11.48 Generation Y's entitlement mentality. The current workforce is dominated by "Generation Y"—people born between 1982 and 1999. These workers have a reputation as having an entitlement mentality (e.g., they believe they have a right to a high-paying job, without the work ethic). The reasons behind this phenomenon were investigated in *Proceedings of the Academy of Educational Leadership* (Vol. 16, 2011). A sample of 272 undergraduate business students was administered a questionnaire designed to capture the behaviors that lead to an entitlement mentality. The responses were used to measure the following two quantitative variables for each student: entitlement score (y)—where higher scores indicate a greater level of entitlement, and "helicopter parents" score (x)—where higher scores indicate that the student's parents had a higher level of involvement in his or her everyday experiences and problems.

a. Give the equation of a simple linear regression model relating y to x.

b. The researchers theorize that helicopter parents lead to an entitlement mentality. Based on this theory, would you expect β_0 to be positive or negative (or are you unsure)? Would you expect β_1 to be positive or negative (or are you unsure)? Explain.

c. The p-value for testing H_0: $\beta_1 = 0$ versus H_a: $\beta_1 > 0$ was reported as .002. Use this result to test the researchers' entitlement theory at $\alpha = .01$.

11.49 Drug controlled-release rate study. Refer to the simple linear regression analysis relating y = drug release rate to x = surface-area-to-volume ratio, Exercise 11.17 (p. 615). Use the results of the regression to form a 90% confidence interval for the slope, β_1. Interpret the result.
DOW

11.50 Sweetness of orange juice. Refer to the simple linear regression relating y = sweetness index of an orange juice sample with x = amount of water-soluble pectin, Exercise 11.22 (p. 616). Use the results of the regression to form a 95% confidence interval for the slope, β_1. Interpret the result.
OJUICE

Applying the Concepts—Intermediate

11.51 Software millionaires and birthdays. Refer to Exercise 11.19 (p. 615) and the study of whether birth decade can predict the number of software millionaires born in the decade. The data are reproduced in the next table (p. 630).
BDAYS

Model parameters:

Source	Value	Standard error	t	Pr > |t|	Lower bound (95%)	Upper bound (95%)
Intercept	9877.8300	829.0411	11.9148	< 0.0001	8086.7957	11668.8643
SEARCHFR	-163.6024	41.9014	-3.9045	0.0018	-254.1249	-73.0799

Equation of the model:

CATCH = 9877.82997–163.60242*SEARCHFREQ

XLSTAT output for Exercise 11.46

Data for Exercise 11.51

Decade	Total U.S. Births (millions)	Number of Software Millionaire Birthdays	Number of CEO Birthdays (in a random sample of 70 companies from the *Fortune* 500 list)
1920	28.582	3	2
1930	24.374	1	2
1940	31.666	10	23
1950	40.530	14	38
1960	38.808	7	9
1970	33.309	4	0

Source: Sauro, J. "Were most software millionaires born around 1955?" *Measuring Usability,* November 17, 2010.

a. Construct a 95% confidence interval for the slope of the model, $E(y) = \beta_0 + \beta_1 x$, where x = total number of U.S. births and y = number of software millionaire birthdays. Give a practical interpretation of the interval.

b. Construct a 95% confidence interval for the slope of the model, $E(y) = \beta_0 + \beta_1 x$, where x = number of CEO birthdays (in a sample of 70 companies) and y = number of software millionaire birthdays. Give a practical interpretation of the interval.

c. Can you conclude that number of software millionaires born in a decade is linearly related to total number of people born in the United States? Number of CEOs born in the decade?

11.52 Beauty and electoral success. Are good looks an advantage when running for political office? This was the question of interest in an article published in the *Journal of Public Economics* (Feb. 2010). The researchers focused on a sample of 641 nonincumbent candidates for political office in Finland. Photos of each candidate were evaluated by non-Finnish subjects; each evaluator assigned a beauty rating—measured on a scale of 1 (lowest rating) to 5 (highest rating)—to each candidate. The beauty ratings for each candidate were averaged, then the average was divided by the standard deviation for all candidates to yield a beauty index for each candidate. (*Note:* A 1-unit increase in the index represents a 1-standard-deviation increase in the beauty rating.) The relative success (measured as a percentage of votes obtained) of each candidate was used as the dependent variable (y) in a regression analysis. One of the independent variables in the model was beauty index (x).

a. Write the equation of a simple linear regression relating y to x.

b. Does the y-intercept of the equation, part **a,** have a practical interpretation? Explain.

c. The article reported the estimated slope of the equation, part **a,** as 22.91. Give a practical interpretation of this value.

d. The standard error of the slope estimate was reported as 3.73. Use this information and the estimate from part **c** to conduct a test for a positive slope at $\alpha = .01$. Give the appropriate conclusion in the words of the problem.

11.53 Ranking driving performance of professional golfers. Refer to *The Sport Journal* (Winter 2007) study of a new method for ranking the total driving performance of golfers on the PGA tour, Exercise 11.21 (p. 616). You fit a straight-line model relating driving accuracy (y) to driving distance (x) to the data saved in the file.

PGA

a. Give the null and alternative hypotheses for testing whether driving accuracy (y) decreases linearly as driving distance (x) increases.

b. Find the test statistic and p-value of the test, part **a.**

c. Make the appropriate conclusion at $\alpha = .01$.

11.54 Are geography journals worth their cost? Refer to the *Geoforum* (Vol. 37, 2006) study of whether the price of a geography journal is correlated with quality, Exercise 11.38 (p. 623).

GEOJRN

a. In Exercise 11.38a, you fit a straight-line model relating cost (y) to JIF (x). Find and interpret a 95% confidence interval for the slope of the line.

b. In Exercise 11.38b, you fit a straight-line model relating cost (y) to number of citations (x). Find and interpret a 95% confidence interval for the slope of the line.

c. In Exercise 11.38c, you fit a straight-line model relating cost (y) to RPI (x). Find and interpret a 95% confidence interval for the slope of the line.

11.55 Survey of the top business schools. Refer to the *Wall Street Journal* (Sep. 25, 2005) Business School Survey, Exercise 11.25 (p. 618). If you pay more in tuition to go to a top business school, will it necessarily result in a higher probability of a job offer at graduation? Let y = percentage of graduates with job offers and x = tuition cost; then fit the simple linear model, $E(y) = \beta_0 + \beta_1 x$, to the data in the file. Is there sufficient evidence (at $\alpha = .10$) of a positive linear relationship between y and x?

TOPBUS

11.56 Public corruption and bad weather. Refer to the *Journal of Law and Economics* (Nov. 2008) study of the link between Federal Emergency Management Agency (FEMA) disaster relief and public corruption, Exercise 11.20 (p. 616). Evaluate the overall adequacy of the straight-line model relating a state's average annual number of public corruption convictions (y) to the state's average annual FEMA relief (x). Use $\alpha = .01$.

FEMA

Applying the Concepts—Advanced

11.57 Does elevation impact hitting performance in baseball? Refer to the *Chance* (Winter 2006) investigation of the effects of elevation on slugging percentage in Major League Baseball, Exercise 2.125 (p. 104). Recall that data were compiled on players' composite slugging percentage at each of 29 cities for a recent season, as well as each city's elevation (feet above sea level). The data are saved in the file. (Selected observations are shown in the table on the following page.) Consider a straight-line model relating slugging percentage (y) to elevation (x).

MLBPKS

a. Is there sufficient evidence (at $\alpha = .01$) of a positive linear relationship between elevation (x) and slugging percentage (y)?.

Selected data for Exercise 11.57

City	Slug Pct.	Elevation
Anaheim	.480	160
Arlington	.605	616
Atlanta	.530	1,050
Baltimore	.505	130
Boston	.505	20
⋮	⋮	⋮
Denver	.625	5,277
⋮	⋮	⋮
Seattle	.550	350
San Francisco	.510	63
St. Louis	.570	465
Tampa	.500	10
Toronto	.535	566

Source: Based on Schaffer, J., & Heiny, E.L. "The effects of elevation on slugging percentage in Major League Baseball," *Chance*, Vol. 19, No. 1, Winter 2006 (adapted from Figure 2, p. 30).

b. Construct a scatterplot for the data and draw the least squares line on the graph. Locate the data point for Denver on the graph. What do you observe?

c. You learned in Exercise 2.125 that the Colorado Rockies, who play their home games in Coors Field, Denver, typically lead the league in team slugging percentage. Many baseball experts attribute this to the "thin air" of Denver—called the "mile-high" city due to its elevation. Remove the data point for Denver from the data set and refit the straight-line model to the remaining data. What conclusions can you draw about the "thin air" theory from this analysis?

11.58 Spreading rate of spilled liquid. Refer to the *Chemical Engineering Progress* (Jan. 2005) study of the rate at which a spilled volatile liquid will spread across a surface, Exercise 11.26 (p. 618). Recall that the data on mass of the spill and elapsed time of the spill are saved in the file. Is there sufficient evidence (at $\alpha = .05$) to indicate that the mass of the spill tends to diminish linearly as time increases? If so, give an interval estimate (with 95% confidence) of the decrease in spill mass for each minute of elapsed time.

LSPILL

11.5 The Coefficients of Correlation and Determination

In this section, we present two statistics that describe the adequacy of a model: the *coefficient of correlation* and the *coefficient of determination.*

Coefficient of Correlation

Recall (from Section 2.10) that a **bivariate relationship** describes a relationship—or correlation—between two variables, x and y. Scatterplots are used to graphically describe a bivariate relationship. In this section, we will discuss the concept of **correlation** and show how it can be used to measure the linear relationship between two variables x and y. A numerical descriptive measure of the linear association between x and y is provided by the *coefficient of correlation, r.*

The **coefficient of correlation,*** r, is a measure of the strength of the *linear* relationship between two variables x and y. It is computed (for a sample of n measurements on x and y) as follows:

$$r = \frac{SS_{xy}}{\sqrt{SS_{xx}SS_{yy}}}$$

where

$$SS_{xy} = \Sigma(x - \bar{x})(y - \bar{y})$$
$$SS_{xx} = \Sigma(x - \bar{x})^2$$
$$SS_{yy} = \Sigma(y - \bar{y})^2$$

Note that the computational formula for the correlation coefficient r given in the definition involves the same quantities that were used in computing the least squares prediction equation. In fact, because the numerators of the expressions for $\hat{\beta}_1$ and r are

*The value of r is often called the *Pearson correlation coefficient* to honor its developer, Karl Pearson. (See Biography, p. 566.)

identical, you can see that $r = 0$ when $\hat{\beta}_1 = 0$ (the case where x contributes no information for the prediction of y), and r is positive when the slope is positive and negative when the slope is negative. Unlike $\hat{\beta}_1$, the correlation coefficient r is *scaleless* and assumes a value between -1 and $+1$, regardless of the units of x and y.

A value of r near or equal to 0 implies little or no linear relationship between y and x. In contrast, the closer r comes to 1 or -1, the stronger the linear relationship between y and x. And if $r = 1$ or $r = -1$, all the sample points fall exactly on the least squares line. Positive values of r imply a positive linear relationship between y and x; that is, y increases as x increases. Negative values of r imply a negative linear relationship between y and x; that is, y decreases as x increases. Each of these situations is portrayed in Figure 11.16.

Now Work Exercise 11.60

We demonstrate how to calculate the coefficient of correlation r using the data in Table 11.1 for the advertising-sales example. The quantities needed to calculate r are SS_{xy}, SS_{xx}, and SS_{yy}. The first two quantities have been calculated previously as $SS_{xy} = 7$ and $SS_{xx} = 10$. The calculation for $SS_{yy} = \Sigma(y - \bar{y})^2$ is shown on the last column of the Excel spreadsheet, Figure 11.5 (p. 000). The result is $SS_{yy} = 6$.

We now find the coefficient of correlation:

$$r = \frac{SS_{xy}}{\sqrt{SS_{xx}SS_{yy}}} = \frac{7}{\sqrt{(10)(6)}} = \frac{7}{\sqrt{60}} = .904$$

The fact that r is positive and near 1 in value indicates that the sales revenue y tends to increase as advertising expenditure x increases—*for this sample of 5 months.* This is the same conclusion we reached when we found the calculated value of the least squares slope to be positive.

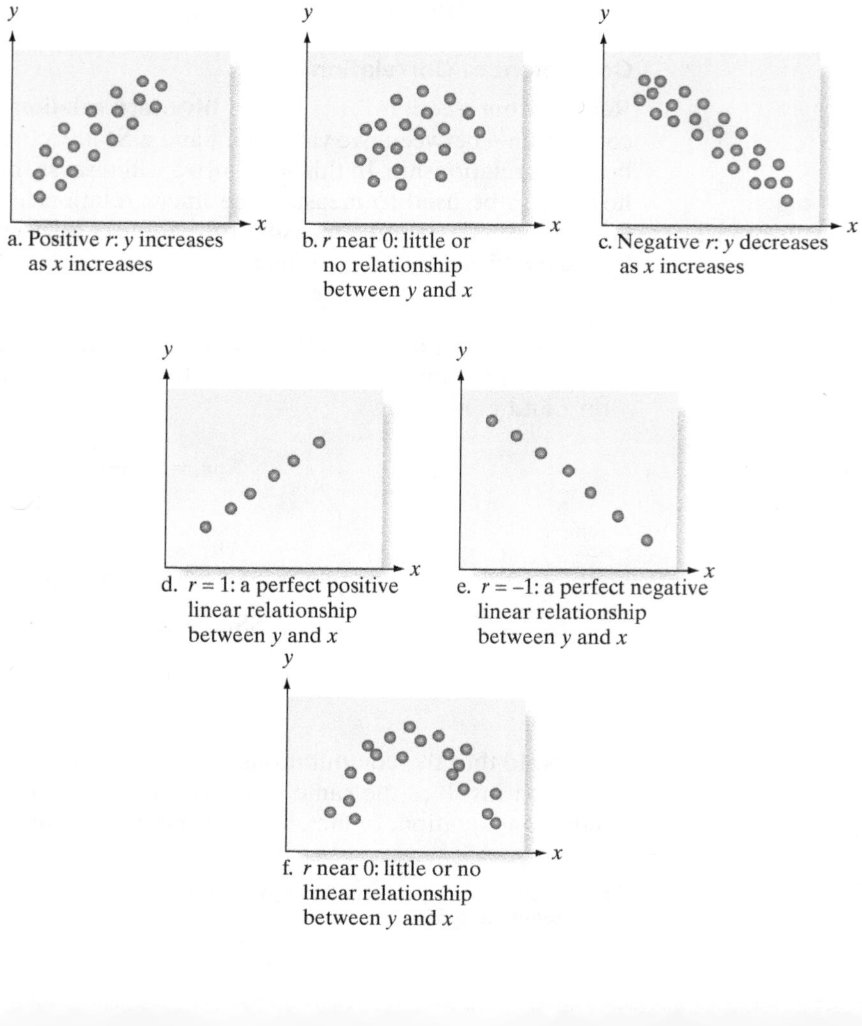

Figure 11.16
Values of r and their implications

Example 11.4

Using the Correlation Coefficient—Relating Crime Rate and Casino Employment

Problem Legalized gambling is available on several riverboat casinos operated by a city in Mississippi. The mayor of the city wants to know the correlation between the number of casino employees and the yearly crime rate. The records for the past 10 years are examined, and the results listed in Table 11.3 are obtained. Calculate the coefficient of correlation r for the data. Interpret the result.

Table 11.3 Data on Casino Employees and Crime Rate, Example 11.4

Year	Number of Casino Employees, x (thousands)	Crime Rate, y (number of crimes per 1,000 population)
2003	15	1.35
2004	18	1.63
2005	24	2.33
2006	22	2.41
2007	25	2.63
2008	29	2.93
2009	30	3.41
2010	32	3.26
2011	35	3.63
2012	38	4.15

Data Set: CASINO

Solution Rather than use the computing formula given in the definition, we resort to using a statistical software package. The data of Table 11.3 were entered into a computer, and Minitab was used to compute r. The Minitab printout is shown in Figure 11.17.

Correlations: EMPLOYEES, CRIMERAT

```
Pearson correlation of EMPLOYEES and CRIMERAT = 0.987
P-Value = 0.000
```

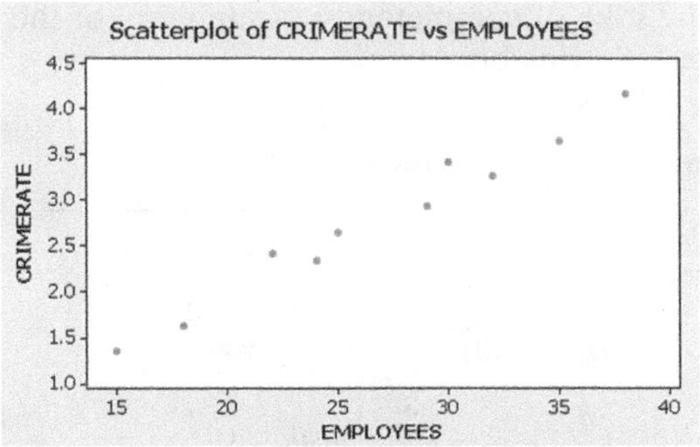

Figure 11.17
Minitab correlation printout for Example 11.4

The coefficient of correlation, highlighted at the top on the printout, is $r = .987$. Thus, the size of the casino workforce and crime rate in this city are very highly correlated—at least over the past 10 years. The implication is that a strong positive linear relationship exists between these variables (see the scatterplot at the bottom of Figure 11.17). We must be careful, however, not to jump to any unwarranted conclusions. For instance, the mayor may be tempted to conclude that hiring more casino workers next year will increase the crime rate—that is, that there is a *causal relationship* between the two variables. However, high correlation does not imply causality. The fact is, many things have probably contributed both to the increase in the casino workforce and to the increase in crime rate. The city's tourist trade has undoubtedly grown since riverboat casinos were legalized, and it is likely that the casinos have expanded both in services offered and in number. *We cannot infer a causal relationship on the basis of high sample correlation. When a high correlation is observed in the sample data, the only safe conclusion is that a linear trend may exist between* x *and* y.

ETHICS in STATISTICS

Intentionally using the correlation coefficient only to make an inference about the relationship between two variables in situations where a nonlinear relationship may exist is considered *unethical statistical practice.*

Look Back Another variable, such as the increase in tourism, may be the underlying cause of the high correlation between x and y.

Now Work Exercise 11.75

> ⚠ **CAUTION** When using the sample correlation coefficient, r, to infer the nature of the relationship between x and y, two caveats exist: (1) A *high correlation* does not necessarily imply that a causal relationship exists between x and y—only that a linear trend may exist; (2) a *low correlation* does not necessarily imply that x and y are unrelated—only that x and y are not strongly *linearly* related.

Keep in mind that the correlation coefficient r measures the linear association between x values and y values in the sample, and a similar linear coefficient of correlation exists for the population from which the data points were selected. The **population correlation coefficient** is denoted by the symbol ρ (rho). As you might expect, ρ is estimated by the corresponding sample statistic, r. Or, instead of estimating ρ, we might want to test the null hypothesis H_0: $\rho = 0$ against H_a: $\rho \neq 0$—that is, we can test the hypothesis that x contributes no information for the prediction of y by using the straight-line model against the alternative that the two variables are at least linearly related.

However, we already performed this *identical* test in Section 11.4 when we tested H_0: $\beta_1 = 0$ against H_a: $\beta_1 \neq 0$—that is, the null hypothesis H_0: $\rho = 0$ is equivalent to the hypothesis H_0: $\beta_1 = 0$.* When we tested the null hypothesis H_0: $\beta_1 = 0$ in connection with the advertising-sales example, the data led to a rejection of the null hypothesis at the $\alpha = .05$ level. This rejection implies that the null hypothesis of a 0 correlation between the two variables (sales revenue and advertising expenditure) can also be rejected at the $\alpha = .05$ level. The only real difference between the least squares slope $\hat{\beta}_1$ and the coefficient of correlation r is the measurement scale. Therefore, the information they provide about the usefulness of the least squares model is to some extent redundant. Consequently, we will use the slope to make inferences about the existence of a positive or negative linear relationship between two variables.

For the sake of completeness, a summary of the test for linear correlation is provided in the following boxes.

A Test for Linear Correlation

One-Tailed Test	Two-Tailed Test
H_0: $\rho = 0$	H_0: $\rho = 0$
H_a: $\rho > 0$ (or H_a: $\rho < 0$)	H_a: $\rho \neq 0$

$$\text{Test statistic: } t = \frac{r\sqrt{n-2}}{\sqrt{1-r^2}} = \frac{\hat{\beta}_1}{s_{\hat{\beta}_1}}$$

Rejection region: $t > t_\alpha$ (or $t < -t_\alpha$)	*Rejection region:* $\lvert t\rvert > t_{\alpha/2}$

where the distribution of t depends on $(n - 2)$ df.

Condition Required for a Valid Test of Correlation

The sample of (x, y) values is randomly selected from a normal population.

Coefficient of Determination

Another way to measure the usefulness of the model is to measure the contribution of x in predicting y. To accomplish this, we calculate how much the errors of prediction of y were reduced by using the information provided by x. To illustrate, consider the sample

*The two tests are equivalent in simple linear regression only.

shown in the scatterplot of Figure 11.18a. If we assume that x contributes no information for the prediction of y, the best prediction for a value of y is the sample mean $\bar{y}$, which is shown as the horizontal line in Figure 11.18b. The vertical line segments in Figure 11.18b are the deviations of the points about the mean $\bar{y}$. Note that the sum of squares of deviations for the prediction equation $\hat{y} = \bar{y}$ is

$$SS_{yy} = \sum (y_i - \bar{y})^2$$

Now suppose you fit a least squares line to the same set of data and locate the deviations of the points about the line as shown in Figure 11.18c. Compare the deviations about the prediction lines in Figures 11.18b and 11.18c. You can see that

1. If x contributes little or no information for the prediction of y, the sums of squares of deviations for the two lines,

$$SS_{yy} = \sum (y_i - \bar{y})^2 \quad \text{and} \quad SSE = \sum (y_i - \hat{y}_i)^2$$

will be nearly equal.

2. If x does contribute information for the prediction of y, the SSE will be smaller than SS_{yy}. In fact, if all the points fall on the least squares line, then SSE $= 0$.

Then the reduction in the sum of squares of deviations that can be attributed to x, expressed as a proportion of SS_{yy}, is

$$\frac{SS_{yy} - SSE}{SS_{yy}}$$

Note that SS_{yy} is the "total sample variation" of the observations around the mean $\bar{y}$ and that SSE is the remaining "unexplained sample variability" after fitting the line $\bar{y}$. Thus,

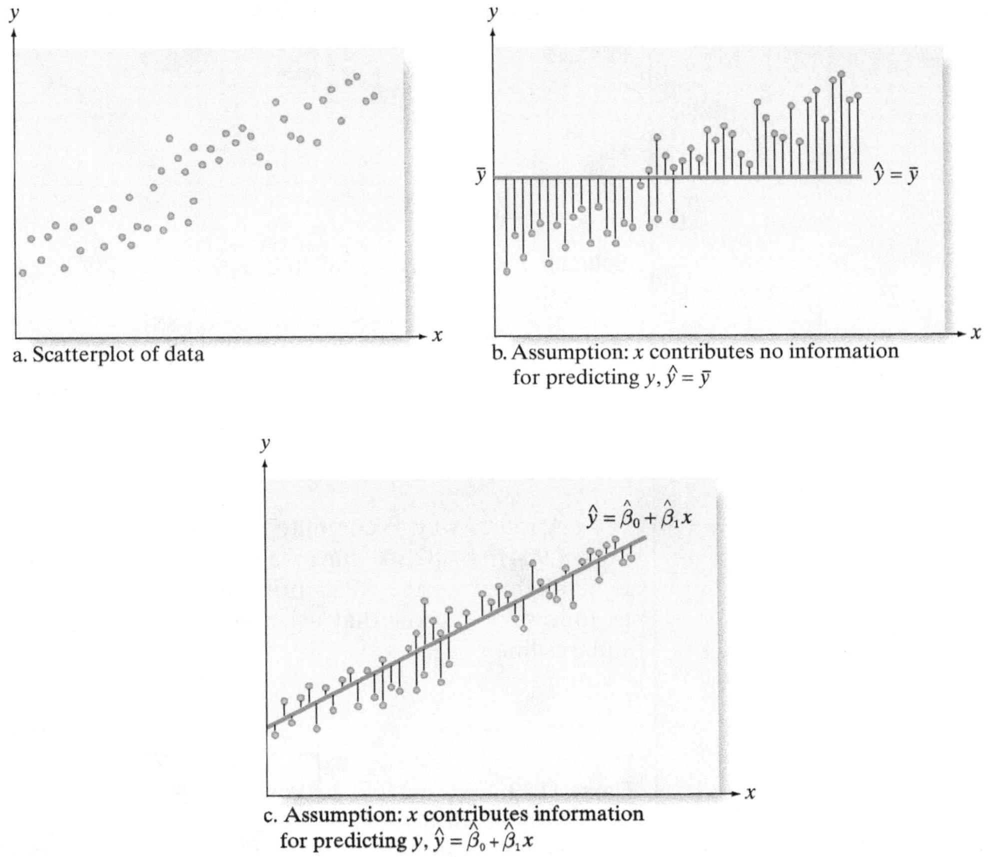

Figure 11.18
A comparison of the sum of squares of deviations for two models

the difference (SS_{yy} − SSE) is the "explained sample variability" attributable to the linear relationship with x. Then a verbal description of the proportion is

$$\frac{SS_{yy} - SSE}{SS_{yy}} = \frac{\text{Explained sample variability}}{\text{Total sample variablity}}$$

$$= \text{Proportion of total sample variability explained by the linear relationship}$$

In simple linear regression, it can be shown that this proportion—called the *coefficient of determination*—is equal to the square of the simple linear coefficient of correlation r.

Coefficient of Determination

$$r^2 = \frac{SS_{yy} - SSE}{SS_{yy}} = 1 - \frac{SSE}{SS_{yy}}$$

It represents the proportion of the total sample variability around $\bar{y}$ that is explained by the linear relationship between y and x. (In simple linear regression, it may also be computed as the square of the coefficient of correlation r.)

Note that r^2 is always between 0 and 1 because r is between −1 and +1. Thus, an r^2 of .60 means that the sum of squares of deviations of the y values about their predicted values has been reduced 60% by the use of the least squares equation $\hat{y}$, instead of $\bar{y}$, to predict y.

Example 11.5

Obtaining the Value of r^2—Sales Revenue Model

Problem Calculate the coefficient of determination for the advertising-sales example. The data are repeated in Table 11.4 for convenience. Interpret the result.

Table 11.4 Advertising-Sales Data

Advertising Expenditure, x ($100s)	Sales Revenue, y ($1,000s)
1	1
2	1
3	2
4	2
5	4

Data Set: ADSALE

Solution From previous calculations,

$$SS_{yy} = 6 \quad \text{and} \quad SSE = \sum(y - \hat{y})^2 = 1.10$$

Then, from the definition, the coefficient of determination is given by

$$r^2 = \frac{SS_{yy} - SSE}{SS_{yy}} = \frac{6.0 - 1.1}{6.0} = \frac{4.9}{6.0} = .82$$

Another way to compute r^2 is to recall (Section 11.2) that $r = .904$. Then we have $r^2 = (.904)^2 = .82$. A third way to obtain r^2 is from a computer printout. This value is highlighted on the SPSS printout reproduced in Figure 11.19. Our interpretation is as follows: We know that using advertising expenditure, x, to predict y with the least squares line

$$\hat{y} = -.1 + .7x$$

Model Summary

Model	R	R Square	Adjusted R Square	Std. Error of the Estimate
1	.904[a]	.817	.756	.606

a. Predictors: (Constant), ADVEXP_X

Figure 11.19
Portion of SPSS printout for advertising-sales regression

accounts for 82% of the total sum of squares of deviations of the five sample y values about their mean. Or, stated another way, 82% of the sample variation in sales revenue (y) can be "explained" by using advertising expenditure (x) in a straight-line model.

Now Work Exercise 11.64a

Practical Interpretation of the Coefficient of Determination, r^2

About $100(r^2)$% of the sample variation in y (measured by the total sum of squares of deviations of the sample y values about their mean $\bar{y}$) can be explained by (or attributed to) using x to predict y in the straight-line model.

Using the Coefficient of Correlation and the Coefficient of Determination

In the previous *Statistics in Action Revisited* (p. 627), we discovered that cumulative 6-month advertising expenditures was a statistically useful linear predictor of number of new PI cases but not a useful linear predictor of number of new WC cases. Both the coefficients of correlation and determination (highlighted on the Minitab printouts in Figures SIA11.4 and SIA11.5) also support this conclusion.

Regression Analysis: NewPI versus AdvExp6

```
The regression equation is
NewPI = 7.77 + 0.113 AdvExp6

Predictor      Coef  SE Coef     T      P
Constant      7.767    3.385  2.29  0.027
AdvExp6     0.11289  0.02793  4.04  0.000

S = 9.67521   R-Sq = 29.0%   R-Sq(adj) = 27.2%

Analysis of Variance

Source          DF      SS      MS      F      P
Regression       1  1529.5  1529.5  16.34  0.000
Residual Error  40  3744.4    93.6
Total           41  5273.9
```

Correlations: NewPI, AdvExp6

```
Pearson correlation of NewPI and AdvExp6 = 0.539
P-Value = 0.000
```

Figure SIA11.4
Minitab printout with coefficients of correlation and determination for y = number of new PI cases

Regression Analysis: NewWC versus AdvExp6

```
The regression equation is
NewWC = 24.6 + 0.0098 AdvExp6

Predictor      Coef  SE Coef     T      P
Constant     24.574    3.367  7.30  0.000
AdvExp6     0.00982  0.02778  0.35  0.725

S = 9.62296   R-Sq = 0.3%   R-Sq(adj) = 0.0%

Analysis of Variance

Source          DF       SS     MS     F      P
Regression       1    11.58  11.58  0.13  0.725
Residual Error  40  3704.06  92.60
Total           41  3715.64
```

Correlations: NewWC, AdvExp6

```
Pearson correlation of NewWC and AdvExp6 = 0.056
P-Value = 0.725
```

Figure SIA11.5
Minitab printout with coefficients of correlation and determination for y = number of new WC cases

STATISTICS in ACTION REVISITED CONTINUED

For y = number of new PI cases, the correlation coefficient value of $r = .539$ is statistically significantly different from 0 and indicates a moderate positive linear relationship between the variables. The coefficient of determination, $r^2 = .29$, implies that almost 30% of the sample variation in number of new PI cases can be explained by using advertising expenditure (x) in the straight-line model. In contrast, for y = number of new WC cases, $r = .056$ is not statistically different from 0 and $r^2 = .003$ implies that only 0.3% of the sample variation in number of new WC cases can be explained by using advertising expenditure (x) in the straight-line model. ◘

Exercises 11.59–11.75

Learning the Mechanics

11.59 Describe the slope of the least squares line if

a. $r = .7$ **b.** $r = -.7$

c. $r = 0$ **d.** $r^2 = .64$

11.60 NW Explain what each of the following sample correlation coefficients tells you about the relationship between the x and y values in the sample:

a. $r = 1$ **b.** $r = -1$

c. $r = 0$ **d.** $r = -.90$

e. $r = .10$ **f.** $r = -.88$

11.61 Calculate r^2 for the least squares line in each of the following exercises. Interpret their values.

a. Exercise 11.10 **b.** Exercise 11.13

11.62 Construct a scatterplot for each data set. Then calculate r and r^2 for each data set. Interpret their values.

a.

x	−2	−1	0	1	2
y	−2	1	2	5	6

b.

x	−2	−1	0	1	2
y	6	5	3	2	0

c.

x	1	2	2	3	3	3	4
y	2	1	3	1	2	3	2

d.

x	0	1	3	5	6
y	0	1	2	1	0

Applet Exercise 11.2

Use the applet *Correlation by Eye* to explore the relationship between the pattern of data in a scatterplot and the corresponding correlation coefficient.

a. Run the applet several times. Each time, guess the value of the correlation coefficient. Then click *Show r* to see the actual correlation coefficient. How close is your value to the actual value of r? Click *New data* to reset the applet.

b. Click the trash can to clear the graph. Use the mouse to place five points on the scatterplot that are approximately in a straight line. Then guess the value of the correlation coefficient. Click *Show r* to see the actual correlation coefficient. How close were you this time?

c. Continue to clear the graph and plot sets of five points with different patterns among the points. Guess the value of r. How close do you come to the actual value of r each time?

d. Based on your experiences with the applet, explain why we need to use more reliable methods of finding the correlation coefficient than just "eyeing" it.

Applying the Concepts—Basic

11.63 Going for it on fourth-down in the NFL. Each week coaches in the National Football League (NFL) face a decision during the game. On fourth-down, should the team punt the ball or go for a first-down? To aid in the decision-making process, statisticians at California State University, Northridge, developed a regression model for predicting the number of points scored (y) by a team that has a first-down with a given number of yards (x) from the opposing goal line (*Chance*, Winter 2009). One of the models fit to data collected on five NFL teams from a recent season was the simple linear regression model, $E(y) = \beta_0 + \beta_1 x$. The regression yielded the following results: $\hat{y} = 4.42 - 048x$, $r^2 = .18$.

a. Give a practical interpretation of the coefficient of determination, r^2.

b. Compute the value of the coefficient of correlation, r, from the value of r^2. Is the value of r positive or negative? Why?

11.64 Lobster fishing study. Refer to the *Bulletin of Marine Science* (April 2010) study of teams of fishermen fishing TRAPS for the red spiny lobster in Baja California Sur, Mexico, Exercise 11.46 (p. 629). Recall that simple linear regression was used to model y = total catch of lobsters (in kilograms) during the season as a function of x = average percentage of traps allocated per day to exploring areas of unknown catch (called *search frequency*). Another portion of the XLSTAT printout of the analysis is shown on the next page.

NW **a.** Locate and interpret the coefficient of determination, r^2, on the printout.

b. Locate and interpret the coefficient of correlation, r, on the printout.

c. In Exercise 11.46, you conducted a test to determine that total catch (y) is negatively linearly related to search frequency (x). Which of the two statistics, r or r^2, can be used to partially support this inference? Explain.

XLSTAT output for Exercise 11.64

Correlation matrix:

Variables	SEARCHFREQ	CATCH
SEARCHFREQ	1.0000	-0.7347
CATCH	-0.7347	1.0000

Regression of variable CATCH:

Goodness of fit statistics:

Observations	15.0000
Sum of weights	15.0000
DF	13.0000
R^2	0.5397
Adjusted R^2	0.5043
MSE	1902741.2024
RMSE	1379.3989
DW	1.4475

11.65 RateMyProfessors.com. A popular Web site among college students is RateMyProfessors.com (RMP). Established over 10 years ago, RMP allows students to post quantitative ratings of their instructors. In *Practical Assessment, Research & Evaluation* (May 2007), University of Maine researchers investigated whether instructor ratings posted on RMP are correlated with the formal in-class student evaluations of teaching (SET) that all universities are required to administer at the end of the semester. Data collected for $n = 426$ University of Maine instructors yielded a correlation between RMP and SET ratings of .68.

a. Give the equation of a linear model relating SET rating (y) to RMP rating (x).

b. Give a practical interpretation of the value $r = .68$.

c. Is the estimated slope of the line, part **a**, positive or negative? Explain.

d. A test of the null hypothesis H_0: $\rho = 0$ yielded a p-value of .001. Interpret this result.

e. Compute the coefficient of determination, r^2, for the regression analysis. Interpret the result.

11.66 In business, do nice guys finish first or last? Refer to the *Nature* (March 20, 2008) study of the use of punishment in cooperation games, Exercise 11.14 (p. 614). Recall that college students repeatedly played a version of the game "prisoner's dilemma," and the researchers recorded the average payoff and the number of times cooperation, defection, and punishment were used for each player.

a. A test of no correlation between cooperation use (x) and average payoff (y) yielded a p-value of .33. Interpret this result.

b. A test of no correlation between defection use (x) and average payoff (y) yielded a p-value of .66. Interpret this result.

c. A test of no correlation between punishment use (x) and average payoff (y) yielded a p-value of .001. Interpret this result.

11.67 Women in top management. An empirical analysis of women in upper management positions at U.S. firms was published in the *Journal of Organizational Culture, Communications and Conflict* (July 2007). Monthly data ($n = 252$ months) were collected for several variables, including the number of females in managerial positions, the number of females with a college degree, and the number of female high school graduates with no college degree. Similar data were collected for males.

a. The correlation coefficient relating number of females in managerial positions and number of females with a college degree was reported as $r = .983$. Interpret this result.

b. The correlation coefficient relating number of females in managerial positions and number of female high school graduates with no college degree was reported as $r = .074$. Interpret this result.

c. The correlation coefficient relating number of males in managerial positions and number of males with a college degree was reported as $r = .722$. Interpret this result.

d. The correlation coefficient relating number of males in managerial positions and number of male high school graduates with no college degree was reported as $r = .528$. Interpret this result.

11.68 Last name and acquisition timing. Refer to the *Journal of Consumer Research* (August 2011) study of the speed with which consumers decide to purchase a product, Exercise 8.13 (p. 433). Recall that the researchers theorized that consumers with last names that begin with letters later in the alphabet would tend to acquire items faster than those whose last names begin with letters earlier in the alphabet (i.e., the *last name effect*). Each in a sample of 50 MBA students was offered free tickets to attend a college basketball game for which there was a limited supply of tickets. The first letter of the last name of those who responded to an e-mail offer in time to receive the tickets was noted and given a numerical value (e.g., "A" = 1, "B" = 2, etc.). Each student's response time (measured in minutes) was also recorded.

a. The researchers computed the correlation between the two variables as $r = -.271$. Interpret this result.

b. The observed significance level for testing for a negative correlation in the population was reported as p-value $= .018$. Interpret this result for $\alpha = .05$.

c. Does this analysis support the researchers' *last name effect* theory? Explain.

Applying the Concepts—Intermediate

11.69 Software millionaires and birthdays. Refer to Exercise 11.19 (p. 615) and the study of the seemingly disproportionate number of software millionaires born around the year 1955. The data are reproduced in the table on the following page.

BDAYS

a. Find the coefficient of determination for the simple linear regression model relating number (y) of software millionaire birthdays in a decade to total number (x) of U.S. births. Interpret the result.

b. Find the coefficient of determination for the simple linear regression model relating number (y) of software millionaire birthdays in a decade to number (x) of CEO birthdays. Interpret the result.

c. The consulting statistician argued that the software industry appears to be no different from any other industry with respect to producing millionaires in a decade. Do you agree? Explain.

Data for Exercise 11.69

Decade	Total U.S. Births (millions)	Number of Software Millionaire Birthdays	Number of CEO Birthdays (in a random sample of 70 companies from the *Fortune* 500 list)
1920	28.582	3	2
1930	24.374	1	2
1940	31.666	10	23
1950	40.530	14	38
1960	38.808	7	9
1970	33.309	4	0

Source: Sauro, J. "Were most software millionaires born around 1955?" *Measuring Usability,* November 17, 2010.

11.70 Child labor in diamond mines. The role of child laborers on Africa's colonial-era diamond mines was the subject of research published in the *Journal of Family History* (Vol. 35, 2010). One particular mining company lured children to the mines by offering incentives for adult male laborers to relocate their families close to the diamond mine. The success of the incentive program was examined by determining the annual *accompaniment rate,* i.e., the percentage of wives (or sons, or daughters) who accompanied their husbands (or fathers) in relocating to the mine. Information from the journal article was used to simulate accompaniment rates for nine consecutive years. Those rates are shown in the table below.

MINES

a. Find the correlation coefficient relating the accompaniment rates for wives and sons. Interpret this value.

b. Find the correlation coefficient relating the accompaniment rates for wives and daughters. Interpret this value.

c. Find the correlation coefficient relating the accompaniment rates for sons and daughters. Interpret this value.

Year	Wives	Sons	Daughters
1	28.7	2.4	14.3
2	41.6	1.7	13.1
3	37.2	0.5	10
4	39.3	3.7	19.6
5	39.5	5.6	19.4
6	39.9	11.2	21.7
7	40.2	12.1	15.3
8	31.3	8.8	15.1
9	25.3	7.6	19.6

Source: Based on Cleveland, T., "Minors in name only: Child laborers on the diamond mines of the *Companhia de Diamantes de Angola* (Diamang), 1917–1975." *Journal of Family History,* Vol. 35, No. 1, 2010 (Table 1).

11.71 Sweetness of orange juice. Refer to the simple linear regression relating y = sweetness index of an orange juice sample with x = amount of water-soluble pectin, Exercise 11.22 (p. 616) and the data saved in the file. Find and interpret the coefficient of determination, r^2, and the coefficient of correlation, r.

OJUICE

11.72 Performance ratings of government agencies. The U.S. Office of Management and Budget (OMB) requires government agencies to produce annual performance and accounting reports (PARS) each year. Refer to *The Public Manager* (Summer 2008) listing of PARS evaluation scores for 24 government agencies, Exercise 2.129 (p. 105). Recall that evaluation scores ranged from 12 (lowest) to 60 (highest). The PARS evaluation scores for two consecutive years are reproduced in the following table.

PARS

a. Calculate and interpret the coefficient of correlation between the PARS scores in year 1 and year 2.

b. Is there sufficient evidence of a positive linear relationship between year 2 PARS score (y) and year 1 PARS score (x)? Test using $\alpha = .05$.

Agency	Year 1	Year 2
Transportation	55	53
Labor	53	51
Veterans	51	51
NRC	39	34
Commerce	37	36
HHS	37	35
DHS	37	30
Justice	35	37
Treasury	35	35
GSA	34	40
Agriculture	33	35
EPA	33	36
Social Security	33	33
USAID	32	42
Education	32	36
Interior	32	31
NASA	32	32
Energy	31	34
HUD	31	30
NSF	31	31
State	31	50
OPM	27	28
SBA	22	31
Defense	17	32

Source: Ellig, J., & Wray, H. "Measuring performance reporting quality," *The Public Manager,* Vol. 37, No. 2, Summer 2008 (p. 66).

11.73 Survey of the top business schools. Refer to the *Wall Street Journal* (Sep. 25, 2005) Business School Survey, Exercise 11.25 (p. 618) and the data saved in the file. Find and interpret r and r^2 for the simple linear regression relating y = percentage of graduates with job offers and x = tuition cost and then fit the simple linear model.

TOPBUS

11.74 Spreading rate of spilled liquid. Refer to the *Chemical Engineering Progress* (Jan. 2005) study of the rate at which a spilled volatile liquid will spread across a surface, Exercise 11.26 (p. 618) and the data saved in the file. Find and interpret r and r^2 for the simple linear regression y = mass of the spill and x = elapsed time of the spill.

SPILL

Applying the Concepts—Advanced

11.75 Salary linked to height. Are short people short-changed when it comes to salary? According to Business Professors T. A. Judge (University of Florida) and D. M. Cable (University of North Carolina), tall people tend to earn more money over their careers than short people (*Journal of Applied Psychology,* June 2004). Using data collected from participants in the National Longitudinal Surveys begun in 1979, the researchers computed the correlation between average earnings from 1985 to 2000 (in dollars) and height (in inches) for several occupations. The results are given in the table. Are average earnings positively related to height? For all occupations? If so, can you conclude that a person taller than you will earn a higher salary? Explain.

NW

Occupation	Correlation, r	Sample Size, n
Sales	.41	117
Managers	.35	455
Blue Collar	.32	349
Service Workers	.31	265
Professional/ Technical	.30	453
Clerical	.25	358
Crafts/ Forepersons	.24	250

Source: Judge, T. A., & Cable, D. M. "The effect of physical height on workplace success and income: Preliminary test of a theoretical model," *Journal of Applied Psychology,* Vol. 89, No. 3, June 2004 (Table 5).

11.6 Using the Model for Estimation and Prediction

If we are satisfied that a useful model has been found to describe the relationship between x and y, we are ready for step 5 in our regression modeling procedure: using the model for estimation and prediction.

The most common uses of a probabilistic model for making inferences can be divided into two categories. The first is using the model to estimate the mean value of y, E(y), *for a specific value of* x. For our advertising-sales example, we may want to estimate the mean sales revenue for *all* months during which \$400 ($x = 4$) is expended on advertising.

The second use of the model entails predicting a new individual y *value for a given* x. That is, if we decide to expend \$400 in advertising next month, we may want to predict the firm's sales revenue for that month.

In the first case, we are attempting to *estimate the mean value of* y *for a very large number of experimental units at the given* x *value.* In the second case, we are trying to *predict the outcome for a single experimental unit at the given* x *value.* Which of these model uses—estimating the mean value of y or predicting an individual new value of y (for the same value of x)—can be accomplished with the greater accuracy?

Before answering this question, we first consider the problem of choosing an estimator (or predictor) of the mean (or a new individual) y value. We will use the least squares prediction equation

$$\hat{y} = \hat{\beta}_0 + \hat{\beta}_1 x$$

both to estimate the mean value of y and to predict a specific new value of y for a given value of x. For our example, we found

$$\hat{y} = -.1 + .7x$$

so that the estimated mean sales revenue for all months when $x = 4$ (advertising is \$400) is

$$\hat{y} = -.1 + .7(4) = 2.7$$

or \$2,700. (Recall that the units of y are thousands of dollars.) The same value is used to predict a new y value when $x = 4$—that is, both the estimated mean and the predicted value of y are $\hat{y} = 2.7$ when $x = 4$, as shown in Figure 11.20.

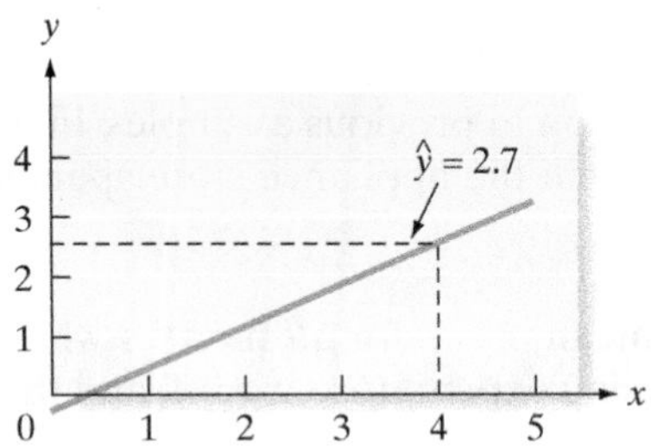

Figure 11.20
Estimated mean value and predicted individual value of sales revenue y for $x = 4$

The difference between these two model uses lies in the relative accuracy of the estimate and the prediction. These accuracies are best measured by using the sampling errors of the least squares line when it is used as an estimator and as a predictor, respectively. These errors are reflected in the standard deviations given in the next box.

Sampling Errors for the Estimator of the Mean of y and the Predictor of an Individual New Value of y

1. The *standard deviation* of the sampling distribution of the estimator $\hat{y}$ of the *mean value of y* at a specific value of x, say x_p, is

$$\sigma_{\hat{y}} = \sigma\sqrt{\frac{1}{n} + \frac{(x_p - \bar{x})^2}{SS_{xx}}}$$

where σ is the standard deviation of the random error ε. We refer to $\sigma_{\hat{y}}$ as the **standard error of $\hat{y}$.**

2. The *standard deviation* of the prediction error for the predictor $\hat{y}$ of an individual *new y value* at a specific value of x is

$$\sigma_{(y-\hat{y})} = \sigma\sqrt{1 + \frac{1}{n} + \frac{(x_p - \bar{x})^2}{SS_{xx}}}$$

where σ is the standard deviation of the random error ε. We refer to $\sigma_{(y-\hat{y})}$ as the **standard error of the prediction.**

The true value of σ is rarely known, so we estimate σ by s and calculate the estimation and prediction intervals as shown in the next two boxes.

A 100(1 − α)% Confidence Interval for the Mean Value of y at $x = x_p$

$$\hat{y} \pm t_{\alpha/2}\,(\text{Estimated standard error of } \hat{y})$$

or

$$\hat{y} \pm t_{\alpha/2}\, s\sqrt{\frac{1}{n} + \frac{(x_p - \bar{x})^2}{SS_{xx}}}$$

where $t_{\alpha/2}$ is based on $(n - 2)$ degrees of freedom.

A 100(1 − α)% Prediction Interval* for an Individual New Value of y at $x = x_p$

$$\hat{y} \pm t_{\alpha/2}\,(\text{Estimated standard error of prediction})$$

or

$$\hat{y} \pm t_{\alpha/2}\, s\sqrt{1 + \frac{1}{n} + \frac{(x_p - \bar{x})^2}{SS_{xx}}}$$

where $t_{\alpha/2}$ is based on $(n - 2)$ degrees of freedom.

Example 11.6

Estimating the Mean of y—Sales Revenue Model

Problem Refer to the sales-appraisal simple linear regression in previous examples. Find a 95% confidence interval for the mean monthly sales when the appliance store spends \$400 on advertising.

Solution Here, we desire a confidence interval for the mean, $E(y)$, for *all* months when the store spends \$400 on advertising. For a \$400 advertising expenditure, $x = 4$, and the confidence interval for the mean value of y is

$$\hat{y} \pm t_{\alpha/2}\, s\sqrt{\frac{1}{n} + \frac{(x_p - \bar{x})^2}{SS_{xx}}} = \hat{y} \pm t_{.025}\, s\sqrt{\frac{1}{5} + \frac{(4 - \bar{x})^2}{SS_{xx}}}$$

*The term *prediction interval* is used when the interval formed is intended to enclose the value of a random variable. The term *confidence interval* is reserved for the estimation of population parameters (such as the mean).

where $t_{.025}$ is based on $n - 2 = 5 - 2 = 3$ degrees of freedom. Recall that $\hat{y} = 2.7$, $s = .61$, $\bar{x} = 3$, and $SS_{xx} = 10$. From Table III in Appendix D, $t_{.025} = 3.182$. Thus, we have

$$\begin{aligned} 2.7 \pm (3.182)(.61)\sqrt{\frac{1}{5} + \frac{(4-3)^2}{10}} &= 2.7 \pm (3.182)(.61)(.55) \\ &= 2.7 \pm (3.182)(.34) \\ &= 2.7 \pm 1.1 = (1.6, 3.8) \end{aligned}$$

Therefore, when the store spends $400 a month on advertising, we are 95% confident that the mean sales revenue for these months is between $1,600 and $3,800.

Look Back Note that we used a small amount of data (small in size) for purposes of illustration in fitting the least squares line. The interval would probably be narrower if more information had been obtained from a larger sample.

■ **Now Work Exercise 11.76a–d**

Example 11.7

Predicting an Individual value of *y*—Sales Revenue Model

Problem Refer, again, to the sales-appraisal regression. Predict the monthly sales for next month if $400 is spent on advertising. Use a 95% prediction interval.

Solution Here, our focus is on a *single* month when the store spends $400 on advertising. To predict the sales for a particular month for which $x_p = 4$, we calculate the 95% prediction interval as

$$\begin{aligned} \hat{y} \pm t_{\alpha/2} s\sqrt{1 + \frac{1}{n} + \frac{(x_p - \bar{x})^2}{SS_{xx}}} &= 2.7 \pm (3.182)(.61)\sqrt{1 + \frac{1}{5} + \frac{(4-3)^2}{10}} \\ &= 2.7 \pm (3.182)(.61)(1.14) \\ &= 2.7 \pm (3.182)(.70) \\ &= 2.7 \pm 2.2 = (.5, 4.9) \end{aligned}$$

Therefore, we predict with 95% confidence that the sales revenue next month (a month in which we spend $400 in advertising) will fall in the interval from $500 to $4,900.

Look Back Like the confidence interval for the mean value of *y*, the prediction interval for *y* is quite large. This is because we have chosen a simple example (only five data points) to fit the least squares line. The width of the prediction interval could be reduced by using a larger number of data points.

■ **Now Work Exercise 11.76e**

Both the confidence interval for $E(y)$ and prediction interval for y can be obtained using a statistical software package. Figure 11.21 is a Minitab printout showing the confidence interval and prediction interval for the data in the advertising-sales example. The 95% confidence interval for $E(y)$ when $x = 4$, highlighted under "95% CI" in Figure 11.21, is (1.645, 3.755). The 95% prediction interval for y when $x = 4$, highlighted in Figure 11.21 under "95% PI," is (.503, 4.897). Both intervals agree with the ones computed in Examples 11.6–11.7.

```
Predicted Values for New Observations

New
Obs    Fit  SE Fit      95% CI            95% PI
  1  2.700   0.332  (1.645, 3.755)   (0.503, 4.897)


Values of Predictors for New Observations

New
Obs  ADVEXP_X
  1      4.00
```

Figure 11.21
Minitab printout giving 95% confidence interval for $E(y)$ and 95% prediction interval for y

Note that the prediction interval for an individual new value of y is *always* wider than the corresponding confidence interval for the mean value of y. To see this, consider the following. The error in estimating the mean value of y, $E(y)$, for a given value of x, say x_p, is the distance between the least squares line and the true line of means, $E(y) = \beta_0 + \beta_1 x$. This error, $[\hat{y} - E(y)]$, is shown in Figure 11.22. In contrast, *the error* $(y_p - \hat{y})$ *in predicting some future value of* y *is the sum of two errors*—the error of estimating the mean of y, $E(y)$, plus the random error that is a component of the value of y to be predicted (see Figure 11.23). Consequently, the error of predicting a particular value of y will be larger than the error of estimating the mean value of y for a particular value of x. Note from their formulas that both the error of estimation and the error of prediction take their smallest values when $x_p = \bar{x}$. The farther x_p lies from $\bar{x}$, the larger will be the errors of estimation and prediction. You can see why this is true by noting the deviations for different values of x_p between the line of means $E(y) = \beta_0 + \beta_1 x$ and the predicted line of means $\hat{y} = \hat{\beta}_0 + \hat{\beta}_1 x$ shown in Figure 11.23. The deviation is larger at the extremes of the interval where the largest and smallest values of x in the data set occur.

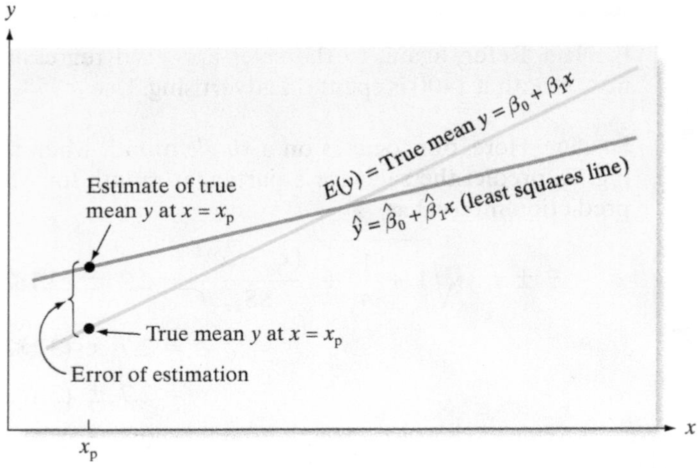

Figure 11.22
Error of estimating the mean value of y for a given value of x

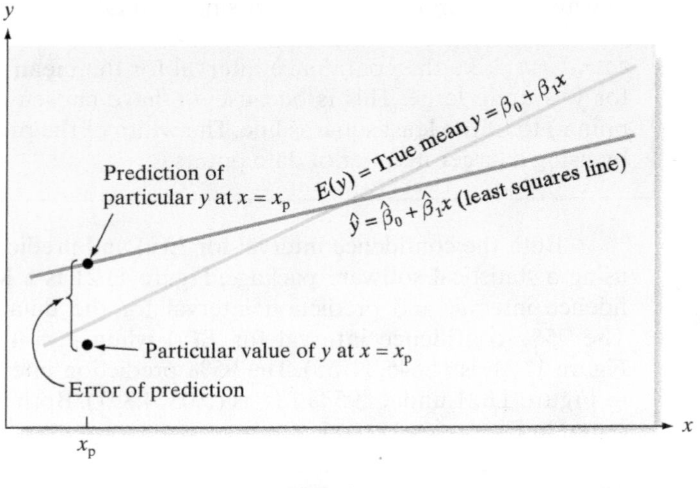

Figure 11.23
Error of predicting a future value of y for a given value of x

Both the confidence intervals for mean values and the prediction intervals for new values are depicted over the entire range of the regression line in Figure 11.24. You can see that the confidence interval is always narrower than the prediction interval, and they are both narrowest at the mean $\bar{x}$, increasing steadily as the distance $|x - \bar{x}|$ increases. In fact, when x is selected far enough away from $\bar{x}$ so that it falls outside the range of the sample data, it is dangerous to make any inferences about $E(y)$ or y.

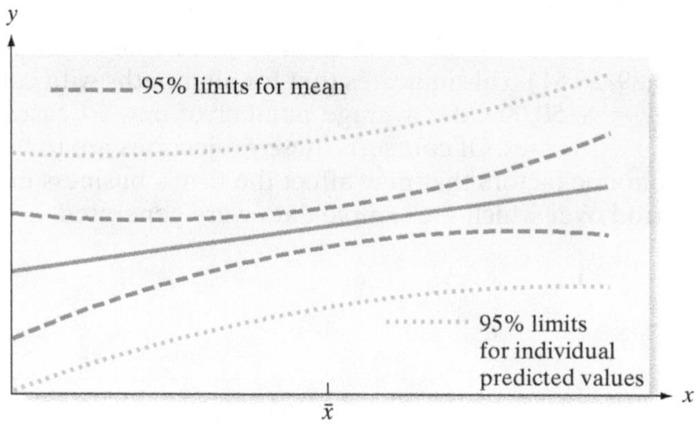

Figure 11.24
Confidence intervals for mean values and prediction intervals for new values

> ⚠ **CAUTION** Using the least squares prediction equation to estimate the mean value of y or to predict a particular value of y for values of x that fall *outside the range* of the values of x contained in your sample data may lead to errors of estimation or prediction that are much larger than expected. Although the least squares model may provide a very good fit to the data over the range of x values contained in the sample, it could give a poor representation of the true model for values of x outside this region.

The confidence interval width grows smaller as n is increased; thus, in theory, you can obtain as precise an estimate of the mean value of y as desired (at any given x) by selecting a large enough sample. The prediction interval for a new value of y also grows smaller as n increases, but there is a lower limit on its width. If you examine the formula for the prediction interval, you will see that the interval can get no smaller than $\hat{y} \pm z_{\alpha/2}\sigma$.* Thus, the only way to obtain more accurate predictions for new values of y is to reduce the standard deviation of the regression model, σ. This can be accomplished only by improving the model, either by using a curvilinear (rather than linear) relationship with x or by adding new independent variables to the model, or both. Methods of improving the model are discussed in Chapter 12.

Prediction Using the Straight-Line Model

In the two previous *Statistics in Action Revisited* sections, we demonstrated that x = cumulative 6-month advertising expenditures is a useful linear predictor of y = the number of new PI cases. The Minitab printout shown in Figure SIA11.6 gives a 95% prediction interval for the number of new PI cases in a month where cumulative spending on advertising over the past 6 months is $x = \$150{,}000$. The highlighted interval is (4.78, 44.62). Thus, we can be 95% confident that for a given month with a 6-month cumulative advertising expenditure of $150,000, the law firm will add between 5 and 44 new PI cases that month.

```
Predicted Values for New Observations

New
Obs    Fit  SE Fit        95% CI           95% PI
  1  24.70    1.89  (20.89, 28.51)  (4.78, 44.62)


Values of Predictors for New Observations

New
Obs  AdvExp6
  1      150
```

Figure SIA11.6
Minitab prediction interval for legal advertising straight-line model

*The result follows from the facts that, for large n, $t_{\alpha/2} \approx z_{\alpha/2}$, $s \approx \sigma$, and the last two terms under the radical in the standard error of the predictor are approximately 0.

STATISTICS in ACTION REVISITED CONTINUED

The 95% *confidence interval for the mean of y* (also highlighted on the printout) is (20.89, 28.51). This indicates that for all months with cumulative spending on advertising of $x = \$150{,}000$, the average number of new PI cases each month will range between 21 and 28 cases. Of course, if these projections are to be useful for future planning, other economic factors that may affect the firm's business must be similar to those during the period over which the sample data were generated.

Exercises 11.76–11.90

Learning the Mechanics

11.76 Consider the following pairs of measurements:
NW
L11076

x	−2	0	2	4	6	8	10
y	0	3	2	3	8	10	11

a. Construct a scatterplot for these data.
b. Find the least squares line and plot it on your scatterplot.
c. Find s^2 and s.
d. Find a 90% confidence interval for the mean value of y when $x = 3$. Plot the upper and lower bounds of the confidence interval on your scatterplot.
e. Find a 90% prediction interval for a new value of y when $x = 3$. Plot the upper and lower bounds of the prediction interval on your scatterplot.
f. Compare the widths of the intervals you constructed in parts **d** and **e.** Which is wider and why?

11.77 Consider the pairs of measurements shown in the table. For these data, $SS_{xx} = 38.9$, $SS_{yy} = 33.6$, $SS_{xy} = 32.8$, and $\hat{y} = -.414 + .843x$.
L11077

x	4	6	0	5	2	3	2	6	2	1
y	3	5	−1	4	3	2	0	4	1	1

a. Construct a scatterplot for these data.
b. Plot the least squares line on your scatterplot.
c. Use a 95% confidence interval to estimate the mean value of y when $x_p = 6$. Plot the upper and lower bounds of the interval on your scatterplot.
d. Repeat part **c** for $x_p = 3.2$ and $x_p = 0$.
e. Compare the widths of the three confidence intervals you constructed in parts **c** and **d** and explain why they differ.

11.78 Refer to Exercise 11.77.
a. Using no information about x, estimate and calculate a 95% confidence interval for the mean value of y. [*Hint:* Use the one-sample t methodology of Section 5.4.]
b. Plot the estimated mean value and the confidence interval as horizontal lines on your scatterplot.
c. Compare the confidence intervals you calculated in parts **c** and **d** of Exercise 11.77 with the one you calculated in part **a** of this exercise. Does x appear to contribute information about the mean value of y?
d. Check the answer you gave in part **c** with a statistical test of the null hypothesis H_0: $\beta_1 = 0$ against H_a: $\beta_1 \neq 0$. Use $\alpha = .05$.

11.79 In fitting a least squares line to $n = 10$ data points, the following quantities were computed:

$SS_{xx} = 32$ $\bar{x} = 3$ $SS_{yy} = 26$ $\bar{y} = 4$ $SS_{xy} = 28$

a. Find the least squares line.
b. Graph the least squares line.
c. Calculate SSE.
d. Calculate s^2.
e. Find a 95% confidence interval for the mean value of y when $x_p = 2.5$.
f. Find a 95% prediction interval for y when $x_p = 4$.

Applying the Concepts—Basic

11.80 In business, do nice guys finish first or last? Refer to the *Nature* (March 20, 2008) study of the use of punishment in cooperation games, Exercise 11.14 (p. 614). Recall that simple linear regression was used to model a player's average payoff (y) as a straight-line function of the number of times punishment was used (x) by the player.
a. If the researchers want to predict average payoff for a single player who used punishment 10 times, how should they proceed?
b. If the researchers want to predict the mean of the average payoffs for all players who used punishment 10 times, how should they proceed?

11.81 Lobster fishing study. Refer to the *Bulletin of Marine Science* (April 2010) study of teams of fishermen fishing for the red spiny lobster in Baja California Sur, Mexico, Exercise 11.16 (p. 614). Recall that simple linear regression was used to model y = total catch of lobsters (in kilograms) during the season as a function of x = average percentage of traps allocated per day to exploring areas of unknown catch (called *search frequency*). A portion of the Minitab printout giving a 95% confidence interval for $E(y)$ and a 95% prediction interval for y when $x = 25$ is shown below.
TRAPS

```
Predicted Values for New Observations

New Obs   Fit  SE Fit       95% CI           95% PI
      1  5788     465  (4783, 6792)   (2643, 8933)


Values of Predictors for New Observations

New Obs  SEARCHFREQ
      1        25.0
```

a. Locate and interpret the 95% confidence interval for $E(y)$.
b. Locate and interpret the 95% prediction interval for y.

XLSTAT output for Exercise 11.82

Predictions for the new observations:

Observation	Pred(RelRate)	Lower bound 90% (Mean)	Upper bound 90% (Mean)	Lower bound 90% (Observation)	Upper bound 90% (Observation)
1.5	61.08	57.26	64.91	55.33	66.83
1.05	44.92	42.99	46.85	40.21	49.63
0.9	39.53	37.78	41.29	34.90	44.17
0.75	34.15	32.17	36.12	29.42	38.87
0.6	28.76	26.27	31.25	23.80	33.72
0.65	30.55	28.26	32.85	25.69	35.42

11.82 Drug controlled-release rate study. Refer to the *Drug Development and Industrial Pharmacy* (Vol. 28, 2002) drug controlled-release rate study, Exercise 11.17 (p. 615). Recall that data for six drug tablets were used to fit the simple linear model, $E(y) = \beta_0 + \beta_1 x$, where y = drug release rate and x = surface-area-to-volume ratio. An Excel/XLSTAT printout giving a 90% prediction interval for each of the $n = 6$ observations in the sample is shown above. Select an observation and give a practical interpretation for this prediction interval.

DOW

11.83 Sweetness of orange juice. Refer to the simple linear regression of sweetness index y and amount of pectin x for $n = 24$ orange juice samples, Exercise 11.22 (p. 616). A 90% confidence interval for the mean sweetness index, $E(y)$, for each of the first 12 runs is shown on the SPSS spreadsheet below. Select an observation and interpret this interval.

OJUICE

11.84 Public corruption and bad weather. Refer to the *Journal of Law and Economics* (Nov. 2008) study of the link between Federal Emergency Management Agency (FEMA) disaster relief and public corruption, Exercise 11.56 (p. 630). You determined that the p-value for testing the adequacy of the straight-line model relating a state's average annual number of public corruption convictions (y) to the state's average annual FEMA relief (x) was $p = .102$. Based on this result, would you recommend using the model to predict the number of public corruption convictions in a state with an annual FEMA relief of $x = 5$ thousand dollars? Explain.

FEMA

Applying the Concepts—Intermediate

11.85 Software millionaires and birthdays. Refer to Exercise 11.35 (p. 622) and the study of software millionaires and their birthdays. The data are reproduced on the next page. Recall that simple linear regression was used to model number (y) of software millionaire birthdays in a decade as a straight-line function of number (x) of CEO birthdays.

BDAYS

a. Consider a future decade where the number of CEO birthdays (in a random sample of 70 companies) is 25. Find a 95% prediction interval for the number of software millionaire birthdays in this decade. Interpret the result.

b. Consider another future decade where the number of CEO birthdays (in a random sample of 70 companies) is 10. Will the 95% prediction interval for the number of software millionaire birthdays in this decade be narrower or wider than the interval, part **b?** Explain.

	run	sweet	pectin	lower90m	upper90m
1	1	5.2	220	5.64898	5.83848
2	2	5.5	227	5.63898	5.81613
3	3	6.0	259	5.57819	5.72904
4	4	5.9	210	5.66194	5.87173
5	5	5.8	224	5.64337	5.82560
6	6	6.0	215	5.65564	5.85493
7	7	5.8	231	5.63284	5.80379
8	8	5.6	268	5.55553	5.71011
9	9	5.6	239	5.61947	5.78019
10	10	5.9	212	5.65946	5.86497
11	11	5.4	410	5.05526	5.55416
12	12	5.6	256	5.58517	5.73592
13	13	5.8	306	5.43785	5.65219
14	14	5.5	259	5.57819	5.72904
15	15	5.3	284	5.50957	5.68213
16	16	5.3	383	5.15725	5.57694
17	17	5.7	271	5.54743	5.70434
18	18	5.5	264	5.56591	5.71821
19	19	5.7	227	5.63898	5.81613
20	20	5.3	263	5.56843	5.72031
21	21	5.9	232	5.63125	5.80075
22	22	5.8	220	5.64898	5.83848
23	23	5.8	246	5.60640	5.76091
24	24	5.9	241	5.61587	5.77454

SPSS output for Exercise 11.83

Data for Exercise 11.85

Decade	Total U.S. Births (millions)	Number of Software Millionaire Birthdays	Number of CEO Birthdays (in a random sample of 70 companies from the *Fortune* 500 list)
1920	28.582	3	2
1930	24.374	1	2
1940	31.666	10	23
1950	40.530	14	38
1960	38.808	7	9
1970	33.309	4	0

Source: Sauro, J. "Were most software millionaires born around 1955?" *Measuring Usability,* November 17, 2010. Copyright © 2010 by Measuring Usability LLC. Reprinted with permission.

11.86 Ranking driving performance of professional golfers. Refer to *The Sport Journal* (Winter 2007) study of a new method for ranking the total driving performance of golfers on the PGA tour, Exercise 11.21 (p. 616). You fit a straight-line model relating driving accuracy (y) to driving distance (x) to the data saved in the file. Of interest is predicting y and estimating $E(y)$ when $x = 300$ yards.

PGA

a. Find and interpret a 95% prediction interval for y.

b. Find and interpret a 95% confidence interval for $E(y)$.

c. If you are interested in knowing the average driving accuracy of all PGA golfers who have a driving distance of 300 yards, which of the intervals is relevant? Explain.

11.87 Spreading rate of spilled liquid. Refer to the *Chemical Engineering Progress* (Jan. 2005) study of the rate at which a spilled volatile liquid will spread across a surface, Exercise 11.26 (p. 618). Recall that simple linear regression was used to model y = mass of the spill as a function of x = elapsed time of the spill.

LSPILL

a. Find a 99% confidence interval for the mean mass of all spills with an elapsed time of 15 minutes. Interpret the result.

b. Find a 99% prediction interval for the mass of a single spill with an elapsed time of 15 minutes. Interpret the result.

c. Compare the intervals, parts **a** and **b.** Which interval is wider? Will this always be the case? Explain.

11.88 Forecasting managerial needs. Managers are an important part of any organization's resource base. Accordingly, the organization should be just as concerned about forecasting its future managerial needs as it is with forecasting its needs for, say, the natural resources used in its production process (Northcraft and Neale, *Organizational Behavior: A Management Challenge,* 2001). A common forecasting procedure is to model the relationship between sales and the number of managers needed because the demand for managers is the result of the increases and decreases in the demand for products and services that a firm offers its customers. To develop this relationship, the data shown in the following table are collected from a firm's records.

MANDEM

a. Test the usefulness of the model. Use $\alpha = .05$. State your conclusion in the context of the problem.

b. The company projects that it will sell 39 units next month. Use the least squares model to construct a 90% prediction interval for the number of managers needed next month.

c. Interpret the interval in part **b.** Use the interval to determine the reliability of the firm's projection.

Units Sold, x	Managers, y	Units Sold, x	Managers, y
5	10	30	22
4	11	31	25
8	10	36	30
7	10	38	30
9	9	40	31
15	10	41	31
20	11	51	32
21	17	40	30
25	19	48	32
24	21	47	32

11.89 Predicting quit rates in manufacturing. The reasons given by workers for quitting their jobs generally fall into one of two categories: (1) worker quits to seek or take a different job, or (2) worker quits to withdraw from the labor force. Economic theory suggests that wages and quit rates are related. The table below lists quit rates (quits per 100 employees) and the average hourly wage in a sample of 15 manufacturing industries. Consider the simple linear regression of quit rate y on average wage x.

QUIT

Industry	Quit Rate, y	Average Wage, x
1	1.4	$ 8.20
2	.7	10.35
3	2.6	6.18
4	3.4	5.37
5	1.7	9.94
6	1.7	9.11
7	1.0	10.59
8	.5	13.29
9	2.0	7.99
10	3.8	5.54
11	2.3	7.50
12	1.9	6.43
13	1.4	8.83
14	1.8	10.93
15	2.0	8.80

a. Do the data present sufficient evidence to conclude that average hourly wage rate contributes useful information for the prediction of quit rates? What does your model suggest about the relationship between quit rates and wages?

b. Find a 95% prediction interval for the quit rate in an industry with an average hourly wage of $9.00. Interpret the result.

c. Find a 95% confidence interval for the mean quit rate for industries with an average hourly wage of $9.00. Interpret this result.

Applying the Concepts—Advanced

11.90 Life tests of cutting tools. Refer to the data saved in the file, Exercise 11.40 (p. 623).

TOOLS

a. Use a 90% confidence interval to estimate the mean useful life of a brand A cutting tool when the cutting speed is 45 meters per minute. Repeat for brand B. Compare the widths of the two intervals and comment on the reasons for any difference.

b. Use a 90% prediction interval to predict the useful life of a brand A cutting tool when the cutting speed is 45 meters per minute. Repeat for brand B. Compare the widths of the two intervals to each other and to the two intervals you calculated in part **a.** Comment on the reasons for any differences.

c. Note that the estimation and prediction you performed in parts **a** and **b** were for a value of x that was not included in the original sample—that is, the value $x = 45$ was not part of the sample. However, the value is within the range of x values in the sample, so the regression model spans the x value for which the estimation and prediction were made. In such situations, estimation and prediction represent *interpolations.* Suppose you were asked to predict the useful life of a brand A cutting tool for a cutting speed of $x = 100$ meters per minute. Because the given value of x is outside the range of the sample x values, the prediction is an example of **extrapolation.** Predict the useful life of a brand A cutting tool that is operated at 100 meters per minute and construct a 95% prediction interval for the actual useful life of the tool. What additional assumption do you have to make in order to ensure the validity of an extrapolation?

11.7 A Complete Example

In the preceding sections, we have presented the basic elements necessary to fit and use a straight-line regression model. In this section, we will assemble these elements by applying them in an example with the aid of a computer.

Suppose a fire insurance company wants to relate the amount of fire damage in major residential fires to the distance between the burning house and the nearest fire station. The study is to be conducted in a large suburb of a major city; a sample of 15 recent fires in this suburb is selected. The amount of damage, y, and the distance between the fire and the nearest fire station, x, are recorded for each fire. The results are shown in Table 11.5 and saved in the **RFIRES** file.

Step 1: First, we hypothesize a model to relate fire damage, y, to the distance from the nearest fire station, x. We hypothesize a straight-line probabilistic model:

$$y = \beta_0 + \beta_1 x + \varepsilon$$

Step 2: Next, we open the **RFIRES** file and use a statistical software package to estimate the unknown parameters in the deterministic component of the hypothesized model. The Excel printout for the simple linear regression analysis is

Table 11.5 Fire Damage Data

Distance from Fire Station, x (miles)	Fire Damage, y (thousands of dollars)
3.4	26.2
1.8	17.8
4.6	31.3
2.3	23.1
3.1	27.5
5.5	36.0
.7	14.1
3.0	22.3
2.6	19.6
4.3	31.3
2.1	24.0
1.1	17.3
6.1	43.2
4.8	36.4
3.8	26.1

Data Set: RFIRES

Regression Analysis						
Regression Statistics						
Multiple R	0.960977715					
R Square	0.923478169					
Adjusted R Square	0.917591874					
Standard Error	2.316346184					
Observations	15					
ANOVA						
	df	*SS*	*MS*	*F*	*Significance F*	
Regression	1	841.766358	841.766358	156.8861596	1.2478E-08	
Residual	13	69.75097535	5.365459643			
Total	14	911.5173333				
	Coefficients	*Standard Error*	*t Stat*	*P-value*	*Lower 95%*	*Upper 95%*
Intercept	10.27792855	1.420277811	7.236562082	6.58556E-06	7.209605476	13.34625162
DISTANCE	4.919330727	0.392747749	12.52542054	1.2478E-08	4.070850963	5.767810491

Figure 11.25
Excel printout for fire damage regression analysis

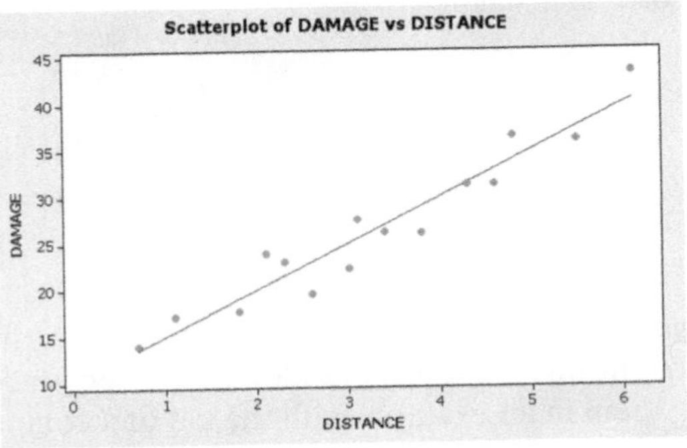

Figure 11.26
Minitab scatterplot with least squares line for fire damage regression analysis

shown in Figure 11.25. The least squares estimates of the slope β_1 and intercept β_0, highlighted on the printout, are

$$\hat{\beta}_1 = 4.919331$$
$$\hat{\beta}_0 = 10.277929$$

and the least squares equation is (rounded)

$$\hat{y} = 10.278 + 4.919x$$

This prediction equation is graphed in the Minitab scatterplot, Figure 11.26.

The least squares estimate of the slope, $\hat{\beta}_1 = 4.919$, implies that the estimated mean damage increases by \$4,919 for each additional mile from the fire station. This interpretation is valid over the range of x, or from .7 to 6.1 miles from the station. The estimated y-intercept, $\hat{\beta}_0 = 10.278$, has the interpretation that a fire 0 miles from the fire station has an estimated mean damage of \$10,278. Although this would seem to apply to the fire station itself, remember that the y-intercept is meaningfully interpretable only if $x = 0$ is within the sampled range of the independent variable. Because $x = 0$ is outside the range in this case, $\hat{\beta}_0$ has no practical interpretation.

Step 3: Now we specify the probability distribution of the random error component ε. The assumptions about the distribution are identical to those listed in Section 11.3. Although we know that these assumptions are not completely satisfied (they rarely are for practical problems), we are willing to assume they are approximately satisfied for this example. The estimate of the standard deviation σ of ε, highlighted on the Excel printout (Figure 11.25) is

$$s = 2.31635$$

This implies that most of the observed fire damage (y) values will fall within approximately $2s = 4.64$ thousand dollars of their respective predicted values when using the least squares line. [*Note:* A more precise prediction interval for y is given in step 5.]

Step 4: We can now check the usefulness of the hypothesized model—that is, whether x really contributes information for the prediction of y using the straight-line model. First, test the null hypothesis that the slope β_1 is 0—that is, that there is no linear relationship between fire damage and the distance from the nearest fire station, against the alternative hypothesis that fire damage increases as the distance increases. We test

$$H_0: \beta_1 = 0$$
$$H_a: \beta_1 > 0$$

The test statistic value (highlighted on the printout) is $t = 12.53$. Also, the two-tailed observed significance level for testing $H_a: \beta_1 \neq 0$, (highlighted on the printout) is approximately 0. When we divide this value in half, the p-value for our one-tailed test is also approximately 0. This small p-value leaves little doubt that mean fire damage and distance between the fire and station are at least linearly related, with mean fire damage increasing as the distance increases.

We gain additional information about the relationship by forming a 95% confidence interval for the slope β_1. The lower and upper endpoints of this interval are highlighted on the Excel printout shown in Figure 11.25.

This yields the interval (4.070, 5.768). We estimate (with 95% confidence) that the interval from \$4,070 to \$5,768 encloses the mean increase (β_1) in fire damage per additional mile distance from the fire station.

Another measure of the utility of the model is the coefficient of determination, r^2. The value (highlighted on Figure 11.25) is $r^2 = .9235$, which implies that about 92% of the sample variation in fire damage (y) is explained by the distance (x) between the fire and the fire station.

The coefficient of correlation, r, that measures the strength of the linear relationship between y and x is not shown on the Excel printout and must be calculated. Using the facts that $r = \sqrt{r^2}$ in simple linear regression and that r and $\hat{\beta}_1$ have the same sign, we find

$$r = +\sqrt{r^2} = \sqrt{.9235} = .96$$

The high correlation confirms our conclusion that β_1 is greater than 0; it appears that fire damage and distance from the fire station are positively correlated. All signs point to a strong linear relationship between y and x.

Step 5: We are now prepared to use the least squares model. Suppose the insurance company wants to predict the fire damage if a major residential fire were to occur 3.5 miles from the nearest fire station. A 95% confidence interval for $E(y)$ and prediction interval for y when $x = 3.5$ are shown on the Minitab printout, Figure 11.27. The predicted value (highlighted on the printout) is $\hat{y} = 27.496$, while the 95% prediction interval (also highlighted) is (22.3239, 32.6672). Therefore, with 95% confidence we predict fire damage in a major residential fire 3.5 miles from the nearest station to be between \$22,324 and \$32,667.

```
Predicted Values for New Observations

New
Obs     Fit  SE Fit          95% CI              95% PI
  1  27.496   0.604  (26.190, 28.801)  (22.324, 32.667)


Values of Predictors for New Observations

New
Obs  DISTANCE
  1      3.50
```

Figure 11.27
Minitab confidence and prediction intervals for fire damage regression

CAUTION We would not use this prediction model to make predictions outside the scope of the model, i.e., for homes less than .7 mile or more than 6.1 miles from the nearest fire station. A look at the data in Table 11.7 reveals that all the x values fall between .7 and 6.1. It is dangerous to use the model to make predictions outside the region in which the sample data fall. A straight line might not provide a good model for the relationship between the mean value of y and the value of x when stretched over a wider range of x values.

Exercises 11.91–11.93

Applying the Concepts—Intermediate

11.91 Prices of recycled materials. Prices of recycled materials (e.g., plastics, paper, and glass) are highly volatile due to the fact that supply is constant, rather than tied to demand. An exploratory study of the prices of recycled products in the United Kingdom was published in *Resources, Conservation, and Recycling* (Vol. 60, 2012). The researchers employed simple linear regression to model y = the monthly price of recycled colored plastic bottles as a function of x = the monthly price of naphtha (a primary material in plastics). The following results were obtained for monthly data collected over a recent 10-year period (n = 120 months):

$\hat{y} = -32.35 + 4.82x$, $t = 16.60$ (for testing H_0: $\beta_1 = 0$)
$r = .83$, $r^2 = .69$

Use this information to conduct the first four steps of a complete simple linear regression analysis. Give your conclusions in the words of the problem.

11.92 Forecasting movie revenues with Twitter. Refer to the *IEEE International Conference on Web Intelligence and Intelligent Agent Technology* (2010) study of how social media (e.g., Twitter.com) may influence the products consumers buy, Exercise 11.23 (p. 617). Recall that opening weekend box office revenue (in millions of dollars) and *tweet rate* (average number of tweets referring to the movie per hour) were collected for a sample of 23 recent movies. The data are reproduced in the table. Conduct a complete simple linear regression analysis of the relationship between revenue (y) and tweet rate (x). Write all your conclusions in the words of the problem.

TWEETS

Tweet Rate	Revenue (millions)
1365.8	142
1212.8	77
581.5	61
310.1	32
455	31
290	30
250	21
680.5	18
150	18
164.5	17
113.9	16
144.5	15
418	14
98	14
100.8	12
115.4	11
74.4	10
87.5	9
127.6	9
52.2	9
144.1	8
41.3	2
2.75	0.3

11.93 An MBA's work-life balance. The importance of having employees with a healthy work-life balance has been recognized by U.S. companies for decades. Many business schools offer courses that assist MBA students with developing good work-life balance habits, and most large companies have developed work-life balance programs for their employees. In April 2005, the Graduate Management Admission Council (GMAC) conducted a survey of over 2,000 MBA alumni to explore the work-life balance issue. (For example, one question asked alumni to state their level of agreement with the statement "My personal and work demands are overwhelming.") Based on these responses, the GMAC determined a work-life balance scale score for each MBA alumnus. Scores ranged from 0 to 100, with lower scores indicating a higher imbalance between work and life. Many other variables, including average number of hours worked per week, were also measured. The data for the work-life balance study are saved in the file. (The first 15 observations are listed in the accompanying table.) Let x = average number of hours worked per week and y = work-life balance scale score for each MBA alumnus. Investigate the link between these two variables by conducting a complete simple linear regression analysis of the data. Summarize your findings in a professional report.

GMAC

WLB Score	Hours
75.22	50
64.98	45
49.62	50
44.51	55
70.10	50
54.74	60
55.98	55
21.24	60
59.86	50
70.10	50
29.00	70
64.98	45
36.75	40
35.45	40
45.75	50

Source: Schoenfeld, G. "Work-life balance: An MBA alumni report," *Graduate Management Admission Council (GMAC) Research Report* (Oct. 13, 2005). Copyright © 2005 by the Graduate Management Admissions Council (GMAC). Reprinted with permission.

Chapter Notes

Key Terms

Key Symbols/Notation

y	Dependent variable (variable to be predicted)
x	Independent variable (variable used to predict y)
$E(y)$	Expected value (mean) of y
β_0	y-intercept of true line
β_1	Slope of true line
$\hat{\beta}_0$	Least squares estimate of y-intercept
$\hat{\beta}_1$	Least squares estimate of slope
ε	Random error
$\hat{y}$	Predicted value of y for a given x-value
$(y - \hat{y})$	Estimated error of prediction
SSE	Sum of squared errors of prediction
r	Coefficient of correlation
r^2	Coefficient of determination
x_p	Value of x used to predict y
$r^2 = \dfrac{SS_{yy} - SSE}{SS_{yy}}$	Coefficient of determination
$\hat{y} \pm t_{\alpha/2} s\sqrt{\dfrac{1}{n} + \dfrac{(x_p - \bar{x})^2}{SS_{xx}}}$	$100\%(1 - \alpha)$ confidence interval for $E(y)$ when $x = x_p$
$\hat{y} \pm t_{\alpha/2} s\sqrt{1 + \dfrac{1}{n} + \dfrac{(x_p - \bar{x})^2}{SS_{xx}}}$	$100\%(1 - \alpha)$ prediction interval for y when $x = x_p$

Key Ideas

Simple Linear Regression variables

y = **Dependent** variable (quantitative)
x = **Independent** variable (quantitative)

Method of Least Squares Properties

1. average error of prediction = 0
2. sum of squared errors is minimum

Practical Interpretation of y-Intercept

Predicted y-value when $x = 0$

(no practical interpretation if $x = 0$ is either nonsensical or outside range of sample data)

Practical Interpretation of Slope

Increase (or decrease) in mean y for every 1-unit increase in x

First-Order (Straight-Line) Model

$$E(y) = \beta_0 + \beta_1 x$$

where $E(y)$ = mean of y

β_0 = **y-intercept** of line (point where line intecepts y-axis)
β_1 = **slope** of line (change in mean of y for every 1-unit change in x)

Coefficient of Correlation, r

1. ranges between -1 and $+1$
2. measures strength of *linear relationship* between y and x

Coefficient of Determination, r^2

1. ranges between 0 and 1
2. measures proportion of sample variation in y "explained" by the model

Practical Interpretation of Model Standard Deviation, s

Ninety-five percent of y-values fall within $2s$ of their respected predicted values

Width of *confidence interval for $E(y)$* will always be **narrower** than width of prediction interval for y

Guide to Simple Linear Regression

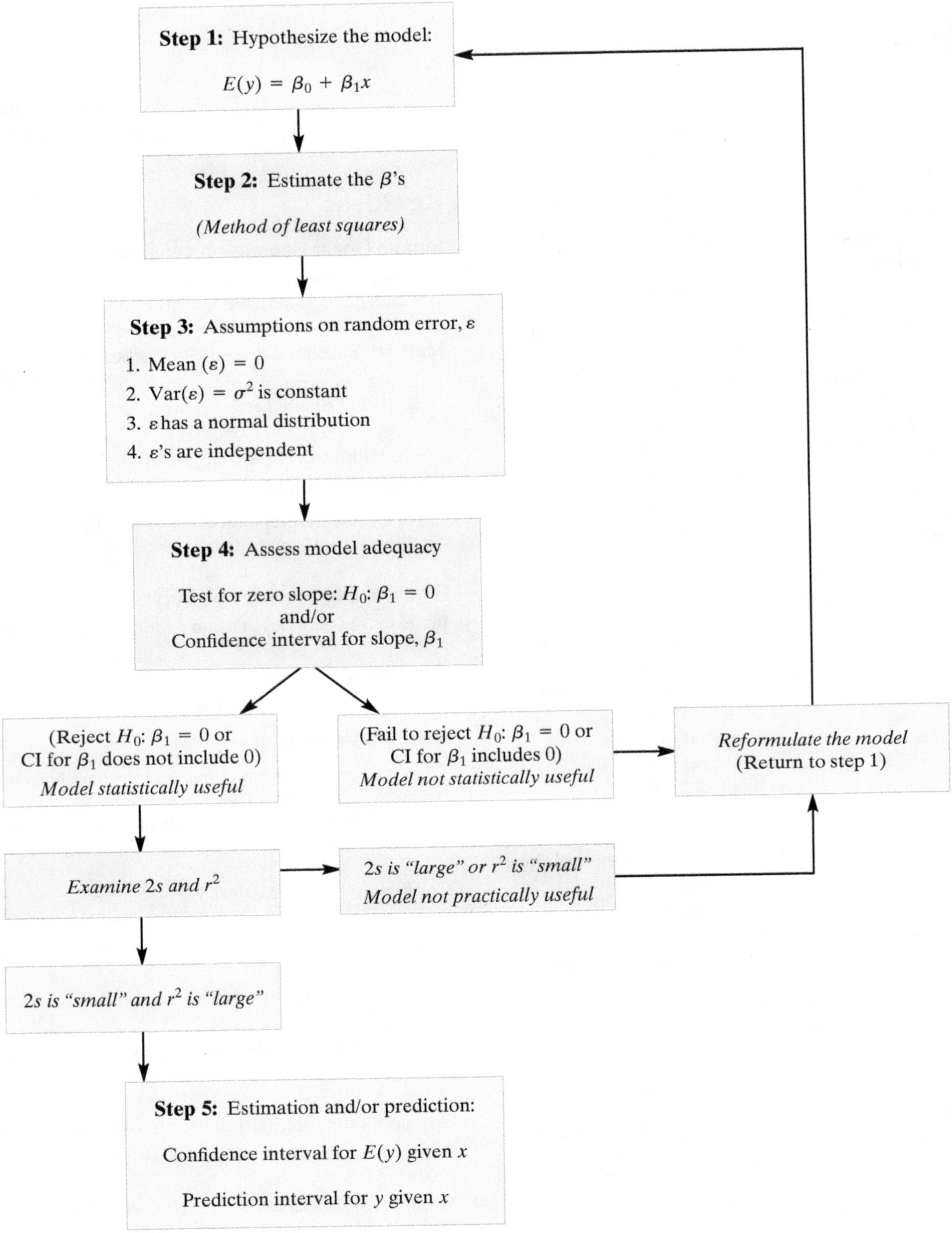

Supplementary Exercises 11.94–11.112

Learning the Mechanics

11.94 Consider the following sample data:

y	5	1	3
x	5	1	3

a. Construct a scatterplot for the data.

b. It is possible to find many lines for which $\Sigma(y - \hat{y}) = 0$. For this reason, the criterion $\Sigma(y - \hat{y}) = 0$ is not used for identifying the "best-fitting" straight line. Find two lines that have $\Sigma(y - \hat{y}) = 0$.

c. Find the least squares line.

d. Compare the value of SSE for the least squares line to that of the two lines you found in part **b.** What principle of least squares is demonstrated by this comparison?

11.95 In fitting a least squares line to $n = 15$ data points, the following quantities were computed: $SS_{xx} = 55$, $SS_{yy} = 198$, $SS_{xy} = -88$, $\bar{x} = 1.3$, and $\bar{y} = 35$.

a. Find the least squares line.

b. Graph the least squares line.

c. Calculate SSE.

d. Calculate s^2.

e. Find a 90% confidence interval for β_1. Interpret this estimate.

f. Find a 90% confidence interval for the mean value of y when $x = 15$.

g. Find a 90% prediction interval for y when $x = 15$.

11.96 Consider the following 10 data points:

L11096

x	3	5	6	4	3	7	6	5	4	7
y	4	3	2	1	2	3	3	5	4	2

a. Plot the data on a scatterplot.

b. Calculate the values of r and r^2.

c. Is there sufficient evidence to indicate that x and y are linearly correlated? Test at the $\alpha = .10$ level of significance.

Applying the Concepts—Basic

11.97 "Metaskills" and career management. Effective management of one's own career requires a skill set that includes adaptability, tolerance for ambiguity, self-awareness, and ability to identify change. Management professors at Pace University (New York) used correlation coefficients to investigate the relationship between these "metaskills" and effective career management (*International Journal of Manpower,* Aug. 2000). Data were collected for 446 business graduates who had all completed a management metaskills course. Two of the many variables measured were self-knowledge skill level (x) and goal-setting ability (y). The correlation coefficient for these two variables was $r = .70$.

a. Give a practical interpretation of the value of r.

b. The p-value for a test of no correlation between the two variables was reported as p-value $= .001$. Interpret this result.

c. Find the coefficient of determination, r^2, and interpret the result.

11.98 Burnout of human services professionals. Emotional exhaustion, or *burnout,* is a significant problem for people with careers in the field of human services. Regression analysis was used to investigate the relationship between burnout and aspects of the human services professional's job and job-related behavior (*Journal of Applied Behavioral Science,* Vol. 22, 1986). Emotional exhaustion was measured with the Maslach Burnout Inventory, a questionnaire. One of the independent variables considered, called *concentration,* was the proportion of social contacts with individuals who belong to a person's work group. The next table lists the values of the emotional exhaustion index (higher values indicate greater exhaustion) and concentration for a sample of 25 human services professionals who work in a large public hospital. A Minitab printout of the simple linear regression is provided below.

BRNOUT

Exhaustion Index, y	Concentration, x	Exhaustion Index, y	Concentration, x
100	20%	493	86%
525	60	892	83
300	38	527	79
980	88	600	75
310	79	855	81
900	87	709	75
410	68	791	77
296	12	718	77
120	35	684	77
501	70	141	17
920	80	400	85
810	92	970	96
506	77		

```
The regression equation is
EXHAUST = - 29 + 8.87 CONCEN


Predictor     Coef   SE Coef       T      P
Constant     -29.5     106.7   -0.28  0.785
CONCEN       8.865     1.471    6.03  0.000


S = 174.207    R-Sq = 61.2%    R-Sq(adj) = 59.5%


Analysis of Variance

Source          DF        SS        MS      F      P
Regression       1   1102408   1102408  36.33  0.000
Residual Error  23    698009     30348
Total           24   1800417


Predicted Values for New Observations

New
Obs     Fit  SE Fit        95% CI               95% PI
  1   679.7    38.7  (599.7, 759.8)   (310.6, 1048.9)


Values of Predictors for New Observations

New
Obs  CONCEN
  1    80.0
```

a. Construct a scatterplot for the data. Do the variables x and y appear to be related?
b. Find the correlation coefficient for the data and interpret its value. Does your conclusion mean that concentration causes emotional exhaustion? Explain.
c. Test the usefulness of the straight-line relationship with concentration for predicting burnout. Use $\alpha = .05$.
d. Find the coefficient of determination for the model and interpret it.
e. Find a 95% confidence interval for the slope β_1. Interpret the result.
f. Use a 95% confidence interval to estimate the mean exhaustion level for all professionals who have 80% of their social contacts within their work groups. Interpret the interval.

11.99 Retaliation against company "whistle-blowers." Individuals who report perceived wrongdoing of a corporation or public agency are known as *whistle-blowers.* Two researchers developed an index to measure the extent of retaliation against a whistle-blower (*Journal of Applied Psychology,* 1986). The index was based on the number of forms of reprisal actually experienced, the number of forms of reprisal threatened, and the number of people within the organization (e.g., coworkers or immediate supervisor) who retaliated against them. The table below lists the retaliation index (higher numbers indicate more extensive retaliation) and salary for a sample of 15 whistle-blowers from federal agencies.

RETAL

Retaliation Index	Salary	Retaliation Index	Salary
301	$62,000	535	$19,800
550	36,500	455	44,000
755	21,600	615	46,600
327	24,000	700	15,100
500	30,100	650	70,000
377	35,000	630	21,000
290	47,500	360	16,900
452	54,000		

Source: Based on Near, J. P., & Miceli, M. P. "Retaliation against whistle blowers: Predictors and effects," *Journal of Applied Psychology,* Vol. 71, No. 1, 1986, pp. 137–145.

a. Construct a scatterplot for the data. Does it appear that the extent of retaliation increases, decreases, or stays the same with an increase in salary? Explain.
b. Use the method of least squares to fit a straight line to the data.
c. Graph the least squares line on your scatterplot. Does the least squares line support your answer to the question in part **a**? Explain.
d. Interpret the y-intercept, $\hat{\beta}_0$ of the least squares line in terms of this application. Is the interpretation meaningful?
e. Interpret the slope, $\hat{\beta}_1$, of the least squares line in terms of this application. Over what range of x is this interpretation meaningful?
f. Test the adequacy of the model using $\alpha = .05$.

11.100 Buying income of households. *Sales and Marketing Management* determined the "effective buying income" (EBI) of the average household in a state. Can the EBI be used to predict retail sales per household in the store-group category "eating and drinking places"?

EBI

a. Use the data for 13 states given in the table below to find the least squares line relating retail sales per household (y) to average household EBI (x).
b. Plot the least squares line, as well as the actual data points, on a scatterplot.
c. Based on the graph, part **b**, give your opinion regarding the predictive ability of the least squares line.
d. Find a 95% confidence interval for the slope of the line.
e. Use the results, part **d**, to assess the adequacy of the straight-line model.

State	Average Household Buying Income ($)	Retail Sales: Eating and Drinking Places ($ per household)
Connecticut	60,998	2,553.8
New Jersey	63,853	2,154.8
Michigan	46,915	2,523.3
Minnesota	44,717	2,278.6
Florida	42,442	2,475.8
South Carolina	37,848	2,358.4
Mississippi	34,490	1,538.4
Oklahoma	34,830	2,063.1
Texas	44,729	2,363.5
Colorado	44,571	3,214.9
Utah	43,421	2,653.8
California	50,713	2,215.0
Oregon	40,597	2,144.0

Source: "The survey of buying power," *Sales and Marketing Management,* 1995. Copyright © 1995 by Sales and Marketing Management. Reprinted with permission.

11.101 Diamonds sold at retail. Refer to the *Journal of Statistics Education* study of 308 diamonds sold on the open market, Exercise 2.158 (p. 117). Recall that you related the size of the diamond (number of carats) to the asking price (dollars) using a scatterplot.

DIAMND

a. Write the equation of a straight-line model relating asking price (y) to number of carats (x).
b. An XLSTAT simple linear regression printout for the analysis is shown on the following page. Find the equation of the least squares line.
c. Give a practical interpretation of the y-intercept of the least squares line. If a practical interpretation is not possible, explain why.
d. Locate a 95% confidence interval for the slope of the least squares line on the printout and practically interpret the result. Over what range is the interpretation meaningful?
e. Locate the estimated standard deviation of the random error on the printout and practically interpret this value.
f. Specify the null and alternative hypotheses for determining whether a positive linear relationship exists between asking price and size.
g. Locate the p-value of the test, part **f**, on the printout. Interpret the result if $\alpha = .05$.
h. Locate the coefficient of determination, r^2, on the printout and interpret the result.
i. Locate the coefficient of correlation, r, on the printout and interpret the result.
j. Locate a 95% prediction interval for the asking price when carat size is .5 on the printout and practically interpret the result.

XLSTAT output for Exercise 11.101

Variables	CARAT	PRICE
CARAT	**1.0000**	0.9447
PRICE	0.9447	**1.0000**

Regression of variable PRICE:

Goodness of fit statistics:

Observatic	308.0000
Sum of we	308.0000
DF	306.0000
R²	0.8925
Adjusted R	0.8922
MSE	1248949.7531
RMSE	1117.5642
DW	1.2156

Analysis of variance:

Source	DF	Sum of squares	Mean squares	F	Pr > F
Model	1	3173248722.4667	3173248722.4667	2540.7337	< 0.0001
Error	306	382178624.4521	1248949.7531		
Corrected	307	3555427346.9188			

Computed against model Y=Mean(Y)

Model parameters:

Source	Value	Standard error	t	Pr > |t|	Lower bound (95%)	Upper bound (95%)
Intercept	-2298.3576	158.5306	-14.4979	< 0.0001	-2610.3056	-1986.4096
CARAT	11598.8840	230.1106	50.4057	< 0.0001	11146.0846	12051.6834

Equation of the model:

PRICE = -2298.35760+11598.88401*CARAT

Predictions for the new observations:

Observation	Pred(PRICE)	Lower bound 95% (Mean)	Upper bound 95% (Mean)	Lower bound 95% (Observation)	Upper bound 95% (Observation)
0.5	3501.0844	3362.4670	3639.7018	1297.6366	5704.5322

k. Locate a 95% confidence interval for the mean asking price when carat size is .5 on the printout and practically interpret the result.

11.102 Sports news on local TV broadcasts. *The Sports Journal* (Winter 2004) published the results of a study conducted to assess the factors that impact the time allotted to sports news on local television news broadcasts. Information on total time (in minutes) allotted to sports and audience ratings of the TV news broadcast (measured on a 100-point scale) was obtained from a national sample of 163 news directors. A correlation analysis on the data yielded $r = .43$.

a. Interpret the value of the correlation coefficient, r.

b. Find and interpret the value of the coefficient of determination, r^2.

Applying the Concepts—Intermediate

11.103 Evaluating managerial success. H. Mintzberg's classic book *The Nature of Managerial Work* (1973) identified the roles found in all managerial jobs. An observational study of 19 managers from a medium-sized manufacturing plant extended Mintzberg's work by investigating which activities *successful* managers actually perform (*Journal of Applied Behavioral Science,* Aug. 1985). To measure success, the researchers devised an index based on the manager's length of time in the organization and his or her level within the firm; the higher the index, the more successful the manager. The table on the following page presents data that can be used to determine whether managerial success is related to the extensiveness of a manager's network-building interactions with people outside the manager's work unit. Such interactions include phone and face-to-face meetings with customers and suppliers, attending outside meetings, and doing public relations work.

MINDEX

a. Construct a scatterplot for the data.

b. Find the prediction equation for managerial success.

c. Find s for your prediction equation. Interpret the standard deviation s in the context of this problem.

d. Plot the least squares line on your scatterplot of part **a.** Does it appear that the number of interactions

Data for Exercise 11.103

Manager	Manager Success Index, y	Number of Interactions with Outsiders, x
1	40	12
2	73	71
3	95	70
4	60	81
5	81	43
6	27	50
7	53	42
8	66	18
9	25	35
10	63	82
11	70	20
12	47	81
13	80	40
14	51	33
15	32	45
16	50	10
17	52	65
18	30	20
19	42	21

with outsiders contributes information for the prediction of managerial success? Explain.

e. Conduct a formal statistical hypothesis test to answer the question posed in part **d.** Use $\alpha = .05$.

f. Construct a 95% confidence interval for β_1. Interpret the interval in the context of the problem.

g. A particular manager was observed for 2 weeks, as in the *Journal of Applied Behavioral Science* study. She made 55 contacts with people outside her work unit. Predict the value of the manager's success index. Use a 90% prediction interval.

h. A second manager was observed for 2 weeks. This manager made 110 contacts with people outside his work unit. Why should caution be exercised in using the least squares model developed from the given data set to construct a prediction interval for this manager's success index?

i. In the context of this problem, determine the value of x for which the associated prediction interval for y is the narrowest.

11.104 Doctors and ethics. Refer to the *Journal of Medical Ethics* (Vol. 32, 2006) study of physicians' use of ethics consultation, Exercise 2.131 (p. 106). Recall that the medical researchers measured the *length of time in practice* (i.e., years of experience) and the *amount of exposure to ethics in medical school* (number of hours) for a sample of 118 physicians. Consider a straight-line regression model relating hours of exposure (y) to time in practice (x).

ETHICS

a. Fit the model to the data saved in the file and conduct a test (at $\alpha = .05$) for a linear relationship between the two variables.

b. In Exercise 2.132 you identified a highly suspect outlier for hours of exposure. Remove this outlier from the data set and rerun the analysis, part **a.** What do you observe?

11.105 Do New Jersey banks serve minority communities? Financial institutions have a legal and social responsibility to serve all communities. Do banks adequately serve both inner-city and suburban neighborhoods, both poor and wealthy communities? In New Jersey, banks have been charged with withdrawing from urban areas with a high percentage of minorities. To examine this charge, a regional New Jersey newspaper, the *Asbury Park Press,* compiled county-by-county data on the number (y) of people in each county per branch bank in the county and the percentage (x) of the population in each county that is minority. These data for each of New Jersey's 21 counties are provided in the table below.

BANKS

County	Number of People per Bank Branch	Percentage of Minority Population
Atlantic	3,073	23.3
Bergen	2,095	13.0
Burlington	2,905	17.8
Camden	3,330	23.4
Cape May	1,321	7.3
Cumberland	2,557	26.5
Essex	3,474	48.8
Gloucester	3,068	10.7
Hudson	3,683	33.2
Hunterdon	1,998	3.7
Mercer	2,607	24.9
Middlesex	3,154	18.1
Monmouth	2,609	12.6
Morris	2,253	8.2
Ocean	2,317	4.7
Passaic	3,307	28.1
Salem	2,511	16.7
Somerset	2,333	12.0
Sussex	2,568	2.4
Union	3,048	25.6
Warren	2,349	2.8

Source: D'Ambrosio, P., & Chambers, S. "No checks and balances," *Asbury Park Press,* September 10, 1995. Copyright © 1995 by Asbury Park Press. Reprinted with permission.

a. Plot the data in a scatterplot. What pattern, if any, does the plot reveal?

b. Consider the linear model $E(y) = \beta_0 + \beta_1 x$. If, in fact, the charge against the New Jersey banks is true, then an increase in the percentage of minorities (x) will lead to a decrease in the number of bank branches in a county and therefore will result in an increase in the number of people (y) per branch. Will the value of β_1 be positive or negative in this situation?

c. Do these data support or refute the charge made against the New Jersey banking community? Test using $\alpha = .01$.

11.106 Monetary values of NFL teams. Refer to the *Forbes* magazine 2011 report on the financial standings of each team in the National Football League (NFL), Exercise 2.26 (p. 60). The table listing the current value (without deduction for debt, except stadium debt) and operating income for each team is reproduced on the next page.

NFL

a. Propose a straight-line model relating an NFL team's current value (y) to its operating income (x).

b. Fit the model to the data using the method of least squares.

c. Interpret the least squares estimates of the slope and y-intercept in the words of the problem.

d. Statistically assess the adequacy of the model. Do you recommend using it to predict an NFL team's value?

Data for Exercise 11.106

Rank	Team	Current Value ($mil)	1-Yr Value Change (%)	Debt/Value (%)	Revenue ($mil)	Operating Income ($mil)
1	Dallas Cowboys	1,850	2	18	406	119
2	Washington Redskins	1,555	0	26	352	65.6
3	New England Patriots	1,400	2	19	333	42.9
4	New York Giants	1,300	10	50	293	40.6
5	New York Jets	1,223	7	61	285	25.1
6	Houston Texans	1,202	3	17	283	41
7	Philadelphia Eagles	1,164	4	9	274	28.9
8	Chicago Bears	1,093	2	11	266	43.4
9	Green Bay Packers	1,089	7	2	259	12
10	Baltimore Ravens	1,088	1	25	262	24.9
11	Indianapolis Colts	1,057	2	4	252	32.8
12	Denver Broncos	1,046	0	14	255	28.5
13	Pittsburgh Steelers	1,018	2	25	255	28.3
14	Miami Dolphins	1,012	0	40	253	12.9
15	Carolina Panthers	1,002	−3	19	257	31.2
16	Seattle Seahawks	997	1	12	249	7.8
17	San Francisco 49ers	990	7	14	234	1.5
18	Kansas City Chiefs	986	2	14	252	14.5
19	Tampa Bay Buccaneers	981	−5	18	245	50.8
20	Cleveland Browns	977	−4	15	247	−2.9
21	New Orleans Saints	965	1	13	261	28.9
22	Tennessee Titans	964	−3	13	250	21.8
23	San Diego Chargers	920	1	14	241	34.2
24	Arizona Cardinals	901	−2	17	240	56.4
25	Cincinnati Bengals	875	−3	11	236	44.7
26	Detroit Lions	844	3	33	228	−7.7
27	Atlanta Falcons	814	−2	34	233	27.2
28	Minnesota Vikings	796	3	41	227	3.7
29	Buffalo Bills	792	−1	16	236	40.9
30	St. Louis Rams	775	−1	15	228	24.6
31	Oakland Raiders	761	0	16	217	23
32	Jacksonville Jaguars	725	0	17	236	32.8

Source: Based on "Football's Most Valuable Teams," *Forbes*, September 7, 2011.

11.107 Evaluating a truck weigh-in-motion program. The Minnesota Department of Transportation installed a state-of-the-art weigh-in-motion scale in the concrete surface of the eastbound lanes of Interstate 494 in Bloomington, Minnesota. After installation, a study was undertaken to determine whether the scale's readings correspond with the static weights of the vehicles being monitored. (Studies of this type are known as *calibration studies.*) After some preliminary comparisons using a two-axle, six-tire truck carrying different loads (see the accompanying table), calibration adjustments were made in the software of the weigh-in-motion system, and the scales were reevaluated.

WEIGHN

Trial Number	Static Weight of Truck, x (thousand pounds)	Weigh-in-Motion Reading Prior to Calibration Adjustment, y_1 (thousand pounds)	Weigh-in-Motion Reading After Calibration Adjustment, y_2 (thousand pounds)
1	27.9	26.0	27.8
2	29.1	29.9	29.1
3	38.0	39.5	37.8
4	27.0	25.1	27.1
5	30.3	31.6	30.6
6	34.5	36.2	34.3
7	27.8	25.1	26.9
8	29.6	31.0	29.6
9	33.1	35.6	33.0
10	35.5	40.2	35.0

Source: Based on Wright, J. L., Owen, F., and Pena, D. "Status of MN/DOT's weigh-in-motion program," St. Paul: Minnesota Department of Transportation, January 1983.

a. Construct two scatterplots, one of y_1 versus x and the other of y_2 versus x.

b. Use the scatterplots of part **a** to evaluate the performance of the weigh-in-motion scale both before and after the calibration adjustment.

c. Calculate the correlation coefficient for both sets of data and interpret their values. Explain how these correlation coefficients can be used to evaluate the weigh-in-motion scale.

d. Suppose the sample correlation coefficient for y_2 and x was 1. Could this happen if the static weights and the weigh-in-motion readings disagreed? Explain.

11.108 Energy efficiency of buildings. Firms planning to build new plants or make additions to existing facilities have become very conscious of the energy efficiency of proposed new structures and are interested in the relation between yearly energy consumption and the number of square feet of building shell. The table on the next page lists the energy consumption in British thermal units (a BTU is the amount of heat required to raise 1 pound

BTU

of water 1°F) for 22 buildings that were all subjected to the same climatic conditions. Consider a straight-line model relating BTU consumption, y, to building shell area, x.

a. Find the least squares estimates of the intercept β_0 and the slope β_1.

b. Investigate the usefulness of the model you developed in part **a.** Is yearly energy consumption positively linearly related to the shell area of the building? Test using $\alpha = .10$.

c. Find the observed significance level of the test of part **b.** Interpret its value.

d. Find the coefficient of determination r^2 and interpret its value.

e. A company wishes to build a new warehouse that will contain 8,000 square feet of shell area. Find the predicted value of energy consumption and associated 95% prediction interval. Comment on the usefulness of this interval.

f. The application of the model you developed in part **a** to the warehouse problem of part **e** is appropriate only if certain assumptions can be made about the new warehouse. What are these assumptions?

BTU/Year (thousands)	Shell Area (square feet)
3,870,000	30,001
1,371,000	13,530
2,422,000	26,060
672,200	6,355
233,100	4,576
218,900	24,680
354,000	2,621
3,135,000	23,350
1,470,000	18,770
1,408,000	12,220
2,201,000	25,490
2,680,000	23,680
337,500	5,650
567,500	8,001
555,300	6,147
239,400	2,660
2,629,000	19,240
1,102,000	10,700
423,500	9,125
423,500	6,510
1,691,000	13,530
1,870,000	18,860

11.109 Foreign investment risk. One of the most difficult tasks of developing and managing a global portfolio is assessing the risks of potential foreign investments. Duke University researcher C. R. Henry collaborated with two First Chicago Investment Management Company directors to examine the use of country credit ratings as a means of evaluating foreign investments (*Journal of Portfolio Management,* Winter 1995). To be effective, such a measure should help explain and predict the volatility of the foreign market in question. Data on annualized risk (y) and average credit rating (x) for 40 fictitious countries (based on the study results) are saved in the file. (The first and last five countries are shown in the table.)

RISK

a. Do the data provide sufficient evidence to conclude that country credit risk (x) contributes information for the prediction of market volatility (y)?

Country	Annualized Risk (%)	Average Credit Rating
1	85.9	30.7
2	25.8	77.1
3	25.2	82.7
4	20.9	77.3
5	63.7	35.1
⋮	⋮	⋮
36	73.0	31.5
37	20.7	86.5
38	14.3	95.3
39	44.9	43.9
40	34.5	23.4

b. Use a graph to visually locate any unusual data points (outliers).

c. Eliminate the outlier(s), part **b,** from the data set and rerun the simple linear regression analysis. Note any dramatic changes in the results.

Applying the Concepts—Advanced

11.110 Regression through the origin. Sometimes it is known from theoretical considerations that the straight-line relationship between two variables, x and y, passes through the origin of the xy-plane. Consider the relationship between the total weight of a shipment of 50-pound bags of flour, y, and the number of bags in the shipment, x. Because a shipment containing $x = 0$ bags (i.e., no shipment at all) has a total weight of $y = 0$, a straight-line model of the relationship between x and y should pass through the point $x = 0$, $y = 0$. In such a case, you could assume $\beta_0 = 0$ and characterize the relationship between x and y with the following model:

FLOUR2

$$y = \beta_1 x + \varepsilon$$

The least squares estimate of β_1 for this model is

$$\hat{\beta}_1 = \frac{\sum x_i y_i}{\sum x_i^2}$$

From the records of past flour shipments, 15 shipments were randomly chosen, and the data shown in the table below were recorded.

Weight of Shipment	Number of 50-Pound Bags in Shipment
5,050	100
10,249	205
20,000	450
7,420	150
24,685	500
10,206	200
7,325	150
4,958	100
7,162	150
24,000	500
4,900	100
14,501	300
28,000	600
17,002	400
16,100	400

a. Find the least squares line for the given data under the assumption that $\beta_0 = 0$. Plot the least squares line on a scatterplot of the data.

b. Find the least squares line for the given data using the model

$$y = \beta_0 + \beta_1 x + \varepsilon$$

(i.e., do not restrict β_0 to equal 0). Plot this line on the same scatterplot you constructed in part **a.**

c. Refer to part **b.** Why might $\hat{\beta}_0$ be different from 0 even though the true value of β_0 is known to be 0?

d. The estimated standard error of $\hat{\beta}_0$ is equal to

$$s\sqrt{\frac{1}{n} + \frac{\bar{x}^2}{SS_{xx}}}$$

Use the t-statistic

$$t = \frac{\hat{\beta}_0 - 0}{s\sqrt{(1/n) + (\bar{x}^2/SS_{xx})}}$$

to test the null hypothesis H_0: $\beta_0 = 0$ against the alternative H_a: $\beta_0 \neq 0$. Use $\alpha = .10$. Should you include β_0 in your model?

Critical Thinking Challenges

11.111 Comparing cost functions. Managers are interested in modeling past cost behavior in order to make more accurate predictions of future costs. Models of past cost behavior are called *cost functions.* Factors that influence costs are called *cost drivers* (Horngren, Datar, and Rajan, *Cost Accounting,* 2011). The cost data shown below are from a rug manufacturer. Indirect manufacturing labor costs consist of machine maintenance costs and setup labor costs. Machine-hours and direct manufacturing labor-hours are cost drivers. Your task is to estimate and compare two alternative cost functions for indirect manufacturing labor costs. In the first, machine-hours is the independent variable; in the second, direct manufacturing labor-hours is the independent variable. Prepare a report that compares the two cost functions and recommends which should be used to explain and predict indirect manufacturing labor costs. Be sure to justify your choice.

RUG

Week	Indirect Manufacturing Labor Costs	Machine-Hours	Direct Manufacturing Labor-Hours
1	$1,190	68	30
2	1,211	88	35
3	1,004	62	36
4	917	72	20
5	770	60	47
6	1,456	96	45
7	1,180	78	44
8	710	46	38
9	1,316	82	70
10	1,032	94	30
11	752	68	29
12	963	48	38

Source: Based on Horngren, C. T., Datar, S. M., & Rajan, M. *Cost Accounting: A Managerial Emphasis*, 14th ed. Upper Saddle River, N.J.: Prentice Hall, 2011.

11.112 Spall damage in bricks. A civil suit revolved around a five-building brick apartment complex located in the Bronx, New York, which began to suffer *spalling* damage (i.e., a separation of some portion of the face of a brick from its body). The owner of the complex alleged that the bricks were defectively manufactured. The brick manufacturer countered that poor design and shoddy management led to the damage. To settle the suit, an estimate of the rate of damage per 1,000 bricks, called the *spall rate,* was required (*Chance,* Summer 1994). The owner estimated the spall rate using several *scaffold-drop* surveys. (With this method, an engineer lowers a scaffold down at selected places on building walls and counts the number of visible spalls for every 1,000 bricks in the observation area.) The brick manufacturer conducted its own survey by dividing the walls of the complex into 83 wall segments and taking a photograph of each wall segment. (The number of spalled bricks that could be made out from each photo was recorded, and the sum over all 83 wall segments was used as an estimate of total spall damage.) In this court case, the jury was faced with the following dilemma: The scaffold-drop survey provided the most accurate estimate of spall rates in a given wall segment. Unfortunately, the drop areas were not selected at random from the entire complex; rather, drops were made at areas with high spall concentrations, leading to an overestimate of the total damage. On the other hand, the photo survey was complete in that all 83 wall segments in the complex were checked for spall damage. But the spall rate estimated by the photos, at least in areas of high spall concentration, was biased low (spalling damage cannot always be seen from a photo), leading to an underestimate of the total damage.

BRICKS

Drop Location	Drop Spall Rate (per 1,000 bricks)	Photo Spall Rate (per 1,000 bricks)
1	0	0
2	5.1	0
3	6.6	0
4	1.1	.8
5	1.8	1.0
6	3.9	1.0
7	11.5	1.9
8	22.1	7.7
9	39.3	14.9
10	39.9	13.9
11	43.0	11.8

Source: Fairley, W. B., et al. "Bricks, buildings, and the Bronx: Estimating masonry deterioration," *Chance,* Vol. 7. No. 3, Summer 1994, p. 36 (Figure 3). Reprinted with permission from *Chance.* [*Note:* The data points are estimated from the points shown on a scatterplot.]

The data in the table are the spall rates obtained using the two methods at 11 drop locations. Use the data, as did expert statisticians who testified in the case, to help the jury estimate the true spall rate at a given wall segment. Then explain how this information, coupled with the data (not given here) on all 83 wall segments, can provide a reasonable estimate of the total spall damage (i.e., total number of damaged bricks).

Activity 11.1 Applying Simple Linear Regression to Your Favorite Data

Many dependent variables in business serve as the subjects of regression modeling efforts. We list five such variables here:

1. Rate of return of a stock
2. Annual unemployment rate
3. Grade point average of an accounting student
4. Gross domestic product of the United States
5. Salary cap space available for your favorite NFL team

Choose one of these dependent variables, or choose some other dependent variable, for which you want to construct a prediction model. There may be a large number of independent variables that should be included in a prediction equation for the dependent variable you choose. List three potentially important independent variables, x_1, x_2, and x_3, that you think might be (individually) strongly related to your dependent variable. Next, obtain 25 data values, each of which consists of a measure of your dependent variable y and the corresponding values of x_1, x_2, and x_3.

a. Use the least squares formulas given in this chapter to fit three straight-line models–one for each independent variable–for predicting y.

b. Interpret the sign of the estimated slope coefficient $\hat{\beta}_1$ in each case, and test the utility of each model by testing H_0: $\beta_1 = 0$ against H_a: $\beta_1 \neq 0$. What assumptions must be satisfied to ensure the validity of these tests?

c. Calculate the coefficient of determination, r^2, for each model. Which of the independent variables predicts y best for the 25 sampled sets of data? Is this variable necessarily best in general (i.e., for the entire population)? Explain.

Be sure to keep the data and the results of your calculations, since you will need them for the Activity section in Chapter 12.

References

Chatterjee, S., & Price, B. *Regression Analysis by Example,* 2nd ed. New York: Wiley, 1991.

Draper, N., & Smith, H. *Applied Regression Analysis,* 3rd ed. New York: Wiley, 1987.

Gitlow, H., Oppenheim, A., & Oppenheim, R. *Quality Management: Tools and Methods for Improvement,* 2nd ed. Burr Ridge, Ill.: Irwin, 1995.

Graybill, F. *Theory and Application of the Linear Model.* North Scituate, Mass.: Duxbury, 1976.

Kleinbaum, D., & Kupper, L. *Applied Regression Analysis and Other Multivariable Methods,* 2nd ed. North Scituate, Mass.: Duxbury, 1997.

Kutner, M., Nachtsheim, C., Neter, J., & Li, W. *Applied Linear Statistical Models,* 5th ed. New York: McGraw-Hill, 2006.

Mendenhall, W. *Introduction to Linear Models and the Design and Analysis of Experiments.* Belmont, CA.: Wadsworth, 1968.

Mendenhall, W., & Sincich, T. A. *Second Course in Statistics: Regression Analysis,* 7th ed. Upper Saddle River, N.J.: Prentice Hall, 2011.

Montgomery, D., Peck, E., & Vining, G. *Introduction to Linear Regression Analysis,* 3rd ed. New York: Wiley, 2001.

Mosteller, F., & Tukey, J. W. *Data Analysis and Regression: A Second Course in Statistics.* Reading, Mass.: Addison-Wesley, 1977.

Rousseeuw, P. J., & Leroy, A. M. *Robust Regression and Outlier Detection.* New York: Wiley, 1987.

Weisburg, S. *Applied Linear Regression,* 2nd ed. New York: Wiley, 1985.

USING TECHNOLOGY Technology images shown here are taken from SPSS Statistics Professional 20.0, Minitab 16, XLSTAT for Pearson, and Excel 2010.

SPSS: Simple Linear Regression

Regression Analysis

Step 1 Access the SPSS spreadsheet file that contains the two quantitative variables (dependent and independent variables).

Step 2 Click on the "Analyze" button on the SPSS menu bar and then click on "Regression" and "Linear," as shown in Figure 11.S.1.

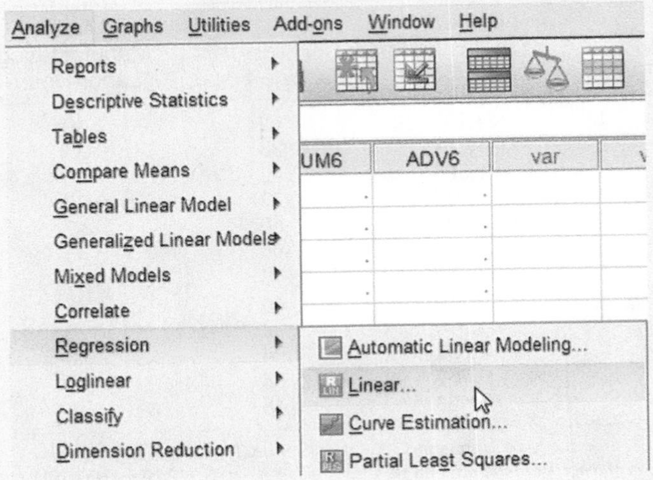

Figure 11.S.1 SPSS menu options for regression

Step 3 On the resulting dialog box (see Figure 11.S.2), specify the dependent variable in the "Dependent" box and the independent variable in the "Independent(s)" box. Be sure to select "Enter" in the "Method" box.

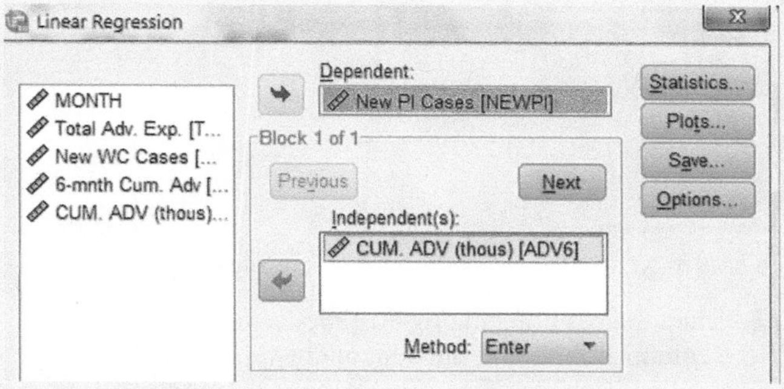

Figure 11.S.2 SPSS linear regression dialog box

Step 4 To produce confidence intervals for the model parameters, click the "Statistics" button and check the appropriate menu items in the resulting menu list.

Step 5 To obtain prediction intervals for y and confidence intervals for $E(y)$, click the "Save" button and check the appropriate items in the resulting menu list, as shown in Figure 11.S.3. (The prediction intervals will be added as new columns to the SPSS data spreadsheet.)

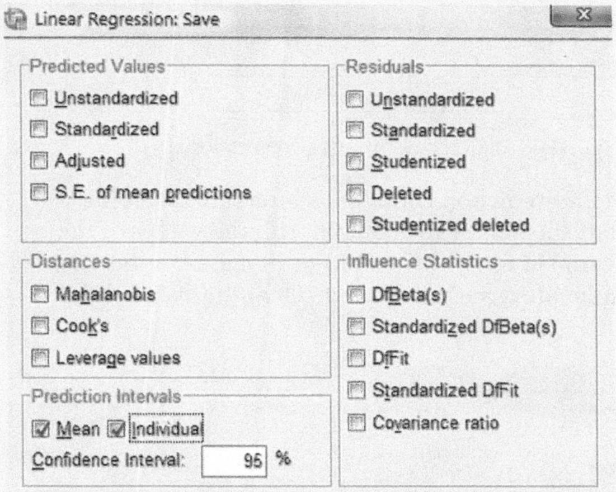

Figure 11.S.3 SPSS linear regression save dialog box

Step 6 To return to the main Regression dialog box from any of these optional screens, click "Continue." Click "OK" on the Regression dialog box to view the linear regression results.

Correlation Analysis

Step 1 Click on the "Analyze" button on the main menu bar and then click on "Correlate" (see Figure 11.S.1).

Step 2 Click on "Bivariate." The resulting dialog box appears in Figure 11.S.4.

Step 3 Enter the variables of interest in the "Variables" box and check the "Pearson" option.

Step 4 Click "OK" to obtain a printout of the correlation.

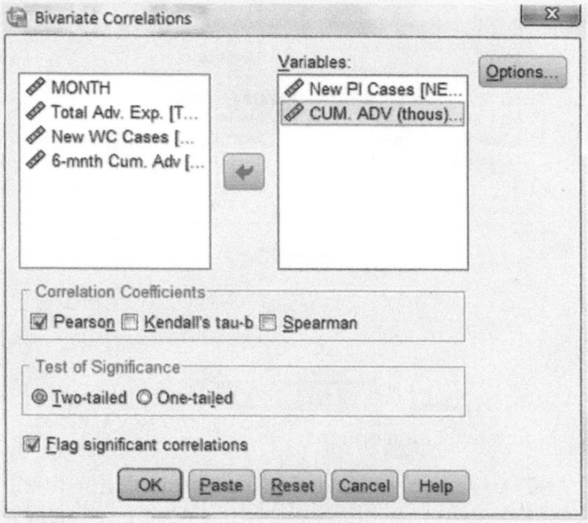

Figure 11.S.4 SPSS correlation dialog box

Minitab: Simple Linear Regression

Regression Analysis

Step 1 Access the Minitab worksheet file that contains the two quantitative variables (dependent and independent variables).

Step 2 Click on the "Stat" button on the Minitab menu bar and then click on "Regression" and "Regression" again, as shown in Figure 11.M.1.

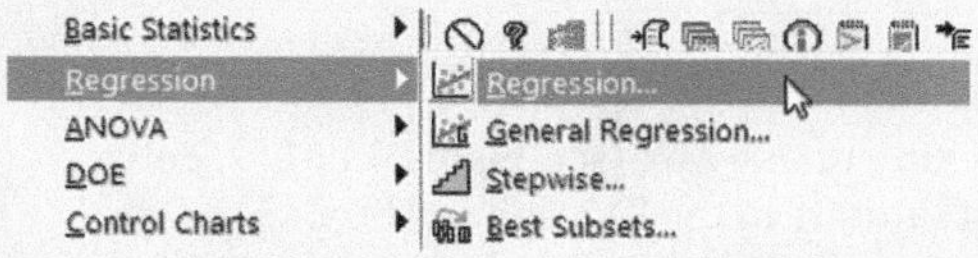

Figure 11.M.1 Minitab menu options for regression

Step 3 On the resulting dialog box (see Figure 11.M.2), specify the dependent variable in the "Response" box and the independent variable in the "Predictors" box.

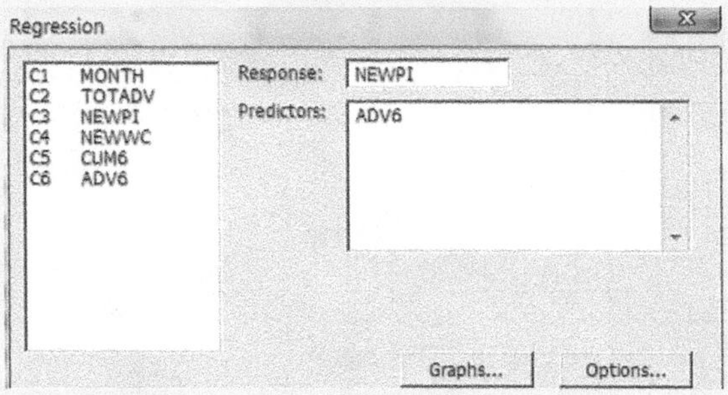

Figure 11.M.2 Minitab regression dialog box

Step 4 To produce prediction intervals for y and confidence intervals for $E(y)$, click the "Options" button. The resulting dialog box is shown in Figure 11.M.3.

Step 5 Check "Confidence limits" and/or "Prediction limits," specify the "Confidence level," and enter the value of x in the "Prediction intervals for new observations" box.

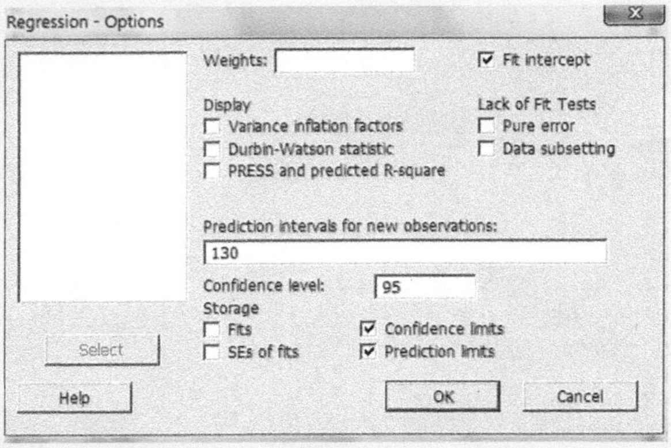

Figure 11.M.3 Minitab regression options

Step 6 Click "OK" to return to the main Regression dialog box and then click "OK" again to produce the Minitab simple linear regression printout.

Correlation Analysis

Step 1 Click on the "Stat" button on the Minitab main menu bar, then click on "Basic Statistics," and then click on "Correlation," as shown in Figure 11.M.4.

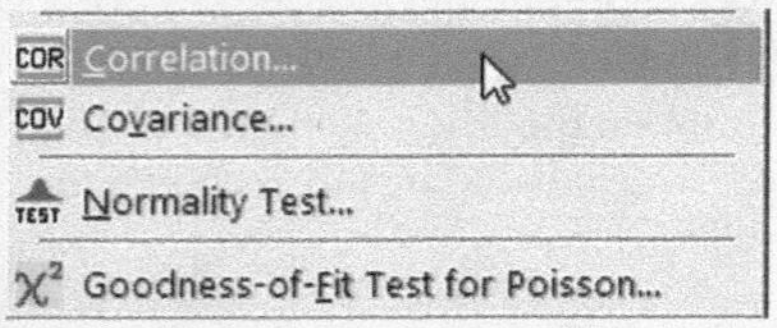

Figure 11.M.4 Minitab menu options for correlation

Step 2 On the resulting dialog box (see Figure 11.M.5), enter the two variables of interest in the "Variables" box.

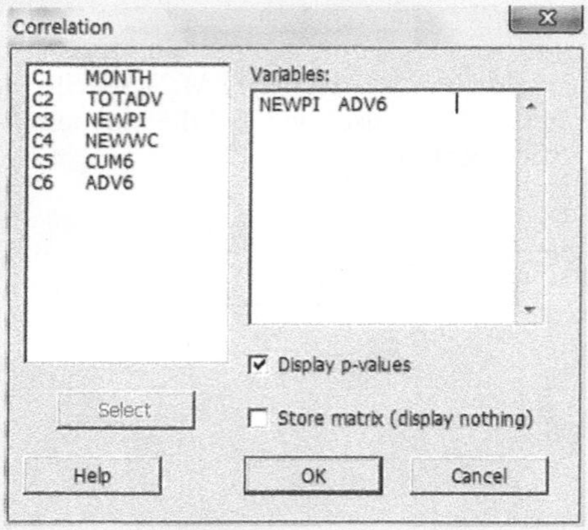

Figure 11.M.5 Minitab correlation dialog box

Step 3 Click "OK" to obtain a printout of the correlation.

Excel/XLSTAT: Simple Linear Regression

Regression/Correlation Analysis

Step 1 First, create a workbook with two columns, one representing the quantitative dependent variable and the other the quantitative independent variable.

Step 2 Click the "XLSTAT" button on the Excel main menu bar, select "Modeling data," then click "Linear regression," as shown in Figure 11.E.1.

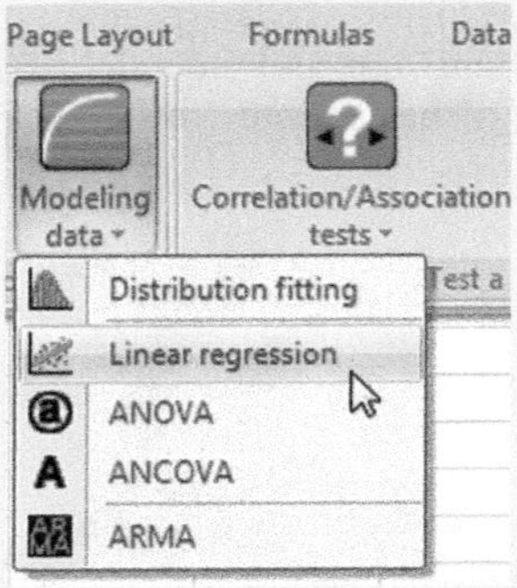

Figure 11.E.1 XLSTAT menu options for simple linear regression

Step 3 When the resulting dialog box appears (Figure 11.E.2), enter the column containing the dependent variable in the "Y / Dependent variables" box. Check the "Quantitative" option and then enter the column containing the independent variable in the "X / Explanatory variables" box.

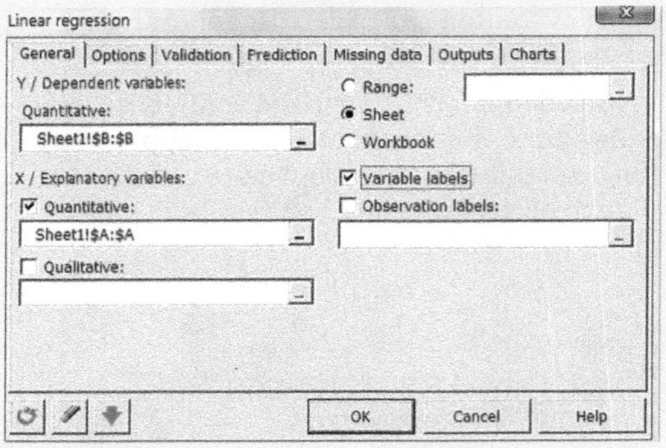

Figure 11.E.2 XLSTAT dialog box for linear regression

Step 4 To obtain prediction/confidence intervals, select the "Prediction" tab, then enter the column with the values of the independent variable for which you want to make predictions in the "X / Explanatory variables" and "Quantitative" box, as shown in Figure 11.E.3.

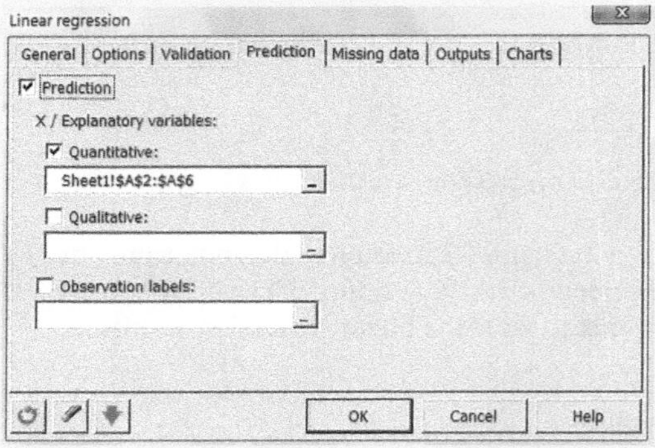

Figure 11.E.3 XLSTAT dialog box for predictions

Step 5 Click "OK," then "Continue" to display the test results.

TI-84 Graphing Calculator: Simple Linear Regression

Finding the Least Squares Regression Equation

Step 1 *Enter the data*

- Press **STAT** and select **1:Edit**

Note: If a list already contains data, clear the old data.

- Use the up arrow to highlight the list name, "**L1**" or "**L2**"
- Press **CLEAR ENTER**
- Enter your *x*-data in **L1** and your *y*-data in **L2**

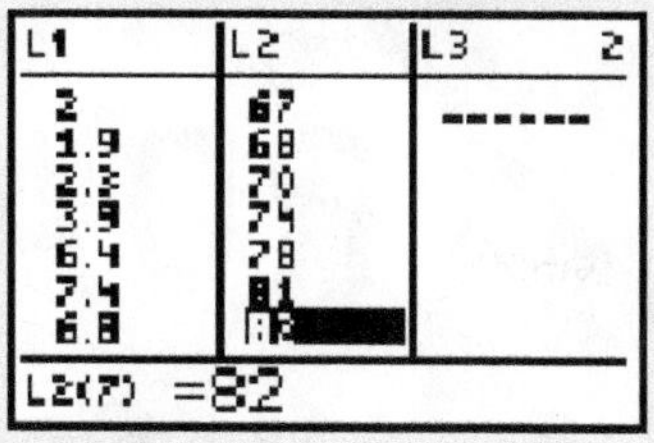

Step 2 *Find the equation*

- Press **STAT** and highlight **CALC**
- Press **4** for **LinReg(ax + b)**
- Press **ENTER**
- The screen will show the values for a and b in the equation $y = ax + b$.

Finding r and r^2

Use this procedure if r and r^2 do not already appear on the LinReg screen from part I:

Step 1 *Turn the diagnostics feature on*

- Press **2nd 0** for **CATALOG**
- Press the **ALPHA** key and $\mathbf{x^{-1}}$ for **D**
- Press the down **ARROW** until **DiagnosticsOn** is highlighted
- Press **ENTER** twice

Step 2 *Find the regression equation as shown in part I above*

The values for r and r^2 will appear on the screen as well.

Graphing the Least Squares Line with the Scatterplot

Step 1 *Enter the data as shown in part I above*

Step 2 *Set up the data plot*

- Press **Y=** and **CLEAR** all functions from the Y registers
- Press **2ndY=** for **STAT PLOT**
- Press **1** for **Plot1**
- Set the cursor so that **ON** is flashing and press **ENTER**
- For **Type,** use the **ARROW** and **ENTER** keys to highlight and select the scatterplot (first icon in the first row)
- For **Xlist,** choose the column containing the *x*-data
- For **Ylist,** choose the column containing the *y*-data

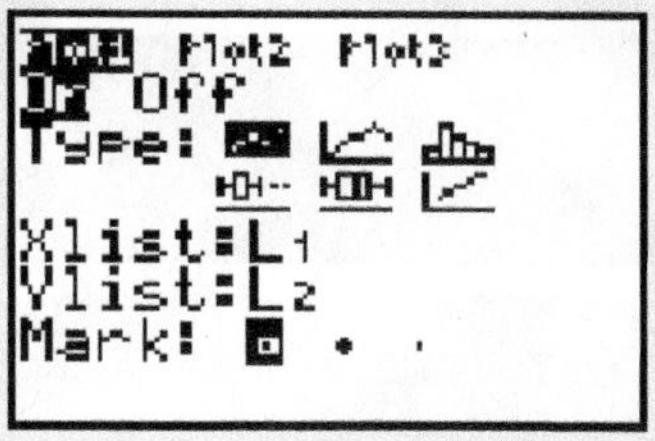

Step 3 *Find the regression equation and store the equation in Y1*

- Press **STAT** and highlight **CALC**
- Press **4** for **LinReg(ax + b)** (Note: Don't press ENTER here because you want to store the regression equation in Y1.)
- Press **VARS**
- Use the right arrow to highlight **Y-VARS**
- Press **ENTER** to select **1:Function**
- Press **ENTER** to select **1:Y1**
- Press **ENTER**

Step 4 *View the scatterplot and regression line*

- Press **ZOOM** and then press **9** to select **9:ZoomStat**

You should see the data graphed along with the regression line.

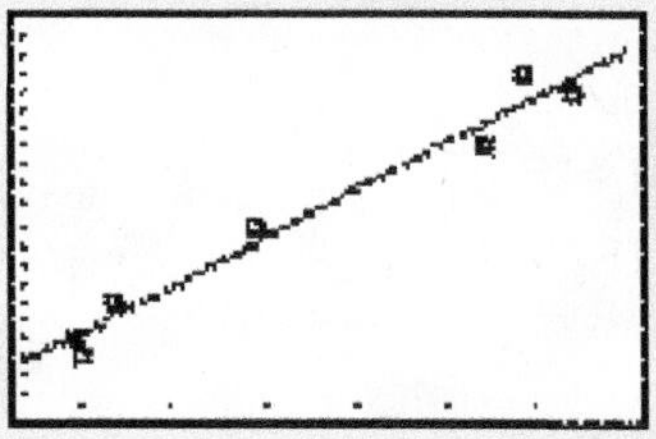

12

CONTENTS

Where We've Been

- Introduced the straight-line model relating a dependent variable y to a single independent variable x
- Demonstrated how to estimate the parameters of the straight-line model using the method of least squares
- Showed how to statistically assess the adequacy of the model
- Showed how to use the model to Estimate $E(y)$ and predict y for a given value of x

Multiple Regression and Model Building

STATISTICS in ACTION

Bid Rigging in the Highway Construction Industry

In the United States, commercial contractors bid for the right to construct state highways and roads. A state government agency, usually the Department of Transportation (DOT), notifies various contractors of the state's intent to build a highway. Sealed bids are submitted by the contractors, and the contractor with the lowest bid (building cost) is awarded the road construction contract. The bidding process works extremely well in competitive markets but has the potential to increase construction costs if the markets are noncompetitive or if collusive practices are present. The latter occurred in the 1980s in Florida. Numerous road contractors either admitted or were found guilty of price fixing (i.e., setting the cost of construction above the fair, or competitive, cost through bid rigging or other means).

This Statistics in Action involves data collected by the Florida attorney general shortly following the price-fixing crisis. The attorney general's objective is to build a model for the cost (y) of a road construction contract awarded using the sealed-bid system. The **FLAG** file contains data for a sample of 235 road contracts. The variables measured for each contract are listed in Table SIA12.1. Ultimately, the attorney general wants to use the model to predict the costs of future road contracts in the state.

In several Statistics in Action Revisited sections in this chapter, we show how to analyze the data using a multiple regression analysis.

Where We're Going

- Introduce a *multiple regression* model as a means of relating a dependent variable *y* to two or more independent variables (12.1)
- Present several different multiple regression models involving both quantitative and qualitative independent variables (12.2, 12.5–12.8)
- Assess how well the multiple regression model fits the sample data (12.3)
- Demonstrate how to use the model for prediction (12.4)
- Present some model-building techniques (12.9–12.10)
- Show how an analysis of the model's *residuals* can aid in detecting violations of model assumptions and in identifying model modifications (12.11)
- Alert the analyst to some regression pitfalls (12.12)

Table SIA12.1 Variables in the FLAG Data File

Variable Name	Type	Description
CONTRACT	Quantitative	Road contract number
COST	Quantitative	Low bid contract cost (thousands of dollars)
DOTEST	Quantitative	DOT engineer's cost estimate (thousands of dollars)
STATUS	Qualitative	Bid status (1 = fixed, 0 = competitive)
B2B1RAT	Quantitative	Ratio of second lowest bid to low bid
B3B1RAT	Quantitative	Ratio of third lowest bid to low bid
BHB1RAT	Quantitative	Ratio of highest bid to low bid
DISTRICT	Qualitative	Location of road (1 = south Florida, 0 = north Florida)
BTPRATIO	Quantitative	Ratio of number of bidders to number of plan holders
DAYSEST	Quantitative	DOT engineer's estimate of number of workdays required

Data Set: FLAG

STATISTICS in ACTION REVISITED

- Evaluating a First-Order Model **(p. 687)**
- Variable Screening and Model Building **(p. 735)**
- A Residual Analysis **(p. 752)**

12.1 Multiple Regression Models

Most practical applications of regression analysis employ models that are more complex than the simple straight-line model. For example, a realistic probabilistic model for monthly sales revenue would include more than just the amount of advertising expenditure. Factors such as last month's sales, number of sales competitors, and advertising medium are some of the many variables that might be related to sales revenue. Thus, we would want to incorporate these and other potentially important independent variables into the model in order to make accurate predictions.

Probabilistic models that include more than one independent variable are called **multiple regression models.** The general form of these models is

$$y = \beta_0 + \beta_1 x_1 + \beta_2 x_2 + \cdots + \beta_k x_k + \varepsilon$$

The dependent variable y is now written as a function of k independent variables, $x_1, x_2, \ldots, x_k$. The random error term is added to make the model probabilistic rather than deterministic. The value of the coefficient β_i determines the contribution of the independent variable x_i, and β_0 is the y-intercept. The coefficients $\beta_0, \beta_1, \ldots, \beta_k$ are usually unknown because they represent population parameters.

At first glance it might appear that the regression model shown above would not allow for anything other than straight-line relationships between y and the independent variables, but this is not true. Actually, $x_1, x_2, \ldots, x_k$ can be functions of variables as long as the functions do not contain unknown parameters. For example, the monthly sales revenue, y, could be a function of the independent variables

$$x_1 = \text{Advertising expenditure}$$
$$x_2 = \text{Number of sales competitors}$$
$$x_3 = (x_1)^2$$
$$x_4 = 1 \text{ if TV advertising, 0 if not}$$

The x_3 term is called a **higher-order term** because it is the value of a quantitative variable (x_1) squared (i.e., raised to the second power). The x_4 term is a **coded variable** representing a qualitative variable (advertising medium). The multiple regression model is quite versatile and can be made to model many different types of response variables.

The General Multiple Regression Model*

$$y = \beta_0 + \beta_1 x_1 + \beta_2 x_2 + \cdots + \beta_k x_k + \varepsilon$$

where

y is the dependent variable.

$x_1, x_2, \ldots, x_k$ are the independent variables.

$E(y) = \beta_0 + \beta_1 x_1 + \beta_2 x_2 + \cdots + \beta_k x_k$ is the deterministic portion of the model.

β_i determines the contribution of the independent variable x_i.

Note: The symbols $x_1, x_2, \ldots, x_k$ may represent higher-order terms for quantitative predictors or terms that represent qualitative predictors.

As shown in the box, the steps used to develop the multiple regression model are similar to those used for the simple linear regression model.

Analyzing a Multiple Regression Model

Step 1 Hypothesize the deterministic component of the model. This component relates the mean, $E(y)$, to the independent variables $x_1, x_2, \ldots, x_k$. This involves the choice of the independent variables to be included in the model (Sections 12.2, 12.5–12.10).

Step 2 Use the sample data to estimate the unknown model parameters $\beta_0, \beta_1, \beta_2, \ldots, \beta_k$ in the model (Section 12.2).

Step 3 Specify the probability distribution of the random error term, ε, and estimate the standard deviation of this distribution, σ (Section 12.3).

Step 4 Check that the assumptions on ε are satisfied and make model modifications if necessary (Section 12.11).

Step 5 Statistically evaluate the usefulness of the model (Sections 12.3).

Step 6 When satisfied that the model is useful, use it for prediction, estimation, and other purposes (Section 12.4).

The assumptions we make about the random error ε of the multiple regression model are also similar to those in a simple linear regression (see Section 11.3). These are summarized below.

Assumptions for Random Error ε

For any given set of values of $x_1, x_2, \ldots, x_k$, the random error ε has a probability distribution with the following properties:

1. Mean equal to 0
2. Variance equal to σ^2
3. Normal distribution
4. Random errors are independent (in a probabilistic sense).

Throughout this chapter, we introduce several different types of models that form the foundation of **model building** (or useful model construction). In the next several sections, we consider the most basic multiple regression model, called the *first-order model.*

*Technically, this model is referred to as a general multiple *linear* regression model since the equation is a linear function of the β's.

PART I: FIRST-ORDER MODELS WITH QUANTITATIVE INDEPENDENT VARIABLES

12.2 Estimating and Making Inferences about the β Parameters

BIOGRAPHY

GEORGE U. YULE (1871–1951)
Yule Processes

Born on a small farm in Scotland, George Yule received an extensive childhood education. After graduating from University College (London), where he studied civil engineering, Yule spent a year employed in engineering workshops. However, he made a career change in 1893, accepting a teaching position back at University College under the guidance of statistician Karl Pearson (see p. 566). Inspired by Pearson's work, Yule produced a series of important articles on the statistics of regression and correlation. Yule is considered the first to apply the method of least squares in regression analysis, and he developed the theory of multiple regression. He eventually was appointed a lecturer in statistics at Cambridge University and later became the president of the prestigious Royal Statistical Society. Yule made many other contributions to the field, including the invention of time series analysis and the development of Yule processes and the Yule distribution.

A model that includes terms only for *quantitative* independent variables, called a **first-order model,** is described in the box. Note that the first-order model does not include any higher-order terms (such as x_1^2).

A First-Order Model in Five Quantitative Independent (Predictor) Variables*

$$E(y) = \beta_0 + \beta_1 x_1 + \beta_2 x_2 + \beta_3 x_3 + \beta_4 x_4 + \beta_5 x_5$$

where $x_1, x_2, \ldots, x_5$ are all quantitative variables that *are not* functions of other independent variables.

Note: β_i represents the slope of the line relating y to x_i when all the other x's are held fixed.

The method of fitting first-order models—and multiple regression models in general—is identical to that of fitting the simple straight-line model: the **method of least squares**—that is, we choose the estimated model

$$\hat{y} = \hat{\beta}_0 + \hat{\beta}_1 x_1 + \cdots + \hat{\beta}_k x_k$$

that (1) has an average error of prediction of 0, i.e., $\Sigma(y - \hat{y}) = 0$
and (2) minimizes SSE $= (y - \hat{y})^2$

As in the case of the simple linear model, the sample estimates $\hat{\beta}_0, \hat{\beta}_1, \ldots, \hat{\beta}_k$ are obtained as a solution to a set of simultaneous linear equations.†

The primary difference between fitting the simple and multiple regression models is computational difficulty. The $(k + 1)$ simultaneous linear equations that must be solved to find the $(k + 1)$ estimated coefficients $\hat{\beta}_0, \hat{\beta}_1, \ldots, \hat{\beta}_k$ cannot be written in simple equation form; rather, the estimates are obtained using matrices and matrix algebra. Instead of presenting the complex matrix algebra required to fit the models, we resort to statistical software and present output from SPSS, Minitab, and Excel.

Example 12.1

Fitting a First-Order Model: Price of an Antique Clock

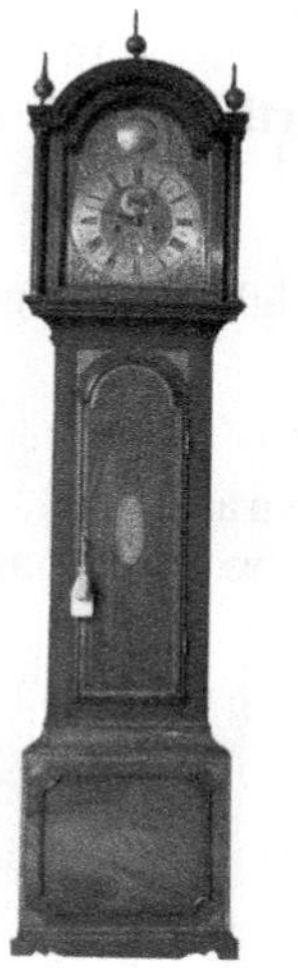

Problem A collector of antique grandfather clocks sold at auction believes that the price received for the clocks depends on both the age of the clocks and the number of bidders at the auction. Thus, he hypothesizes the first-order model

$$y = \beta_0 + \beta_1 x_1 + \beta_2 x_2 + \varepsilon$$

where

$$y = \text{Auction price (dollars)}$$
$$x_1 = \text{Age of clock (years)}$$
$$x_2 = \text{Number of bidders}$$

A sample of 32 auction prices of grandfather clocks, along with their age and the number of bidders, is given in Table 12.1.

a. Use scatterplots to plot the sample data. Interpret the plots.

b. Use the method of least squares to estimate the unknown parameters β_0, β_1, and β_2 of the model.

*The terminology *first order* is derived from the fact that each x in the model is raised to the first power.

†Students who are familiar with calculus should note that $\hat{\beta}_0, \hat{\beta}_1, \ldots, \hat{\beta}_k$ are the solutions to the set of equations $\partial\text{SSE}/\partial\hat{\beta}_0 = 0, \partial\text{SSE}/\partial\hat{\beta}_1 = 0, \ldots, \partial\text{SSE}/\partial\hat{\beta}_k = 0$. The solution is usually given in matrix form, but we do not present the details here. See the references for details.

Table 12.1 Auction Price Data

Age, x_1	Number of Bidders, x_2	Auction Price, y	Age, x_1	Number of Bidders, x_2	Auction Price, y
127	13	$1,235	170	14	$2,131
115	12	1,080	182	8	1,550
127	7	845	162	11	1,884
150	9	1,522	184	10	2,041
156	6	1,047	143	6	845
182	11	1,979	159	9	1,483
156	12	1,822	108	14	1,055
132	10	1,253	175	8	1,545
137	9	1,297	108	6	729
113	9	946	179	9	1,792
137	15	1,713	111	15	1,175
117	11	1,024	187	8	1,593
137	8	1,147	111	7	785
153	6	1,092	115	7	744
117	13	1,152	194	5	1,356
126	10	1,336	168	7	1,262

Data Set: CLOCKS

c. Find the value of SSE that is minimized by the least squares method.

d. Estimate σ, the standard deviation of the model, and interpret the result.

Solution

a. Minitab side-by-side scatterplots for examining the bivariate relationships between y and x_1, and between y and x_2, are shown in Figure 12.1. Of the two variables, age (x_1) appears to have the stronger linear relationship with auction price (y).

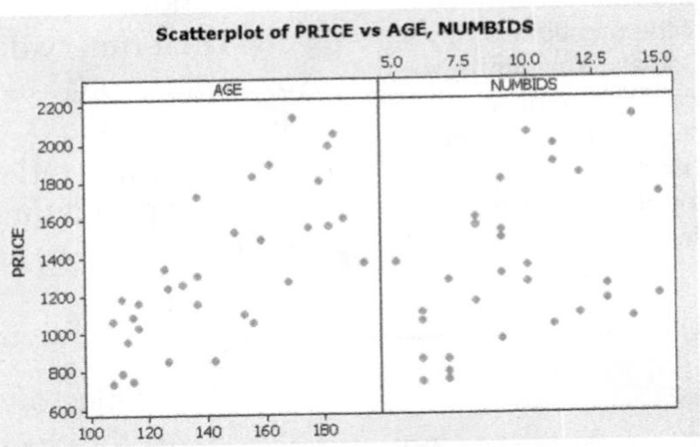

Figure 12.1
Minitab side-by-side scatterplots for the data of Table 12.1

b. The model hypothesized is fit to the data of Table 12.1 with Minitab. A portion of the printout is reproduced in Figure 12.2. The least squares estimates of the β parameters (highlighted) are $\hat{\beta}_0 = -1{,}339$, $\hat{\beta}_1 = 12.74$, and $\hat{\beta}_2 = 85.95$. Therefore, the equation that minimizes SSE for this data set (i.e., the **least squares prediction equation**) is

$$\hat{y} = -1{,}339 + 12.74x_1 + 85.95x_2$$

c. The minimum value of the sum of the squared errors, also highlighted in Figure 12.2, is SSE $= 516{,}727$.

d. Recall that the estimator of σ^2 for the straight-line model is $s^2 = \text{SSE}/(n-2)$, and note that the denominator is (n − number of estimated β parameters), which is $(n-2)$ in the straight-line model. Because we must estimate the three parameters β_0, β_1, and β_2 for the first-order model, the estimator of σ^2 is

$$s^2 = \frac{\text{SSE}}{n-3} = \frac{\text{SSE}}{32-3} = \frac{516{,}727}{29} = 17{,}818$$

This value, often called the **mean square for error (MSE),** is also highlighted at the bottom of the Minitab printout in Figure 12.2. The estimate of σ, then, is

$$s = \sqrt{17{,}818} = 133.5$$

Regression Analysis: PRICE versus AGE, NUMBIDS

```
The regression equation is
PRICE = - 1339 + 12.7 AGE + 86.0 NUMBIDS

Predictor      Coef  SE Coef      T      P
Constant    -1339.0    173.8  -7.70  0.000
AGE         12.7406   0.9047  14.08  0.000
NUMBIDS      85.953    8.729   9.85  0.000

S = 133.485   R-Sq = 89.2%   R-Sq(adj) = 88.5%

Analysis of Variance

Source          DF       SS       MS       F      P
Regression       2  4283063  2141531  120.19  0.000
Residual Error  29   516727    17818
Total           31  4799790
```

Figure 12.2
Minitab analysis of the auction price model

which is highlighted in the middle of the Minitab printout in Figure 12.2. One useful interpretation of the estimated standard deviation s is that the interval $\pm 2s$ will provide a rough approximation to the accuracy with which the model will predict future values of y for given values of x. Thus, we expect the model to provide predictions of auction price to within about $\pm 2s = \pm 2(133.5) = \pm 267$ dollars.*

Look Back As with simple linear regression, we will use the estimator of σ^2 both to check the utility of the model (Section 12.3) and to provide a measure of reliability of predictions and estimates when the model is used for those purposes (Section 12.4). Thus, you can see that the estimation of σ^2 plays an important part in the development of a regression model.

■ **Now Work Exercise 12.2a–c**

Estimator of σ^2 for a Multiple Regression Model with k Independent Variables

$$s^2 = \frac{\text{SSE}}{n - \text{number of estimated } \beta \text{ parameters}} = \frac{\text{SSE}}{n - (k + 1)}$$

After obtaining the least squares prediction equation, the analyst will usually want to make meaningful interpretations of the β estimates. Recall that in the straight-line model (Chapter 11)

$$y = \beta_0 + \beta_1 x + \varepsilon$$

β_0 represents the y-intercept of the line, and β_1 represents the slope of the line. From our discussion in Chapter 11, β_1 has a practical interpretation—it represents the mean change in y for every 1-unit increase in x. When the independent variables are quantitative, the β parameters in the first-order model specified in Example 12.1 have similar interpretations. The difference is that when we interpret the β that multiplies one of the variables (e.g., x_1), we must be certain to hold the values of the remaining independent variables (e.g., x_2, x_3) fixed.

To see this, suppose that the mean $E(y)$ of a response y is related to two quantitative independent variables, x_1 and x_2, by the first-order model

$$E(y) = 1 + 2x_1 + x_2$$

In other words, $\beta_0 = 1$, $\beta_1 = 2$, and $\beta_2 = 1$.

Now, when $x_2 = 0$, the relationship between $E(y)$ and x_1 is given by

$$E(y) = 1 + 2x_1 + (0) = 1 + 2x_1$$

*The $\pm 2s$ approximation will improve as the sample size is increased. We will provide more precise methodology for the construction of prediction intervals in Section 12.4.

A Minitab graph of this relationship (a straight line) is shown in Figure 12.3. Similar graphs of the relationship between $E(y)$ and x_1 for $x_2 = 1$,

$$E(y) = 1 + 2x_1 + (1) = 2 + 2x_1$$

and for $x_2 = 2$,

$$E(y) = 1 + 2x_1 + (2) = 3 + 2x_1$$

also are shown in Figure 12.3. Note that the slopes of the three lines are all equal to $\beta_1 = 2$, the coefficient that multiplies x_1.

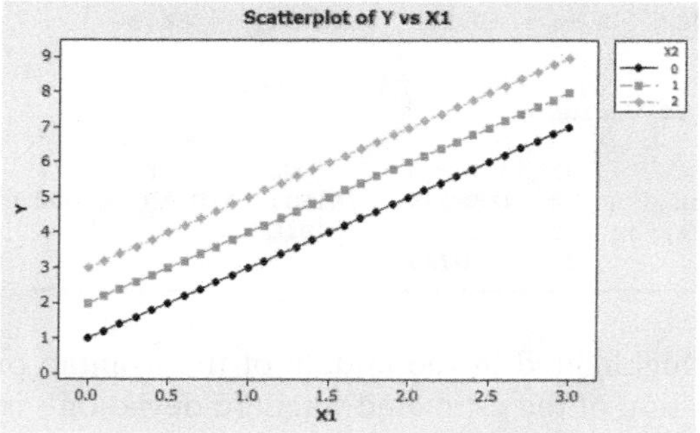

Figure 12.3
Minitab graph of $E(y) = 1 + 2x_1 + x_2$ for $x_2 = 0, 1, 2$

Figure 12.3 exhibits a characteristic of all first-order models: If you graph $E(y)$ versus any one variable—say, x_1—for fixed values of the other variables, the result will always be a *straight line* with slope equal to β_1. If you repeat the process for other values of the fixed independent variables, you will obtain a set of *parallel* straight lines. This indicates that the effect of the independent variable x_i on $E(y)$ is independent of all the other independent variables in the model, and this effect is measured by the slope β_i (see the box on page 669).

A Minitab three-dimensional graph of the model $E(y) = 1 + 2x_1 + x_2$ is shown in Figure 12.4. Note that the model graphs as a plane. If you slice the plane at a particular value of x_2 (say, $x_2 = 0$), you obtain a straight line relating $E(y)$ to x_1 (e.g., $E[y] = 1 + 2x_1$). Similarly, if you slice the plane at a particular value of x_1, you obtain a straight line relating $E(y)$ to x_2. Because it is more difficult to visualize three-dimensional and, in general, k-dimensional surfaces, we will graph all the models presented in this chapter in two dimensions. *The key to obtaining these graphs is to hold fixed all but one of the independent variables in the model.*

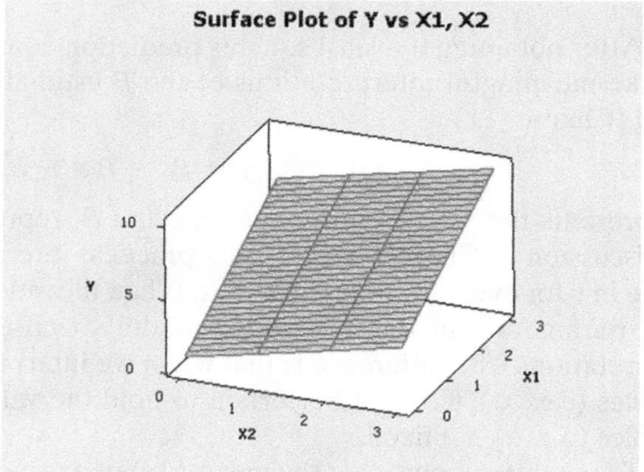

Figure 12.4
Minitab 3-dimensional graph of $E(y) = 1 + 2x_1 + x_2$

Example 12.2

Interpreting the β Estimates: Clock Auction Price Model

Problem Refer to the first-order model for auction price (y) considered in Example 12.1. Interpret the estimates of the β parameters in the model.

Solution The least squares prediction equation, as given in Example 12.1, is $\hat{y} = -1{,}339 + 12.74x_1 + 85.95x_2$. We know that with first-order models, β_1 represents the slope of the line relating y to x_1 for fixed x_2. That is, β_1 measures the change in $E(y)$ for every 1-unit increase in x_1 when the other independent variable in the model is held fixed. A similar statement can be made about β_2: β_2 measures the change in $E(y)$ for every 1-unit increase in x_2 when the other x in the model is held fixed. Consequently, we obtain the following interpretations:

$\hat{\beta}_1 = 12.74$: We estimate the mean auction price $E(y)$ of an antique clock to increase \$12.74 for every 1-year increase in age (x_1) when the number of bidders (x_2) is held fixed.

$\hat{\beta}_2 = 85.95$: We estimate the mean auction price $E(y)$ of an antique clock to increase \$85.95 for every 1-bidder increase in the number of bidders (x_2) when age (x_1) is held fixed.

The value $\hat{\beta}_0 = -1{,}339$ does not have a meaningful interpretation in this example. To see this, note that $\hat{y} = \hat{\beta}_0$ when $x_1 = x_2 = 0$. Thus, $\hat{\beta}_0 = -1{,}339$ represents the estimated mean auction price when the values of all the independent variables are set equal to 0. Because an antique clock with these characteristics—an age of 0 years and 0 bidders on the clock—is not practical, the value of $\hat{\beta}_0$ has no meaningful interpretation.

Look Back In general, $\hat{\beta}_0$ will not have a practical interpretation unless it makes sense to set the values of the x's simultaneously equal to 0.

■ **Now Work Exercise 12.14a, b**

CAUTION The interpretation of the β parameters in a multiple regression model will depend on the terms specified in the model. The interpretations above are for a first-order linear model only. In practice, you should be sure that a first-order model is the correct model for $E(y)$ before making these β interpretations. (We discuss alternative models for $E(y)$ in Sections 12.5–12.8.)

Inferences about the individual β parameters in a model are obtained using either a confidence interval or a test of hypothesis, as outlined in the following two boxes.*

A 100(1 − α)% Confidence Interval for a β Parameter

$$\hat{\beta}_i \pm t_{\alpha/2} s_{\hat{\beta}_i}$$

where $t_{\alpha/2}$ is based on $n - (k + 1)$ degrees of freedom and

n = Number of observations

$k + 1$ = Number of β parameters in the model

Test of an Individual Parameter Coefficient in the Multiple Regression Model

One-Tailed Test	Two-Tailed Test
$H_0: \beta_i = 0$	$H_0: \beta_i = 0$
$H_a: \beta_i < 0$ [or $H_a: \beta_i > 0$]	$H_a: \beta_i \neq 0$

Test statistic: $t = \dfrac{\hat{\beta}_i}{s_{\hat{\beta}_i}}$

Rejection region: $t < -t_\alpha$ [or $t > t_\alpha$ when $H_a: \beta_i > 0$] | *Rejection region:* $|t| > t_{\alpha/2}$

where t_α and $t_{\alpha/2}$ are based on $n - (k + 1)$ degrees of freedom and

n = Number of observations

$k + 1$ = Number of β parameters in the model

*The formulas for computing $\hat{\beta}_i$ and its standard error are so complex that the only reasonable way to present them is by using matrix algebra. We do not assume a prerequisite of matrix algebra for this text, and, in any case, we think the formulas can be omitted in an introductory course without serious loss. They are programmed into almost all statistical software packages with multiple regression routines and are presented in some of the texts listed in the references.

Conditions Required for Valid Inferences about the β Parameters

Refer to the four assumptions about the probability distribution for the random error ε. (p. 668).

We illustrate these methods with another example.

Example 12.3

Inferences about the β Parameters—Auction Price Model

Problem Refer to Examples 12.1 and 12.2. The collector of antique grandfather clocks knows that the price (y) received for the clocks increases linearly with the age (x_1) of the clocks. Moreover, the collector hypothesizes that the auction price (y) will increase linearly as the number of bidders (x_2) increases. Use the information on the Minitab printout shown in Figure 12.2 (p. 671) to

a. Test the hypothesis that the mean auction price of a clock increases as the number of bidders increases when age is held constant, that is, test $\beta_2 > 0$. Use $\alpha = .05$.

b. Form a 90% confidence interval for β_1 and interpret the result.

Solution

a. The hypotheses of interest concern the parameter β_2. Specifically,

$$H_0\colon \beta_2 = 0$$
$$H_a\colon \beta_2 > 0$$

The test statistic is a t-statistic formed by dividing the sample estimate $\hat{\beta}_2$ of the parameter β_2 by the estimated standard error of $\hat{\beta}_2$ (denoted $s_{\hat{\beta}_2}$). These estimates, $\hat{\beta}_2 = 85.953$ and $s_{\hat{\beta}_2} = 8.729$, as well as the calculated t-value,

$$\textit{Test statistic: } t = \frac{\hat{\beta}_2}{s_{\hat{\beta}_2}} = \frac{85.953}{8.729} = 9.85$$

are highlighted on the Minitab printout in Figure 12.2.

The rejection region for the test is found in exactly the same way as the rejection regions for the t-tests in previous chapters—that is, we consult Table III in Appendix D to obtain an upper-tail value of t. This is a value t_α such that $P(t > t_\alpha) = \alpha$. We can then use this value to construct rejection regions for either one-tailed or two-tailed tests.

For $\alpha = .05$ and $n - (k + 1) = 32 - (2 + 1) = 29$ df, the critical t-value obtained from Table III is $t_{.05} = 1.699$. Therefore,

$$\textit{Rejection region: } t > 1.699 \text{ (see Figure 12.5)}$$

Because the test statistic value, $t = 9.85$, falls in the rejection region, we have sufficient evidence to reject H_0. Thus, the collector can conclude that the mean auction price of a clock increases as the number of bidders increases, when age is held constant. Note that the two-tailed observed significance level of the test is also highlighted on the printout. Because the one-tailed p-value (half this value) is p-value ≈ 0, any nonzero α (e.g., $\alpha = .01$) will lead us to reject H_0.

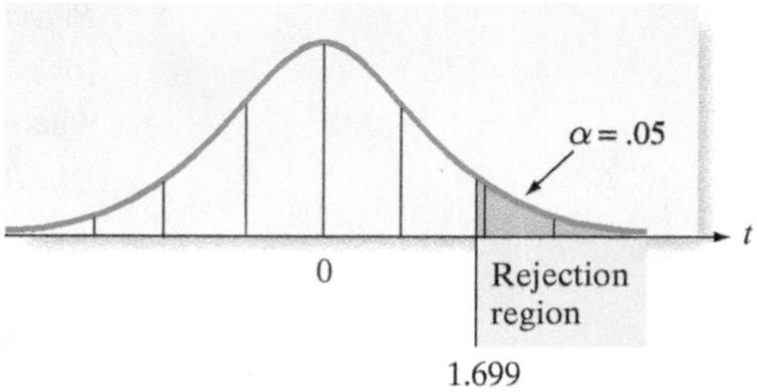

Figure 12.5
Rejection region for $H_0\colon \beta_2 = 0$ vs. $H_a\colon \beta_2 > 0$

b. A 90% confidence interval for β_1 is:

$$\hat{\beta}_1 \pm t_{\alpha/2}s_{\hat{\beta}_1} = \hat{\beta}_1 \pm t_{.05}s_{\hat{\beta}_1}$$

Substituting $\hat{\beta}_1 = 12.74$, $s_{\hat{\beta}_1} = .905$ (both obtained from the Minitab printout, Figure 12.2), and $t_{.05} = 1.699$ (from part **a**) into the equation, we obtain

$$12.74 \pm 1.699(.905) = 12.74 \pm 1.54$$

or (11.20, 14.28). Thus, we are 90% confident that β_1 falls between 11.20 and 14.28. Because β_1 is the slope of the line relating auction price (y) to age of the clock (x_1), we conclude that the price increases between \$11.20 and \$14.28 for every 1-year increase in age, holding number of bidders (x_2) constant.

Look Back When interpreting the β multiplied by one x, be sure to hold fixed the values of the other x's in the model.

■ **Now Work Exercise 12.14c, d**

12.3 Evaluating Overall Model Utility

In Section 12.2, we demonstrated the use of t-tests in making inferences about β parameters in the multiple regression model. There are caveats, however, with conducting these t-tests for the purposes of determining which x's are useful for predicting y. Several of these are listed next.

Use Caution when Conducting t-Tests on the β Parameters

It is dangerous to conduct t-tests on the individual β parameters in a *first-order linear model* for the purpose of determining which independent variables are useful for predicting y and which are not. If you fail to reject H_0: $\beta_i = 0$, several conclusions are possible:

1. There is no relationship between y and x_i.
2. A straight-line relationship between y and x exists (holding the other x's in the model fixed), but a Type II error occurred.
3. A relationship between y and x_i (holding the other x's in the model fixed) exists but is more complex than a straight-line relationship (e.g., a curvilinear relationship may be appropriate). The most you can say about a β parameter test is that there is either sufficient (if you reject H_0: $\beta_i = 0$) or insufficient (if you do not reject H_0: $\beta_i = 0$) evidence of a *linear* (*straight-line*) relationship between y and x_i.

In addition, conducting t-tests on each β parameter in a model is *not* the best way to determine whether the overall model is contributing information for the prediction of y. If we were to conduct a series of t-tests to determine whether the independent variables are contributing to the predictive relationship, we would be very likely to make one or more errors in deciding which terms to retain in the model and which to exclude.

For example, suppose you fit a first-order model in 10 quantitative x variables and decide to conduct t-tests on all 10 of the individual β's in the model, each at $\alpha = .05$. Even if all the β parameters (except β_0) are equal to 0, approximately 40% of the time you will incorrectly reject the null hypothesis at least once and conclude that some β parameter differs from 0.* Thus, in multiple regression models for which a large number

*The proof of this result (assuming independence of tests) proceeds as follows:

$P(\text{Reject } H_0 \text{ at least once} \mid \beta_1 = \beta_2 = \cdots = \beta_{10} = 0)$
$= 1 - P(\text{Reject } H_0 \text{ no times} \mid \beta_1 = \beta_2 = \cdots = \beta_{10} = 0)$
$\leq 1 - [P(\text{Accept } H_0\text{: } \beta_1 = 0 \mid \beta_1 = 0) \cdot P(\text{Accept } H_0\text{: } \beta_2 = 0 \mid \beta_2 = 0) \cdot \cdots \cdot P(\text{Accept } H_0\text{: } \beta_{10} = 0 \mid \beta_{10} = 0)]$
$= 1 - [(1 - \alpha)^{10}] = 1 - (.95)^{10} = .401$

For dependent tests, the Bonferroni inequality states that
$P(\text{Reject } H_0 \text{ at least once} \mid \beta_1 = \beta_2 = \cdots = \beta_{10} = 0) \leq 10(\alpha) = 10(.05) = .50.$

of independent variables are being considered, conducting a series of t-tests may include a large number of insignificant variables and exclude some useful ones. To test the utility of a multiple regression model, we need a *global test* (one that encompasses all the β parameters). We would also like to find some statistical quantity that measures how well the model fits the data.

We commence with the easier problem—finding a measure of how well a linear model fits a set of data. For this we use the multiple regression equivalent of r^2, the coefficient of determination for the straight-line model (Chapter 11), as shown in the box.

The **multiple coefficient of determination, R^2,** is defined as

$$R^2 = 1 - \frac{SSE}{SS_{yy}} = \frac{SS_{yy} - SSE}{SS_{yy}} = \frac{\text{Explained variablilty}}{\text{Total variability}}$$

Just like r^2 in the simple linear model, R^2 represents the fraction of the sample variation of the y values (measured by SS_{yy}) that is explained by the least squares prediction equation. Thus, $R^2 = 0$ implies a complete lack of fit of the model to the data, and $R^2 = 1$ implies a perfect fit, with the model passing through every data point. In general, the larger the value of R^2, the better the model fits the data.

To illustrate, the value $R^2 = .892$ for the auction price model of Examples 12.1–12.3 is highlighted on the SPSS printout for the analysis shown in Figure 12.6. This high value of R^2 implies that using the independent variables age and number of bidders in a first-order model explains 89.2% of the total *sample variation* (measured by SS_{yy}) in auction price (y). Thus, R^2 is a sample statistic that tells how well the model fits the data and thereby represents a measure of the usefulness of the entire model.

Model Summary

Model	R	R Square	Adjusted R Square	Std. Error of the Estimate
1	.945[a]	.892	.885	133.485

a. Predictors: (Constant), NUMBIDS, AGE

ANOVA[b]

Model		Sum of Squares	df	Mean Square	F	Sig.
1	Regression	4283062.960	2	2141531.480	120.188	.000[a]
	Residual	516726.540	29	17818.157		
	Total	4799789.500	31			

a. Predictors: (Constant), NUMBIDS, AGE

b. Dependent Variable: PRICE

Coefficients[a]

Model		Unstandardized Coefficients		Standardized Coefficients	t	Sig.	95% Confidence Interval for B	
		B	Std. Error	Beta			Lower Bound	Upper Bound
1	(Constant)	−1338.951	173.809		−7.704	.000	−1694.432	−983.471
	AGE	12.741	.905	.887	14.082	.000	10.890	14.591
	NUMBIDS	85.953	8.729	.620	9.847	.000	68.101	103.805

a. Dependent Variable: PRICE

Figure 12.6
SPSS analysis of the auction price model

A large value of R^2 computed from the *sample* data does not necessarily mean that the model provides a good fit to all of the data points in the *population*. For example, a first-order linear model that contains three parameters will provide a perfect fit to a sample of three data points, and R^2 will equal 1. Likewise, you will always obtain a perfect fit ($R^2 = 1$) to a set of n data points if the model contains exactly n parameters. Consequently, if you want to use the value of R^2 as a measure of how useful the model will be for predicting y, it should be based on a sample that contains substantially more data points than the number of parameters in the model.

> **CAUTION** In a multiple regression analysis, use the value of R^2 as a measure of how useful a linear model will be for predicting y only if the sample contains substantially more data points than the number of β parameters in the model.

As an alternative to using R^2 as a measure of model adequacy, the *adjusted multiple coefficient of determination,* denoted R_a^2, is often reported. The formula for R_a^2 is shown in the box.

The **adjusted multiple coefficient of determination** is given by

$$R_a^2 = 1 - \left[\frac{(n-1)}{n-(k+1)}\right]\left(\frac{\text{SSE}}{\text{SS}_{yy}}\right)$$

$$= 1 - \left[\frac{(n-1)}{n-(k+1)}\right](1 - R^2)$$

Note: $R_a^2 \le R^2$

R^2 and R_a^2 have similar interpretations. However, unlike R^2, R_a^2 takes into account ("adjusts" for) both the sample size n and the number of β parameters in the model. R_a^2 will always be smaller than R^2 and, more importantly, cannot be "forced" to 1 by simply adding more and more independent variables to the model. Consequently, analysts prefer the more conservative R_a^2 when choosing a measure of model adequacy. The value of R_a^2 is also highlighted in Figure 12.6. Note that $R_a^2 = .885$, a value only slightly smaller than R^2.

Despite their utility, R^2 and R_a^2 are only sample statistics. Therefore, it is dangerous to judge the global usefulness of a model based solely on these values. A better method is to conduct a test of hypothesis involving *all* the β parameters (except β_0) in a model. In particular, for the general multiple regression model $E(y) = \beta_0 + \beta_1 x_1 + \beta_2 x_2 + \cdots + \beta_k x_k$, we would test

$$H_0: \beta_1 = \beta_2 = \cdots = \beta_k = 0$$

H_a: At least one of the coefficients is nonzero.

The test statistic used to test this hypothesis is an F-statistic, and several equivalent versions of the formula can be used (although we will usually rely on the computer to calculate the F-statistic):

$$\textit{Test statistic: } F = \frac{(\text{SS}_{yy} - \text{SSE})/k}{\text{SSE}/[n-(k+1)]}$$

$$= \frac{\text{Mean Square (Model)}}{\text{Mean Square (Error)}} = \frac{R^2/k}{(1-R^2)/[n-(k+1)]}$$

These formulas indicate that the F-statistic is the ratio of the *explained* variability divided by the model degrees of freedom to the *unexplained* variability divided by the error degrees of freedom. Thus, the larger the proportion of the total variability accounted for by the model, the larger the F-statistic.

To determine when the ratio becomes large enough that we can confidently reject the null hypothesis and conclude that the model is more useful than no model at all for predicting y, we compare the calculated F-statistic to a tabulated F value with k df in the numerator and $[n - (k + 1)]$ df in the denominator. Recall that tabulations of the F-distribution for various values of α are given in Tables V, VI, VII, and VIII in Appendix D.

Rejection region: $F > F_\alpha$, where F is based on k numerator and $n - (k + 1)$ denominator degrees of freedom.

The analysis of variance F-test for testing the usefulness of the model is summarized in the next box.

Testing Global Usefulness of the Model: The Analysis of Variance F-Test

H_0: $\beta_1 = \beta_2 = \cdots = \beta_k = 0$ (All model terms are unimportant for predicting y.)

H_a: At least one $\beta_i \neq 0$ (At least one model term is useful for predicting y.)

$$\textit{Test statistic: } F = \frac{(SS_{yy} - SSE)/k}{SSE/[n - (k + 1)]} = \frac{R^2/k}{(1 - R^2)/[n - (k + 1)]}$$

$$= \frac{\text{Mean Square (Model)}}{\text{Mean Square (Error)}}$$

where n is the sample size and k is the number of terms in the model.

Rejection region: $F > F_\alpha$, with k numerator degrees of freedom and $[n - (k + 1)]$ denominator degrees of freedom.

Conditions Required for the Global F-Test in Regression to Be Valid

refer to the standard regression assumptions about the random error component (Section 12.1).

CAUTION A rejection of the null hypothesis H_0: $\beta_1 = \beta_2 = \cdots = \beta_k$ in the *global F-test* leads to the conclusion [with $100(1 - \alpha)\%$ confidence] that the model is statistically useful. However, statistically "useful" does not necessarily mean "best." Another model may prove even more useful in terms of providing more reliable estimates and predictions. This global F-test is usually regarded as a test that the model *must* pass to merit further consideration.

Example 12.4

Assessing Overall Adequacy—Clock Auction Price Model

Problem Refer to Examples 12.1–12.3, in which an antique collector modeled the auction price (y) of grandfather clocks as a function of the age of the clock (x_1) and the number of bidders (x_2). Recall that the hypothesized first-order model is

$$y = \beta_0 + \beta_1 x_1 + \beta_2 x_2 + \varepsilon$$

The SPSS printout for the analysis is shown in Figure 12.6 (p. 676).

a. Find and interpret the adjusted coefficient of determination R_a^2.

b. Conduct the global F-test of model usefulness at the $\alpha = .05$ level of significance.

Solution

a. The R_a^2 value (highlighted in Figure 12.6) is .885. This implies that the least squares model has explained about 88.5% of the total sample variation in y values (auction prices), after adjusting for sample size and number of independent variables in the model.

b. The elements of the global test of the model follow:

H_0: $\beta_1 = \beta_2 = 0$ (*Note:* $k = 2$)

H_a: At least one of the two model coefficients, β_1 and β_2, is nonzero.

$$\textit{Test statistic: } F = \frac{\text{MS (Model)}}{\text{MSE}} = \frac{2{,}141{,}531}{17{,}818} = 120.19 \text{ (see Figure 12.6)}$$

p-value ≈ 0

Conclusion: Because $\alpha = .05$ exceeds the observed significance level, ($p \approx 0$), the data provide strong evidence that at least one of the model coefficients is nonzero. The overall model appears to be statistically useful for predicting auction prices.

Look Back Can we be sure that the best prediction model has been found if the global F-test indicates that a model is useful? Unfortunately, we cannot. The addition of other independent variables may improve the usefulness of the model. (See the box on p. 678.) We consider more complex multiple regression models in Sections 12.5–12.8.

■ Now Work Exercise 12.15d–h

In this section, we discussed several different statistics for assessing the utility of a multiple regression model: t-tests on individual β parameters, R^2, R_a^2, and the global F-test. Both R^2 and R_a^2 are indicators of how well the prediction equation fits the data. Intuitive evaluations of the contribution of the model based on R^2 must be examined with care. Unlike R_a^2, the value of R^2 increases as more and more variables are added to the model. Consequently, you could force R^2 to take a value very close to 1 even though the model contributes no information for the prediction of y. In fact, R^2 equals 1 when the number of terms in the model (including β_0) equals the number of data points. Therefore, you should not rely solely on the value of R^2 (or even R_a^2) to tell you whether the model is useful for predicting y.

Conducting t-tests on all of the individual β parameters is also not the best method of testing the global utility of the model because these multiple tests result in a high probability of making at least one Type I error. Use the F-test for testing the global utility of the model.

After we have determined that the overall model is useful for predicting y using the F-test, we may elect to conduct one or more t-tests on the individual β parameters. However, the test (or tests) to be conducted should be decided a priori—that is, prior to fitting the model. Also, we should limit the number of t-tests conducted to avoid the potential problem of making too many Type I errors. Generally, the regression analyst will conduct t-tests only on the "most important" β's. We provide insight in identifying the most important β's in a linear model in Sections 12.5–12.8.

Recommendation for Checking the Utility of a Multiple Regression Model

1. First, conduct a test of overall model adequacy using the F-test—that is, test

$$H_0: \beta_1 = \beta_2 = \cdots = \beta_k = 0$$

If the model is deemed adequate (that is, if you reject H_0), then proceed to step 2. Otherwise, you should hypothesize and fit another model. The new model may include more independent variables or higher-order terms.

2. Conduct t-tests on those β parameters in which you are particularly interested (that is, the "most important" β's). As we will see in Sections 12.5 and 12.6, these usually involve only the β's associated with higher-order terms (x^2, x_1x_2, etc.). However, it is a safe practice to limit the number of β's that are tested. Conducting a series of t-tests leads to a high overall Type I error rate α.

Exercises 12.1–12.24

Learning the Mechanics

12.1 Write a first-order model relating $E(y)$ to
- **a.** two quantitative independent variables.
- **b.** four quantitative independent variables.
- **c.** five quantitative independent variables.

12.2 NW Minitab was used to fit the model $E(y) = \beta_0 + \beta_1x_1 + \beta_2x_2$ to $n = 20$ data points, and the printout shown on the next page was obtained.
- **a.** What are the sample estimates of β_0, β_1, and β_2?
- **b.** What is the least squares prediction equation?
- **c.** Find SSE, MSE, and s. Interpret the standard deviation in the context of the problem.
- **d.** Test H_0: $\beta_1 = 0$ against H_0: $\beta_1 \neq 0$. Use $\alpha = .05$.
- **e.** Use a 95% confidence interval to estimate β_2.
- **f.** Find R^2 and R_a^2 and interpret these values.
- **g.** Find the test statistic for testing H_0: $\beta_1 = \beta_2 = 0$.
- **h.** Find the observed significance level of the test, part **g**. Interpret the result.

Minitab output for Exercise 12.2

```
The regression equation is
Y = 506.35 - 941.9 X1 - 429.1 X2


Predictor      Coef  SE Coef      T      P
Constant    506.346    45.17  11.21  0.000
X1         -941.900   275.08  -3.42  0.003
X2         -429.060   379.83  -1.13  0.274


S = 94.251    R-Sq = 45.9%    R-Sq(adj) = 39.6%


Analysis of Variance

Source          DF      SS     MS     F      P
Regression       2  128329  64165  7.22  0.005
Residual Error  17  151016   8883
Total           19  279345
```

12.3 Suppose you fit the multiple regression model

$$y = \beta_0 + \beta_1 x_1 + \beta_2 x_2 + \beta_3 x_3 + \varepsilon$$

to $n = 30$ data points and obtain the following result:

$$\hat{y} = 3.4 - 4.6x_1 + 2.7x_2 + .93x_3$$

The estimated standard errors of $\hat{\beta}_2$ and $\hat{\beta}_3$ are 1.86 and .29, respectively.

a. Test the null hypothesis H_0: $\beta_2 = 0$ against the alternative hypothesis H_a: $\beta_2 \neq 0$. Use $\alpha = .05$.

b. Test the null hypothesis H_0: $\beta_3 = 0$ against the alternative hypothesis H_a: $\beta_3 \neq 0$. Use $\alpha = .05$.

c. The null hypothesis H_0: $\beta_2 = 0$ is not rejected. In contrast, the null hypothesis H_0: $\beta_3 = 0$ is rejected. Explain how this can happen even though $\hat{\beta}_2 > \hat{\beta}_3$.

12.4 Suppose you fit the first-order multiple regression model

$$y = \beta_0 + \beta_1 x_1 + \beta_2 x_2 + \varepsilon$$

to $n = 25$ data points and obtain the prediction equation

$$\hat{y} = 6.4 + 3.1x_1 + .92x_2$$

The estimated standard deviations of the sampling distributions of $\hat{\beta}_1$ and $\hat{\beta}_2$ are 2.3 and .27, respectively.

a. Test H_0: $\beta_1 = 0$ against H_a: $\beta_1 > 0$. Use $\alpha = .05$.

b. Test H_0: $\beta_2 = 0$ against H_a: $\beta_2 \neq 0$. Use $\alpha = .05$.

c. Find a 90% confidence interval for β_1. Interpret the interval.

d. Find a 99% confidence interval for β_2. Interpret the interval.

12.5 How is the number of degrees of freedom available for estimating σ^2 (the variance of ε) related to the number of independent variables in a regression model?

12.6 Consider the first-order model equation in three quantitative independent variables

$$E(y) = 1 + 2x_1 + x_2 - 3x_3$$

a. Graph the relationship between y and x_1 for $x_2 = 1$ and $x_3 = 3$.

b. Repeat part **a** for $x_2 = -1$ and $x_3 = 1$.

c. How do the graphed lines in parts **a** and **b** relate to each other? What is the slope of each line?

d. If a linear model is first-order in three independent variables, what type of geometric relationship will you obtain when $E(y)$ is graphed as a function of one of the independent variables for various combinations of values of the other independent variables?

12.7 Suppose you fit the first-order model

$$y = \beta_0 + \beta_1 x_1 + \beta_2 x_2 + \beta_3 x_3 + \beta_4 x_4 + \beta_5 x_5 + \varepsilon$$

to $n = 30$ data points and obtain

$$SSE = .33 \quad R^2 = .92$$

a. Do the values of SSE and R^2 suggest that the model provides a good fit to the data? Explain.

b. Is the model of any use in predicting y? Test the null hypothesis H_0: $\beta_1 = \beta_2 = \beta_3 = \beta_4 = \beta_5 = 0$ against the alternative hypothesis H_a: At least one of the parameters $\beta_1, \beta_2, \ldots, \beta_5$ is nonzero. Use $\alpha = .05$.

12.8 If the analysis of variance F-test leads to the conclusion that at least one of the model parameters is nonzero, can you conclude that the model is the best predictor for the dependent variable y? Can you conclude that all of the terms in the model are important for predicting y? What is the appropriate conclusion?

Applying the Concepts—Basic

12.9 Usability professionals salary survey. The Usability Professionals' Association (UPA) supports people who research, design, and evaluate the user experience of products and services. Recently, the UPA conducted a salary survey of its members (*UPA Salary Survey*, August 18, 2009). One of the report's authors, Jeff Sauro, investigated how much having a PhD affects salaries in this profession and discussed his analysis on the blog, www.measuringusability.com. Sauro fit a first-order multiple regression model for salary (y, in dollars) as a function of years of experience (x_1), PhD status ($x_2 = 1$ if PhD, 0 if not), and manager status ($x_3 = 1$ if manager, 0 if not). The following prediction equation was obtained:

$$\hat{y} = 52{,}484 + 2{,}941x_1 + 16{,}880x_2 + 11{,}108x_3$$

a. Predict the salary of a UPA member with 10 years of experience who does not have a PhD, but is a manager.

b. Predict the salary of a UPA member with 10 years of experience who does have a PhD, but is not a manager.

c. The following coefficient was reported: $R_a^2 = .32$. Give a practical interpretation of this value.

d. A 95% confidence interval for β_1 was reported as (2700, 3200). Give a practical interpretation of this result.

e. A 95% confidence interval for β_2 was reported as (11,500, 22,300). Give a practical interpretation of this result.

f. A 95% confidence interval for β_3 was reported as (7,600, 14,600). Give a practical interpretation of this result.

12.10 Forecasting movie revenues with Twitter. Refer to the *IEEE International Conference on Web Intelligence and Intelligent Agent Technology* (2010) study on using the volume of chatter on Twitter.com to forecast movie box office revenue, Exercise 11.23 (p. 617). Recall that opening weekend box office revenue data (in millions of dollars) were collected for a sample of 24 recent movies. In addition to each movie's *tweet rate*, i.e., the average number of tweets referring to the movie per hour 1 week prior to the movie's release, the researchers also computed the ratio of positive to negative tweets (called the *PN-ratio*).

a. Give the equation of a first-order model relating revenue (y) to both tweet rate (x_1) and PN-ratio (x_2).

b. Which β in the model, part **a,** represents the change in revenue (y) for every 1-tweet increase in the tweet rate (x_1), holding PN-ratio (x_2) constant?

c. Which β in the model, part **a,** represents the change in revenue (y) for every 1-unit increase in the PN-ratio (x_2), holding tweet rate (x_1) constant?

d. The following coefficients were reported: $R^2 = .945$ and $R_a^2 = .940$. Give a practical interpretation for both R^2 and R_a^2.

e. Conduct a test of the null hypothesis, $H_0{:}\beta_1 = \beta_2 = 0$. Use $\alpha = .05$.

f. The researchers reported the p-values for testing $H_0{:}\ \beta_1 = 0$ and $H_0{:}\ \beta_2 = 0$ as both less than .0001. Interpret these results (use $\alpha = .01$).

12.11 Accounting and Machiavellianism. Refer to the *Behavioral Research in Accounting* (Jan. 2008) study of Machiavellian traits (e.g., manipulation, cunning, duplicity, deception, and bad faith) in accountants, Exercise 9.8 (p. 492). Recall that a Mach rating score was determined for each in a sample of accounting alumni of a large southwestern university. For one portion of the study, the researcher modeled an accountant's Mach score (y) as a function of age, gender, education, and income. Data on $n = 198$ accountants yielded the results shown in the table.

Independent Variable	t-value for $H_0{:}\ \beta_i = 0$	p-value
Age (x_1)	0.10	> .10
Gender (x_2)	−0.55	> .10
Education (x_3)	1.95	< .01
Income (x_4)	0.52	> .10
Overall model: $R^2 = .13$, $F = 4.74$ (p-value < .01)		

a. Conduct a test of overall model utility. Use $\alpha = .05$.

b. Interpret the coefficient of determination, R^2.

c. Is there sufficient evidence (at $\alpha = .05$) to say that income is a statistically useful predictor of Mach score?

12.12 Characteristics of lead users. During new product development, companies often involve "lead users," i.e., creative individuals who are on the leading edge of an important market trend. *Creativity and Innovation Management* (Feb. 2008) published an article on identifying the social network characteristics of lead users of children's computer games. Data were collected for $n = 326$ children, and the following variables were measured: lead-user rating (y, measured on a 5-point scale), gender ($x_1 = 1$ if female, 0 if male), age (x_2, years), degree of centrality (x_3, measured as the number of direct ties to other peers in the network), and betweenness centrality (x_4, measured as the number of shortest paths between peers). A first-order model for y was fit to the data, yielding the following least squares prediction equation:

$$\hat{y} = 3.58 + .01x_1 - .06x_2 - .01x_3 + .42x_4$$

a. Give two properties of the errors of prediction that result from using the method of least squares to obtain the parameter estimates.

b. Give a practical interpretation of the estimate of β_4 in the model.

c. A test of $H_0{:}\ \beta_4 = 0$ resulted in a p-value of .002. Make the appropriate conclusion at $\alpha = .05$.

12.13 Highway crash data analysis. Researchers at Montana State University have written a tutorial on an empirical method for analyzing before and after highway crash data (Montana Department of Transportation, Research Report, May 2004). The initial step in the methodology is to develop a Safety Performance Function (SPF)—a mathematical model that estimates crash occurrence for a given roadway segment. Using data collected for over 100 roadway segments, the researchers fit the model, $E(y) = \beta_0 + \beta_1x_1 + \beta_2x_2$, where y = number of crashes per 3 years, x_1 = roadway length (miles), and x_2 = AADT = average annual daily traffic (number of vehicles). The results are shown in the following tables.

Interstate Highways

Variable	Parameter Estimate	Standard Error	t-value
Intercept	1.81231	.50568	3.58
Length (x_1)	.10875	.03166	3.44
AADT (x_2)	.00017	.00003	5.19

Noninterstate Highways

Variable	Parameter Estimate	Standard Error	t-value
Intercept	1.20785	.28075	4.30
Length (x_1)	.06343	.01809	3.51
AADT (x_2)	.00056	.00012	4.86

a. Give the least squares prediction equation for the interstate highway model.

b. Give practical interpretations of the β estimates, part **a.**

c. Refer to part **a.** Find a 99% confidence interval for β_1 and interpret the result.

d. Refer to part **a.** Find a 99% confidence interval for β_2 and interpret the result.

e. Repeat parts **a–d** for the noninterstate highway model.

12.14 Predicting runs scored in baseball. In *Chance* (Fall 2000), statistician Scott Berry built a multiple regression model for predicting total number of runs scored by a Major League Baseball team during a season. Using data on all teams over a 9-year period (a sample of $n = 234$), the results in the following table were obtained.

NW

Independent Variable	β Estimate	Standard Error
Intercept	3.70	15.00
Walks (x_1)	.34	.02
Singles (x_2)	.49	.03
Doubles (x_3)	.72	.05
Triples (x_4)	1.14	.19
Home runs (x_5)	1.51	.05
Stolen bases (x_6)	.26	.05
Caught stealing (x_7)	−.14	.14
Strikeouts (x_8)	−.10	.01
Outs (x_9)	−.10	.01

Source: Table from Berry, S. M. "A statistician reads the sports pages: Modeling offensive ability in baseball," *Chance*, Vol. 13, No. 4, Fall 2000, pp. 56–59 (Table 2). Reprinted with permission from *Chance*. © 2000 by the American Statistical Association. Reprinted with permission.

a. Write the least squares prediction equation for y = total number of runs scored by a team in a season.
b. Interpret, practically, the β estimates in the model.
c. Conduct a test of H_0: $\beta_7 = 0$ against H_a: $\beta_7 < 0$ at $\alpha = .05$. Interpret the results.
d. Form a 95% confidence interval for β_5. Interpret the results.

Applying the Concepts—Intermediate

12.15 Novelty of a vacation destination. Many tourists choose a vacation destination based on the newness or uniqueness (i.e., the novelty) of the itinerary. Texas A&M University professor J. Petrick investigated the relationship between novelty and vacationing golfers' demographics (*Annals of Tourism Research*, Vol. 29, 2002). Data were obtained from a mail survey of 393 golf vacationers to a large coastal resort in the southeastern United States. Several measures of novelty level (on a numerical scale) were obtained for each vacationer, including "change from routine," "thrill," "boredom-alleviation," and "surprise." The researcher employed four independent variables in a regression model to predict each of the novelty measures. The independent variables were x_1 = number of rounds of golf per year, x_2 = total number of golf vacations taken, x_3 = number of years played golf, and x_4 = average golf score.
NW

a. Give the hypothesized equation of a first-order model for y = change from routine.
b. A test of H_0: $\beta_3 = 0$ versus H_a: $\beta_3 < 0$ yielded a p-value of .005. Interpret this result if $\alpha = .01$.
c. The estimate of β_3 was found to be negative. Based on this result (and the result of part **b**), the researcher concluded that "those who have played golf for more years are less apt to seek change from their normal routine in their golf vacations." Do you agree with this statement? Explain.
d. The regression results for three dependent novelty measures, based on data collected for n = 393 golf vacationers, are summarized in the table below. Give the null hypothesis for testing the overall adequacy of the first-order regression model.
e. Give the rejection region for the test, part **d,** for $\alpha = .01$.
f. Use the test statistics reported in the table and the rejection region from part **e** to conduct the test for each of the dependent measures of novelty.
g. Verify that the p-values reported in the table support your conclusions in part **f.**
h. Interpret the values of R^2 reported in the table.

Dependent Variable	F-value	p-value	R^2
Thrill	5.56	<.001	.055
Change from routine	3.02	.018	.030
Surprise	3.33	.011	.023

Source: Based on Petrick, J. F. "An examination of golf vacationers' novelty," *Annals of Tourism Research*, Vol. 29, No. 2, 2002, pp. 384–400.

12.16 Arsenic in groundwater. *Environmental Science & Technology* (Jan. 2005) reported on a study of the reliability of a commercial kit to test for arsenic in groundwater. The field kit was used to test a sample of 328 groundwater wells in Bangladesh. In addition to the arsenic level (micrograms per liter), the latitude (degrees), longitude (degrees), and depth (feet) of each well were measured. The data are saved in the file. (The first and last 5 observations are listed in the table below.)
WELLS

Well ID	Latitude	Longitude	Depth	Arsenic
10	23.7887	90.6522	60	331
14	23.7886	90.6523	45	302
30	23.7880	90.6517	45	193
59	23.7893	90.6525	125	232
85	23.7920	90.6140	150	19
⋮	⋮	⋮	⋮	⋮
7353	23.7949	90.6515	40	48
7357	23.7955	90.6515	30	172
7890	23.7658	90.6312	60	175
7893	23.7656	90.6315	45	624
7970	23.7644	90.6303	30	254

a. Write a first-order model for arsenic level (y) as a function of latitude, longitude, and depth.
b. Fit the model to the data using the method of least squares.
c. Give practical interpretations of the β estimates.
d. Find the model standard deviation, s, and interpret its value.
e. Find and interpret the values of R^2 and R_a^2.
f. Conduct a test of overall model utility at $\alpha = .05$.
g. Based on the results, parts **d–f**, would you recommend using the model to predict arsenic level (y)? Explain.

12.17 Reality TV and cosmetic surgery. How much influence does the media, especially reality television programs, have on one's decision to undergo cosmetic surgery? This was the question of interest to psychologists who published an article in *Body Image: An International Journal of Research* (March 2010). In the study, 170 college students answered questions about their impressions of reality TV shows featuring cosmetic surgery, level of self-esteem, satisfaction with one's own body, and desire to have cosmetic surgery to alter one's body. The variables analyzed in the study were measured as follows: DESIRE—scale ranging from 5 to 25, where the higher the value, the greater the interest in having cosmetic surgery; GENDER—1 if male, 0 if female; SELFESTM—scale ranging from 4 to 40, where the higher the value, the greater the level of self-esteem; BODYSAT—scale ranging from 1 to 9, where the higher the value, the greater the satisfaction with one's own body; and IMPREAL—scale ranging from 1 to 7, where the higher the value, the more one believes reality television shows featuring cosmetic surgery are realistic. The data for the study (simulated based on statistics reported in the journal article) are saved in the file. Selected observations are listed in the next table on page 683. The psychologists used multiple regression to model desire to have cosmetic surgery (y) as a function of gender (x_1), self-esteem (x_2), body satisfaction (x_3), and impression of reality TV (x_4).
BDYIMG

a. Fit the first-order model, $E(y) = \beta_0 + \beta_1 x_1 + \beta_2 x_2 + \beta_3 x_3 + \beta_4 x_4$, to the data in the file. Give the least squares prediction equation.
b. Interpret the β estimates in the words of the problem.

Data for Exercise 12.17 (first and last five observations)

STUDENT	DESIRE	GENDER	SELFESTM	BODYSAT	IMPREAL
1	11	0	24	3	4
2	13	0	20	3	4
3	11	0	25	4	5
4	11	1	22	9	4
5	18	0	8	1	6
⋮	⋮	⋮	⋮	⋮	⋮
166	18	0	25	3	5
167	13	0	26	4	5
168	9	1	13	5	6
169	14	0	20	3	2
170	6	1	27	8	3

c. Is the overall model statistically useful for predicting desire to have cosmetic surgery? Test using $\alpha = .01$.

d. Which statistic, R^2 or R_a^2, is the preferred measure of model fit? Practically interpret the value of this statistic.

e. Conduct a test to determine whether desire to have cosmetic surgery decreases linearly as level of body satisfaction increases. Use $\alpha = .05$.

f. Find a 95% confidence interval for β_4. Practically interpret the result.

12.18 Contamination from a plant's discharge. Refer to the U.S. Army Corps of Engineers data (Example 1.5, p. 13) on fish contaminated from the toxic discharges of a chemical plant located on the banks of the Tennessee River in Alabama. Recall that the engineers measured the length (in centimeters), weight (in grams), and DDT level (in parts per million) for 144 captured fish. In addition, the number of miles upstream from the river was recorded. The data are saved in the file. (The first and last five observations are shown in the table in the next column.)

DDT

a. Fit the first-order model, $E(y) = \beta_0 + \beta_1x_1 + \beta_2x_2 + \beta_3x_3$, to the data, where y = DDT level, x_1 = mile, x_2 = length, and x_3 = weight. Report the least squares prediction equation.

b. Find the estimate of the standard deviation of ε for the model and give a practical interpretation of its value.

c. Conduct a test of the global utility of the model. Use $\alpha = .05$.

River	Mile	Species	Length	Weight	DDT
FC	5	CHANNELCATFISH	42.5	732	10.00
FC	5	CHANNELCATFISH	44.0	795	16.00
FC	5	CHANNELCATFISH	41.5	547	23.00
FC	5	CHANNELCATFISH	39.0	465	21.00
FC	5	CHANNELCATFISH	50.5	1,252	50.00
⋮	⋮	⋮	⋮	⋮	⋮
TR	345	LARGEMOUTHBASS	23.5	358	2.00
TR	345	LARGEMOUTHBASS	30.0	856	2.20
TR	345	LARGEMOUTHBASS	29.0	793	7.40
TR	345	LARGEMOUTHBASS	17.5	173	0.35
TR	345	LARGEMOUTHBASS	36.0	1,433	1.90

d. Do the data provide sufficient evidence to conclude that DDT level increases as length increases? Report the observed significance level of the test and reach a conclusion using $\alpha = .05$.

e. Find and interpret a 95% confidence interval for β_3.

12.19 Cooling method for gas turbines. Refer to the *Journal of Engineering for Gas Turbines and Power* (Jan. 2005) study of a high-pressure inlet fogging method for a gas turbine engine, Exercise 7.40 (p. 378). Recall that the heat rate (kilojoules per kilowatt per hour) was measured for each in a sample of 67 gas turbines augmented with high-pressure inlet fogging. In addition, several other variables were measured, including cycle speed (revolutions per minute), inlet temperature (°C), exhaust gas temperature (°C), cycle pressure ratio, and air mass flow rate (kilograms per second). The data are saved in the file. (The first and last five observations are listed in the table at the bottom of the page.)

GASTRB

a. Write a first-order model for heat rate (y) as a function of speed, inlet temperature, exhaust temperature, cycle pressure ratio, and airflow rate.

b. Fit the model to the data using the method of least squares.

c. Give practical interpretations of the β estimates.

d. Find the model standard deviation, s, and interpret its value.

e. Conduct a test for overall model utility using $\alpha = .01$.

f. Find and interpret R_a^2.

g. Is there sufficient evidence (at $\alpha = .01$) to indicate that heat rate (y) is linearly related to inlet temperature?

Data for Exercise 12.19 (selected observations)

RPM	CP Ratio	Inlet Temp.	Exhaust Temp.	Airflow	Heat Rate
27,245	9.2	1,134	602	7	14,622
14,000	12.2	950	446	15	13,196
17,384	14.8	1,149	537	20	11,948
11,085	11.8	1,024	478	27	11,289
14,045	13.2	1,149	553	29	11,964
⋮	⋮	⋮	⋮	⋮	⋮
18,910	14.0	1,066	532	8	12,766
3,600	35.0	1,288	448	152	8,714
3,600	20.0	1,160	456	84	9,469
16,000	10.6	1,232	560	14	11,948
14,600	13.4	1,077	536	20	12,414

Source: Based on Bhargava, R., & Meher-Homji, C. B. "Parametric analysis of existing gas turbines with inlet evaporative and overspray fogging," *Journal of Engineering for Gas Turbines and Power*, Vol. 127, No. 1, Jan. 2005, pp. 145–158.

12.20 Extracting water from oil. In the oil industry, water that mixes with crude oil during production and transportation must be removed. Chemists have found that the oil can be extracted from the water/oil mix electrically. Researchers at the University of Bergen (Norway) conducted a series of experiments to study the factors that influence the voltage (y) required to separate the water from the oil (*Journal of Colloid and Interface Science*, Aug. 1995). The seven independent variables investigated in the study are listed in the table below. (Each variable was measured at two levels—a "low" level and a "high" level.) Sixteen water/oil mixtures were prepared using different combinations of the independent variables; then each emulsion was exposed to a high electric field. In addition, three mixtures were tested when all independent variables were set to 0. The data for all 19 experiments are saved in the file (selected observations are shown in the table at the bottom of the page).

H2OOIL

a. Propose a first-order model for y as a function of all seven independent variables.

b. Use a statistical software package to fit the model to the data in the table.

c. Fully interpret the β estimates.

d. Evaluate the overall utility of the model at $\alpha = .10$.

12.21 Occupational safety study. An important goal in occupational safety is "active caring." Employees demonstrate active caring (AC) about the safety of their coworkers when they identify environmental hazards and unsafe work practices and then implement appropriate corrective actions for these unsafe conditions or behaviors. Three factors hypothesized to increase the propensity for an employee to actively care for safety are (1) high self-esteem, (2) optimism, and (3) group cohesiveness. *Applied & Preventive Psychology* (Winter 1995) attempted to establish empirical support for the AC hypothesis by fitting the model $E(y) = \beta_0 + \beta_1 x_1 + \beta_2 x_2 + \beta_3 x_3$, where

y = AC score (active caring score, 15-point scale)

x_1 = Self-esteem score

x_2 = Optimism score

x_3 = Group cohesion score

The regression analysis, based on data collected for $n = 31$ hourly workers at a large fiber-manufacturing plant, yielded a multiple coefficient of determination of $R^2 = .362$.

a. Interpret the value of R^2.

b. Use the R^2 value to test the global utility of the model. Use $\alpha = .05$.

12.22 R^2 and model fit. Because the coefficient of determination R^2 always increases when a new independent variable is added to the model, it is tempting to include many variables in a model to force R^2 to be near 1. However, doing so reduces the degrees of freedom available for estimating σ^2, which adversely affects our ability to make reliable inferences. Suppose you want to use 18 economic indicators to predict next year's gross domestic product (GDP). You fit the model

$$y = \beta_0 + \beta_1 x_1 + \beta_2 x_2 + \cdots + \beta_{17} x_{17} + \beta_{18} x_{18} + \varepsilon$$

where y = GDP and $x_1, x_2, \ldots, x_{18}$ are the economic indicators. Only 20 years of data ($n = 20$) are used to fit the model, and you obtain $R^2 = .95$. Test to see whether this impressive-looking R^2 is large enough for you to infer that the model is useful—that is, that at least one term in the model is important for predicting GDP. Use $\alpha = .05$.

Applying the Concepts—Advanced

12.23 Bordeaux wine sold at auction. The vineyards in the Bordeaux region of France are known for producing excellent red wines. However, the uncertainty of the weather during the growing season, the phenomenon that wine tastes better with age, and the fact that some Bordeaux vineyards produce better wines than others encourage speculation concerning the value of a case of wine produced by a certain vineyard during a certain year (or vintage). As a result, many wine experts attempt to predict the auction price of a case of Bordeaux wine. The publishers of a newsletter titled *Liquid Assets: The International Guide to Fine Wine* discussed a multiple regression approach to predicting the London auction price of red Bordeaux wine in *Chance* (Fall 1995). The natural logarithm of the price y (in dollars) of a case containing a dozen bottles of red wine was modeled as a function of weather during growing season and age of vintage using data collected for the vintages of 1952–1980. Three models were fit to the data. The results of the regressions are summarized in the table on the next page.

Data for Exercise 12.20 (selected observations)

Experiment Number	Voltage, y (kw/cm)	Disperse Phase Volume, x_1 (%)	Salinity, x_2 (%)	Temperature, x_3 (°C)	Time Delay, x_4 (hours)	Surfactant Concentration, x_5 (%)	Span: Triton, x_6	Solid Particles, x_7 (%)
1	.64	40	1	4	.25	2	.25	.5
2	.80	80	1	4	.25	4	.25	2
3	3.20	40	4	4	.25	4	.75	.5
4	.48	80	4	4	.25	2	.75	2
5	1.72	40	1	23	.25	4	.75	2
⋮	⋮	⋮	⋮	⋮	⋮	⋮	⋮	⋮
16	.72	80	4	23	24	4	.75	2
17	1.08	0	0	0	0	0	0	0
18	1.08	0	0	0	0	0	0	0
19	1.04	0	0	0	0	0	0	0

Source: Based on Førdedal, H., et al. "A multivariate analysis of W/O emulsions in high external electric fields as studied by means of dielectric time domain spectroscopy," *Journal of Colloid and Interface Science*, Vol. 173, No. 2, Aug. 1995, p. 398 (Table 2).

Results for Exercise 12.23

Independent Variables	Beta Estimates (Standard Errors)		
	Model 1	Model 2	Model 3
x_1 = Vintage year	.0354 (.0137)	.0238 (.00717)	.0240 (.00747)
x_2 = Average growing season temperature(°C)	(not included)	.616 (.0952)	.608 (.116)
x_3 = Sept./Aug. rainfall (cm)	(not included)	−.00386 (.00081)	−.00380 (.00095)
x_4 = Rainfall in months preceding vintage (cm)	(not included)	.0001173 (.000482)	.00115 (.000505)
x_5 = Average Sept. temperature(°C)	(not included)	(not included)	.00765 (.565)
	R^2 = .212	R^2 = .828	R^2 = .828
	s = .575	s = .287	s = .293

Source: Ashenfelter, O., Ashmore, D., & LaLonde, R. "Bordeaux wine vintage quality and weather," *Chance*, Vol. 8, No. 4, Fall 1995, p. 116 (Table 2).

a. For each model, conduct a t-test (at $\alpha = .05$) for each of the β parameters in the model. Interpret the results.

b. When the natural log of y is used as a dependent variable, the antilogarithm of a β coefficient minus 1—that is $e^{\beta_i} - 1$—represents the percentage change in y for every 1-unit increase in the associated x value. Use this information to interpret the β estimates of each model.

c. Based on the values of R^2 and s, which of the three models would you recommend for predicting Bordeaux wine prices? Explain.

12.24 Cost analysis for a shipping department. Multiple regression is used by accountants in cost analysis to shed light on the factors that cause costs to be incurred and the magnitudes of their effects. Sometimes, it is desirable to use physical units instead of cost as the dependent variable in a cost analysis (e.g., if the cost associated with the activity of interest is a function of some physical unit, such as hours of labor). The advantage of this approach is that the regression model will provide estimates of the number of labor hours required under different circumstances, and these hours can then be costed at the current labor rate (Horngren, Foster, and Datar, *Cost Accounting*, 2006). The sample data shown in the table below have been collected from a firm's accounting and production records to provide cost information about the firm's shipping department. These data are saved in the file. Consider the model

SHIP

$$y = \beta_0 + \beta_1 x_1 + \beta_2 x_2 + \beta_3 x_3 + \varepsilon$$

a. Find the least squares prediction equation.

b. Use an F-test to investigate the usefulness of the model specified in part **a.** Use $\alpha = .01$ and state your conclusion in the context of the problem.

c. Test $H_0: \beta_2 = 0$ versus $H_a: \beta_2 \neq 0$ using $\alpha = .05$. What do the results of your test suggest about the magnitude of the effects of x_2 on labor costs?

d. Find R^2 and interpret its value in the context of the problem.

e. If shipping department employees are paid $7.50 per hour, how much less, on average, will it cost the company per week if the average number of pounds per shipment increases from a level of 20 to 21? Assume that x_1 and x_2 remain unchanged. Your answer is an estimate of what is known in economics as the *expected marginal cost* associated with a 1-pound increase in x_3.

f. With what approximate precision can this model be used to predict the hours of labor? [*Note:* The precision of multiple regression predictions is discussed in Section 12.4.]

g. Can regression analysis alone indicate what factors *cause* costs to increase? Explain.

Data for Exercise 12.24

Week	Labor, y (hr)	Pounds Shipped, x_1 (1,000s)	Percentage of Units Shipped by Truck, x_2	Average Shipment Weight, x_3(lb)
1	100	5.1	90	20
2	85	3.8	99	22
3	108	5.3	58	19
4	116	7.5	16	15
5	92	4.5	54	20
6	63	3.3	42	26
7	79	5.3	12	25
8	101	5.9	32	21
9	88	4.0	56	24
10	71	4.2	64	29
11	122	6.8	78	10
12	85	3.9	90	30
13	50	3.8	74	28
14	114	7.5	89	14
15	104	4.5	90	21
16	111	6.0	40	20
17	110	8.1	55	16
18	100	2.9	64	19
19	82	4.0	35	23
20	85	4.8	58	25

12.4 Using the Model for Estimation and Prediction

In Section 11.6, we discussed the use of the least squares line for estimating the mean value of y, $E(y)$, for some particular value of x, say $x = x_p$. We also showed how to use the same fitted model to predict, when $x = x_p$, some new value of y to be observed in the future. Recall that the least squares line yielded the same value for both the estimate of $E(y)$ and the prediction of some future value of y—that is, both are the result of substituting x_p into the prediction equation $\hat{y} = \hat{\beta}_0 + \hat{\beta}_1 x$ and calculating $\hat{y}_p$. There the equivalence ends. The confidence interval for the mean $E(y)$ is narrower than the prediction interval for y because of the additional uncertainty attributable to the random error ε when predicting some future value of y.

These same concepts carry over to the multiple regression model. Consider a first-order model relating sale price (y) of a residential property to land value (x_1), appraised improvements value (x_2), and home size (x_3). Suppose we want to estimate the mean sale price for a given property with x_1 = \$15,000, x_2 = \$50,000, and x_3 = 1,800 square feet. Assuming that the first-order model represents the true relationship between sale price and the three independent variables, we want to estimate

$$E(y) = \beta_0 + \beta_1 x_1 + \beta_2 x_2 + \beta_3 x_3 = \beta_0 + \beta_1(15{,}000) + \beta_2(50{,}000) + \beta_3(1{,}800)$$

After obtaining the least squares estimates $\hat{\beta}_0, \hat{\beta}_1, \hat{\beta}_2$, and $\hat{\beta}_3$, the estimate of $E(y)$ will be

$$\hat{y} = \hat{\beta}_0 + \hat{\beta}_1(15{,}000) + \hat{\beta}_2(50{,}000) + \hat{\beta}_3(1{,}800)$$

To form a confidence interval for the mean, we need to know the standard deviation of the sampling distribution for the estimator $\hat{y}$. For multiple regression models, the form of this standard deviation is rather complex. However, the regression routines of statistical computer software packages allow us to obtain the confidence intervals for mean values of y for any given combination of values of the independent variables. We illustrate with an example.

Example 12.5

Estimating $E(y)$ and Predicting y—Auction Price Model

Problem Refer to Examples 12.1–12.4 and the first-order model, $E(y) = \beta_0 + \beta_1 x_1 + \beta_2 x_2$, where y = auction price of a grandfather clock, x_1 = age of the clock, and x_2 = number of bidders.

a. Estimate the average auction price for all 150-year-old clocks sold at auction with 10 bidders using a 95% confidence interval. Interpret the result.

b. Predict the auction price for a single 150-year-old clock sold at an auction with 10 bidders using a 95% prediction interval. Interpret the result.

c. Suppose you want to predict the auction price for one clock that is 50 years old and has 2 bidders. How should you proceed?

Solution

a. Here, the key words *average* and *for all* imply we want to estimate the mean of y, $E(y)$. We want a 95% confidence interval for $E(y)$ when x_1 = 150 years and x_2 = 10 bidders. A Minitab printout for this analysis is shown in Figure 12.7. The confidence interval (highlighted under **"95% CI"**) is (1,381.4, 1,481.9). Thus, we are 95% confident that the mean auction price for all 150-year-old clocks sold at an auction with 10 bidders lies between \$1,381.40 and \$1,481.90.

b. The key words *predict* and *for a single* imply that we want a 95% prediction interval for y when x_1 = 150 years and x_2 = 10 bidders. This interval (highlighted under "95% PI" on the Minitab printout, Figure 12.7) is (1,154.1, 1,709.3). We say, with 95% confidence, that the auction price for a single 150-year-old clock sold at an auction with 10 bidders falls between \$1,154.10 and \$1,709.30.

c. Now, we want to predict the auction price, y, for a single (*one*) grandfather clock when x_1 = 50 years and x_2 = 2 bidders. Consequently, we desire a 95% prediction interval for y. However, before we form this prediction interval, we should check

Regression Analysis: PRICE versus AGE, NUMBIDS

```
The regression equation is
PRICE = - 1339 + 12.7 AGE + 86.0 NUMBIDS

Predictor       Coef   SE Coef      T      P
Constant     -1339.0     173.8  -7.70  0.000
AGE          12.7406    0.9047  14.08  0.000
NUMBIDS       85.953     8.729   9.85  0.000

S = 133.485    R-Sq = 89.2%    R-Sq(adj) = 88.5%

Analysis of Variance

Source           DF       SS       MS       F      P
Regression        2  4283063  2141531  120.19  0.000
Residual Error   29   516727    17818
Total            31  4799790

Predicted Values for New Observations

New
Obs     Fit  SE Fit          95% CI              95% PI
  1  1431.7    24.6  (1381.4, 1481.9)  (1154.1, 1709.3)

Values of Predictors for New Observations

New
Obs  AGE  NUMBIDS
  1  150     10.0
```

Figure 12.7
Minitab printout with 95% confidence intervals for grandfather clock model

to make sure that the selected values of the independent variables, $x_1 = 50$ and $x_2 = 2$, are both reasonable and within their respective sample ranges. If you examine the sample data shown in Table 12.1 (p. 670), you will see that the range for age is $108 \le x_1 \le 194$, and the range for number of bidders is $5 \le x_2 \le 15$. Thus, both selected values fall well *outside* their respective ranges. Recall the *Caution* box in Section 11.6 (p. 645) warning about the dangers of using the model to predict y for a value of an independent variable that is not within the range of the sample data. Doing so may lead to an unreliable prediction.

Look Back If we want to make the prediction requested in part **c**, we would need to collect additional data on clocks with the requested characteristics (i.e., $x_1 = 50$ years and $x_2 = 2$ bidders) and then refit the model.

Now Work Exercise 12.29

Evaluating a First-Order Model

The Florida attorney general wants to develop a model for the cost (y) of a road construction contract awarded using the sealed-bid system and to use the model to predict the costs of future road contracts in the state. In addition to contract cost, the **FLAG** file contains data on eight potential predictor variables for a sample of 235 road contracts. (See Table SIA12.1 on p. 667.) Minitab scatterplots (with the dependent variable, COST, plotted against each of the potential predictors) for the data are shown in Figure SIA12.1. From the scatterplots, it appears that the DOT engineer's cost estimate (DOTEST) and estimate of work days (DAYSEST) would be good predictors of contract cost. [In a future Statistics in Action Revisited section (p. 735), we will learn that the two best predictors of contract cost are actually DOTEST and the fixed or competitive status (STATUS) of the contract.] However, in this section, we will fit the first-order regression model using all eight independent variables.

The Minitab printout for the regression analysis is shown in Figure SIA12.2. The global F-statistic ($F = 1{,}166.68$) and associated p-value (.000) shown on the printout indicate that the overall model is statistically useful for predicting construction cost. The value of R^2 indicates that the model can explain 97.6% of the sample variation in contract cost. Both of these results provide strong statistical support for using the model for estimation and prediction.

STATISTICS in ACTION REVISITED CONTINUED

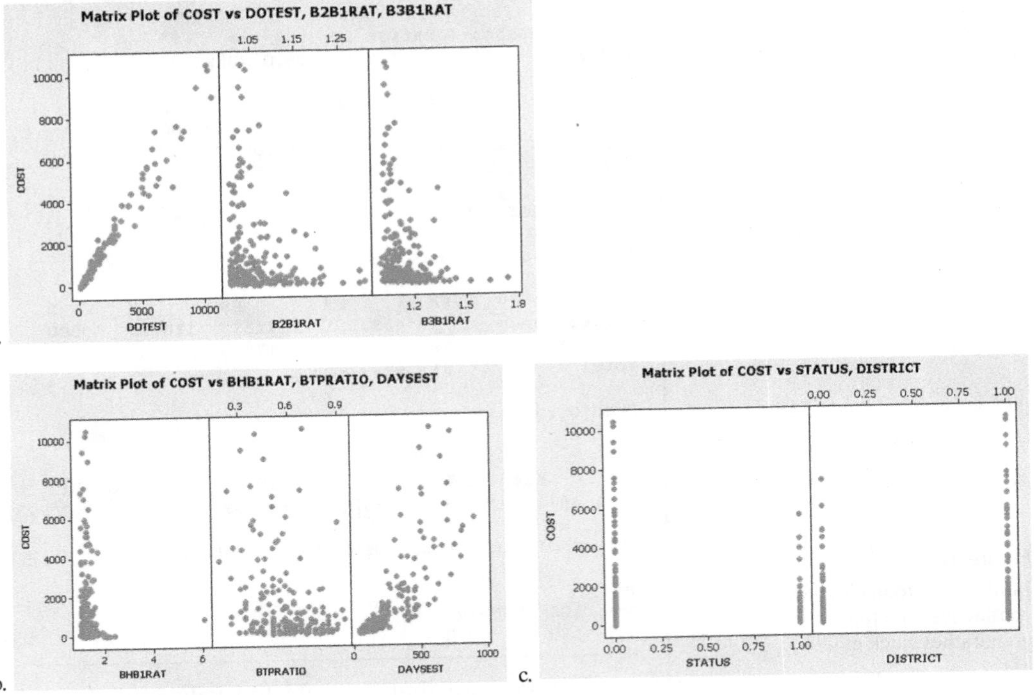

Figure SIA12.1
Minitab scatterplots for **FLAG** data

```
The regression equation is
COST = 124 + 0.906 DOTEST - 147 B2B1RAT - 84 B3B1RAT - 59.1 BHB1RAT + 148 STA>>
       + 37.8 DISTRICT + 218 BTPRATIO + 0.344 DAYSEST


Predictor      Coef  SE Coef      T      P
Constant      123.9    426.8   0.29  0.772
DOTEST      0.90647  0.01659  54.64  0.000
B2B1RAT      -147.1    419.0  -0.35  0.726
B3B1RAT       -83.8    245.4  -0.34  0.733
BHB1RAT      -59.09    54.90  -1.08  0.283
STATUS       148.16    51.48   2.88  0.004
DISTRICT      37.75    43.07   0.88  0.382
BTPRATIO      217.6    139.6   1.56  0.120
DAYSEST      0.3439   0.1803   1.91  0.058


S = 304.589   R-Sq = 97.6%   R-Sq(adj) = 97.6%


Analysis of Variance

Source           DF         SS         MS        F      P
Regression        8  865907936  108238492  1166.68  0.000
Residual Error  226   20967037      92774
Total           234  886874973
```

Figure SIA12.2
Minitab regression output for first-order model of road construction cost

[*Note:* Not all of the independent variables have statistically significant t-values. However, we caution against dropping the insignificant variables from the model at this stage. One reason (discussed in Section 12.3) is that performing a large number of t-tests will yield an inflated probability of at least one Type I error. In later sections of this chapter, we develop other reasons for why the multiple t-test approach is not a good strategy for determining which independent variables to keep in the model.]

The Minitab printout shown in Figure SIA12.3 gives a 95% prediction interval for cost and a 95% confidence interval for the mean cost for the x-values associated with the last observation (contract) in the **FLAG** file. These x-values are engineer's cost estimate (DOTEST) = 497 thousand dollars, ratio of second lowest bid to lowest bid (B2B1RAT) = 1.07, ratio of third lowest bid to lowest bid (B3B1RAT) = 1.08, ratio of highest bid to lowest bid (BHB1RAT) = 1.19, competitive bid (STATUS = 0), south

Florida contract (DISTRICT = 1), bidders to planholders ratio (BTPRATIO) = 0.5, and estimated work days (DAYSEST) = 90. The 95% confidence interval of (339.2, 528.2) implies that for all road contracts with these x-values, the mean contract cost falls between 339.2 and 528.2 thousand dollars, with 95% confidence.

```
Predicted Values for New Observations

New
Obs    Fit  SE Fit        95% CI              95% PI
  1  433.7    48.0  (339.2, 528.2)  (-173.9, 1041.2)


Values of Predictors for New Observations

New
Obs  DOTEST  B2B1RAT  B3B1RAT  BHB1RAT    STATUS  DISTRICT  BTPRATIO  DAYSEST
  1     497     1.07     1.08     1.19  0.000000      1.00     0.500     90.0
```

Figure SIA12.3
Minitab printout with 95% confidence and prediction intervals

The 95% prediction interval of (−173.9, 1,041.2) implies that for an individual road contract with these x-values, the contract cost falls between 0 (because cost cannot be negative) and 1,041.2 thousand dollars, with 95% confidence. Note the wide range of the prediction interval. This is due to the large magnitude of the model standard deviation, $s = 305$ thousand dollars. Although the model is deemed statistically useful for predicting contract cost, it may not be "practically" useful. To reduce the magnitude of s, we will need to improve the model's predictive ability. (We consider such a model in the next Statistics in Action Revisited section.)

Data Set: FLAG

Exercises 12.25–12.33

Applying the Concepts—Basic

12.25 Characteristics of lead users. Refer to the *Creativity and Innovation Management* (Feb. 2008) study of lead users of children's computer games, Exercise 12.12 (p. 681). Recall that the researchers modeled lead-user rating (y, measured on a 5-point scale) as a function of gender ($x_1 = 1$ if female, 0 if male), age (x_2, years), degree of centrality (x_3, measured as the number of direct ties to other peers in the network), and betweenness centrality (x_4, measured as the number of shortest paths between peers). The least squares prediction equation was $\hat{y} = 3.58 + .01x_1 - .06x_2 - .01x_3 + .42x_4$.

a. Compute the predicted lead-user rating of a 10-year-old female child with 5 direct ties to other peers in her social network and with 2 shortest paths between peers.

b. Compute an estimate for the mean lead-user rating of all 8-year-old male children with 10 direct ties to other peers and with 4 shortest paths between peers.

12.26 Predicting runs scored in baseball. Refer to the *Chance* (Fall 2000) study of runs scored in Major League Baseball games, Exercise 12.14 (p. 681). Multiple regression was used to model total number of runs scored (y) of a team during the season as a function of number of walks (x_1), number of singles (x_2), number of doubles (x_3), number of triples (x_4), number of home runs (x_5), number of stolen bases (x_6), number of times caught stealing (x_7), number of strikeouts (x_8), and total number of outs (x_9). Using the β estimates given in Exercise 12.14, predict the number of runs scored by your favorite Major League Baseball team last year. How close is the predicted value to the actual number of runs scored by your team? [*Note:* You can find data on your favorite team on the Internet at www.mlb.com.]

12.27 Reality TV and cosmetic surgery. Refer to the *Body Image: An International Journal of Research* (March 2010) study of the impact of reality TV shows on one's desire to undergo cosmetic surgery, Exercise 12.17 (p. 682). Recall that psychologists used multiple regression to model desire to have cosmetic surgery (y) as a function of gender (x_1), self-esteem (x_2), body satisfaction (x_3), and impression of reality TV (x_4). The SPSS printout below shows a confidence interval for $E(y)$ for each of the first five students in the study.

a. Interpret the confidence interval for $E(y)$ for student 1.

b. Interpret the confidence interval for $E(y)$ for student 4.

12.28 Chemical plant contamination. Refer to Exercise 12.18 (p. 683) and the U.S. Army Corps of Engineers study. You DDT fit the first-order model, $E(y) = \beta_0 + \beta_1 x_1 + \beta_2 x_2 + \beta_3 x_3$,

	STUDENT	DESIRE	GENDER	SELFESTM	BODYSAT	IMPREAL	Lower95CL_Mean	Upper95CL_Mean
1	1	11	0	24	3	4	13.42	14.31
2	2	13	0	20	3	4	13.56	14.55
3	3	11	0	25	4	5	13.42	14.56
4	4	11	1	22	9	4	8.79	10.89
5	5	18	0	8	1	6	15.18	17.34

SPSS output for Exercise 12.27

XLSTAT output for Exercise 12.28

Predictions for the new observations:

Observation	Pred(DDT)	Lower bound 90% (Mean)	Upper bound 90% (Mean)	Lower bound 90% (Observation)	Upper bound 90% (Observation)
MILE=300, LNGTH=40, WT=1000	18.8803	3.8650	33.8956	-143.2178	180.9784

to the data, where y = DDT level (parts per million), x_1 = number of miles upstream, x_2 = length (centimeters), and x_3 = weight (grams). Use the Excel/XLSTAT printout above to predict, with 90% confidence, the DDT level of a fish caught 300 miles upstream with a length of 40 centimeters and a weight of 1,000 grams. Interpret the result.

12.29 Cooling method for gas turbines. Refer to the *Journal of Engineering for Gas Turbines and Power* (Jan. 2005) study of a high-pressure inlet fogging method for a gas turbine engine, Exercise 12.19 (p. 683). Recall that you fit a first-order model for heat rate (y) as a function of speed (x_1), inlet temperature (x_2), exhaust temperature (x_3), cycle pressure ratio (x_4), and airflow rate (x_5). A Minitab printout with both a 95% confidence interval for $E(y)$ and prediction interval for y for selected values of the x's is shown below.

GASTRB NW

a. Interpret the 95% prediction interval for y in the words of the problem.

b. Interpret the 95% confidence interval for $E(y)$ in the words of the problem.

c. Will the confidence interval for $E(y)$ always be narrower than the prediction interval for y? Explain.

```
Predicted Values for New Observations

New
Obs      Fit  SE Fit           95% CI                  95% PI
  1  12632.5   237.3  (12157.9, 13107.1)  (11599.6, 13665.5)

Values of Predictors for New Observations

New
Obs   RPM  INLET-TEMP  EXH-TEMP  CPRATIO  AIRFLOW
  1  7500        1000       525     13.5     10.0
```

Applying the Concepts—Intermediate

12.30 Arsenic in groundwater. Refer to the *Environmental Science & Technology* (Jan. 2005) study of the reliability of a commercial kit to test for arsenic in groundwater, Exercise 12.16 (p. 682). You fit a first-order model for arsenic level (y) as a function of latitude, longitude, and depth. Based on the model statistics, the researchers concluded that the arsenic level is highest at a low latitude, high longitude, and low depth. Do you agree? If so, find a 95% prediction interval for arsenic level for the lowest latitude, highest longitude, and lowest depth that are within the range of the sample data. Interpret the result.

WELLS

12.31 Pay-for-performance efficiency of CEOs. In Chapter 1 (p. 4), we presented *Forbes* magazine's "Executive Compensation Scoreboard." *Forbes* (April 13, 2011) determined which CEOs are worth their pay based on a comparison of the firm's stock performance and the CEO's annual salary. Data for 175 of the top performers are saved in the file. Some of the variables measured for each CEO include pay-for-performance efficiency rating (x_1), value of shares owned (x_2), age (x_3), and the CEO's average salary over the past 5 years (y). (Recall that the lower the efficiency rating, the more the CEO is worth his/her pay.) Consider the first-order model $E(y) = \beta_0 + \beta_1 x_1 + \beta_2 x_2 + \beta_3 x_3$.

TOP175

a. Fit the model to the data and give the least squares prediction equation.

b. Conduct a test of overall model adequacy using $\alpha = .05$.

c. Predict, with 95% confidence, the 5-year pay of a CEO with $x_1 = 173$, x_2 = \$102.9 million, and $x_3 = 59$ years. (*Note:* These values represent the data for Sam Palmisano, CEO of IBM.) Interpret the result.

12.32 Extracting water from oil. Refer to Exercise 12.20 (p. 684) and the study on separating water from oil. The researchers concluded that "in order to break a water-oil mixture with the lowest possible voltage, the volume fraction of the disperse phase (x_1) should be high, while the salinity (x_2) and the amount of surfactant (x_5) should be low." Use this information and the first-order model of Exercise 12.20 to find a 95% prediction interval for this "low" voltage (y). Interpret the interval.

H2OOIL

12.33 Boiler drum production. In a production facility, an accurate estimate of man-hours needed to complete a task is crucial to management in making such decisions as the proper number of workers to hire, an accurate deadline to quote a client, or cost-analysis decisions regarding budgets. A manufacturer of boiler drums wants to use regression to predict the number of man-hours needed to erect the drums in future projects. To accomplish this, data for 35 boilers were collected. In addition to man-hours (y), the variables measured were boiler capacity (x_1 = lb/hr), boiler design pressure (x_2 = pounds per square inch or psi), boiler type (x_3 = 1 if industry field erected, 0 if utility field erected), and drum type (x_4 = 1 if steam, 0 if mud). The data are saved in the file. (The first five and last five observations are listed in the accompanying table.)

BOILER

a. Fit the model $E(y) = \beta_0 + \beta_1 x_1 + \beta_2 x_2 + \beta_3 x_3 + \beta_4 x_4$ to the data. Give the estimates of the β's.

b. Conduct a test for the global utility of the model. Use $\alpha = .01$.

c. Find a 95% confidence interval for $E(y)$ when x_1 = 150,000, x_2 = 500, x_3 = 1, and x_4 = 0. Interpret the result.

Man-Hours, y	Boiler Capacity, x_1	Design Pressure, x_2	Boiler Type, x_3	Drum Type, x_4
3,137	120,000	375	1	1
3,590	65,000	750	1	1
4,526	150,000	500	1	1
10,825	1,073,877	2,170	0	1
4,023	150,000	325	1	1
⋮	⋮	⋮	⋮	⋮
4,206	441,000	410	1	0
4,006	441,000	410	1	0
3,728	627,000	1,525	0	0
3,211	610,000	1,500	0	0
1,200	30,000	325	1	0

Source: Dr. Kelly Uscategui.

PART II: MODEL BUILDING IN MULTIPLE REGRESSION

12.5 Interaction Models

In Section 12.2, we demonstrated the relationship between $E(y)$ and the independent variables in a first-order model. When $E(y)$ is graphed against any one variable (say, x_1) for fixed values of the other variables, the result is a set of *parallel* straight lines (see Figure 12.3, p. 672). When this situation occurs (as it always does for a first-order model), we say that the relationship between $E(y)$ and any one independent variable *does not depend* on the values of the other independent variables in the model.

However, if the relationship between $E(y)$ and x_1 does, in fact, depend on the values of the remaining x's held fixed, then the first-order model is not appropriate for predicting y. In this case, we need another model that will take into account this dependence. Such a model includes the *cross products* of two or more x's.

For example, suppose that the mean value $E(y)$ of a response y is related to two quantitative independent variables, x_1 and x_2, by the model

$$E(y) = 1 + 2x_1 - x_2 + 3x_1x_2$$

A graph of the relationship between $E(y)$ and x_1 for $x_2 = 0, 1,$ and 2 is displayed in the Minitab graph, Figure 12.8.

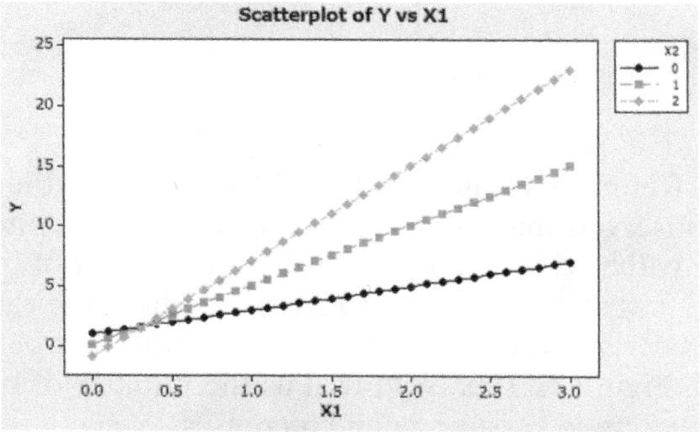

Figure 12.8
Minitab graphs of $1 + 2x_1 - x_2 + 3x_1x_2$ for $x_2 = 0, 1, 2$

Note that the graph shows three nonparallel straight lines. You can verify that the slopes of the lines differ by substituting each of the values $x_2 = 0, 1,$ and 2 into the equation.

For $x_2 = 0$:

$$E(y) = 1 + 2x_1 - (0) + 3x_1(0) = 1 + 2x_1 \qquad \text{(slope = 2)}$$

For $x_2 = 1$,

$$E(y) = 1 + 2x_1 - (1) + 3x_1(1) = 0 + 5x_1 \qquad \text{(slope = 5)}$$

For $x_2 = 2$,

$$E(y) = 1 + 2x_1 - (2) + 3x_1(2) = -1 + 8x_1 \qquad \text{(slope = 8)}$$

Note that the slope of each line is represented by $\beta_1 + \beta_3x_2 = 2 + 3x_2$. Thus, the effect on $E(y)$ of a change in x_1 (i.e., the slope) now *depends* on the value of x_2. When this situation occurs, we say that x_1 and x_2 **interact.** The cross-product term, x_1x_2, is called an **interaction term,** and the model $E(y) = \beta_0 + \beta_1x_1 + \beta_2x_2 + \beta_3x_1x_2$ is called an **interaction model** with two quantitative variables.

An Interaction Model Relating $E(y)$ to Two Quantitative Independent Variables

$$E(y) = \beta_0 + \beta_1x_1 + \beta_2x_2 + \beta_3x_1x_2$$

where

$(\beta_1 + \beta_3x_2)$ represents the change in $E(y)$ for every 1-unit increase in x_1, holding x_2 fixed

$(\beta_2 + \beta_3x_1)$ represents the change in $E(y)$ for every 1-unit increase in x_2, holding x_1 fixed

A three-dimensional graph (generated in Minitab) of the interaction model in two quantitative x's is shown in Figure 12.9. Unlike the flat planar surface displayed in Figure 12.4, the interaction model traces a ruled surface (twisted plane) in three-dimensional space. If we slice the twisted plane at a fixed value of x_2, we obtain a straight line relating $E(y)$ to x_1; however, the slope of the line will change as we change the value of x_2. Consequently, an interaction model is appropriate when the linear relationship between y and one independent variable depends on the value of another independent variable. The next example illustrates this idea.

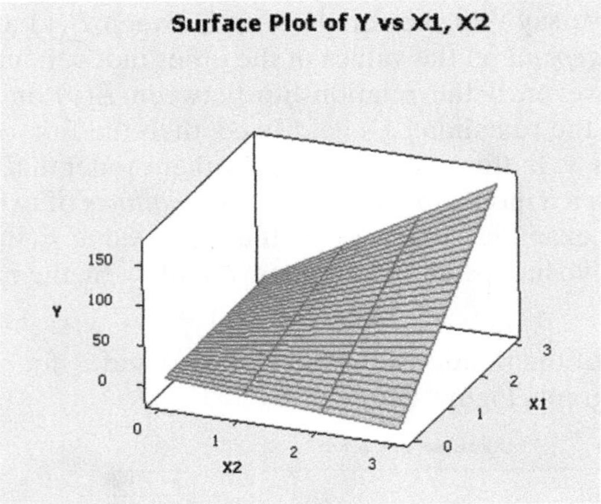

Figure 12.9
Minitab 3-dimensional graph of $1 + 2x_1 - x_2 + 3x_1x_2$

Example 12.6

Evaluating an Interaction Model—Clock Auction Prices

Problem Refer to Examples 12.1–12.4. Suppose the collector of grandfather clocks, having observed many auctions, believes that the *rate of increase* of the auction price with age will be driven upward by a large number of bidders. Thus, instead of a relationship like that shown in Figure 12.10a, in which the rate of increase in price with age is the same for any number of bidders, the collector believes the relationship is like that shown in Figure 12.10b. Note that as the number of bidders increases from 5 to 15, the slope of the price versus age line increases.

Consequently, the interaction model is proposed:

$$y = \beta_0 = \beta_1 x_1 + \beta_2 x_2 + \beta_3 x_1 x_2 + \varepsilon$$

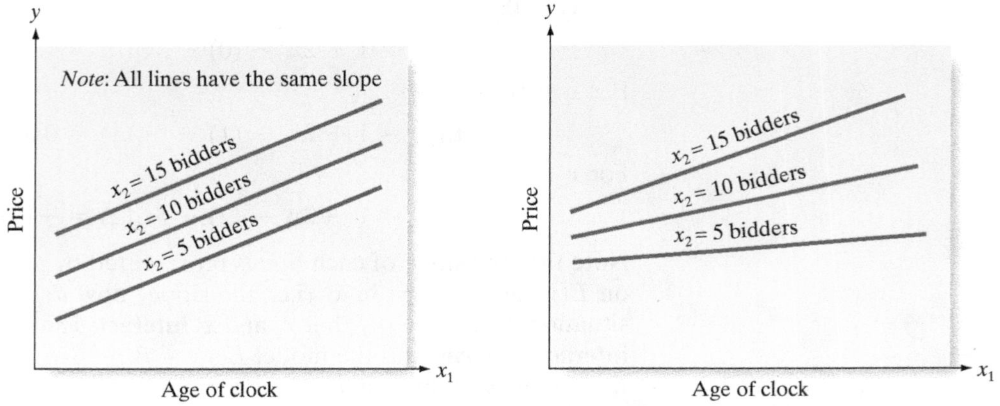

a. No interaction between x_1 and x_2

b. Interaction between x_1 and x_2

Figure 12.10
Examples of no-interaction and interaction models

The 32 data points listed in Table 12.1 (p. 670) were used to fit the model with interaction. A portion of the Minitab printout is shown in Figure 12.11.

a. Test the overall utility of the model using the global F-test at $\alpha = .05$.

b. Test the hypothesis (at $\alpha = .05$) that the price-age slope increases as the number of bidders increases—that is, that age and number of bidders, x_2, interact positively.

c. Estimate the change in auction price of a 150-year-old grandfather clock, y, for each additional bidder.

Regression Analysis: PRICE versus AGE, NUMBIDS, AGEBID

```
The regression equation is
PRICE = 320 + 0.88 AGE - 93.3 NUMBIDS + 1.30 AGEBID
```

Predictor	Coef	SE Coef	T	P
Constant	320.5	295.1	1.09	0.287
AGE	0.878	2.032	0.43	0.669
NUMBIDS	-93.26	29.89	-3.12	0.004
AGEBID	1.2978	0.2123	6.11	0.000

S = 88.9145   R-Sq = 95.4%   R-Sq(adj) = 94.9%

Analysis of Variance

Source	DF	SS	MS	F	P
Regression	3	4578427	1526142	193.04	0.000
Residual Error	28	221362	7906		
Total	31	4799790			

Figure 12.11
Minitab printout for interaction model of auction price

Solution

a. The global F-test is used to test the null hypothesis

$$H_0: \beta_1 = \beta_2 = \beta_3 = 0$$

The test statistic and p-value of the test (highlighted on the Minitab printout) are $F = 193.04$ and p-value $= 0$, respectively. Because $\alpha = .05$ exceeds the p-value, there is sufficient evidence to conclude that the model fit is a statistically useful predictor of auction price, y.

b. The hypotheses of interest to the collector concern the interaction parameter β_3. Specifically,

$$H_0: \beta_3 = 0$$
$$H_a: \beta_3 > 0$$

Because we are testing an individual β parameter, a t-test is required. The test statistic and two-tailed p-value (highlighted on the printout) are $t = 6.11$ and p-value $= 0$, respectively. The upper-tailed p-value, obtained by dividing the two-tailed p-value in half, is $0/2 = 0$. Because $\alpha = .05$ exceeds the p-value, the collector can reject H_0 and conclude that the rate of change of the mean price of the clocks with age increases as the number of bidders increases; that is, x_1 and x_2 interact positively. Thus, it appears that the interaction term should be included in the model.

c. To estimate the change in auction price, y, for every 1-unit increase in number of bidders, x_2, we need to estimate the slope of the line relating y to x_2 when the age of the clock, x_1, is 150 years old. An analyst who is not careful may estimate this slope as $\hat{\beta}_2 = -93.26$. Although the coefficient of x_2 is negative, this does *not* imply that auction price decreases as the number of bidders increases. Since interaction is present, the rate of change (slope) of mean auction price with the number of bidders *depends* on x_1, the age of the clock. For a fixed value of age (x_1), we can rewrite the interaction model as follows:

$$E(y) = \beta_0 + \beta_1 x_1 + \beta_2 x_2 + \beta_3 x_1 x_2 = \underbrace{(\beta_0 + \beta_1 x_1)}_{y\text{-intercept}} + \underbrace{(\beta_2 + \beta_3 x_1)}_{\text{slope}} x_2$$

Thus, the estimated rate of change of y for a 1-unit increase in x_2 (one new bidder) for a 150-year-old clock is

$$\text{Estimated slope of the } y \text{ versus } x_2 \text{ line} = \hat{\beta}_2 + \hat{\beta}_3 x_1$$
$$= -93.26 + 1.30(150) = 101.74$$

In other words, we estimate that the auction price of a 150-year-old clock will *increase* by about \$101.74 for every additional bidder.

Look Back Although the rate of increase will vary as x_1 is changed, it will remain positive for the range of values of x_1 included in the sample. Extreme care is needed in interpreting the signs and sizes of coefficients in a multiple regression model.

■ **Now Work Exercise 12.40**

Example 12.6 illustrates an important point about conducting t-tests on the β parameters in the interaction model. The key β parameter in this model is the interaction β, β_3. [Note that this β is also the one associated with the highest-order term in the model, x_1x_2.]* Consequently, we will want to test H_0: $\beta_3 = 0$ after we have determined that the overall model is useful for predicting y. Once interaction is detected (as in Example 12.6), however, tests on the first-order terms x_1 and x_2 should *not* be conducted because they are meaningless tests; the presence of interaction implies that both x's are important.

CAUTION Once interaction has been deemed important in the model $E(y) = \beta_0 + \beta_1x_1 + \beta_2x_2 + \beta_3x_1x_2$, do not conduct t-tests on the β coefficients of the first-order terms x_1 and x_2. These terms should be kept in the model regardless of the magnitude of their associated p-values shown on the printout.

Exercises 12.34–12.48

Learning the Mechanics

12.34 Write an interaction model relating the mean value of y, $E(y)$ to

a. two quantitative independent variables

b. three quantitative independent variables [*Hint:* Include all possible two-way cross-product terms.]

12.35 Suppose the true relationship between $E(y)$ and the quantitative independent variables x_1 and x_2 is

$$E(y) = 3 + x_1 + 2x_2 - x_1x_2$$

a. Describe the corresponding three-dimensional response surface.

b. Plot the linear relationship between y and x_2 for $x_1 = 0, 1, 2$, where $0 \le x_2 \le 5$.

c. Explain why the lines you plotted in part **b** are not parallel.

d. Use the lines you plotted in part **b** to explain how changes in the settings of x_1 and x_2 affect $E(y)$.

e. Use your graph from part **b** to determine how much $E(y)$ changes when x_1 is changed from 2 to 0 and x_2 is simultaneously changed from 4 to 5.

12.36 Suppose you fit the interaction model

$$y = \beta_0 + \beta_1x_1 + \beta_2x_2 + \beta_3x_1x_2 + \varepsilon$$

to $n = 32$ data points and obtain the following results:

$SS_{yy} = 479$ $SSE = 21$ $\hat{\beta}_3 = 10$ $s_{\hat{\beta}_3} = 4$

a. Find R^2 and interpret its value.

b. Is the model adequate for predicting y? Test at $\alpha = .05$.

c. Use a graph to explain the contribution of the x_1x_2 term to the model.

d. Is there evidence that x_1 and x_2 interact? Test at $\alpha = .05$.

12.37 The Minitab printout below was obtained from fitting the model

$$y = \beta_0 + \beta_1x_1 + \beta_2x_2 + \beta_3x_1x_2 + \varepsilon$$

to $n = 15$ data points.

a. What is the prediction equation for the response surface?

b. Describe the geometric form of the response surface of part **a.**

```
The regression equation is
Y = -2.55 + 3.82 X1 + 2.63 X2 -1.29 X1X2

Predictor      Coef   SE Coef       T       P
Constant     -2.550     1.142   -2.23   0.043
X1            3.815     0.529    7.22   0.000
X2            2.630     0.344    7.64   0.000
X1X2         -1.285     0.159   -8.06   0.000

S = 0.713        R-Sq = 85.6%     R-Sq(adj) = 81.6%

Analysis of Variance

Source            DF        SS        MS        F       P
Regression         3    33.149    11.050    21.75   0.000
Residual Error    11     5.587     0.508
Total             14    38.736
```

*The order of a term is equal to the sum of the exponents of the quantitative variables included in the term. Thus, when x_1 and x_2 are both quantitative variables, the cross product, x_1x_2, is a second-order term.

c. Plot the prediction equation for the case when $x_2 = 1$. Do this twice more on the same graph for the cases when $x_2 = 3$ and $x_2 = 5$.
d. Explain what it means to say that x_1 and x_2 interact. Explain why your graph of part **c** suggests that x_1 and x_2 interact.
e. Specify the null and alternative hypotheses you would use to test whether x_1 and x_2 interact.
f. Conduct the hypothesis test of part **e** using $\alpha = .01$.

Applying the Concepts—Basic

12.38 Tipping behavior in restaurants. By law, food servers at restaurants are not entitled to minimum wages since they are tipped by customers. Can food servers increase their tips by complimenting the customers they are waiting on? To answer this question, researchers collected data on the customer tipping behavior for a sample of 348 dining parties and reported their findings in the *Journal of Applied Social Psychology* (Vol. 40, 2010). Tip size (y, measured as a percentage of the total food bill) was modeled as a function of size of the dining party (x_1) and whether or not the server complimented the customers' choice of menu items (x_2). One theory states that the effect of size of the dining party on tip size is independent of whether or not the server compliments the customers' menu choices. A second theory hypothesizes that the effect of size of the dining party on tip size is greater when the server compliments the customers' menu choices as opposed to when the server refrains from complimenting menu choices.

a. Write a model for $E(y)$ as a function of x_1 and x_2 that corresponds to Theory 1.
b. Write a model for $E(y)$ as a function of x_1 and x_2 that corresponds to Theory 2.
c. The researchers summarized the results of their analysis with the following graph. Based on the graph, which of the two models would you expect to fit the data better? Explain.

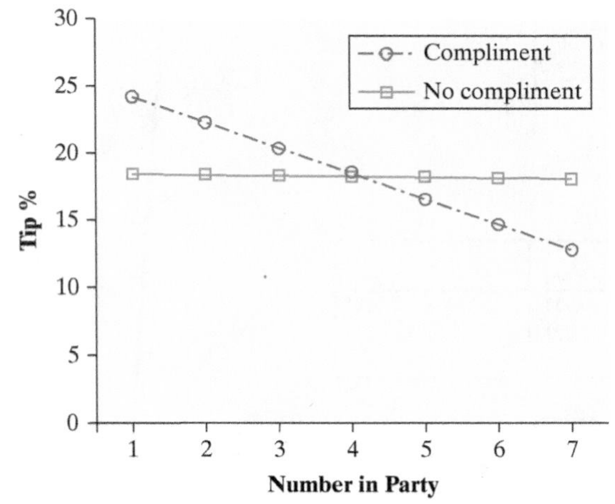

12.39 Forecasting movie revenues with Twitter. Refer to the *IEEE International Conference on Web Intelligence and Intelligent Agent Technology* (2010) study on using the volume of chatter on Twitter.com to forecast movie box office revenue, Exercise 12.10 (p. 680). The researchers modeled a movie's opening weekend box office revenue (y) as a function of tweet rate (x_1) and ratio of positive to negative tweets (x_2) using a first-order model.

a. Write the equation of an interaction model for $E(y)$ as a function of x_1 and x_2.
b. In terms of the β's in the model, part **a**, what is the change in revenue (y) for every 1-tweet increase in the tweet rate (x_1), holding PN-ratio (x_2) constant at a value of 2.5?
c. In terms of the β's in the model, part **a,** what is the change in revenue (y) for every 1-tweet increase in the tweet rate (x_1), holding PN-ratio (x_2) constant at a value of 5.0?
d. In terms of the β's in the model, part **a,** what is the change in revenue (y) for every 1-unit increase in the PN-ratio (x_2), holding tweet rate (x_1) constant at a value of 100?
e. Give the null hypothesis for testing whether tweet rate (x_1) and PN-ratio (x_2) interact to affect revenue (y).

12.40 Role of retailer interest on shopping behavior. NW Retail interest is defined by marketers as the level of interest a consumer has in a given retail store. Marketing professors at the University of Tennessee at Chattanooga and the University of Alabama investigated the role of retailer interest in consumers' shopping behavior (*Journal of Retailing*, Summer 2006). Using survey data collected for $n = 375$ consumers, the professors developed an interaction model for y = willingness of the consumer to shop at a retailer's store in the future (called *repatronage intentions*) as a function of x_1 = consumer satisfaction and x_2 = retailer interest. The regression results are shown below.

Variable	$\hat{\beta}$	*t*-value	*p*-value
Satisfaction (x_1)	.426	7.33	$< .01$
Retailer interest (x_2)	.044	0.85	$> .10$
Interaction (x_1x_2)	−.157	−3.09	$< .01$
$R^2 = .65$, $F = 226.35$, p-value $< .001$			

a. Is the overall model statistically useful for predicting y? Test using $\alpha = .05$.
b. Conduct a test for interaction at $\alpha = .05$.
c. Use the β estimates to sketch the estimated relationship between repatronage intentions (y) and satisfaction (x_1) when retailer interest is $x_2 = 1$ (a low value).
d. Repeat part **c** when retailer interest is $x_2 = 7$ (a high value).
e. Sketch the two lines, parts **c** and **d,** on the same graph to illustrate the nature of the interaction.

12.41 Defects in nuclear missile housing parts. The technique of multivariable testing (MVT) was discussed in the *Journal of the Reliability Analysis Center* (First Quarter, 2004). MVT was shown to improve the quality of carbon-foam rings used in nuclear missile housings. The rings are produced via a casting process that involves mixing ingredients, oven curing, and carving the finished part. One type of defect analyzed was the number y of black streaks in the manufactured ring. Two variables found to impact the number of defects were turntable speed (revolutions per minute), x_1, and cutting-blade position (inches from center), x_2.

a. The researchers discovered "an interaction between blade position and turntable speed." Hypothesize a regression model for $E(y)$ that incorporates this interaction.
b. The researchers reported a positive linear relationship between number of defects (y) and turntable speed (x_1)

but found that the slope of the relationship was much steeper for lower values of cutting-blade position (x_2). What does this imply about the interaction term in the model, part **a**? Explain.

12.42 Consumer behavior while waiting in line. While waiting in a long line for service (e.g., to use an ATM or at the post office), at some point you may decide to leave the queue. The *Journal of Consumer Research* (Nov. 2003) published a study of consumer behavior while waiting in a queue. A sample of $n = 148$ college students was asked to imagine that they were waiting in line at a post office to mail a package and that the estimated waiting time is 10 minutes or less. After a 10-minute wait, students were asked about their level of negative feelings (annoyed, anxious) on a scale of 1 (strongly disagree) to 9 (strongly agree). Before answering, however, the students were informed about how many people were ahead of them and behind them in the line. The researchers used regression to relate negative feelings score (y) to number ahead in line (x_1) and number behind in line (x_2).

a. The researchers fit an interaction model to the data. Write the hypothesized equation of this model.

b. In the words of the problem, explain what it means to say that "x_1 and x_2 interact to affect y."

c. A t-test for the interaction β in the model resulted in a p-value greater than .25. Interpret this result.

d. From their analysis, the researchers concluded that "the greater the number of people ahead, the higher the negative feeling score" and "the greater the number of people behind, the lower the negative feeling score." Use this information to determine the signs of β_1 and β_2 in the model.

Applying the Concepts—Intermediate

12.43 Reality TV and cosmetic surgery. Refer to the *Body Image: An International Journal of Research* (March 2010) study of the impact of reality TV shows on a college student's decision to undergo cosmetic surgery, Exercise 12.17 (p. 682). Recall that the data for the study (simulated based on statistics reported in the journal article) are saved in the file. Consider the interaction model, $E(y) = \beta_0 + \beta_1 x_1 + \beta_2 x_4 + \beta_3 x_1 x_4$, where y = desire to have cosmetic surgery (25-point scale), x_1 = {1 if male, 0 if female}, and x_4 = impression of reality TV (7-point scale). The model was fit to the data and the resulting SPSS printout appears at the bottom of the page.

BDYIMG

a. Give the least squares prediction equation.

b. Find the predicted level of desire (y) for a male college student with an impression-of-reality-TV-scale score of 5.

c. Conduct a test of overall model adequacy. Use $\alpha = .10$.

d. Give a practical interpretation of R_a^2.

e. Give a practical interpretation of s.

f. Conduct a test (at $\alpha = .10$) to determine if gender (x_1) and impression of reality TV show (x_4) interact in the prediction of level of desire for cosmetic surgery (y).

12.44 Factors that impact an auditor's judgment. A study was conducted to determine the effects of linguistic delivery style and client credibility on auditors' judgments (*Advances in Accounting and Behavioral Research,* 2004). Two hundred auditors from Big 5 accounting firms were each asked to assume that he or she was an audit team supervisor of a new manufacturing client and was performing an analytical review of the client's financial statement. The researchers gave the auditors different information on the client's credibility and linguistic delivery style of the client's explanation. Each auditor then provided an assessment of the likelihood that the client-provided explanation accounted for the fluctuation in the financial statement. The three variables of interest—credibility (x_1), linguistic delivery style (x_2), and likelihood (y)—were all measured on a numerical scale. Regression analysis was used to fit the interaction model, $y = \beta_0 + \beta_1 x_1 + \beta_2 x_2 + \beta_3 x_1 x_2 + \varepsilon$. The results are summarized in the table on the next page.

Model Summary

Model	R	R Square	Adjusted R Square	Std. Error of the Estimate
1	.670[a]	.449	.439	2.350

a. Predictors: (Constant), GENDER_IMPREAL, IMPREAL, GENDER

ANOVA[a]

Model		Sum of Squares	df	Mean Square	F	Sig.
1	Regression	747.001	3	249.000	45.086	.000[b]
	Residual	916.787	166	5.523		
	Total	1663.788	169			

a. Dependent Variable: DESIRE

b. Predictors: (Constant), GENDER_IMPREAL, IMPREAL, GENDER

Coefficients[a]

Model		Unstandardized Coefficients B	Std. Error	Standardized Coefficients Beta	t	Sig.
1	(Constant)	11.779	.674		17.486	.000
	GENDER	-1.972	1.179	-.303	-1.672	.096
	IMPREAL	.585	.162	.258	3.617	.000
	GENDER_IMPREAL	-.553	.276	-.378	-2.004	.047

a. Dependent Variable: DESIRE

SPSS output for Exercise 12.43

Results for Exercise 12.44

	Beta Estimate	Std Error	*t*-statistic	*p*-value
Constant	15.865	10.980	1.445	0.150
Client credibility (x_1)	0.037	0.339	0.110	0.913
Linguistic delivery style (x_2)	−0.678	0.328	−2.064	0.040
Interaction (x_1x_2)	0.036	0.009	4.008	< 0.005
F-statistic $= 55.35$ ($p < 0.0005$): $R_a^2 = .450$				

a. Interpret the phrase *client credibility and linguistic delivery style interact* in the words of the problem.
b. Give the null and alternative hypotheses for testing the overall adequacy of the model.
c. Conduct the test, part **b,** using the information in the table.
d. Give the null and alternative hypotheses for testing whether client credibility and linguistic delivery style interact.
e. Conduct the test, part **d,** using the information in the table.
f. The researchers estimated the slope of the likelihood–linguistic delivery style line at a low level of client credibility ($x_1 = 22$). Obtain this estimate and interpret it in the words of the problem.
g. The researchers also estimated the slope of the likelihood–linguistic delivery style line at a high level of client credibility ($x_1 = 46$). Obtain this estimate and interpret it in the words of the problem.

12.45 Arsenic in groundwater. Refer to the *Environmental Science & Technology* (Jan. 2005) study of the reliability of a commercial kit to test for arsenic in groundwater, Exercise 12.16 (p. 682). Recall that you fit a first-order model for arsenic level (y) as a function of latitude (x_1), longitude (x_2), and depth (x_3).
WELLS
a. Write a model for arsenic level (y) that includes first-order terms for latitude, longitude, and depth, as well as terms for interaction between latitude and depth and interaction between longitude and depth.
b. Use statistical software to fit the interaction model, part **a,** to the data. Give the least squares prediction equation.
c. Conduct a test (at $\alpha = .05$) to determine whether latitude and depth interact to affect arsenic level.
d. Conduct a test (at $\alpha = .05$) to determine whether longitude and depth interact to affect arsenic level.
e. Practically interpret the results of the tests, parts **c** and **d.**

12.46 Cooling method for gas turbines. Refer to the *Journal of Engineering for Gas Turbines and Power* (Jan. 2005) study of a high-pressure inlet fogging method for a gas turbine engine, Exercise 12.19 (p. 683). Recall that you fit a first-order model for heat rate (y) as a function of speed (x_1), inlet temperature (x_2), exhaust temperature (x_3), cycle pressure ratio (x_4), and airflow rate (x_5).
GASTRB
a. Researchers hypothesize that the linear relationship between heat rate (y) and temperature (both inlet and exhaust) depends on airflow rate. Write a model for heat rate that incorporates the researchers' theories.
b. Use statistical software to fit the interaction model, part **a,** to the data. Give the least squares prediction equation.
c. Conduct a test (at $\alpha = .05$) to determine whether inlet temperature and airflow rate interact to affect heat rate.
d. Conduct a test (at $\alpha = .05$) to determine whether exhaust temperature and airflow rate interact to affect heat rate.
e. Practically interpret the results of the tests, parts **c** and **d.**

12.47 Extracting water from oil. Refer to the *Journal of Colloid and Interface Science* study of water/oil mixtures, Exercise 12.20 (p. 684). Recall that three of the seven variables used to predict voltage (y) were volume (x_1), salinity (x_2), and surfactant concentration (x_5). The model the researchers fit is
H2OOIL

$$E(y) = \beta_0 + \beta_1x_1 + \beta_2x_2 + \beta_3x_5 + \beta_4x_1x_2 + \beta_5x_1x_5$$

a. Note that the model includes interaction between disperse phase volume (x_1) and salinity (x_2) as well as interaction between disperse phase volume (x_1) and surfactant concentration (x_5). Discuss how these interaction terms affect the hypothetical relationship between y and x_1. Draw a sketch to support your answer.
b. Fit the interaction model to the data. Does this model appear to fit the data better than the first-order model in Exercise 12.20? Explain.
c. Interpret the β estimates of the interaction model.

12.48 Therapists' reactions to child-abuse reports. Licensed therapists are mandated by law to report child abuse by their clients. This requires the therapist to breach confidentiality and possibly lose the client's trust. A national survey of licensed psychotherapists was conducted to investigate clients' reactions to legally mandated child-abuse reports (*American Journal of Orthopsychiatry,* Jan. 1997). The sample consisted of 303 therapists who had filed a child-abuse report against one of their clients. The researchers were interested in finding the best predictors of a client's reaction (y) to the report, where y is measured on a 30-point scale. (The higher the value, the more favorable the client's response to the report.) The independent variables found to have the most predictive power are listed here.

x_1 = Therapist's age (years)
x_2 = Therapist's gender (1 if male, 0 if female)
x_3 = Degree of therapist's role strain (25-point scale)
x_4 = Strength of client-therapist relationship (40-point scale)
x_5 = Type of case (1 if family, 0 if not)
x_1x_2 = Age × gender interaction

a. Hypothesize a first-order model relating y to each of the five independent variables.
b. Give the null hypothesis for testing the contribution of x_4, strength of client-therapist relationship, to the model.
c. The test statistic for the test, part **b,** was $t = 4.408$ with an associated p-value of .001. Interpret this result.
d. The estimated β coefficient for the x_1x_2 interaction term was positive and highly significant ($p < .001$). According to the researchers, "This interaction suggests that … as the age of the therapist increased, … male therapists were less likely to get negative client reactions than were female therapists." Do you agree?
e. For this model, $R^2 = .2946$. Interpret this value.

12.6 Quadratic and Other Higher-Order Models

All of the models discussed in the previous sections proposed straight-line relationships between $E(y)$ and each of the independent variables in the model. In this section, we consider models that allow for curvature in the two-dimensional relationship between y and an independent variable. Each of these models is a **second-order model** because it will include an x^2 term.

First, we consider a model that includes only one independent variable x. The form of this model, called the **quadratic model,** is

$$y = \beta_0 + \beta_1 x + \beta_2 x^2 + \varepsilon$$

The term involving x^2, called a **quadratic term** (or **second-order term**), enables us to hypothesize curvature in the graph of the response model relating y to x. Graphs of the quadratic model for two different values of β_2 are shown in Figure 12.12. When the curve opens upward, the sign of β_2 is positive (see Figure 12.12a); when the curve opens downward, the sign of β_2 is negative (see Figure 12.12b).

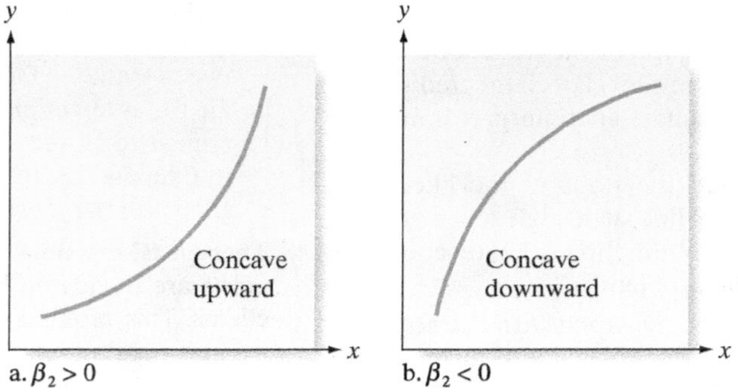

Figure 12.12
Graphs for two quadratic models

A Quadratic (Second-Order) Model in a Single Quantitative Independent Variable

$$E(y) = \beta_0 + \beta_1 x + \beta_2 x^2$$

where

β_0 is the y-intercept of the curve.
β_1 is a shift parameter.
β_2 is the rate of curvature.

Example 12.7

Analyzing a Quadratic Model—Predicting Electrical Usage

Problem In all-electric homes, the amount of electricity expended is of interest to consumers, builders, and groups involved with energy conservation. Suppose we wish to investigate the monthly electrical usage, y, in all-electric homes and its relationship to the size, x, of the home. Moreover, suppose we think that monthly electrical usage in all-electric homes is related to the size of the home by the quadratic model

$$y = \beta_0 + \beta_1 x + \beta_2 x^2 + \varepsilon$$

To fit the model, the values of y and x are collected for 15 homes during a particular month. The data are shown in Table 12.2.

a. Construct a scatterplot for the data. Is there evidence to support the use of a quadratic model?

b. Use the method of least squares to estimate the unknown parameters β_0, β_1, and β_2 in the quadratic model.

c. Graph the prediction equation and assess how well the model fits the data, both visually and numerically.

d. Interpret the β estimates.

Table 12.2 Home Size–Electrical Usage Data

Size of Home, x (sq. ft.)	Monthly Usage, y (kilowatt-hours)
1,290	1,182
1,350	1,172
1,470	1,264
1,600	1,493
1,710	1,571
1,840	1,711
1,980	1,804
2,230	1,840
2,400	1,986
2,710	2,007
2,930	1,984
3,000	1,960
3,210	2,001
3,240	1,928
3,520	1,945

Data Set: KWHRS

e. Is the overall model useful (at $\alpha = .01$) for predicting electrical usage y?

f. Is there sufficient evidence of downward curvature in the home size–electrical usage relationship? Test using $\alpha = .01$.

Solution

a. A Minitab scatterplot for the data in Table 12.2 is shown in Figure 12.13. The figure illustrates that electrical usage appears to increase in a curvilinear manner with the size of the home. This provides some support for the inclusion of the quadratic term x^2 in the model.

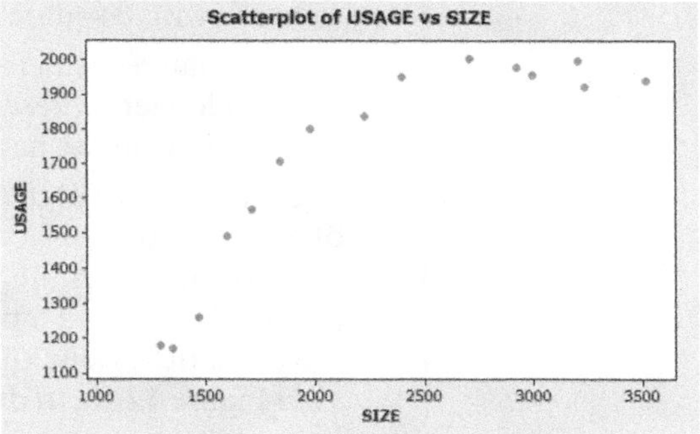

Figure 12.13
Minitab scatterplot for electrical usage data

b. We used Excel to fit the model to the data in Table 12.2. Part of the Excel regression output is displayed in Figure 12.14. The least squares estimates of the β parameters (highlighted) are $\hat{\beta}_0 = -806.7$, $\hat{\beta}_1 = 1.9616$, and $\hat{\beta}_2 = -.00034$. Therefore, the equation that minimizes the SSE for the data is

$$\hat{y} = -806.7 + 1.9616x - .00034x^2$$

SUMMARY OUTPUT

Regression Statistics	
Multiple R	0.988576
R Square	0.977283
Adjusted R Square	0.973496
Standard Error	50.19975
Observations	15

ANOVA

	df	*SS*	*MS*	*F*	*Significance F*
Regression	2	1300900.218	650450.1	258.1135719	0.0000000001
Residual	12	30240.18169	2520.015		
Total	14	1331140.4			

	Coefficients	*Standard Error*	*t Stat*	*P-value*	*Lower 95%*	*Upper 95%*
Intercept	-806.717	166.8720911	-4.83434	0.0004089596	-1170.299712	-443.134
SIZE	1.961617	0.152524384	12.861	0.0000000223	1.629294434	2.293939
SIZESQ	-0.00034	0.00003212	-10.599	0.0000001903	-0.000410426	-0.00027

Figure 12.14
Excel regression output for electrical usage model

c. Figure 12.15 is a Minitab graph of the least squares prediction equation. Note that the graph provides a good fit to the data of Table 12.2. A numerical measure of fit is obtained with the adjusted coefficient of determination, R_a^2. This value (highlighted on Figure 12.14) is $R_a^2 = .973$. This implies that about 97% of the sample variation in electrical usage (y) can be explained by the quadratic model (after adjusting for sample size and degrees of freedom).

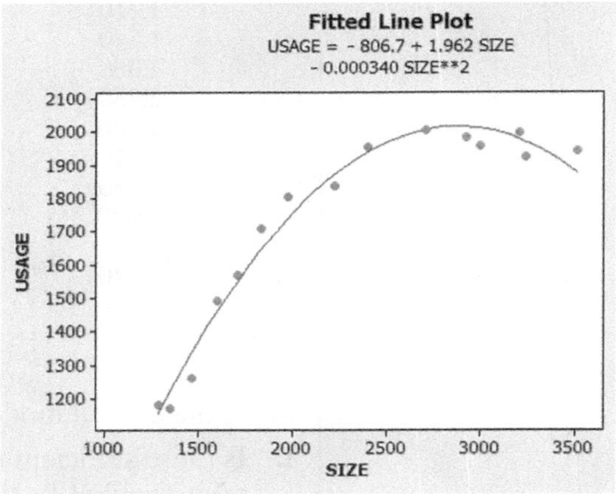

Figure 12.15
Minitab plot of least squares model for electrical usage

d. The interpretation of the estimated coefficients in a quadratic model must be undertaken cautiously. First, the estimated y-intercept, $\hat{\beta}_0$, can be meaningfully interpreted only if the range of the independent variable includes zero—that is, if $x = 0$ is included in the sampled range of x. Although $\hat{\beta}_0 = -806.7$ seems to imply that the estimated electrical usage is negative when $x = 0$, this zero point is not in the range of the sample (the lowest value of x is 1,290 square feet), and the value is nonsensical (a home with 0 square feet); thus the interpretation of $\hat{\beta}_0$ is not meaningful.

The estimated coefficient of x is $\hat{\beta}_1 = 1.9616$, but in the presence of the quadratic term x^2, it no longer represents a slope.* The estimated coefficient of the first-order term x will not, in general, have a meaningful interpretation in the quadratic model.

The sign of the coefficient, $\hat{\beta}_2 = -.00034$, of the quadratic term, x^2, is the indicator of whether the curve is concave downward (mound-shaped) or concave upward (bowl-shaped). A negative $\hat{\beta}_2$ implies downward concavity, as in this example (Figure 12.15), and a positive $\hat{\beta}_2$ implies upward concavity. Rather than interpreting the numerical value of $\hat{\beta}_2$ itself, we employ a graphical representation of the model, as in Figure 12.15, to describe the model.

Note that Figure 12.15 implies that the estimated electrical usage is leveling off as the home sizes increase beyond 2,500 square feet. In fact, the convexity of the model would lead to decreasing usage estimates if we were to display the model out to 4,000 square feet and beyond (see Figure 12.16). However, model interpretations are not meaningful outside the range of the independent variable, which has a maximum value of 3,520 square feet in this example. Thus, although the model appears to support the hypothesis that the *rate of increase* per square foot *decreases* for home sizes near the high end of the sampled values, the conclusion that usage will actually begin to decrease for very large homes would be a *misuse* of the model because no homes of 3,600 square feet or more were included in the sample.

e. To test whether the quadratic model is statistically useful, we conduct the global F-test:

$$H_0: \beta_1 = \beta_2 = 0$$

H_a: At least one of the above coefficients is nonzero.

*For students with knowledge of calculus, note that the slope of the quadratic model is the first derivative $\partial y/\partial x = \beta_1 + 2\beta_2 x$. Thus, the slope varies as a function of x, rather than the constant slope associated with the straight-line model.

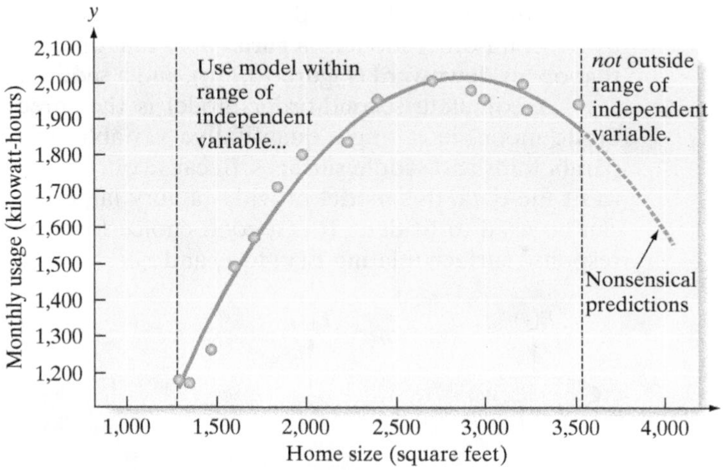

Figure 12.16
Potential misuse of quadratic model

From the Excel printout, Figure 12.14, the test statistic (highlighted) is $F = 258.11$ with an associated p-value of approximately 0. For any reasonable α, we reject H_0 and conclude that the overall model is a useful predictor of electrical usage, y.

f. Figure 12.15 shows concave downward curvature in the relationship between size of a home and electrical usage in the sample of 15 data points. To determine if this type of curvature exists in the population, we want to test

H_0: $\beta_2 = 0$ (no curvature in the response curve)

H_a: $\beta_2 < 0$ (downward concavity exists in the response curve)

The test statistic for testing β_2, highlighted on the printout, is $t = -10.599$, and the associated two-tailed p-value is .0000002. Because this is a one-tailed test, the appropriate p-value is $(.0000002)/2 = .0000001$. Now $\alpha = .01$ exceeds this p-value. Thus, there is very strong evidence of downward curvature in the population—that is, electrical usage increases more slowly per square foot for large homes than for small homes.

Look Back Note that the Excel printout in Figure 12.14 also provides the t-test statistic and corresponding two-tailed p-values for the tests of H_0: $\beta_0 = 0$ and H_0: $\beta_1 = 0$. Because the interpretation of these parameters is not meaningful for this model, the tests are not of interest.

Now Work Exercise 12.56

When two or more quantitative independent variables are included in a second-order model, we can incorporate squared terms for each x in the model, as well as the interaction between the two independent variables. A model that includes all possible second-order terms in two independent variables—called a **complete second-order model**—is given in the box below.

Complete Second-Order Model with Two Quantitative Independent Variables

$$E(y) = \beta_0 + \beta_1 x_1 + \beta_2 x_2 + \beta_3 x_2 x_2 + \beta_4 x_1^2 + \beta_5 x_2^2$$

Comments on the Parameters

β_0: y-intercept, the value of $E(y)$ when $x_1 = x_2 = 0$

β_1, β_2: Changing β_1 and β_2 causes the surface to shift along the x_1- and x_2-axes

β_3: Controls the rotation of the surface

β_4, β_5: Signs and values of these parameters control the type of surface and the rates of curvature.

Three types of three-dimensional graphs (called **response surfaces**) are produced by a second-order model:* a **paraboloid** that opens upward (Figure 12.17a), a paraboloid that opens downward (Figure 12.17b), and a **saddle-shaped surface** (Figure 12.17c).

A complete second-order model is the three-dimensional equivalent of a quadratic model in a single quantitative variable. Instead of tracing parabolas, it traces paraboloids and saddle surfaces. Because only a portion of the complete surface is used to fit the data, this model provides a very large variety of gently curving surfaces that can be used to fit data. It is a good choice for a model if you expect curvature in the response surface relating $E(y)$ to x_1 and x_2.

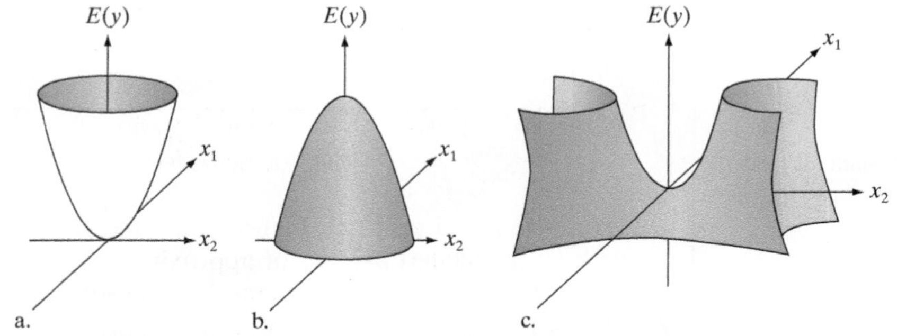

Figure 12.17
Graphs for three second-order surfaces

Example 12.8

A More Complex Second-Order Model—Predicting Hours Worked per Week

Problem A social scientist would like to relate the number of hours worked per week (outside the home) by a married woman to the number of years of formal education she has completed and the number of children in her family.

a. Identify the dependent variable and the independent variables.
b. Write the first-order model for this example.
c. Modify the model in part **b** to include an interaction term.
d. Write a complete second-order model for $E(y)$.

Solution

a. The dependent variable is

$$y = \text{Number of hours worked per week by a married woman}$$

The two independent variables, both quantitative in nature, are

$$x_1 = \text{Number of years of formal education completed by the woman}$$
$$x_2 = \text{Number of children in the family}$$

b. The first-order model is

$$E(y) = \beta_0 + \beta_1 x_1 + \beta_2 x_2$$

This model would probably not be appropriate in this situation because x_1 and x_2 may interact and/or curvature terms corresponding to x_1^2 and x_2^2 may be needed to obtain a good model for $E(y)$.

c. Adding the interaction term, we obtain

$$E(y) = \beta_0 + \beta_1 x_1 + \beta_2 x_2 + \beta_3 x_1 x_2$$

This model should be better than the model in part **b** because we have now allowed for interaction between x_1 and x_2.

*The saddle-shaped surface (Figure 12.17c) is produced when $\beta_3^2 > 4\beta_4\beta_5$; the paraboloid opens upward (Figure 12.17a) when $\beta_4 + \beta_5 > 0$ and opens downward (Figure 12.17b) when $\beta_4 + \beta_5 < 0$.

d. The complete second-order model is

$$E(y) = \beta_0 + \beta_1x_1 + \beta_2x_2 + \beta_3x_1x_2 + \beta_4x_1^2 + \beta_5x_2^2$$

Because it would not be surprising to find curvature in the response surface, the complete second-order model would be preferred to the models in parts **b** and **c.**

Look Back How can we tell whether the complete second-order model really does provide better predictions of hours worked than the models in parts **b** and **c**? The answers to these and similar questions are examined in Section 12.9.

Now Work Exercise 12.59

Most relationships between $E(y)$ and two or more quantitative independent variables are second order and require the use of either the interactive or the complete second-order model to obtain a good fit to a data set. As in the case of a single quantitative independent variable, however, the curvature in the response surface may be very slight over the range of values of the variables in the data set. When this happens, a first-order model may provide a good fit to the data.

Exercises 12.49–12.65

Learning the Mechanics

12.49 Write a second-order model relating the mean of y, $E(y)$, to

a. one quantitative independent variable

b. two quantitative independent variables

c. three quantitative independent variables [*Hint:* Include all possible two-way cross-product terms and squared terms.]

12.50 Suppose you fit the second-order model

$$y = \beta_0 + \beta_1x + \beta_2x^2 + \varepsilon$$

to $n = 25$ data points. Your estimate of β_2 is $\hat{\beta}_2 = .47$, and the estimated standard error of the estimate is .15.

a. Test H_0: $\beta_2 = 0$ against H_a: $\beta_2 \neq 0$. Use $\alpha = .05$.

b. Suppose you want to determine only whether the quadratic curve opens upward; that is, as x increases, the slope of the curve increases. Give the test statistic and the rejection region for the test for $\alpha = .05$. Do the data support the theory that the slope of the curve increases as x increases? Explain.

12.51 Suppose you fit the quadratic model

$$E(y) = \beta_0 + \beta_1x + \beta_2x^2$$

to a set of $n = 20$ data points and found $R^2 = .91$, $SS_{yy} = 29.94$, and SSE $= 2.63$.

a. Is there sufficient evidence to indicate that the model contributes information for predicting y? Test using $\alpha = .05$.

b. What null and alternative hypotheses would you test to determine whether upward curvature exists?

c. What null and alternative hypotheses would you test to determine whether downward curvature exists?

12.52 Consider the following quadratic models:

(1) $y = 1 - 2x + x^2$
(2) $y = 1 + 2x + x^2$
(3) $y = 1 + x^2$
(4) $y = 1 - x^2$
(5) $y = 1 + 3x^2$

a. Graph each of the quadratic models, side by side, on the same sheet of graph paper.

b. What effect does the first-order term ($2x$) have on the graph of the curve?

c. What effect does the second-order term (x^2) have on the graph of the curve?

12.53 Minitab was used to fit the complete second-order model

$$E(y) = \beta_0 + \beta_1x_1 + \beta_2x_2 + \beta_3x_1x_2 + \beta_4x_1^2 + \beta_5x_2^2$$

to $n = 39$ data points. The printout is shown below.

```
The regression equation is
Y = -24.56 + 1.12 X1 + 27.99 X2 - 0.54 X1X2 - 0.004 X1SQ + 0.002 X2SQ

Predictor        Coef     SE Coef       T      P
Constant      -24.563       6.531   -3.76  0.001
X1            1.19848      0.1103   10.86  0.000
X2             27.988      79.489    0.35  0.727
X1X2          -0.5397      1.0338   -0.52  0.605
X1SQ          -0.0043      0.0004  -10.74  0.000
X2SQ           0.0020      0.0033    0.60  0.550

S = 2.762      R-Sq = 79.7%     R-Sq(adj) = 76.6%

Analysis of Variance

Source          DF       SS       MS       F      P
Regression       5   989.30   197.86   25.93  0.000
Residual Error  33   251.81     7.63
Total           38  1241.11
```

Minitab output for Exercise 12.53

a. Is there sufficient evidence to indicate that at least one of the parameters—$\beta_1, \beta_2, \beta_3, \beta_4$, and β_5—is nonzero? Test using $\alpha = .05$.
b. Test H_0: $\beta_4 = 0$ against H_a: $\beta_4 \neq 0$. Use $\alpha = .01$.
c. Test H_0: $\beta_5 = 0$ against H_a: $\beta_5 \neq 0$. Use $\alpha = .01$.
d. Use graphs to explain the consequences of the tests in parts **b** and **c.**

Applying the Concepts—Basic

12.54 Personality traits and job performance. When attempting to predict job performance using personality traits, researchers typically assume that the relationship is linear. A study published in the *Journal of Applied Psychology* (Jan. 2011) investigated a curvilinear relationship between job task performance and a specific personality trait—conscientiousness. Using data collected for 602 employees of a large public organization, task performance was measured on a 30-point scale (where higher scores indicate better performance) and conscientiousness was measured on a scale of −3 to +3 (where higher scores indicate a higher level of conscientiousness).

a. The coefficient of correlation relating task performance score to conscientiousness score was reported as $r = .18$. Explain why the researchers should not use this statistic to investigate the curvilinear relationship between task performance and conscientiousness.
b. Give the equation of a curvilinear (quadratic) model relating task performance score (y) to conscientiousness score (x).
c. The researchers theorized that task performance increases as level of conscientiousness increases, but at a decreasing rate. Draw a sketch of this relationship.
d. If the theory in part **c** is supported, what is the expected sign of β_2 in the model, part **b**?
e. The researchers reported $\hat{\beta}_2 = -.32$ with an associated p-value of less than .05. Use this information to test the researchers' theory at $\alpha = .05$.

12.55 Going for it on fourth-down in the NFL. Refer to the *Chance* (Winter 2009) study of fourth-down decisions by coaches in the National Football League (NFL), Exercise 11.63 (p. 638). Recall that statisticians at California State University, Northridge, fit a straight-line model for predicting the number of points scored (y) by a team that has a first-down with a given number of yards (x) from the opposing goal line. A second model fit to data collected on five NFL teams from a recent season was the quadratic regression model, $E(y) = \beta_0 + \beta_1 x + \beta_2 x^2$. The regression yielded the following results: $\hat{y} = 6.13 + .141x - .0009x^2$, $R^2 = .226$.

a. If possible, give a practical interpretation of each of the β estimates in the model.
b. Give a practical interpretation of the coefficient of determination, R^2.
c. In Exercise 11.63, the coefficient of correlation for the straight-line model was reported as $R^2 = .18$.Does this statistic alone indicate that the quadratic model is a better fit than the straight-line model? Explain.
d. What test of hypothesis would you conduct to determine if the quadratic model is a better fit than the straight-line model?

12.56 Catalytic converters in cars. A quadratic model was applied to motor vehicle toxic emissions data collected in Mexico City (*Environmental Science & Engineering*, Sept. 1, 2000). The following equation was used to predict the percentage (y) of motor vehicles without catalytic converters in the Mexico City fleet for a given year (x):

NW

$$\hat{y} = 325{,}790 - 321.67x + .0794x^2.$$

a. Explain why the value $\hat{\beta}_0 = 325{,}790$ has no practical interpretation.
b. Explain why the value $\hat{\beta}_1 = -321.67$ should not be interpreted as a slope.
c. Examine the value of $\hat{\beta}_2$ to determine the nature of the curvature (upward or downward) in the sample data.
d. The researchers used the model to estimate "that just after the year 2021 the fleet of cars with catalytic converters will completely disappear." Comment on the danger of using the model to predict y in the year 2021. (*Note:* The model was fit to data collected between 1984 and 1999.)

12.57 Testing tires for wear. Underinflated or overinflated tires can increase tire wear. A new tire was tested for wear at different pressures, with the results shown in the following table.

TIRES

Pressure, x (pounds per square inch)	Mileage, y (thousands)
30	29
31	32
32	36
33	38
34	37
35	33
36	26

a. Plot the data on a scatterplot.
b. If you were given only the information for $x = 30, 31, 32, 33$, what kind of model would you suggest? For $x = 33, 34, 35, 36$? For all the data?

12.58 Assertiveness and leadership. Management professors at Columbia University examined the relationship between assertiveness and leadership (*Journal of Personality and Social Psychology*, Feb. 2007). The sample represented 388 people enrolled in a full-time MBA program. Based on answers to a questionnaire, the researchers measured two variables for each subject: assertiveness score (x) and leadership ability score (y). A quadratic regression model was fit to the data, with the following results:

Independent Variable	β Estimate	t-value	p-value
x	.57	2.55	.01
x^2	−.088	−3.97	< .01
Model $R^2 = .12$			

a. Conduct a test of overall model utility. Use $\alpha = .05$.
b. The researchers hypothesized that leadership ability increases at a decreasing rate with assertiveness. Set up the null and alternative hypotheses to test this theory.
c. Use the reported results to conduct the test, part **b.** Give your conclusion (at $\alpha = .05$) in the words of the problem.

12.59 Goal congruence in top management teams. Do chief executive officers (CEOs) and their top managers always

NW

agree on the goals of the company? Goal importance congruence between CEOs and vice presidents (VPs) was studied in the *Academy of Management Journal* (Feb. 2008). The researchers used regression to model a VP's attitude toward the goal of improving efficiency (y) as a function of the two quantitative independent variables level of CEO leadership (x_1) and level of congruence between the CEO and the VP (x_2). A complete second-order model in x_1 and x_2 was fit to data collected for $n = 517$ top management team members at U.S. credit unions.

a. Write the complete second-order model for $E(y)$.

b. The coefficient of determination for the model, part **a,** was reported as $R^2 = .14$. Interpret this value.

c. The estimate of the β-value for the $(x_2)^2$ term in the model was found to be negative. Interpret this result, practically.

d. A t-test on the β-value for the interaction term in the model, x_1x_2, resulted in a p-value of .02. Practically interpret this result, using $\alpha = .05$.

Applying the Concepts—Intermediate

12.60 Shopping on Black Friday. Refer to the *International Journal of Retail and Distribution Management* (Vol. 39, 2011) study of shopping on Black Friday (the day after Thanksgiving), Exercise 6.16 (p. 309). Recall that researchers conducted interviews with a sample of 38 women shopping on Black Friday to gauge their shopping habits. Two of the variables measured for each shopper were age (x) and number of years shopping on Black Friday (y). Data on these two variables for the 38 shoppers are listed in the accompanying table.

BLKFRI

a. Fit the quadratic model, $E(y) = \beta_0 + \beta_1 x + \beta_2 x^2$, to the data using statistical software. Give the prediction equation.

b. Conduct a test of the overall adequacy of the model. Use $\alpha = .01$.

c. Conduct a test to determine if the relationship between age (x) and number of years shopping on Black Friday (y) is best represented by a linear or quadratic function. Use $\alpha = .01$.

Age	Years	Age	Years
32	5	21	5
27	3	52	10
40	12	40	18
62	35	38	5
47	20	56	8
53	30	60	5
24	8	35	15
27	2	50	25
47	24	56	10
40	25	20	2
45	11	20	4
22	11	21	4
25	5	22	5
60	35	50	10
22	3	30	6
50	15	28	16
70	22	25	7
50	10	30	6
21	6	49	30

Source: Thomas, J. B., & Peters, C. "An exploratory investigation of Black Friday consumption rituals," *International Journal of Retail and Distribution Management*, Vol. 39, No. 7, 2011 (Table I). Copyright © 2011 by Emerald Group Publishing Limited. Reprinted with permission.

12.61 Revenues of popular movies. The *Internet Movie Database* (www.imdb.com) monitors the gross revenues for all major motion pictures. The accompanying table gives both the domestic (United States and Canada) and international gross revenues for a sample of 19 popular movies.

IMDB

Movie Title (year)	Domestic Gross ($ millions)	International Gross ($ millions)
Avatar (2009)	760.5	2,021.0
Titanic (1997)	600.8	1,234.6
The Dark Knight (2008)	533.3	464.0
E.T. (1982)	439.9	321.8
Pirates of the Caribbean: Dead Man's Chest (2006)	423.0	642.9
Jurassic Park (1993)	356.8	563.0
Lion King (1994)	328.4	455.0
Harry Potter and the Sorcerer's Stone (2001)	317.6	651.1
Inception (2010)	291.4	468.2
The Hangover (2009)	277.3	201.6
Sixth Sense (1999)	293.5	368.0
Jaws (1975)	260.0	210.6
Ghost (1990)	217.6	300.0
Saving Private Ryan (1998)	216.1	263.2
Gladiator (2000)	187.7	268.6
Dances with Wolves (1990)	184.2	240.0
The Exorcist (1973)	204.6	153.0
My Big Fat Greek Wedding (2002)	241.4	115.1
Rocky IV (1985)	127.9	172.6

Source: Based on information from *The Internet Movie Database* (http://www.imdb.com).

a. Write a first-order model for foreign gross revenues (y) as a function of domestic gross revenues (x).

b. Write a second-order model for international gross revenues y as a function of domestic gross revenues x.

c. Construct a scatterplot for these data. Which of the models from parts **a** and **b** appears to be the better choice for explaining the variation in foreign gross revenues?

d. Fit the model of part **b** to the data and investigate its usefulness. Is there evidence of a curvilinear relationship between international and domestic gross revenues? Try using $\alpha = .05$.

e. Based on your analysis in part **d,** which of the models from parts **a** and **b** better explains the variation in international gross revenues? Compare your answer to your preliminary conclusion from part **c.**

12.62 Estimating change-point dosage. A standard method for studying toxic substances and their effects on humans is to observe the responses of rodents exposed to various doses of the substance over time. In the *Journal of Agricultural, Biological, and Environmental Statistics* (June 2005), researchers used least squares regression to estimate the *change-point* dosage—defined as the largest dose level that has no adverse effects. Data were obtained from a dose-response study of rats exposed to the toxic substance aconiazide. A sample of 50 rats was evenly divided into five dosage groups: 0, 100, 200, 500, and 750 milligrams per kilogram of body weight. The dependent variable y measured was the weight change (in grams) after a

2-week exposure. The researchers fit the quadratic model $E(y) = \beta_0 + \beta_1 x + \beta_2 x^2$, where x = dosage level, with the following results: $\hat{y} = 10.25 + .0053x - .0000266x^2$.

a. Construct a rough sketch of the least squares prediction equation. Describe the nature of the curvature in the estimated model.

b. Estimate the weight change (y) for a rat given a dosage of 500 mg/kg of aconiazide.

c. Estimate the weight change (y) for a rat given a dosage of 0 mg/kg of aconiazide. (This dosage is called the *control* dosage level.)

d. Of the five dosage groups in the study, find the largest dosage level x that yields an estimated weight change that is closest to but below the estimated weight change for the control group. This value is the *change-point* dosage.

12.63 Failure times of silicon wafer microchips. Researchers at National Semiconductor experimented with tin-lead solder bumps used to manufacture silicon wafer integrated circuit chips (International Wafer Level Packaging Conference, Nov. 3–4, 2005). The failure times of the microchips (in hours) was determined at different solder temperatures (degrees Celsius). The data for one experiment are given in the table. The researchers want to predict failure time (y) based on solder temperature (x).

WAFER

a. Construct a scatterplot for the data. What type of relationship, linear or curvilinear, appears to exist between failure time and solder temperature?

b. Fit the model, $E(y) = \beta_0 + \beta_1 x + \beta_2 x^2$, to the data. Give the least squares prediction equation.

c. Conduct a test to determine if there is upward curvature in the relationship between failure time and solder temperature. (Use $\alpha = .05$.)

Temperature (°C)	Time to Failure (hours)
165	200
162	200
164	1,200
158	500
158	600
159	750
156	1,200
157	1,500
152	500
147	500
149	1,100
149	1,150
142	3,500
142	3,600
143	3,650
133	4,200
132	4,800
132	5,000
134	5,200
134	5,400
125	8,300
123	9,700

Source: Gee, S., & Nguyen, L. "Mean time to failure in wafer level-CSP packages with SnPb and SnAgCu solder bmps," International Wafer Level Packaging Conference, San Jose, CA, Nov. 3–4, 2005 (adapted from Figure 7). Reprinted with permission.

12.64 Public perceptions of health risks. In the *Journal of Experimental Psychology: Learning, Memory, and Cognition* (July 2005), University of Basel (Switzerland) psychologists tested the ability of people to judge risk of an infectious disease. The researchers asked German college students to estimate the number of people who are infected with a certain disease in a typical year. The median estimates as well as the actual incidence rate for each in a sample of 24 infections are provided in the table. Consider the quadratic model $E(y) = \beta_0 + \beta_1 x + \beta_2 x^2$, where y = actual incidence rate and x = estimated rate.

INFECT

Infection	Incidence Rate	Estimate
Polio	0.25	300
Diphtheria	1	1,000
Trachoma	1.75	691
Rabbit fever	2	200
Cholera	3	17.5
Leprosy	5	0.8
Tetanus	9	1,000
Hemorrhagic fever	10	150
Trichinosis	22	326.5
Undulant fever	23	146.5
Well's disease	39	370
Gas gangrene	98	400
Parrot fever	119	225
Typhoid	152	200
Q fever	179	200
Malaria	936	400
Syphilis	1,514	1,500
Dysentery	1,627	1,000
Gonorrhea	2,926	6,000
Meningitis	4,019	5,000
Tuberculosis	12,619	1,500
Hepatitis	14,889	10,000
Gastroenteritis	203,864	37,000
Botulism	15	37,500

Source: Hertwig, R., Pachur, T., & Kurzenhauser, S. "Judgments of risk frequencies: Tests of possible cognitive mechanisms," *Journal of Experimental Psychology: Learning, Memory, and Cognition,* Vol. 31, No. 4, July 2005 (Table 1).

a. Fit the quadratic model to the data and then conduct a test to determine if incidence rate is curvilinearly related to estimated rate. (Use $\alpha = .05$.)

b. Construct a scatterplot for the data. Locate the data point for botulism on the graph. What do you observe?

c. Repeat part **a** but omit the data point for botulism from the analysis. Has the fit of the model improved? Explain.

12.65 Orange juice demand study. A chilled orange juice warehousing operation in New York City was experiencing too many out-of-stock situations with its 96-ounce containers. To better understand current and future demand for this product, the company examined the last 40 days of sales, which are shown in the table on the next page. One of the company's objectives is to model demand, y, as a function of sale day, x (where $x = 1, 2, 3, \ldots, 40$).

NYOJ

a. Construct a scatterplot for these data.

b. Does it appear that a second-order model might better explain the variation in demand than a first-order model? Explain.

c. Fit a first-order model to these data.

d. Fit a second-order model to these data.

e. Compare the results in parts **c** and **d** and decide which model better explains variation in demand. Justify your choice.

Data for Exercise 12.65

Sale Day, x	Demand for 96 oz. Containers, y (in cases)	Sale Day, x	Demand for 96 oz. Containers, y (in cases)
1	4,581	21	5,902
2	4,239	22	2,295
3	2,754	23	2,682
4	4,501	24	5,787
5	4,016	25	3,339
6	4,680	26	3,798
7	4,950	27	2,007
8	3,303	28	6,282
9	2,367	29	3,267
10	3,055	30	4,779
11	4,248	31	9,000
12	5,067	32	9,531
13	5,201	33	3,915
14	5,133	34	8,964
15	4,211	35	6,984
16	3,195	36	6,660
17	5,760	37	6,921
18	5,661	38	10,005
19	6,102	39	10,153
20	6,099	40	11,520

Source: Tom Metzler and Rick Campbell.

12.7 Qualitative (Dummy) Variable Models

Multiple regression models can also be written to include **qualitative** (or **categorical**) independent variables. Qualitative variables, unlike quantitative variables, cannot be measured on a numerical scale. Therefore, we must code the values of the qualitative variables (called **levels**) as numbers before we can fit the model. These coded qualitative variables are called **dummy** (or **indicator**) **variables** because the numbers assigned to the various levels are arbitrarily selected.

To illustrate, suppose a female executive at a certain company claims that male executives earn higher salaries, on average, than female executives with the same education, experience, and responsibilities. To support her claim, she wants to model the salary y of an executive using a qualitative independent variable representing the gender of an executive (male or female).

A convenient method of coding the values of a qualitative variable at two levels involves assigning a value of 1 to one of the levels and a value of 0 to the other. For example, the dummy variable used to describe gender could be coded as follows:

$$x = \begin{cases} 1 & \text{if male} \\ 0 & \text{if female} \end{cases}$$

The choice of which level is assigned to 1 and which is assigned to 0 is arbitrary. The model then takes the following form:

$$E(y) = \beta_0 + \beta_1 x$$

The advantage of using a 0–1 coding scheme is that the β coefficients are easily interpreted. The model above allows us to compare the mean executive salary $E(y)$ for males with the corresponding mean for females.

$$\text{Males } (x = 1)\text{: } E(y) = \beta_0 + \beta_1(1) = \beta_0 + \beta_1$$
$$\text{Females } (x = 0)\text{: } E(y) = \beta_0 + \beta_1(0) = \beta_0$$

These two means are illustrated in the bar graph in Figure 12.18.

First note that β_0 represents the mean salary for females (say, μ_F). When a 0–1 coding convention is used, β_0 will always represent the mean response associated with the level of the qualitative variable assigned the value 0 (called the **base level**).

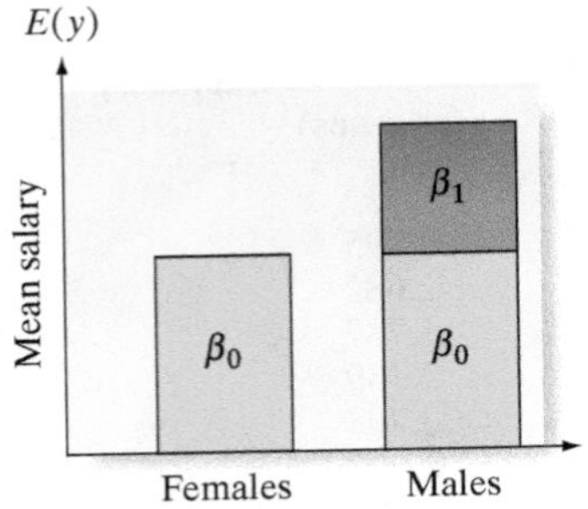

Figure 12.18
Bar graph comparing $E(y)$ for males and females

The difference between the mean salary for males and the mean salary for females, $\mu_M - \mu_F$, is represented by β_1—that is,

$$\mu_M - \mu_F = (\beta_0 + \beta_1) - (\beta_0) = \beta_1$$

This difference is shown in Figure 12.18.* With a 0–1 coding convention, β_1 will always represent the difference between the mean response for the level assigned the value 1 and the mean for the base level. Thus, for the executive salary model, we have

$$\beta_0 = \mu_F$$
$$\beta_1 = \mu_M - \mu_F$$

The model relating a mean response $E(y)$ to a qualitative independent variable at two levels is summarized in the following box.

A Model Relating $E(y)$ to a Qualitative Independent Variable with Two Levels

$$E(y) = \beta_0 + \beta_1 x$$

where

$$x = \begin{cases} 1 & \text{if level A} \\ 0 & \text{if level B} \end{cases}$$

Interpretation of β's:

$$\beta_0 = \mu_B \text{ (mean for base level)}$$
$$\beta_1 = \mu_A - \mu_B$$

Note: μ_i represents the mean of y, $E(y)$, for level i of the dummy variable.

Now carefully examine the model with a single qualitative independent variable at two levels; we will use exactly the same pattern for any number of levels. Moreover, the interpretation of the parameters will always be the same. One level (say, level A) is selected as the base level. Then for the 0–1 coding† for the dummy variables,

$$\mu_A = \beta_0$$

The coding for all dummy variables is as follows: To represent the mean value of y for a particular level, let that dummy variable equal 1; otherwise, the dummy variable is set equal to 0. Using this system of coding,

$$\mu_B = \beta_0 + \beta_1$$
$$\mu_C = \beta_0 + \beta_2$$

and so on. Because $\mu_A = \beta_0$, any other model parameter will represent the difference between means for that level and the base level:

$$\beta_1 = \mu_B - \mu_A$$
$$\beta_2 = \mu_C - \mu_A$$

and so on. Consequently, each β multiplied by a dummy variable represents the difference between $E(y)$ at one level of the qualitative variable and $E(y)$ at the base level.

A Model Relating $E(y)$ to One Qualitative Independent Variable with k Levels

Always use a number of dummy variables that is one less than the number of levels of the qualitative variable. Thus, for a qualitative variable with k levels, use $k - 1$ dummy variables:

$$E(y) = \beta_0 + \beta_1 x_1 + \beta_2 x_2 + \cdots + \beta_{k-1} x_{k-1}$$

*Note that β_1 could be negative. If β_1 were negative, the height of the bar corresponding to males would be *reduced* (rather than increased) from the height of the bar for females by the amount β_1. Figure 12.18 is constructed assuming that β_1 is a positive quantity.

†You do not have to use a 0–1 system of coding for the dummy variables. Any two-value system will work, but the interpretation given to the model parameters will depend on the code. Using the 0–1 system makes the model parameters easy to interpret.

where x_i is the dummy variable for level $i + 1$ and

$$x_i = \begin{cases} 1 & \text{if } y \text{ is observed at level } i + 1 \\ 0 & \text{otherwise} \end{cases}$$

Then, for this system of coding

$$\begin{aligned} \mu_A &= \beta_0 & \quad \text{and} \quad \beta_1 &= \mu_B - \mu_A \\ \mu_B &= \beta_0 + \beta_1 & \beta_2 &= \mu_C - \mu_A \\ \mu_C &= \beta_0 + \beta_2 & \beta_3 &= \mu_D - \mu_A \\ \mu_D &= \beta_0 + \beta_3 & &\vdots \end{aligned}$$

Note: μ_i represents the mean of y, $E(y)$, for level i of the qualitative variable.

Example 12.9

A Model with One Qualitative Independent Variable—Credit Card Debt

Problem Suppose an economist wants to compare the mean dollar amounts owed by delinquent credit card customers in three different socioeconomic classes: (1) lower class, (2) middle class, and (3) upper class. A sample of 10 customers with delinquent accounts is selected from each group, and the amount owed by each is recorded, as shown in Table 12.3.

Table 12.3 Dollars Owed, Example 12.9

Group 1 (lower class)	Group 2 (middle class)	Group 3 (upper class)
$148	$513	$335
76	264	643
393	433	216
520	94	536
236	535	128
134	327	723
55	214	258
166	135	380
415	280	594
153	304	465

Data Set: CCDEBT

a. Hypothesize a regression model for amount owed (y) using socioeconomic class as an independent variable.

b. Interpret the β's in the model.

c. Fit the model to the data and give the least squares prediction equation.

d. Use the model to determine if the mean dollar amounts owed by customers differ significantly for the three socioeconomic groups at $\alpha = .05$.

Solution

a. Note that socioeconomic status (low, middle, upper class) is a qualitative variable (measured on an ordinal scale). For a three-level qualitative variable, we need two dummy variables in the regression model. The model relating $E(y)$ to this single qualitative variable, socioeconomic group, is

$$E(y) = \beta_0 + \beta_1 x_1 + \beta_2 x_2$$

where (arbitrarily choosing group 1 as the base level)

$$x_1 = \begin{cases} 1 & \text{if group 2} \\ 0 & \text{if not} \end{cases} \qquad x_2 = \begin{cases} 1 & \text{if group 3} \\ 0 & \text{if not} \end{cases}$$

b. For this model

$$\begin{aligned} \beta_0 &= \mu_1 \\ \beta_1 &= \mu_2 - \mu_1 \\ \beta_2 &= \mu_3 - \mu_1 \end{aligned}$$

where μ_1, μ_2, and μ_3 are the mean responses for socioeconomic groups 1, 2, and 3, respectively—that is, β_0 represents the mean amount owed for group 1 (lower class), β_1 represents the mean difference in amounts owed for group 2 (middle) and group 1 (lower), and β_2 represents the mean difference in amounts owed for group 3 (upper) and group 1 (lower).

c. The Minitab printout of the regression analysis is shown in Figure 12.19. The least squares estimates of the β's are highlighted on the printout, yielding the following least squares prediction equation:

$$\hat{y} = 229.6 + 80.3x_1 + 198.2x_2$$

Regression Analysis: Amount versus X1, X2

```
The regression equation is
Amount = 230 + 80.3 X1 + 198 X2

Predictor     Coef  SE Coef     T      P
Constant    229.60    53.43  4.30  0.000
X1           80.30    75.56  1.06  0.297
X2          198.20    75.56  2.62  0.014

S = 168.948   R-Sq = 20.5%   R-Sq(adj) = 14.6%

Analysis of Variance

Source          DF      SS     MS     F      P
Regression       2  198772  99386  3.48  0.045
Residual Error  27  770671  28543
Total           29  969443
```

Descriptive Statistics: Amount

```
Variable  Class   N   Mean  StDev  Minimum  Maximum
Amount    L      10  229.6  158.2     55.0    520.0
          M      10  309.9  147.9     94.0    535.0
          U      10  427.8  196.8    128.0    723.0
```

Figure 12.19
Minitab output for model with dummy variables

The interpretations of the β's in part **b** allow us to obtain the β estimates from the sample means associated with the different levels of the qualitative variable.*

Because $\beta_0 = \mu_1$, then the estimate of β_0 is the estimated mean delinquent amount for the lower-class group. This sample mean, highlighted at the bottom of the Minitab printout, is 229.6; thus $\hat{\beta}_0 = 229.6$.

Now $\beta_1 = \mu_2 - \mu_1$; therefore, the estimate of β_1 is the difference between the sample mean delinquent amounts for the middle- and lower-class groups. Based on the sample means highlighted at the bottom of the Minitab printout, we have $\hat{\beta}_1 = 309.9 - 229.6 = 80.3$.

Similarly, the estimate of $\beta_2 = \mu_3 - \mu_1$ is the difference between the sample mean delinquent amounts for the upper- and lower-class groups. From the sample means highlighted at the bottom of the Minitab printout, we have $\hat{\beta}_2 = 427.8 - 229.6 = 198.2$.

d. Testing the null hypothesis that the means for the three groups are equal—that is, $\mu_1 = \mu_2 = \mu_3$—is equivalent to testing

$$H_0: \beta_1 = \beta_2 = 0$$

You can see this by observing that if $\beta_1 = \mu_2 - \mu_1 = 0$, then $\mu_1 = \mu_2$. Similarly, if $\beta_2 = \mu_3 - \mu_1 = 0$, then $\mu_3 = \mu_1$. Thus, if H_0 is true, then μ_1, μ_2, and μ_3 must be equal. The alternative hypothesis is

H_a: At least one of the parameters, β_1 and β_2, differs from 0, which implies that at least two of the three means (μ_1, μ_2, and μ_3) differ.

*The least squares method and the sample means method will yield equivalent β estimates when the sample sizes associated with the different levels of the qualitative variable are equal.

To test this hypothesis, we conduct the global F-test for the model. The value of the F-statistic for testing the adequacy of the model, $F = 3.48$, and the observed significance level of the test, p-value $= .045$, are both highlighted on Figure 12.19. Because $\alpha = .05$ exceeds the p-value, we reject H_0 and conclude that at least one of the parameters, β_1 and β_2, differs from 0. Or, equivalently, we conclude that the data provide sufficient evidence to indicate that the mean indebtedness does vary from one socioeconomic group to another.

Look Back This global F-test is equivalent to the analysis of variance F-test for a completely randomized design of Chapter 9.

Now Work Exercise 12.78

CAUTION A common mistake of regression analysts is to use a single dummy variable x for a qualitative variable at k levels, where $x = 1, 2, 3, \ldots, k$. Such a regression model will have unestimable β's and β's that are difficult to interpret. Remember, when modeling $E(y)$ with a single qualitative independent variable, the number of 0–1 dummy variables to include in the model will always be one less than the number of levels of the qualitative variable.

Exercises 12.66–12.81

Learning the Mechanics

12.66 Write a regression model relating the mean value of y to a qualitative independent variable that can assume two levels. Interpret all the terms in the model.

12.67 Write a regression model relating $E(y)$ to a qualitative independent variable that can assume three levels. Interpret all the terms in the model.

12.68 The Minitab printout below resulted from fitting the following model to $n = 15$ data points:

$$y = \beta_0 + \beta_1 x_1 + \beta_2 x_2 + \varepsilon$$

where

$$x_1 = \begin{cases} 1 & \text{if level 2} \\ 0 & \text{if not} \end{cases} \qquad x_2 = \begin{cases} 1 & \text{if level 3} \\ 0 & \text{if not} \end{cases}$$

a. Report the least squares prediction equation.
b. Interpret the values of β_1 and β_2.
c. Interpret the following hypotheses in terms of μ_1, μ_2, and μ_3:

```
The regression equation is
Y = 80.0 + 16.8 X1 + 40.4 X2


Predictor     Coef   SE Coef      T       P
Constant    80.000     4.082  19.60   0.000
X1          16.800     5.774   2.91   0.013
X2          40.400     5.774   7.00   0.000


S = 9.129     R-Sq = 80.5%    R-Sq(adj) = 77.2%

Analysis of Variance

Source          DF      SS       MS       F       P
Regression       2  4118.9   2059.5   24.72   0.000
Residual Error  12  1000.0     83.3
Total           14  5118.9
```

H_0: $\beta_1 = \beta_2 = 0$
H_a: At least one of the parameters β_1 and β_2 differs from 0

d. Conduct the hypothesis test of part **c.**

12.69 The following model was used to relate $E(y)$ to a single qualitative variable with four levels:

$$E(y) = \beta_0 + \beta_1 x_1 + \beta_2 x_2 + \beta_3 x_3$$

where

$$x_1 = \begin{cases} 1 & \text{if level 2} \\ 0 & \text{if not} \end{cases} \quad x_2 = \begin{cases} 1 & \text{if level 3} \\ 0 & \text{if not} \end{cases} \quad x_3 = \begin{cases} 1 & \text{if level 4} \\ 0 & \text{if not} \end{cases}$$

This model was fit to $n = 30$ data points, and the following result was obtained:

$$\hat{y} = 10.2 - 4x_1 + 12x_2 + 2x_3$$

a. Use the least squares prediction equation to find the estimate of $E(y)$ for each level of the qualitative independent variable.
b. Specify the null and alternative hypotheses you would use to test whether $E(y)$ is the same for all four levels of the independent variable.

Applying the Concepts—Basic

12.70 **Can money spent on gifts buy love?** Refer to the *Journal of Experimental Social Psychology* (Vol. 45, 2009) study of whether buying gifts truly buys love, Exercise 9.9 (p. 492). Recall that study participants were randomly assigned to play the role of gift-giver or gift-receiver. Gift-receivers were asked to provide the level of appreciation (measured on a 7-point scale where 1 = "not at all" and 7 = "to a great extent") they had for the last birthday gift they received from a loved one. Gift-givers were asked to recall the last birthday gift they gave to a loved one and to provide the level of appreciation the loved one had for the gift.

a. Write a dummy variable regression model that will allow the researchers to compare the average level of appreciation for birthday gift-givers (μ_G) to the average for birthday gift-receivers (μ_R).

b. Express each of the model's β parameters in terms of μ_G and μ_R.

c. The researchers hypothesize that the average level of appreciation is higher for birthday gift-givers than for birthday gift-receivers. Explain how to test this hypothesis using the regression model.

12.71 Production technologies, terroir, and quality of Bordeaux wine. In addition to state-of-the-art technologies, the production of quality wine is strongly influenced by the natural endowments of the grape-growing region—called the "terroir." *The Economic Journal* (May 2008) published an empirical study of the factors that yield a quality Bordeaux wine. A quantitative measure of wine quality (y) was modeled as a function of several qualitative independent variables, including grape-picking method (manual or automated), soil type (clay, gravel, or sand), and slope orientation (east, south, west, southeast, or southwest).

a. Create the appropriate dummy variables for each of the qualitative independent variables.

b. Write a model for wine quality (y) as a function of grape-picking method. Interpret the β's in the model.

c. Write a model for wine quality (y) as a function of soil type. Interpret the β's in the model.

d. Write a model for wine quality (y) as a function of slope orientation. Interpret the β's in the model.

12.72 Impact of race on football card values. University of Colorado sociologists investigated the impact of race on the value of professional football players' "rookie" cards (*Electronic Journal of Sociology*, 2007). The sample consisted of 148 rookie cards of National Football League (NFL) players who were inducted into the Football Hall of Fame. The price of the card (in dollars) was modeled as a function of several qualitative independent variables: race of player (black or white), card availability (high or low), and player position (quarterback, running back, wide receiver, tight end, defensive lineman, linebacker, defensive back, or offensive lineman).

a. Create the appropriate dummy variables for each of the qualitative independent variables.

b. Write a model for price (y) as a function of race. Interpret the β's in the model.

c. Write a model for price (y) as a function of card availability. Interpret the β's in the model.

d. Write a model for price (y) as a function of position. Interpret the β's in the model.

12.73 Accuracy of software effort estimates. Periodically, software engineers must provide estimates of their effort in developing new software. In the *Journal of Empirical Software Engineering* (Vol. 9, 2004), multiple regression was used to predict the accuracy of these effort estimates. The dependent variable, defined as the relative error in estimating effort,

$$y = (\text{actual effort} - \text{estimated effort})/(\text{actual effort})$$

was determined for each in a sample of $n = 49$ software development tasks. Several qualitative independent variables were evaluated as potential predictors of relative error. Some of these variables are described in the table.

Estimator role (developer or project leader)
Task complexity (low, medium, or high)
Contract type (fixed price or hourly rate)
Customer priority (time of delivery, cost, or quality)

a. Write a model for $E(y)$ as a function of estimator role. Interpret the β's.

b. Write a model for $E(y)$ as a function of task complexity. Interpret the β's.

c. Write a model for $E(y)$ as a function of contract type. Interpret the β's.

d. Write a model for $E(y)$ as a function of customer priority. Interpret the β's.

12.74 Buy-side vs. sell-side analysts' earnings forecasts. Refer to the *Financial Analysts Journal* (Jul./Aug. 2008) comparison of earnings forecasts of buy-side and sell-side analysts, Exercise 2.86 (p. 86). The Harvard Business School professors used regression to model the relative optimism (y) of the analysts' 3-month horizon forecasts. One of the independent variables used to model forecast optimism was the dummyvariable $x = \{1$ if the analyst worked for a buy-side firm, 0 if the analyst worked for a sell-side firm$\}$.

a. Write the equation of the model for $E(y)$ as a function of type of firm.

b. Interpret the value of β_0 in the model, part **a.**

c. The professors write that the value of β_1 in the model, part **a,** "represents the mean difference in relative forecast optimism between buy-side and sell-side analysts." Do you agree?

d. The professors also argue that "if buy-side analysts make less optimistic forecasts than their sell-side counterparts, the [estimated value of β_1] will be negative." Do you agree?

12.75 Do blondes raise more funds? During fundraising, does the physical appearance of the solicitor impact the level of capital raised? An economist at the University of Nevada-Reno designed an experiment to answer this question and published the results in *Economic Letters* (Vol. 100, 2008). Each in a sample of 955 households was contacted by a female solicitor and asked to contribute to the Center for Natural Hazards Mitigation Research. The level of contribution (in dollars) was recorded as well as the hair color of the solicitor (blond Caucasian, brunette Caucasian, or minority female).

a. Consider a model for the mean level of contribution, $E(y)$, that allows for different means depending on the hair color of the solicitor. Create the appropriate number of dummy variables for hair color. (Use minority female as the base level.)

b. Write the equation of the model, part **a,** incorporating the dummy variables.

c. In terms of the β's in the model, what is the mean level of contribution for households contacted by a blond Caucasian solicitor?

d. In terms of the β's in the model, what is the difference between the mean level of contribution for households contacted by a blond solicitor and those contacted by a minority female?

e. One theory posits that blond solicitors will achieve the highest mean contribution level, but that there will be no difference between the mean contribution levels attained by brunette Caucasian and minority females. If this theory is true, give the expected signs of the β's in the model.

f. The researcher found the β-estimate for the dummy variable for blond Caucasian to be positive and significantly different from 0 (p-value $< .01$). The β-estimate for the dummy variable for brunette Caucasian was also positive, but not significantly different from 0 (p-value $> .10$). Do these results support the theory, part **e**?

Applying the Concepts—Intermediate

12.76 Deferred tax allowance study. A study was conducted to identify accounting choice variables that influence a manager's decision to change the level of the deferred tax asset allowance at the firm (*The Engineering Economist*, Jan./Feb. 2004). Data were collected for a sample of 329 firms that reported deferred tax assets in 2000. The dependent variable of interest (DTVA) is measured as the change in the deferred tax asset valuation allowance divided by the deferred tax asset. The independent variables used as predictors of DTVA are listed as follows:

LEVERAGE: x_1 = ratio of debt book value to shareholder's equity

BONUS: x_2 = 1 if firm maintains a management bonus plan, 0 if not

MVALUE: x_3 = market value of common stock

BBATH: x_4 = 1 if operating earnings negative and lower than last year, 0 if not

EARN: x_5 = change in operating earnings divided by total assets

A first-order model was fit to the data with the following results (p-values in parentheses):

$$R_a^2 = .280$$

$$\hat{y} = .044 + .006x_1 - .035x_2 - .001x_3 + .296x_4 + .010x_5$$

$$(.070) \quad (.228) \quad (.157) \quad (.678) \quad (.001) \quad (.869)$$

a. Interpret the estimate of the β coefficient for x_4.

b. The "Big Bath" theory proposed by the researchers states that the mean DTVA for firms with negative earnings and earnings lower than last year will exceed the mean DTVA of other firms. Is there evidence to support this theory? Test using $\alpha = .05$.

c. Interpret the value of R_a^2.

12.77 Corporate sustainability and firm characteristics. Refer to the *Business and Society* (March 2011) study on how firm size and firm type impact corporate sustainability behaviors, Exercise 9.7 (p. 492). Recall that Certified Public Accountants (CPAs) were surveyed on their firms' likelihood of reporting sustainability policies (measured as a probability between 0 and 1). The CPAs were divided into four groups depending on firm size (large or small) and firm type (public or private): large/public, large/private, small/public, and small/private. One goal of the analysis is to determine whether the mean likelihood of reporting sustainability policies differs depending on firm size and firm type.

a. Consider a single qualitative variable representing the four size/type categories. Create the appropriate dummy variables for representing this qualitative variable as an independent variable in a regression model for predicting likelihood of reporting sustainability policies (y).

b. Give the equation of the model, part **a**, and interpret each of the model parameters.

c. The global F-test for the model resulted in p-value $< .001$. Give a practical interpretation of this result.

d. Now consider treating firm size and firm type as two different qualitative independent variables in a model for likelihood of reporting sustainability policies (y). Create the appropriate dummy variables for representing these qualitative variables in the model.

e. Refer to part **d.** Write a model for $E(y)$ as a function of firm size and firm type, but do not include interaction. (This model is called the *main effects* model.)

f. Refer to the model, part **e.** For each combination of firm size and firm type (e.g., large/public), write $E(y)$ as a function of the model parameters.

g. Use the results, part **f**, to show that for the main effects model, the difference between the mean likelihoods for large and small firms does not depend on firm type.

h. Write a model for $E(y)$ as a function of firm size, firm type, and size × type interaction.

i. Refer to the model, part **h.** For each combination of firm size and firm type (e.g., large/public), write $E(y)$ as a function of the model parameters.

j. Use the results, part **i**, to show that for the interaction model, the difference between the mean likelihoods for large and small firms does depend on firm type.

12.78 Homework assistance for accounting students. Refer to the *Journal of Accounting Education* (Vol. 25, 2007) study of assisting accounting students with their homework, Exercise 9.30 (p. 510). Recall that 175 accounting students took a pretest on a topic not covered in class and then each was given a homework problem to solve on the same topic. The students were assigned to one of three homework assistance groups. Some students received the completed solution, some were given check figures at various steps of the solution, and some received no help at all. After finishing the homework, the students were all given a posttest on the subject. The dependent variable of interest was the knowledge gain (or test score improvement). These data are saved in the file.

NW

ACCHW

a. Propose a model for the knowledge gain (y) as a function of the qualitative variable, homework assistance group.

b. In terms of the β's in the model, give an expression for the difference between the mean knowledge gains of students in the "completed solution" and "no help" groups.

c. Fit the model to the data and give the least squares prediction equation.

d. Conduct the global F-test for model utility using $\alpha = .05$. Interpret the results, practically.

e. Show that the results, part **d**, agree with the conclusions reached in Exercise 9.30.

12.79 Comparing mosquito repellents. Which insect repellents protect best against mosquitoes? *Consumer Reports* (June 2000) tested 14 products that all claim to be an effective mosquito repellent. Each product was classified as either lotion/cream or aerosol/spray. The cost of the product (in dollars) was divided by the amount of the repellent needed to cover exposed areas of the skin (about 1/3 ounce) to obtain a cost-per-use value. Effectiveness was measured as the maximum number of hours of protection (in half-hour

REPELL

increments) provided when human testers exposed their arms to 200 mosquitoes. The data from the report are listed in the table.

Insect Repellent	Type	Cost/ Use	Maximum Protection
Amway Hour Guard 12	Lotion/Cream	\$2.08	13.5 hours
Avon Skin-So-Soft	Aerosol/Spray	0.67	0.5
Avon BugGuard Plus	Lotion/Cream	1.00	2.0
Ben's Backyard Formula	Lotion/Cream	0.75	7.0
Bite Blocker	Lotion/Cream	0.46	3.0
BugOut	Aerosol/Spray	0.11	6.0
Cutter Skinsations	Aerosol/Spray	0.22	3.0
Cutter Unscented	Aerosol/Spray	0.19	5.5
Muskoll Ultra6Hours	Aerosol/Spray	0.24	6.5
Natrapel	Aerosol/Spray	0.27	1.0
Off! Deep Woods	Aerosol/Spray	1.77	14.0
Off! Skintastic	Lotion/Cream	0.67	3.0
Sawyer Deet Formula	Lotion/Cream	0.36	7.0
Repel Permanone	Aerosol/Spray	2.75	24.0

Source: Based on "Buzz off and Insect repellants: Which keep bugs at bay?" *Consumer Reports,* June 2000.

a. Suppose you want to use repellent type to model the cost per use (y). Create the appropriate number of dummy variables for repellent type and write the model.
b. Fit the model, part **a,** to the data.
c. Give the null hypothesis for testing whether repellent type is a useful predictor of cost per use (y).
d. Conduct the test, part **c,** and give the appropriate conclusion. Use $\alpha = .10$.
e. Repeat parts **a–d** if the dependent variable is the maximum number of hours of protection (y).

Applying the Concepts—Advanced

12.80 Manipulating rates of return with stock splits. Some firms have been accused of using stock splits to manipulate their stock prices before being acquired by another firm. An article in *Financial Management* (Winter 2008) investigated the impact of stock splits on long-run stock performance for acquiring firms. A simplified version of the model fit by the researchers follows:

$$E(y) = \beta_0 + \beta_1 x_1 + \beta_2 x_2 + \beta_3 x_1 x_2,$$

where

y = Firm's 3-year buy-and-hold return rate (%)
x_1 = {1 if stock split prior to acquisition, 0 if not}
x_2 = {1 if firm's discretionary accrual is high, 0 if discretionary accrual is low}

a. In terms of the β's in the model, what is the mean buy-and-hold return rate (BAR) for a firm with no stock split and a high discretionary accrual (DA)?
b. In terms of the β's in the model, what is the mean BAR for a firm with no stock split and a low DA?
c. For firms with no stock split, find the difference between the mean BAR for firms with high and low DA. (*Hint:* Use your answers to parts **a** and **b.**)
d. Repeat part **c** for firms with a stock split.
e. Note that the differences, parts **c** and **d,** are not the same. Explain why this illustrates the notion of interaction between x_1 and x_2.
f. A test for H_0: $\beta_3 = 0$ yielded a p-value of .027. Using $\alpha = .05$, interpret this result.
g. The researchers reported that the estimated values of both β_2 and β_3 are negative. Consequently, they conclude that "high-DA acquirers perform worse compared with low-DA acquirers. Moreover, the underperformance is even greater if high-DA acquirers have a stock split before acquistion." Do you agree?

12.81 Study of recall of TV commercials. Refer to the *Journal of Applied Psychology* (June 2002) study of recall of television commercials, Exercise 9.28 (p. 509). Participants were assigned to watch one of three types of TV programs, with nine commercials embedded in each show. Group V watched a TV program with a violent content code rating (e.g., *Tour of Duty*); group S viewed a show with a sex content code rating (e.g., *Strip Mall*); and group N watched a neutral TV program with neither a V nor an S rating (e.g., *Candid Camera*). The dependent variable measured for each participant was a score (y) on his/her recall of the brand names in the commercial messages, with scores ranging from 0 (no brands recalled) to 9 (all brands recalled).
ADREC
a. Write a model for $E(y)$ as a function of viewer group.
b. Fit the model, part **a,** to the data saved in the file. Give the least squares prediction equation.
c. Conduct a test of overall model utility at $\alpha = .01$. Interpret the results.
d. The sample mean recall scores for the three groups were $\bar{y}_V = 2.08$, $\bar{y}_S = 1.71$, and $\bar{y}_N = 3.17$. Show how to find these sample means using only the β estimates obtained in part **b.**

12.8 Models with Both Quantitative and Qualitative Variables

Suppose you want to relate the mean monthly sales $E(y)$ of a company to monthly advertising expenditure x for three different advertising media (say newspaper, radio, and television) and you wish to use first-order (straight-line) models to model the responses for all three media. Graphs of these three relationships might appear as shown in Figure 12.20.

Because the lines in Figure 12.20 are hypothetical, a number of practical questions arise. Is one advertising medium as effective as any other? That is, do the three mean sales lines differ for the three advertising media? Do the increases in mean sales per dollar input in advertising differ for the three advertising media? That is, do the slopes of the three lines differ? Note that the two practical questions have been rephrased into questions about the parameters that define the three lines in Figure 12.20. To answer them, we must write a single regression model that will characterize the three lines of Figure 12.20 and that, by testing hypotheses about the lines, will answer the questions.

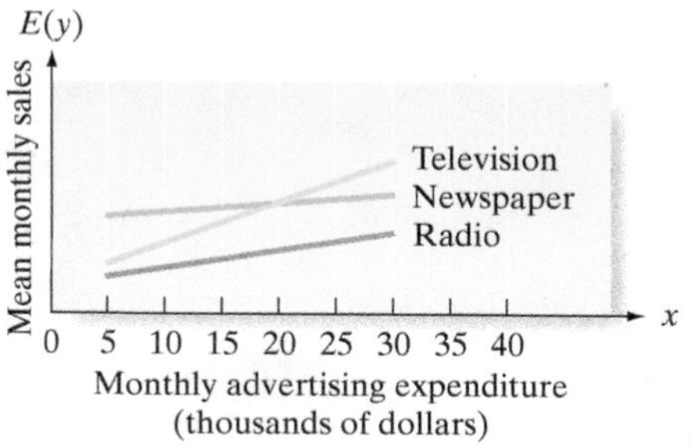

Figure 12.20
Graphs of the relationship between mean sales $E(y)$ and advertising expenditure x

The response described previously, monthly sales, is a function of *two* independent variables, one quantitative (advertising expenditure x_1) and one qualitative (type of medium). We will proceed, in stages, to build a model relating $E(y)$ to these variables and will show graphically the interpretation we would give to the model at each stage. This will help you to see the contributions of the various terms in the model.

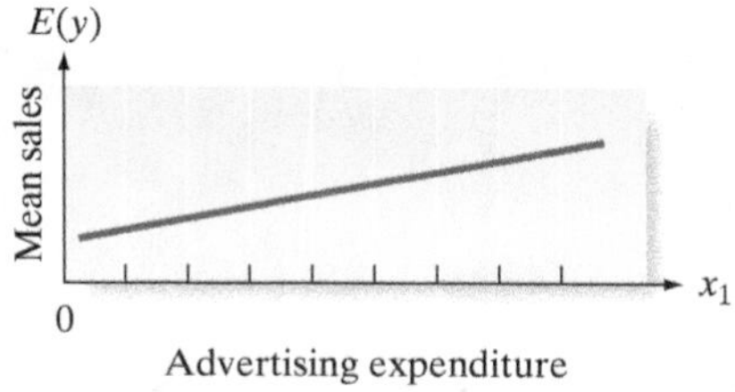

Figure 12.21
The relationship between $E(y)$ and x_1 is the same for all media

1. The straight-line relationship between mean sales $E(y)$ and advertising expenditure is the same for all three media—that is, a single line will describe the relationship between $E(y)$ and advertising expenditure x_1 for all the media (see Figure 12.21).

$$E(y) = \beta_0 + \beta_1 x \qquad \text{where } x_1 = \text{advertising expenditure}$$

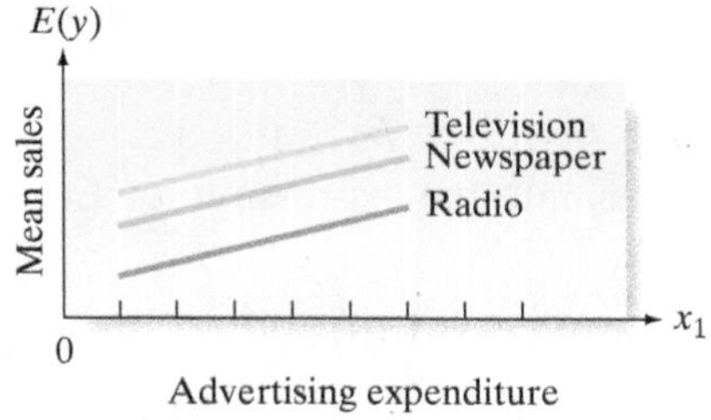

Figure 12.22
Parallel response lines for the three media

2. The straight lines relating mean sales $E(y)$ to advertising expenditure x_1 differ from one medium to another, but the rate of increase in mean sales per increase in dollar advertising expenditure x_1 is the same for all media—that is, the lines are parallel but possess different y-intercepts (see Figure 12.22).

$$E(y) = \beta_0 + \beta_1 x_1 + \beta_2 x_2 + \beta_3 x_3$$

where

$$x_1 = \text{advertising expenditure}$$

$$x_2 = \begin{cases} 1 & \text{if radio medium} \\ 0 & \text{if not} \end{cases}$$

$$x_3 = \begin{cases} 1 & \text{if television medium} \\ 0 & \text{if not} \end{cases}$$

Notice that this model is essentially a combination of a first-order model with a single quantitative variable and the model with a single qualitative variable:

First-order model with a single quantitative variable:	$E(y) = \beta_0 + \beta_1 x_1$
Model with single qualitative variable at three levels:	$E(y) = \beta_0 + \beta_2 x_2 + \beta_3 x_3$

where x_1, x_2, and x_3 are as just defined. The model described here implies no interaction between the two independent variables, which are advertising expenditure x_1 and the qualitative variable (type of advertising medium). The change in $E(y)$ for a 1-unit increase in x_1 is identical (the slopes of the lines are equal) for all three advertising media. The terms corresponding to each of the independent variables are called **main effect terms** because they imply no interaction.

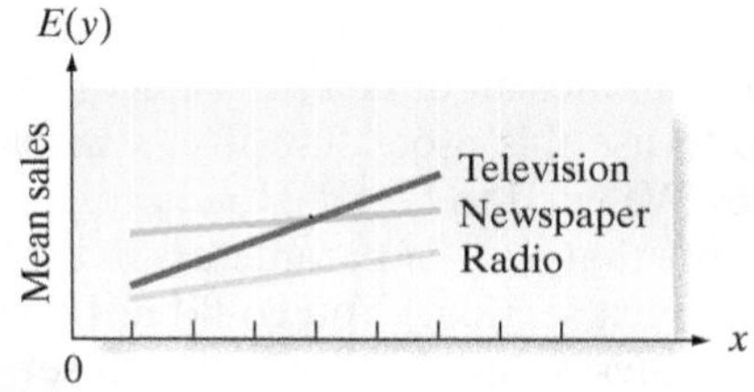

Figure 12.23
Different response lines for the three media

3. The straight lines relating mean sales $E(y)$ to advertising expenditure x_1 differ for the three advertising media—that is, both the line intercepts and the slopes differ (see Figure 12.23). As you will see, this interaction model is obtained by

adding terms involving the cross-product terms, one each from each of the two independent variables:

$$E(y) = \overbrace{\beta_0 + \beta_1 x_1}^{\substack{\text{Main effect,}\\ \text{advertising}\\ \text{expenditure}}} + \overbrace{\beta_2 x_2 + \beta_3 x_3}^{\substack{\text{Main effect,}\\ \text{type of}\\ \text{medium}}} + \overbrace{\beta_4 x_1 x_2 + \beta_5 x_1 x_3}^{\text{Interaction}}$$

Note that each of the preceding models is obtained by adding terms to model 1, the single first-order model used to model the responses for all three media. Model 2 is obtained by adding the main effect terms for type of medium, the qualitative variable. Model 3 is obtained by adding the interaction terms to model 2.

Example 12.10

Interpreting the β's in a Model with Mixed Independent Variables

Problem Substitute the appropriate values of the dummy variables in model 3 (above) to obtain the equations of the three response lines in Figure 12.23.

Solution The complete model that characterizes the three lines in Figure 12.23 is

$$E(y) = \beta_0 + \beta_1 x_1 + \beta_2 x_2 + \beta_3 x_3 + \beta_4 x_1 x_2 + \beta_5 x_1 x_3$$

where

$$x_1 = \text{advertising expenditure}$$

$$x_2 = \begin{cases} 1 & \text{if radio medium} \\ 0 & \text{if not} \end{cases}$$

$$x_3 = \begin{cases} 1 & \text{if television medium} \\ 0 & \text{if not} \end{cases}$$

Examining the coding, you can see that $x_2 = x_3 = 0$ when the advertising medium is newspaper. Substituting these values into the expression for $E(y)$, we obtain the newspaper medium line:

$$E(y) = \beta_0 + \beta_1 x_1 + \beta_2(0) + \beta_3(0) + \beta_4 x_1(0) + \beta_5 x_1(0) = \beta_0 + \beta_1 x_1$$

Similarly, we substitute the appropriate values of x_2 and x_3 into the expression for $E(y)$ to obtain the radio medium line ($x_2 = 1, x_3 = 0$):

$$E(y) = \beta_0 + \beta_1 x_1 + \beta_2(1) + \beta_3(0) + \beta_4 x_1(1) + \beta_5 x_1(0)$$

$$= \overbrace{(\beta_0 + \beta_2)}^{y\text{-intercept}} + \overbrace{(\beta_1 + \beta_4)}^{\text{Slope}} x_1$$

and the television medium line: ($x_2 = 0, x_3 = 1$):

$$E(y) = \beta_0 + \beta_1 x_1 + \beta_2(0) + \beta_3(1) + \beta_4 x_1(0) + \beta_5 x_1(1)$$

$$= \overbrace{(\beta_0 + \beta_3)}^{y\text{-intercept}} + \overbrace{(\beta_1 + \beta_5)}^{\text{Slope}} x_1$$

Look Back If you were to fit model 3, obtain estimates of $\beta_0, \beta_1, \beta_2, \dots, \beta_5$, and substitute them into the equations for the three media lines, you would obtain exactly the same prediction equations as you would obtain if you were to fit three separate straight lines, one to each of the three sets of media data. You may ask why we would not fit the three lines separately. Why bother fitting a model that combines all three lines (model 3) into the same equation? The answer is that you need to use this procedure if you wish to use statistical tests to compare the three media lines. We need to be able to express a practical question about the lines in terms of a hypothesis that a set of parameters in the model equals 0. (We demonstrate this procedure in the next section.) You could not do this if you were to perform three separate regression analyses and fit a line to each set of media data.

■ Now Work Exercise 12.82

Example 12.11

Testing for Two Different Slopes—Worker Productivity

Problem An industrial psychologist conducted an experiment to investigate the relationship between worker productivity and a measure of salary incentive for two manufacturing plants: One plant operates under "disciplined management practices," and the other plant uses a traditional management style. The productivity y per worker was measured by recording the number of machined castings that a worker could produce in a 4-week period of 40 hours per week. The incentive was the amount x_1 of bonus (in cents per casting) paid for all castings produced in excess of 1,000 per worker for the 4-week period. Nine workers were selected from each plant, and three from each group of nine were assigned to receive a 20¢ bonus per casting, three a 30¢ bonus, and three a 40¢ bonus. The productivity data for the 18 workers, three for each plant type and incentive combination, are shown in Table 12.4.

Table 12.4 Productivity Data for Example 12.11

Management style	Incentive								
	20¢/casting			30¢/casting			40¢/casting		
Traditional	1,435	1,512	1,491	1,583	1,529	1,610	1,601	1,574	1,636
Disciplined	1,575	1,512	1,488	1,635	1,589	1,661	1,645	1,616	1,689

Data Set: CAST

a. Write a model for mean productivity, $E(y)$, assuming that the relationship between $E(y)$ and incentive x_1 is first-order.

b. Fit the model and graph the prediction equations for the disciplined and traditional management styles.

c. Do the data provide sufficient evidence to indicate that the rate of increase of worker productivity is different for disciplined and traditional plants? Test at $\alpha = .10$.

Solution

a. If we assume that a first-order model* is adequate to detect a change in mean productivity as a function of incentive x_1, then the model that produces two straight lines, one for each plant, is

$$E(y) = \beta_0 + \beta_1 x_1 + \beta_2 x_2 + \beta_3 x_1 x_2$$

where

$$x_1 = \text{incentive} \qquad x_2 = \begin{cases} 1 & \text{if disciplined management style} \\ 0 & \text{if traditional management style} \end{cases}$$

b. The SPSS printout for the regression analysis is shown in Figure 12.24. Reading the parameter estimates highlighted at the bottom of the printout, you can see that

$$\hat{y} = 1{,}365.833 + 6.217x_1 + 47.778x_2 + .033x_1x_2$$

The prediction equation for the plant using a traditional management style can be obtained (see the coding) by substituting $x_2 = 0$ into the general prediction equation. Then

$$\begin{aligned} \hat{y} &= \hat{\beta}_0 + \hat{\beta}_1 x_1 + \hat{\beta}_2(0) + \hat{\beta}_3 x_1(0) = \hat{\beta}_0 + \hat{\beta}_1 x_1 \\ &= 1{,}365.833 + 6.217x_1 \end{aligned}$$

*Although the model contains a term involving x_1x_2, it is first-order (graphs as a straight line) in the quantitative variable x_1. The variable x_2 is a dummy variable that introduces or deletes terms in the model. The order of a model is determined only by the quantitative variables that appear in the model.

Model Summary

Model	R	R Square	Adjusted R Square	Std. Error of the Estimate
1	.843[a]	.711	.649	40.839

a. Predictors: (Constant), INC_PDUM, INCENTIV, PDUMMY

ANOVA[b]

Model		Sum of Squares	df	Mean Square	F	Sig.
1	Regression	57332.39	3	19110.796	11.459	.000[a]
	Residual	23349.22	14	1667.802		
	Total	80681.61	17			

a. Predictors: (Constant), INC_PDUM, INCENTIV, PDUMMY

b. Dependent Variable: CASTINGS

Coefficients[a]

Model		Unstandardized Coefficients		Standardized Coefficients	t	Sig.
		B	Std. Error	Beta		
1	(Constant)	1365.833	51.836		26.349	.000
	INCENTIV	6.217	1.667	.758	3.729	.002
	PDUMMY	47.778	73.308	.357	.652	.525
	INC_PDUM	.033	2.358	.008	.014	.989

a. Dependent Variable: CASTINGS

Figure 12.24
SPSS printout of the complete model for the casting data

Similarly, the prediction equation for the plant with a disciplined management style can be obtained by substituting $x_2 = 1$ into the general prediction equation. Then

$$\hat{y} = \hat{\beta}_0 + \hat{\beta}_1 x_1 + \hat{\beta}_2 x_2 + \hat{\beta}_3 x_1 x_2$$
$$= \hat{\beta}_0 + \hat{\beta}_1 x_1 + \hat{\beta}_2(1) + \hat{\beta}_3 x_1(1)$$
$$= \underbrace{(\hat{\beta}_0 + \hat{\beta}_2)}_{y\text{-intercept}} + \underbrace{(\hat{\beta}_1 + \hat{\beta}_3)}_{\text{Slope}} x_1$$
$$= (1{,}365.833 + 47.778) + (6.217 + .033)x_1$$
$$= 1{,}413.611 + 6.250x_1$$

A Minitab graph of these prediction equations is shown in Figure 12.25. Note that the slopes of the two lines are nearly identical (6.217 for traditional and 6.250 for disciplined).

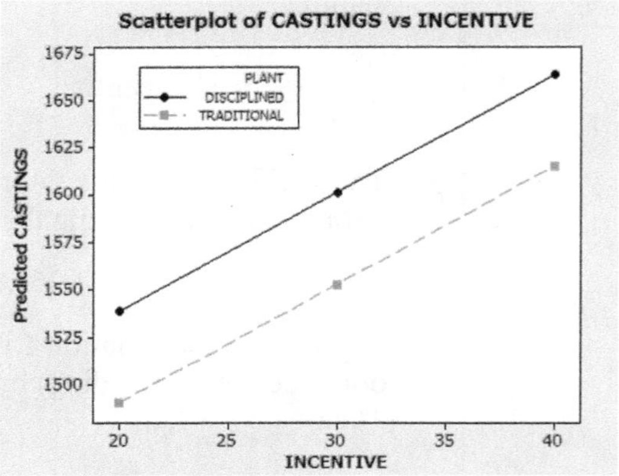

Figure 12.25
Minitab plot of prediction equations for two plants

c. If the rate of increase of productivity with incentive (i.e., the slope) for plants with the disciplined management style is different from the corresponding slope for traditional plants, then the interaction β (i.e., β_3) will differ from 0. Consequently, we want to test

$$H_0: \beta_3 = 0$$
$$H_a: \beta_3 \neq 0$$

This test is conducted using the t-test of Section 12.3. From the SPSS printout, the test statistic and corresponding p-value are

$$t = .014 \qquad p = .989$$

Because $\alpha = .10$ is less than the p-value, we fail to reject H_0. There is insufficient evidence to conclude that the traditional and disciplined shapes differ. Thus, the test supports our observation of two nearly identical slopes in part **b.**

Look Back Because interaction is not significant, we will drop the x_1x_2 term from the model and use the simpler model, $E(y) = \beta_0 + \beta_1x_1 + \beta_2x_2$, to predict productivity.

Now Work Exercise 12.88

Models with both quantitative and qualitative x's may also include higher-order (e.g., second-order) terms. In the problem of relating mean monthly sales $E(y)$ of a company to monthly advertising expenditure x_1 and type of medium, suppose we think that the relationship between $E(y)$ and x_1 is curvilinear. We will construct the model, stage by stage, to enable you to compare the procedure with the stage-by-stage construction of the first-order model in the beginning of this section. The graphical interpretations will help you understand the contributions of the model terms.

1. The mean sales curves are identical for all three advertising media—that is, a single second-order curve will suffice to describe the relationship between $E(y)$ and x_1 for all the media (see Figure 12.26):

$$E(y) = \beta_0 + \beta_1x_1 + \beta_2x_1^2$$

where x_1 = advertising expenditure

2. The response curves possess the same shapes but different y-intercepts (see Figure 12.27):

$$E(y) = \beta_0 + \beta_1x_1 + \beta_2x_1^2 + \beta_3x_2 + \beta_4x_3$$

where

$$x_1 = \text{advertising expenditure}$$

$$x_2 = \begin{cases} 1 & \text{if radio medium} \\ 0 & \text{if not} \end{cases}$$

$$x_3 = \begin{cases} 1 & \text{if television medium} \\ 0 & \text{if not} \end{cases}$$

Figure 12.26
The relationship between $E(y)$ and x_1 is the same for all media

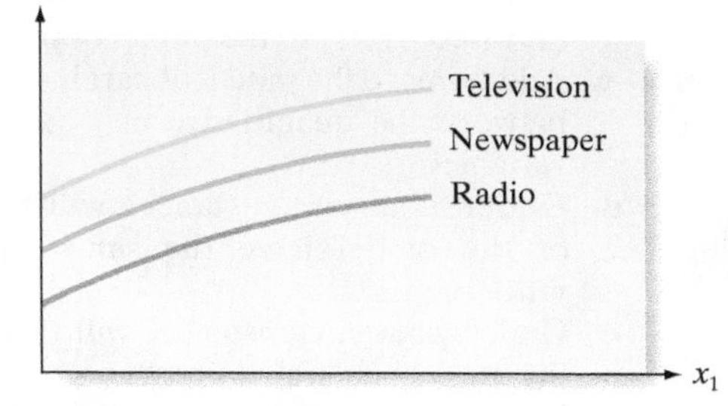

Figure 12.27
The response curves have the same shapes but different y-intercepts

3. The response curves for the three advertising media are different (i.e., advertising expenditure and type of medium interact), as shown in Figure 12.28:

$$E(y) = \beta_0 + \beta_1 x_1 + \beta_2 x_1^2 + \beta_3 x_2 + \beta_4 x_3 + \beta_5 x_1 x_2 + \beta_6 x_1 x_3 + \beta_7 x_1^2 x_2 + \beta_8 x_1^2 x_3$$

Now that you know how to write a model with two independent variables—one qualitative and one quantitative—we ask, Why do it? Why not write a separate second-order model for each type of medium where $E(y)$ is a function of only advertising expenditure? As stated earlier, one reason we wrote the single model representing all three response curves is so that we can test to determine whether the curves are different. We illustrate this procedure in Section 12.9. A second reason for writing a single model is that we obtain a pooled estimate of σ^2, the variance of the random error component ε. If the variance of ε is truly the same for each type of medium, the pooled estimate is superior to three separate estimates calculated by fitting a separate model for each type of medium.

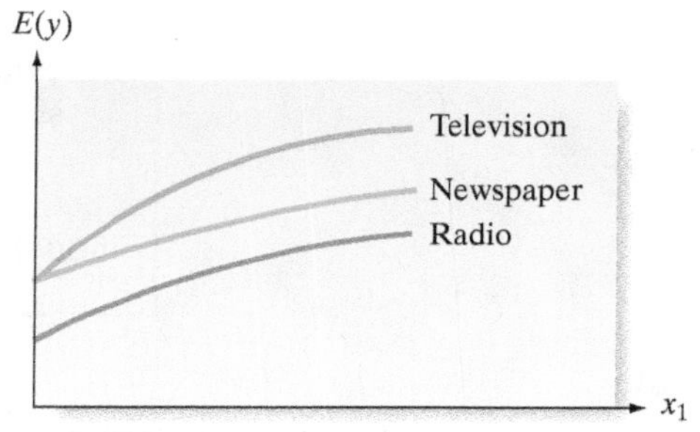

Figure 12.28
The response curves for the three media differ

Exercises 12.82–12.96

Learning the Mechanics

12.82 NW Consider a multiple regression model for a response y, with one quantitative independent variable x_1 and one qualitative variable at three levels.

a. Write a first-order model that relates the mean response $E(y)$ to the quantitative independent variable.

b. Add the main effect terms for the qualitative independent variable to the model of part **a.** Specify the coding scheme you use.

c. Add terms to the model of part **b** to allow for interaction between the quantitative and qualitative independent variables.

d. Under what circumstances will the response lines of the model in part **c** be parallel?

e. Under what circumstances will the model in part **c** have only one response line?

12.83 Refer to Exercise 12.82.

a. Write a complete second-order model that relates $E(y)$ to the quantitative variable.

b. Add the main effect terms for the qualitative variable (at three levels) to the model of part **a.**

c. Add terms to the model of part **b** to allow for interaction between the quantitative and qualitative independent variables.

d. Under what circumstances will the response curves of the model have the same shape but different y-intercepts?

e. Under what circumstances will the response curves of the model be parallel lines?

f. Under what circumstances will the response curves of the model be identical?

12.84 Consider the model:

$$y = \beta_0 + \beta_1 x_1 + \beta_2 x_2 + \beta_3 x_3 + \varepsilon$$

where x_1 is a quantitative variable and x_2 and x_3 are dummy variables describing a qualitative variable at three levels using the coding scheme

$$x_2 = \begin{cases} 1 & \text{if level 2} \\ 0 & \text{otherwise} \end{cases} \qquad x_3 = \begin{cases} 1 & \text{if level 3} \\ 0 & \text{otherwise} \end{cases}$$

The resulting least squares prediction equation is

$$\hat{y} = 44.8 + 2.2x_1 + 9.4x_2 + 15.6x_3$$

a. What is the response line (equation) for $E(y)$ when $x_2 = x_3 = 0$? When $x_2 = 1$ and $x_3 = 0$? When $x_2 = 0$ and $x_3 = 1$?

b. What is the least squares prediction equation associated with level 1? Level 2? Level 3? Plot these on the same graph.

12.85 Consider the model:

$$y = \beta_0 + \beta_1 x_1 + \beta_2 x_1^2 + \beta_3 x_2 + \beta_4 x_3 + \beta_5 x_1 x_2 + \beta_6 x_1 x_3 + \beta_7 x_1^2 x_2 + \beta_8 x_1^2 x_3 + \varepsilon$$

where x_1 is a quantitative variable and

$$x_2 = \begin{cases} 1 & \text{if level 2} \\ 0 & \text{otherwise} \end{cases} \qquad x_3 = \begin{cases} 1 & \text{if level 3} \\ 0 & \text{otherwise} \end{cases}$$

The resulting least squares prediction equation is

$$\hat{y} = 48.8 - 3.4x_1 + .07x_1^2 - 2.4x_2 - 7.5x_3 + 3.7x_1x_2 + 2.7x_1x_3 - .02x_1^2x_2 - .04x_1^2x_3$$

a. What is the equation of the response curve for $E(y)$ when $x_2 = 0$ and $x_3 = 0$? When $x_2 = 1$ and $x_3 = 0$? When $x_2 = 0$ and $x_3 = 1$?

b. On the same graph, plot the least squares prediction equation associated with level 1, with level 2, and with level 3.

12.86 Write a model that relates $E(y)$ to two independent variables—one quantitative and one qualitative at four levels. Construct a model that allows the associated response curves to be second-order but does not allow for interaction between the two independent variables.

Applying the Concepts—Basic

12.87 Reality TV and cosmetic surgery. Refer to the *Body Image: An International Journal of Research* (March 2010) study of the impact of reality TV shows on a college student's decision to undergo cosmetic surgery, Exercise 12.43 (p. 696). The data saved in the file were used to fit the interaction model, $E(y) = \beta_0 + \beta_1 x_1 + \beta_2 x_4 + \beta_3 x_1 x_4$, where y = desire to have cosmetic surgery (25-point scale), x_1 = {1 if male, 0 if female}, and x_4 = impression of reality TV (7-point scale). From the SPSS printout (p. 696), the estimated equation is:

BDYIMG

$$\hat{y} = 11.78 - 1.97x_1 + .58x_4 - .55x_1x_4$$

a. Give an estimate of the change in desire (y) for every 1-point increase in impression of reality TV show (x_4) for female students.

b. Repeat part **a** for male students.

12.88 Do blondes raise more funds? Refer to the *Economic Letters* (Vol. 100, 2008) study of whether the color of a female solicitor's hair impacts the level of capital raised, Exercise 12.75 (p. 712). Recall that 955 households were contacted by a female solicitor to raise funds for hazard mitigation research. In addition to the household's level of contribution (in dollars) and the hair color of the solicitor (blond Caucasian, brunette Caucasian, or minority female), the researcher also recorded the beauty rating of the solicitor (measured quantitatively, on a 10-point scale).

NW

a. Write a first-order model (with no interaction) for mean contribution level, $E(y)$, as a function of a solicitor's hair color and her beauty rating.

b. Refer to the model, part **a.** For each hair color, express the change in contribution level for each 1-point increase in a solicitor's beauty rating in terms of the model parameters.

c. Write an interaction model for mean contribution level, $E(y)$, as a function of a solicitor's hair color and her beauty rating.

d. Refer to the model, part **c.** For each hair color, express the change in contribution level for each 1-point increase in a solicitor's beauty rating in terms of the model parameters.

e. Refer to the model, part **c.** Illustrate the interaction with a graph.

12.89 Impact of race on football card values. Refer to the *Electronic Journal of Sociology* (2007) study of the impact of race on the value of professional football players' "rookie" cards, Exercise 12.72 (p. 712). Recall that the sample consisted of 148 rookie cards of NFL players who were inducted into the Football Hall of Fame (HOF). The researchers modeled the natural logarithm of card price (y) as a function of the following independent variables:

Race:	x_1 = 1 if black, 0 if white
Card availability:	x_2 = 1 if high, 0 if low
Card vintage:	x_3 = year card printed
Finalist:	x_4 = natural logarithm of number of times player on final HOF ballot
Position-QB:	x_5 = 1 if quarterback, 0 if not
Position-RB:	x_7 = 1 if running back, 0 if not
Position-WR:	x_8 = 1 if wide receiver, 0 if not
Position-TE:	x_9 = 1 if tight end, 0 if not
Position-DL:	x_{10} = 1 if defensive lineman, 0 if not
Position-LB:	x_{11} = 1 if linebacker, 0 if not
Position-DB:	x_{12} = 1 if defensive back, 0 if not

[*Note:* For position, offensive lineman is the base level.]

a. The model $E(y) = \beta_0 + \beta_1 x_1 + \beta_2 x_2 + \beta_3 x_3 + \beta_4 x_4 + \beta_5 x_5 + \beta_6 x_6 + \beta_7 x_7 + \beta_8 x_8 + \beta_9 x_9 + \beta_{10} x_{10} + \beta_{11} x_{11} + \beta_{12} x_{12}$ was fit to the data with the following results: $R^2 = .705$, $R_a^2 = .681$, $F = 26.9$. Interpret the results, practically. Make an inference about the overall adequacy of the model.

b. Refer to part **a.** Statistics for the race variable were reported as follows: $\hat{\beta}_1 = -.147$, $s_{\hat{\beta}_1} = .145$, $t = -1.014$, p-value $= .312$. Use this information to make an inference about the impact of race on the value of professional football players' rookie cards.

c. Refer to part **a.** Statistics for the card vintage variable were reported as follows: $\hat{\beta}_3 = -.074$, $s_{\hat{\beta}_3} = .007$, $t = -10.92$, p-value $= .000$. Use this information to make an inference about the impact of card vintage on the value of professional football players' rookie cards.

d. Write a first-order model for $E(y)$ as a function of card vintage (x_3) and position (x_5–x_{12}) that allows for the relationship between price and vintage to vary depending on position.

12.90 Buy-side vs. sell-side analysts' earnings forecasts. Refer to the *Financial Analysts Journal* (Jul./Aug. 2008) comparison of earnings forecasts of buy-side and sell-side analysts, Exercise 12.74 (p. 712). Recall that the Harvard Business School professors used regression to model the relative optimism (y) of the analysts' 3-month horizon forecasts. The following model was fit to data collected on 11,121 forecasts: $E(y) = \beta_0 + \beta_1 x_1 + \beta_2 x_2 + \beta_3 x_3$, where

x_1 = {1 if the analyst worked for a buy-side firm, 0 if the analyst worked for a sell-side firm}

x_2 = number of days between forecast and fiscal year-end (i.e., forecast horizon)

x_3 = natural logarithm of the number of quarters the analyst had worked with the firm

a. The coefficient of determination for the model was reported as $R^2 = .069$. Interpret this value.

b. Use the value of R^2 in part **a** to conduct a test of the global utility of the model. Use $\alpha = .01$.

c. The value of β_1 was estimated as 1.07, with an associated t-value of 4.3. Use this information to test ($\alpha = .01$.) whether x_1 contributes significantly to the prediction of y.

d. The professors concluded that "after controlling for forecast horizon and analyst experience, earnings forecasts by the analysts at buy-side firms are more optimistic than forecasts made by analysts at sell-side firms." Do you agree?

12.91 Workplace bullying and intention to leave. Workplace bullying (e.g., work-related harassment, persistent criticism, withholding key information, spreading rumors, intimidation) has been shown to have a negative psychological effect on victims, often leading the victim to quit or resign. In *Human Resource Management Journal* (Oct. 2008), researchers employed multiple regression to examine whether perceived organizational support (POS) would moderate the relationship between workplace bullying and victims' intention to leave the firm. The dependent variable in the analysis, intention to leave (y), was measured on a quantitative scale. The two key independent variables in the study were bullying (x_1, measured on a quantitative scale) and perceived organizational support (measured qualitatively as "low," "neutral," or "high").

a. Set up the dummy variables required to represent POS in the regression model.

b. Write a model for $E(y)$ as a function of bullying and POS that hypothesizes three parallel straight lines, one for each level of POS.

c. Write a model for $E(y)$ as a function of bullying and POS that hypothesizes three nonparallel straight lines, one for each level of POS.

d. The researchers discovered that the effect of bullying on intention to leave was greater at the low level of POS than at the high level of POS. Which of the two models, parts **b** and **c**, support these findings?

Applying the Concepts—Intermediate

12.92 Agreeableness, gender, and wages. Do agreeable individuals get paid less, on average, than those who are less agreeable on the job? And is this gap greater for males than for females? These questions were addressed in the *Journal of Personality and Social Psychology* (Feb. 2012). Several variables were measured for each in a sample of individuals enrolled in the National Survey of Midlife Development in the U.S. Three of these variables are: (1) level of agreeableness score (where higher scores indicate a greater level of agreeableness), (2) gender (male or female), and (3) annual income (dollars). The researchers modeled mean income, $E(y)$, as a function of both agreeableness score (x_1) and a dummy variable for gender ($x_2 = 1$ if male, 0 if female). Data for a sample of 100 individuals (simulated, based on information provided in the study) are saved in the file. The first 10 observations are listed in the accompanying table.

WAGAP

Data for First 10 Individuals in Study

Income	Agree Score	Gender
44,770	3.0	1
51,480	2.9	1
39,600	3.3	1
24,370	3.3	0
15,460	3.6	0
43,730	3.8	1
48,330	3.2	1
25,970	2.5	0
17,120	3.5	0
20,140	3.2	0

a. Consider the model, $E(y) = \beta_0 + \beta_1x_1 + \beta_2x_2$. The researchers theorized that for either gender, income would decrease as agreeableness score increases. If this theory is true, what is the expected sign of β_1 in the model?

b. The researchers also theorized that the rate of decrease of income with agreeableness score would be steeper for males than for females (i.e., the income gap between males and females would be greater the less agreeable the individuals are). Can this theory be tested using the model, part **a**? Explain.

c. Consider the interaction model, $E(y) = \beta_0 + \beta_1x_1 + \beta_2x_2 + \beta_3x_1x_2$. If the theory, part **b,** is true, give the expected sign of β_1. The expected sign of β_3.

d. Fit the model, part **c**, to the sample data. Check the signs of the estimated β coefficients. How do they compare to the expected values, part **c**?

e. Refer to the interaction model, part **c.** Give the null and alternative hypotheses for testing whether the rate of decrease of income with agreeableness score is steeper for males than for females.

f. Conduct the test, part **e.** Use $\alpha = .05$. Is the researchers' theory supported?

12.93 Chemical plant contamination. Refer to Exercise 12.18 (p. 683) and the model relating the mean DDT level $E(y)$ of contaminated fish to x_1 = miles captured upstream, x_2 = length, and x_3 = weight. Now consider a model for $E(y)$ as a function of both weight and species (channel catfish, largemouth bass, and smallmouth buffalo).

DDT

a. Set up the appropriate dummy variables for species.

b. Write the equation of a model that proposes parallel straight-line relationships between mean DDT level $E(y)$ and weight, one line for each species.

c. Write the equation of a model that proposes nonparallel straight-line relationships between mean DDT level $E(y)$ and weight, one line for each species.

d. Fit the model, part **b**, to the data saved in the file. Give the least squares prediction equation.

e. Refer to part **d.** Interpret the value of the least squares estimate of the beta coefficient multiplied by weight.

f. Fit the model, part **c**, to the data saved in the file. Give the least squares prediction equation.

g. Refer to part **f.** Find the estimated slope of the line relating DDT level (y) to weight for the channel catfish species.

12.94 Personality traits and job performance. Refer to the *Journal of Applied Psychology* (Jan. 2011) study of the relationship between task performance and conscientiousness, Exercise 12.54 (p. 704). Recall that the researchers used a quadratic model to relate y = task performance score (measured on a 30-point scale) to x_1 = conscientiousness score (measured on a scale of −3 to +3). In addition, the researchers included job complexity in the model, where x_2 = {1 if highly complex job, 0 if not}. The complete model took the form

$$E(y) = \beta_0 + \beta_1x_1 + \beta_2(x_1)^2 + \beta_3x_2 + \beta_4x_1x_2 + \beta_5(x_1)^2x_2$$

a. For jobs that are not highly complex, write the equation of the model for $E(y)$ as a function of x_1. (Substitute $x_2 = 0$ into the equation.)

b. Refer to part **a.** What do each of the β's represent in the model?

c. For highly complex jobs, write the equation of the model for $E(y)$ as a function of x_1. (Substitute $x_2 = 1$ into the equation.)

d. Refer to part **c.** What do each of the β's represent in the model?

e. Does the model support the researchers' theory that the curvilinear relationship between task performance score (y) and conscientiousness score (x_1) depends on job complexity (x_2)? Explain.

12.95 Recently sold, single-family homes. The National Association of Realtors maintains a database consisting of sales information on homes sold in the United States. The next table lists the sale prices for a sample of 28 recently sold, single-family homes. The table also identifies the region of the country in which the home is located and the total number of homes sold in the region during the month the home sold.

NAR

Home Price	Region	Sales Volume
$218,200	NE	55,156
235,900	NE	61,025
192,888	NE	48,991
200,990	NE	55,156
345,300	NE	60,324
178,999	NE	51,446
240,855	NW	61,025
183,200	NW	94,166
165,225	NW	92,063
160,633	NW	89,485
173,900	NW	91,772
241,000	NW	99,025
188,950	NW	94,166
192,880	NW	95,688
193,000	S	155,666
211,980	S	160,000
179,500	S	153,540
185,650	S	148,668
250,900	S	163,210
190,990	S	141,822
242,790	S	163,611
258,900	W	109,083
202,420	W	101,111
365,900	W	116,983
219,900	W	108,773
228,250	W	105,106
235,300	W	107,839
269,800	W	109,026

Source: Based on information from National Association of Realtors, www.realtor.org.

a. Propose a complete second-order model for the sale price of a single-family home as a function of region and sales volume.

b. Give the equation of the curve relating sale price to sales volume for homes sold in the West.

c. Repeat part **b** for homes sold in the Northwest.

d. Which β's in the model, part **a,** allow for differences among the mean sale prices for homes in the four regions?

e. Fit the model, part **a,** to the data using an available statistical software package. Is the model statistically useful for predicting sale price? Test using $\alpha = .01$.

12.96 Volatility of foreign stocks. The relationship between country credit ratings and the volatility of the countries' stock markets was examined in the *Journal of Portfolio Management* (Spring 1996). The researchers point out that this volatility can be explained by two factors: the countries' credit ratings and whether the countries in question have developed or emerging markets. Data on the volatility (measured as the standard deviation of stock returns), credit rating (measured as a percentage), and market type (developed or emerging) for a sample of 30 fictitious countries are saved in the file. (Selected observations are shown in the table below.)

VOLATL

a. Write a model that describes the relationship between volatility (y) and credit rating (x_1) as two nonparallel lines, one for each type of market. Specify the dummy variable coding scheme you use.

b. Plot volatility y against credit rating x_1 for all the developed markets in the sample. On the same graph, plot y against x_1 for all emerging markets in the sample. Does it appear that the model specified in part **a** is appropriate? Explain.

c. Fit the model, part **a,** to the data using a statistical software package. Report the least squares prediction equation for each of the two types of markets.

d. Plot the two prediction equations of part **c** on a scatterplot of the data.

e. Is there evidence to conclude that the slope of the linear relationship between volatility y and credit rating x_1 depends on market type? Test using $\alpha = .01$.

Country	Volatility (standard deviation of return), y	Credit Rating, x_1	Developed (D) or Emerging (E), x_2
1	56.9	9.5	E
2	25.1	72.4	D
3	28.4	58.2	E
4	56.2	9.9	E
5	21.5	92.1	D
⋮	⋮	⋮	⋮
26	47.5	16.9	E
27	22.0	89.0	D
28	21.5	91.9	D
29	38.1	30.7	E
30	37.4	32.2	E

12.9 Comparing Nested Models

To be successful model builders, we require a statistical method that will allow us to determine (with a high degree of confidence) which one among a set of candidate models best fits the data. In this section, we present such a technique for *nested models.*

> Two models are **nested** if one model contains all the terms of the second model and at least one additional term. The more complex of the two models is called the **complete** (or **full**) model, and the simpler of the two is called the **reduced** model.

To illustrate the concept of nested models, consider the straight-line interaction model for the mean auction price $E(y)$ of a grandfather clock as a function of two quantitative variables: age of the clock (x_1) and number of bidders (x_2). The interaction model, fit in Example 12.6, is

$$E(y) = \beta_0 + \beta_1 x_1 + \beta_2 x_2 + \beta_3 x_1 x_2$$

If we assume that the relationship between auction price (y), age (x_1), and bidders (x_2) is curvilinear, then the complete second-order model is more appropriate:

$$E(y) = \overbrace{\beta_0 + \beta_1 x_1 + \beta_2 x_2 + \beta_3 x_1 x_2}^{\text{Terms in interaction model}} + \overbrace{\beta_4 x_1^2 + \beta_5 x_2^2}^{\text{Quadratic terms}}$$

Note that the curvilinear model contains quadratic terms for x_1 and x_2, as well as the terms in the interaction model. Therefore, the models are nested models. In this case, the interaction model is nested within the more complex curvilinear model. Thus, the curvilinear model is the *complete* model, and the interaction model is the *reduced* model.

Suppose we want to know whether the more complex curvilinear model contributes more information for the prediction of y than the straight-line interaction model. This is equivalent to determining whether the quadratic terms β_4 and β_5 should be retained in the model. To test whether these terms should be retained, we test the null hypothesis

H_0: $\beta_4 = \beta_5 = 0$ (i.e., quadratic terms are not important for predicting y)

against the alternative hypothesis

H_a: At least one of the parameters β_4 and β_5 is nonzero (i.e., at least one of the quadratic terms is useful for predicting y).

Note that the terms being tested are those additional terms in the complete (curvilinear) model that are not in the reduced (straight-line interaction) model.

In Section 12.3, we presented the t-test for a single β coefficient and the global F-test for *all* the β parameters (except β_0) in the model. We now need a test for a *subset* of the β parameters in the complete model. The test procedure is intuitive. First, we use the method of least squares to fit the reduced model and calculate the corresponding sum of squares for error, SSE_R (the sum of squares of the deviations between observed and predicted y-values). Next, we fit the complete model and calculate its sum of squares for error, SSE_C. Then we compare SSE_R to SSE_C by calculating the difference, $\text{SSE}_\text{R} - \text{SSE}_\text{C}$. If the additional terms in the complete model are significant, then SSE_C should be much smaller than SSE_R, and the difference $\text{SSE}_\text{R} - \text{SSE}_\text{C}$ will be large.

Because SSE will always decrease when new terms are added to the model, the question is whether the difference $\text{SSE}_\text{R} - \text{SSE}_\text{C}$ is large enough to conclude that it is due to more than just an increase in the number of model terms and to chance. The formal statistical test uses an F-statistic, as shown in the box.

When the assumptions listed in Section 12.1 about the random error term are satisfied, this F-statistic has an F-distribution with ν_1 and ν_2 df. Note that ν_1 is the number of

β parameters being tested, and ν_2 is the number of degrees of freedom associated with s^2 in the complete model.

F-Test for Comparing Nested Models

Reduced model: $E(y) = \beta_0 + \beta_1 x_1 + \cdots + \beta_g x_g$

Complete model: $E(y) = \beta_0 + \beta_1 x_1 + \cdots + \beta_g x_g + \beta_{g+1} x_{g+1} + \cdots + \beta_k x_k$

H_0: $\beta_{g+1} = \beta_{g+2} = \cdots = \beta_k = 0$

H_a: At least one of the β parameters under test is nonzero.

$$\text{Test statistic: } F = \frac{(\text{SSE}_\text{R} - \text{SSE}_\text{C})/(k - g)}{\text{SSE}_\text{C}/[n - (k+1)]} = \frac{(\text{SSE}_\text{R} - \text{SSE}_\text{C})/\#\beta\text{'s tested in } H_0}{\text{MSE}_\text{C}}$$

where

SSE_R = Sum of squared errors for the reduced model

SSE_C = Sum of squared errors for the complete model

MSE_C = Mean square error (s^2) for the complete model

$k - g$ = Number of β parameters specified in H_0 (i.e., number of β parameters tested)

$k + 1$ = Number of β parameters in the complete model (including β_0)

n = Total sample size

Rejection region: $F > F_\alpha$

where F is based on $\nu_1 = k - g$ numerator degrees of freedom and $\nu_2 = n - (k + 1)$ denominator degrees of freedom.

Example 12.12

Analyzing a Complete Second-Order Model—Auction Price Data

Problem Refer to the problem of modeling the auction price (y) of an antique grandfather clock, Examples 12.1–12.6. In these examples, we discovered that price was related to both age (x_1) of the clock and number of bidders (x_2), and age and number of bidders had an interactive effect on price. Both the first-order model of Example 12.1 and the interaction model of Example 12.6, however, propose only straight-line (linear) relationships. We did not consider the possibility that the relationship between price (y) and age (x_1) is curvilinear, or that the relationship between price (y) and number of bidders (x_2) is curvilinear.

a. Propose a complete second-order model for price (y) as a function of age (x_1) and number of bidders (x_2).

b. Fit the model to the data for the 32 clocks in Table 12.1 and give the least squares prediction equation.

c. Do the data provide sufficient evidence to indicate that the quadratic terms in the model contribute information for the prediction of price (y)? That is, is there evidence of curvature in the price-age and price-bidders relationships?

Solution

a. Because both age (x_1) and number of bidders (x_2) are quantitative variables, we write the complete second-order model as follows:

$$E(y) = \beta_0 + \beta_1 x_1 + \beta_2 x_2 + \beta_3 x_1 x_2 + \beta_4 (x_1)^2 + \beta_5 (x_2)^2$$

Note that we have added two quadratic terms, $\beta_4 (x_1)^2$ and $\beta_5 (x_2)^2$, to the interaction model of Example 12.6.

Regression Analysis: PRICE versus AGE, NUMBIDS, AGE-BID, AGESQ, NUMBIDSQ

```
The regression equation is
PRICE = - 332 + 3.21 AGE + 14.8 NUMBIDS + 1.12 AGE-BID - 0.0030 AGESQ
        - 4.18 NUMBIDSQ

Predictor        Coef   SE Coef       T      P
Constant       -331.9     764.9   -0.43  0.668
AGE             3.208     8.947    0.36  0.723
NUMBIDS         14.81     62.21    0.24  0.814
AGE-BID        1.1232    0.2316    4.85  0.000
AGESQ        -0.00300   0.02748   -0.11  0.914
NUMBIDSQ       -4.179     2.145   -1.95  0.062

S = 86.1019   R-Sq = 96.0%   R-Sq(adj) = 95.2%

Analysis of Variance

Source          DF       SS      MS       F      P
Regression       5  4607038  921408  124.29  0.000
Residual Error  26   192752    7414
Total           31  4799790
```

Figure 12.29
Minitab analysis of complete second-order model for auction price

b. We used Minitab to fit the model to the data in Table 12.2. The Minitab output is shown in Figure 12.29. The least squares prediction equation, highlighted on the printout, is

$$\hat{y} = -332 + 3.21x_1 + 14.8x_2 + 1.12x_1x_2 - .003(x_1)^2 - 4.18(x_2)^2$$

Note that the estimates of the quadratic terms, β_4 and β_5, are both negative, implying downward curvature in both the price-age and price-bidders relationships.

c. To determine whether the quadratic terms are useful for predicting price (y), we want to test

$$H_0\text{: } \beta_4 = \beta_5 = 0$$

H_a: At least one of the parameters, β_4 and β_5, differs from 0.

Because the null hypothesis involves a subset of β's, we will need to perform a nested model F-test. The complete model is the complete second-order model of part **a.** The reduced model is obtained by dropping the quadratic terms out of the complete model. Doing so yields:

$$\textit{Reduced model: } E(y) = \beta_0 + \beta_1x_1 + \beta_2x_2 + \beta_3x_1x_2$$

We fit this model in Example 12.6. The Minitab printout for this reduced model is reproduced in Figure 12.30.

To conduct this test, we first obtain the SSE values for the complete and reduced models. These values (highlighted, respectively, on Figures 12.29 and 12.30) are

$$\text{SSE}_\text{C} = 192{,}752 \text{ and } \text{SSE}_\text{R} = 221{,}362$$

Also, s^2 for the complete model (highlighted on Figure 12.29) is

$$s^2 = \text{MSE}_\text{C} = 7{,}414$$

Recall that $n = 32$ and that there are $k = 5$ terms in the complete model and $g = 3$ terms in the reduced model. Therefore, the calculated value of the test statistic is

$$\textit{Test statistic: } F = \frac{(\text{SSE}_\text{R} - \text{SSE}_\text{C})/(k - g)}{\text{MSE}_\text{C}} = \frac{(221{,}362 - 192{,}752)/2}{7{,}414} = 1.93$$

The critical F-value for the rejection region is based on $\nu_1 = (k - g) = 2$ numerator df and $\nu_2 = [n - (k + 1)] = 26$ denominator df. If we choose $\alpha = .05$, this critical value is $F_{.05} = 3.37$ and the rejection region is

$$\textit{Rejection region: } F > 3.37$$

Because the test statistic, $F = 1.93$, falls outside the rejection region, we fail to reject H_0. That is, there is insufficient evidence (at $\alpha = .05$) to conclude that at least one

Regression Analysis: PRICE versus AGE, NUMBIDS, AGEBID

```
The regression equation is
PRICE = 320 + 0.88 AGE - 93.3 NUMBIDS + 1.30 AGEBID


Predictor     Coef  SE Coef      T      P
Constant     320.5    295.1   1.09  0.287
AGE          0.878    2.032   0.43  0.669
NUMBIDS     -93.26    29.89  -3.12  0.004
AGEBID      1.2978   0.2123   6.11  0.000


S = 88.9145   R-Sq = 95.4%   R-Sq(adj) = 94.9%


Analysis of Variance

Source          DF       SS       MS       F      P
Regression       3  4578427  1526142  193.04  0.000
Residual Error  28   221362     7906
Total           31  4799790
```

Figure 12.30
Minitab analysis of reduced model for auction price

of the quadratic terms contributes information for the prediction of auction price (y). Consequently, there is no evidence of curvature in either the price-age or price-bidders relationship. It appears that the first-order, interaction (reduced) model is adequate for predicting auction price.

Look Back Some statistical software packages will perform the desired nested model F-test if requested. The test statistic and p-value for the test above are highlighted on the SPSS printout, Figure 12.31. Note that p-value $= .165$ exceeds $\alpha = .05$; thus, there is insufficient evidence to reject H_0.

■ **Now Work Exercise 12.100**

Model Summary

Model	R	R Square	Adjusted R Square	Std. Error of the Estimate	Change Statistics				
					R Square Change	F Change	df1	df2	Sig. F Change
1	.977[a]	.954	.949	88.915	.954	193.041	3	28	.000
2	.980[b]	.960	.952	86.102	.006	1.930	2	26	.165

a. Predictors: (Constant), AGE_BID, AGE, NUMBIDS

b. Predictors: (Constant), AGE_BID, AGE, NUMBIDS, NUMBIDSQ, AGESQ

Figure 12.31
SPSS printout of nested model F-test for auction price

The nested model F-test can be used to determine whether *any* subset of terms should be included in a complete model by testing the null hypothesis that a particular set of β parameters simultaneously equals 0. For example, we may want to test to determine whether a set of interaction terms for quantitative variables or a set of main effect terms for a qualitative variable should be included in a model. If we reject H_0, the complete model is the better of the two nested models. If we fail to reject H_0, as in Example 12.12, we favor the reduced model. Although we must be cautious about accepting H_0, most practitioners of regression analysis adopt the principle of *parsimony*—that is, in situations where two competing models are found to have essentially the same predictive power (as in Example 12.12), the model with the fewer number of β's (i.e., the more parsimonious model) is selected. Based on this principle, we would drop the two quadratic terms and select the first-order, interaction (reduced) model over the second-order (complete) model.

A **parsimonious model** is a general linear model with a small number of β parameters. In situations where two competing models have essentially the same predictive power (as determined by an F-test), choose the more parsimonious of the two.

Guidelines for Selecting Preferred Model in a Nested Model *F*-Test

Conclusion		*Preferred Model*
Reject H_0	→	Complete Model
Fail to reject H_0	→	Reduced Model

When the candidate models in model building are nested models, the *F*-test developed in this section is the appropriate procedure to apply to compare the models. However, if the models are not nested, this *F*-test is not applicable. In this situation, the analyst must base the choice of the best model on statistics such as R_a^2 and *s*. It is important to remember that decisions based on these and other numerical descriptive measures of model adequacy cannot be supported with a measure of reliability and are often very subjective in nature.

Exercises 12.97–12.110

Learning the Mechanics

12.97 Determine which pairs of the following models are "nested" models. For each pair of nested models, identify the complete and reduced model.

a. $E(y) = \beta_0 + \beta_1x_1 + \beta_2x_2$
b. $E(y) = \beta_0 + \beta_1x_1$
c. $E(y) = \beta_0 + \beta_1x_1 + \beta_2x_1^2$
d. $E(y) = \beta_0 + \beta_1x_1 + \beta_2x_2 + \beta_3x_1x_2$
e. $E(y) = \beta_0 + \beta_1x_1 + \beta_2x_2 + \beta_3x_1x_2 + \beta_4x_1^2 + \beta_5x_2^2$

12.98 Suppose you fit the regression model

$$y = \beta_0 + \beta_1x_1 + \beta_2x_2 + \beta_3x_1x_2 + \beta_4x_1^2 + \beta_5x_2^2 + \varepsilon$$

to $n = 30$ data points and wish to test

$$H_0\text{: } \beta_3 = \beta_4 = \beta_5 = 0$$

a. State the alternative hypothesis H_a.
b. Give the reduced model appropriate for conducting the test.
c. What are the numerator and denominator degrees of freedom associated with the *F*-statistic?
d. Suppose the SSE's for the reduced and complete models are $SSE_R = 1{,}250.2$ and $SSE_C = 1{,}125.2$. Conduct the hypothesis test and interpret the results of your test. Test using $\alpha = .05$.

12.99 The complete model

$$y = \beta_0 + \beta_1x_1 + \beta_2x_2 + \beta_3x_3 + \beta_4x_4 + \varepsilon$$

was fit to $n = 20$ data points, with SSE = 152.66. The reduced model, $y = \beta_0 + \beta_1x_1 + \beta_2x_2 + \varepsilon$, was also fit, with SSE = 160.44.

a. How many β parameters are in the complete model? The reduced model?
b. Specify the null and alternative hypotheses you would use to investigate whether the complete model contributes more information for the prediction of *y* than the reduced model.
c. Conduct the hypothesis test of part **b.** Use $\alpha = .05$.

Applying the Concepts—Basic

12.100 **Mental health of a community.** An article in the *Community Mental Health Journal* (Aug. 2000) used multiple regression analysis to model the level of community adjustment of clients of the Department of Mental Health and Addiction Services in Connecticut. The dependent variable, community adjustment (*y*), was measured quantitatively based on staff ratings of the clients. (Lower scores indicate better adjustment.) The complete model was a first-order model with 21 independent variables. The independent variables were categorized as Demographic (4 variables), Diagnostic (7 variables), Treatment (4 variables), and Community (6 variables).
NW

a. Write the equation of $E(y)$ for the complete model.
b. Give the null hypothesis for testing whether the 7 Diagnostic variables contribute information for the prediction of *y*.
c. Give the equation of the reduced model appropriate for the test, part **b.**
d. The test, part **b,** resulted in a test statistic of $F = 59.3$ and *p*-value $< .0001$. Interpret this result in the words of the problem.

12.101 **Buy-side vs. sell-side analysts' earnings forecasts.** Refer to the *Financial Analysts Journal* (Jul./Aug. 2008) comparison of earnings forecasts of buy-side and sell-side analysts, Exercise 12.90 (p. 721). Recall that the Harvard Business School professors used regression to model the relative optimism (*y*) of the analysts' 3-month horizon forecasts as a function of x_1 = {1 if the analyst worked for a buy-side firm, 0 if the analyst worked for a sell-side firm} and x_2 = number of days between forecast and fiscal year-end (i.e., forecast horizon). Consider the complete second-order model

$$E(y) = \beta_0 + \beta_1x_1 + \beta_2x_2 + \beta_3x_1x_2 + \beta_4(x_2)^2 + \beta_5x_1(x_2)^2$$

a. What null hypothesis would you test to determine whether the quadratic terms in the model are statistically useful for predicting relative optimism (*y*)?

b. Give the complete and reduced models for conducting the test, part **a.**

c. What null hypothesis would you test to determine whether the interaction terms in the model are statistically useful for predicting relative optimism (y)?

d. Give the complete and reduced models for conducting the test, part **c.**

e. What null hypothesis would you test to determine whether the dummy variable terms in the model are statistically useful for predicting relative optimism (y)?

f. Give the complete and reduced models for conducting the test, part **e.**

12.102 Workplace bullying and intention to leave. Refer to the *Human Resource Management Journal* (Oct. 2008) study of workplace bullying, Exercise 12.91 (p. 722). Recall that multiple regression was used to model an employee's intention to leave (y) as a function of bullying (x_1, measured on a quantitative scale) and perceived organizational support (measured qualitatively as "low POS," "neutral POS," or "high POS"). In Exercise 12.91b, you wrote a model for $E(y)$ as a function of bullying and POS that hypothesizes three parallel straight lines, one for each level of POS. In Exercise 12.91c, you wrote a model for $E(y)$ as a function of bullying and POS that hypothesizes three nonparallel straight lines, one for each level of POS.

a. Explain why the two models are nested. Which is the complete model? Which is the reduced model?

b. Give the null hypothesis for comparing the two models.

c. If you reject H_0 in part **b,** which model do you prefer? Why?

d. If you fail to reject H_0 in part **b,** which model do you prefer? Why?

12.103 Cooling method for gas turbines. Refer to the *Journal of Engineering for Gas Turbines and Power* (Jan. 2005) study of a high-pressure inlet fogging method for a gas turbine engine, Exercise 12.19 (p. 683). Consider a model for heat rate (kilojoules per kilowatt per hour) of a gas turbine as a function of cycle speed (revolutions per minute) and cycle pressure ratio. The data are saved in the file.

GASTRB

a. Write a complete second-order model for heat rate (y).

b. Give the null and alternative hypotheses for determining whether the curvature terms in the complete second-order model are statistically useful for predicting heat rate (y).

c. For the test in part **b,** identify the complete and reduced model.

d. Portions of the Minitab printouts for the two models are shown below. Find the values of SSE_R, SSE_C, and MSE_C on the printouts.

e. Compute the value of the test statistics for the test of part **b.**

f. Find the rejection region for the test of part **b** using $\alpha = .10$.

g. State the conclusion of the test in the words of the problem.

12.104 Personality traits and job performance. Refer to the *Journal of Applied Psychology* (Jan. 2011) study of the relationship between task performance and conscientiousness, Exercise 12.94 (p. 722). Recall that y = task performance score (measured on a 30-point scale) was modeled as a function of x_1 = conscientiousness score (measured on a scale of -3 to $+3$) and x_2 = {1 if highly complex job, 0 if not} using the complete model

$$E(y) = \beta_0 + \beta_1 x_1 + \beta_2 (x_1)^2 + \beta_3 x_2 + \beta_4 x_1 x_2 + \beta_5 (x_1)^2 x_2$$

a. Specify the null hypothesis for testing the overall adequacy of the model.

Complete Model

```
The regression equation is
HEATRATE = 15583 + 0.078 RPM - 523 CPRATIO + 0.00445 RPM_CPR - 0.000000 RPMSQ
           + 8.84 CPRSQ

S = 563.513   R-Sq = 88.5%   R-Sq(adj) = 87.5%

Analysis of Variance

Source          DF         SS        MS       F      P
Regression       5  148526859  29705372   93.55  0.000
Residual Error  61   19370350    317547
Total           66  167897208
```

Reduced Model

```
The regression equation is
HEATRATE = 12065 + 0.170 RPM - 146 CPRATIO - 0.00242 RPM_CPR

S = 633.842   R-Sq = 84.9%   R-Sq(adj) = 84.2%

Analysis of Variance

Source          DF         SS        MS       F      P
Regression       3  142586570  47528857  118.30  0.000
Residual Error  63   25310639    401756
Total           66  167897208
```

Minitab output for Exercise 12.103

b. Specify the null hypothesis for testing whether task performance score (y) and conscientiousness score (x_1) are curvilinearly related.

c. Specify the null hypothesis for testing whether the curvilinear relationship between task performance score (y) and conscientiousness score (x_1) depends on job complexity (x_2).

d. Explain how each of the tests, parts **a–c,** should be conducted (i.e., give the forms of the test statistic and the reduced model).

Applying the Concepts—Intermediate

12.105 Reality TV and cosmetic surgery. Refer to the *Body Image: An International Journal of Research* (March 2010) study of the influence of reality TV shows on one's desire to undergo cosmetic surgery, Exercise 12.17 (p. 682). Recall that psychologists modeled desire to have cosmetic surgery (y) as a function of gender (x_1), self-esteem (x_2), body satisfaction (x_3), and impression of reality TV (x_4). The psychologists theorized that one's impression of reality TV will "moderate" the impact that each of the first three independent variables has on one's desire to have cosmetic surgery. If so, then x_4 will interact with each of the other independent variables.

BDYIMG

a. Give the equation of the model for $E(y)$ that matches the theory.

b. Fit the model, part **a,** to the simulated data saved in the file. Evaluate the overall utility of the model.

c. Give the null hypothesis for testing the psychologists' theory.

d. Conduct a nested model F-test to test the theory. What do you conclude?

12.106 Study of supervisor-targeted aggression. "Moonlighters" are workers who hold two jobs at the same time. What are the factors that impact the likelihood of a moonlighting worker becoming aggressive toward his/her supervisor? This was the research question of interest in the *Journal of Applied Psychology* (July 2005). Completed questionnaires were obtained from $n = 105$ moonlighters, and the data were used to fit several multiple regression models for supervisor-directed aggression score (y). Two of the models (with R^2 values in parentheses) are given below:

Model 1: $E(y) = \beta_0 + \beta_1(\text{Age}) + \beta_2(\text{Gender}) + \beta_3(\text{Interatctional injustice at 2nd job}) + \beta_4(\text{Abusive supervisor at 2nd job})$

($R^2 = .101$)

Model 2: $E(y) = \beta_0 + \beta_1(\text{Age}) + \beta_2(\text{Gender}) + \beta_3(\text{Interactional injustice at 2nd job}) + \beta_4(\text{Abusive supervisor at 2nd job}) + \beta_5(\text{Self-esteem}) + \beta_6(\text{History of aggression}) + \beta_7(\text{Interactional injustice at primary job}) + \beta_8(\text{Abusive supervisor at primary job})$

($R^2 = .555$)

a. Interpret the R^2 values for the models.

b. Give the null and alternative hypotheses for comparing the fits of models 1 and 2.

c. Are the two models nested? Explain.

d. The nested F-test for comparing the two models resulted in $F = 42.13$ and p-value $< .001$. What can you conclude from these results?

e. A third model was fit, one that hypothesizes all possible pairs of interactions between self-esteem, history of aggression, interactional injustice at primary job, and abusive supervisor at primary job. Give the equation of this model (model 3).

f. A nested F-test to compare models 2 and 3 resulted in a p-value $> .10$. What can you conclude from this result?

12.107 Agreeableness, gender, and wages. Refer to the *Journal of Personality and Social Psychology* (Feb. 2012) study of on-the-job agreeableness and wages, Exercise 12.92 (p. 722). The researchers modeled mean income, $E(y)$, as a function of both agreeableness score (x_1) and a dummy variable for gender ($x_2 = 1$ if male, 0 if female). Suppose the researchers theorize that for either gender, income will decrease at a decreasing rate as agreeableness score increases. Consequently, they want to fit a second-order model.

WAGAP

a. Consider the model, $E(y) = \beta_0 + \beta_1 x_1 + \beta_2(x_1)^2 + \beta_3 x_2$. If the researchers' belief is true, what is the expected sign of β_2 in the model?

b. Draw a sketch of the model, part **a,** showing how gender impacts the income-agreeableness score relationship.

c. Write a complete second-order model for $E(y)$ as a function of x_1 and x_2.

d. Draw a sketch of the model, part **c,** showing how gender impacts the income-agreeableness score relationship.

e. What null hypothesis would you test in order to compare the two models, parts **a** and **c**?

f. Fit the models to the sample data saved in the file and carry out the test, part **e.** What do you conclude? (Test using $\alpha = .10$.)

12.108 Recently sold, single-family homes. Refer to the National Association of Realtors data on sales price (y), region (NE, NW, S, or W), and sales volume for 28 recently sold, single-family homes, Exercise 12.95 (p. 723). You fit a complete second-order model for $E(y)$ as a function of region and sales volume.

NAR

a. Conduct a nested-model F-test to determine whether the quadratic terms in the model are statistically useful for predicting sales price (y). Use $\alpha = .05$.

b. Based on the result, part **a,** which of the nested models (the complete or the reduced model) do you prefer to use in predicting sales price (y)? Explain.

c. Refer to part **b.** Treat the preferred model as the complete model and conduct a nested model F-test to determine whether region and sales volume interact to affect sales price (y). Use $\alpha = .05$.

d. Based on the result, part **c,** which of the nested models (the complete or the reduced model) do you prefer to use in predicting sales price (y)? Explain.

12.109 Glass as a waste encapsulant. Because glass is not subject to radiation damage, encapsulation of waste in glass is considered to be one of the most promising solutions to the problem of low-level nuclear waste in the environment. However, chemical reactions may weaken the glass.

This concern led to a study undertaken jointly by the Department of Materials Science and Engineering at the University of Florida and the U.S. Department of Energy to assess the utility of glass as a waste encapsulant.* Corrosive chemical solutions (called *corrosion baths*) were prepared and applied directly to glass samples containing one of three types of waste (TDS-3A, FE, and AL); the chemical reactions were observed over time. A few of the key variables measured were

y = Amount of silicon (in parts per million) found in solution at end of experiment. (This is both a measure of the degree of breakdown in the glass and a proxy for the amount of radioactive species released into the environment.)

x_1 = Temperature (°C) of the corrosion bath

x_2 = 1 if waste type TDS-3A, 0 if not

x_3 = 1 if waste type FE, 0 if not

(Waste type AL is the base level.) Suppose we want to model amount y of silicon as a function of temperature (x_1) and type of waste (x_2, x_3).

a. Write a model that proposes parallel straight-line relationships between amount of silicon and temperature, one line for each of the three waste types.

b. Add terms for the interaction between temperature and waste type to the model of part **a.**

c. Refer to the model of part **b.** For each waste type, give the slope of the line relating amount of silicon to temperature.

d. Explain how you could test for the presence of temperature–waste type interaction.

Applying the Concepts—Advanced

12.110 Emotional distress in firefighters. The *Journal of Human Stress* (Summer 1987) reported on a study of "psychological response of firefighters to chemical fire." It is thought that the following complete second-order model will be adequate to describe the relationship between emotional distress and years of experience for two groups of firefighters—those exposed to a chemical fire and those unexposed:

$$E(y) = \beta_0 + \beta_1x_1 + \beta_2x_1^2 + \beta_3x_2 + \beta_4x_1x_2 + \beta_5x_1^2x_2$$

where

y = Emotional distress

x_1 = Experience (years)

x_2 = 1 if exposed to chemical fire, 0 if not

a. How would you determine whether the *rate* of increase of emotional distress with experience is different for the two groups of firefighters?

b. How would you determine whether there are differences in mean emotional distress levels that are attributable to exposure group?

12.10 Stepwise Regression

Consider the problem of predicting the salary y of an executive. Perhaps the biggest problem in building a model to describe executive salaries is choosing the important independent variables to be included in the model. The list of potentially important independent variables is extremely long (e.g., age, experience, tenure, education level, etc.), and we need some objective method of screening out those that are not important.

The problem of deciding which of a large set of independent variables to include in a model is a common one. Trying to determine which variables influence the profit of a firm, affect blood pressure of humans, or are related to a student's performance in college are only a few examples.

A systematic approach to building a model with a large number of independent variables is difficult because the interpretation of multivariable interactions and higher-order terms is tedious. We therefore turn to a screening procedure, available in most statistical software packages, known as **stepwise regression.**

The most commonly used stepwise regression procedure works as follows. The user first identifies the response, y, and the set of potentially important independent variables, $x_1, x_2, \dots, x_k$, where k is generally large. [*Note:* This set of variables could include both first-order and higher-order terms. However, we may often include only the main effects of both quantitative variables (first-order terms) and qualitative variables (dummy variables) because the inclusion of second-order terms greatly increases the number of independent variables.] The response and independent variables are then entered into the computer software, and the stepwise procedure begins.

Step 1: The software program fits all possible one-variable models of the form

$$E(y) = \beta_0 + \beta_1x_i$$

*The background information for this exercise was provided by Dr. David Clark, Department of Materials Science and Engineering, University of Florida.

to the data, where x_i is the ith independent variable, $i = 1, 2, \ldots, k$. For each model, the test of the null hypothesis

$$H_0: \beta_1 = 0$$

against the alternative hypothesis

$$H_a: \beta_1 \neq 0$$

is conducted using the t-test (or the equivalent F-test) for a single β parameter. The independent variable that produces the largest (absolute) t-value is declared the best one-variable predictor of y.* Call this independent variable x_1.

Step 2: The stepwise program now begins to search through the remaining $(k - 1)$ independent variables for the best two-variable model of the form

$$E(y) = \beta_0 + \beta_1 x_1 + \beta_2 x_i$$

This is done by fitting all two-variable models containing x_1 and each of the other $(k - 1)$ options for the second variable x_i. The t-values for the test $H_0: \beta_2 = 0$ are computed for each of the $(k - 1)$ models (corresponding to the remaining independent variables, x_i, $i = 2, 3, \ldots, k$), and the variable having the largest t is retained. Call this variable x_2.

At this point, some software packages diverge in methodology. The better packages now go back and check the t-value of $\hat{\beta}_1$ after $\hat{\beta}_2 x_2$ has been added to the model. If the t-value has become nonsignificant at some specified α level (say $\alpha = .10$), the variable x_1 is removed and a search is made for the independent variable with a β parameter that will yield the most significant t-value in the presence of $\hat{\beta}_2 x_2$. Other packages do not recheck the significance of $\hat{\beta}_1$ but proceed directly to step 3.†

The reason the t-value for x_1 may change from step 1 to step 2 is that the meaning of the coefficient $\hat{\beta}_1$ changes. In step 2, we are approximating a complex response surface in two variables with a plane. The best-fitting plane may yield a different value for $\hat{\beta}_1$ than that obtained in step 1. Thus, both the value of $\hat{\beta}_1$ and its significance usually change from step 1 to step 2. For this reason, the software packages that recheck the t-values at each step are preferred.

Step 3: The stepwise procedure now checks for a third independent variable to include in the model with x_1 and x_2—that is, we seek the best model of the form

$$E(y) = \beta_0 + \beta_1 x_1 + \beta_2 x_2 + \beta_3 x_i$$

To do this, we fit all the $(k - 2)$ models using x_1, x_2, and each of the $(k - 2)$ remaining variables, x_i, as a possible x_3. The criterion is again to include the independent variable with the largest t-value. Call this best third variable x_3.

The better programs now recheck the t-values corresponding to the x_1 and x_2 coefficients, removing the variables with t-values that have become nonsignificant. This procedure is continued until no further independent variables can be found that yield significant t-values (at the specified α level) in the presence of the variables already in the model.

The result of the stepwise procedure is a model containing only those terms with t-values that are significant at the specified α level. Thus, in most practical situations, only several of the large number of independent variables remain. However, it is very important *not* to jump to the conclusion that all the independent variables important for predicting y have been identified or that the unimportant independent variables have been eliminated. Remember, the stepwise procedure is using only *sample estimates* of the true model coefficients (β's) to select the important variables. An extremely large

*In step 1, note that the variable with the largest t-value is also the one with the largest (absolute) Pearson product moment correlation, r (Section 11.5), with y.

†*Forward selection* is the name given to stepwise routines that *do not* recheck the significance of each previously entered independent variable. This is in constrast to *stepwise selection* routines, which perform the rechecks. A third approach is to use *backward selection,* where initially, all terms are entered and then eliminated one by one.

number of single β parameter t-tests have been conducted, and the probability is very high that one or more errors have been made in including or excluding variables—that is, we have very probably included some unimportant independent variables in the model (Type I errors) and eliminated some important ones (Type II errors).

There is a second reason why we might not have arrived at a good model. When we choose the variables to be included in the stepwise regression, we may often omit higher-order terms (to keep the number of variables manageable). Consequently, we may have initially omitted several important terms from the model. Thus, we should recognize stepwise regression for what it is: an **objective variable screening procedure.**

Successful model builders will now consider second-order terms (for quantitative variables) and other interactions among variables screened by the stepwise procedure. It would be best to develop this response surface model with a second set of data independent of that used for the screening, so that the results of the stepwise procedure can be partially verified with new data. This is not always possible, however, because in many modeling situations only a small amount of data is available.

Do not be deceived by the impressive-looking t-values that result from the stepwise procedure—it has retained only the independent variables with the largest t-values. Also, be certain to consider second-order terms in systematically developing the prediction model. Finally, if you have used a first-order model for your stepwise procedure, remember that it may be greatly improved by the addition of higher-order terms.

⚠ CAUTION Be wary of using the results of stepwise regression to make inferences about the relationship between $E(y)$ and the independent variables in the resulting first-order model. First, an extremely large number of t-tests have been conducted, leading to a high probability of making one or more Type I or Type II errors. Second, the stepwise model does not include any higher-order or interaction terms. Stepwise regression should be used only when necessary—that is, when you want to determine which of a large number of potentially important independent variables should be used in the model-building process.

Example 12.13

Running a Stepwise Regression—Modeling Executive Salary

Problem An international management consulting company develops multiple regression models for executive salaries of its client firms. The consulting company has found that models that use the natural logarithm of salary as the dependent variable have better predictive power than those using salary as the dependent variable.* A preliminary step in the construction of these models is the determination of the most important independent variables. For one firm, 10 potential independent variables (7 quantitative and 3 qualitative) were measured in a sample of 100 executives. The data, described in Table 12.5, are

Table 12.5 Independent Variables in the Executive Salary Example

Independent Variable	Description	Type
x_1	Experience (years)	Quantitative
x_2	Education (years)	Quantitative
x_3	Bonus eligibility (1 if yes, 0 if no)	Qualitative
x_4	Number of employees supervised	Quantitative
x_5	Corporate assets (millions of dollars)	Quantitative
x_6	Board member (1 if yes, 0 if no)	Qualitative
x_7	Age (years)	Quantitative
x_8	Company profits (past 12 months, millions of dollars)	Quantitative
x_9	Has international responsibility (1 if yes, 0 if no)	Qualitative
x_{10}	Company's total sales (past 12 months, millions of dollars)	Quantitative

Data Set: EXSAL

*This is probably because salaries tend to be incremented in *percentages* rather than dollar values. When a response variable undergoes percentage changes as the independent variables are varied, the logarithm of the response variable will be more suitable as a dependent variable.

saved in the file. Because it would be very difficult to construct a complete second-order model with all of the 10 independent variables, use stepwise regression to decide which of the 10 variables should be included in the building of the final model for the natural log of executive salaries.

Solution We will use stepwise regression with the main effects of the 10 independent variables to identify the most important variables. The dependent variable y is the natural logarithm of the executive salaries. The Minitab stepwise regression printout is shown in Figure 12.32.

```
Alpha-to-Enter: 0.15  Alpha-to-Remove: 0.15

Response is Y on 10 predictors, with N = 100

Step              1        2        3        4        5
Constant     11.091   10.968   10.783   10.278    9.962

X1           0.0278   0.0273   0.0273   0.0273   0.0273
T-Value       12.62    15.13    18.80    24.68    26.50
P-Value       0.000    0.000    0.000    0.000    0.000

X3                     0.197    0.233    0.232    0.225
T-Value                 7.10    10.17    13.30    13.74
P-Value                0.000    0.000    0.000    0.000

X4                             0.00048  0.00055  0.00052
T-Value                           7.32    10.92    11.06
P-Value                          0.000    0.000    0.000

X2                                       0.0300   0.0291
T-Value                                    8.38     8.72
P-Value                                   0.000    0.000

X5                                               0.00196
T-Value                                             3.95
P-Value                                            0.000

S             0.161    0.131    0.106   0.0807   0.0751
R-Sq          61.90    74.92    83.91    90.75    92.06
R-Sq(adj)     61.51    74.40    83.41    90.36    91.64
Mallows C-p   343.9    195.5     93.8     16.8      3.6
```

Figure 12.32
Minitab stepwise regression printout for executive salary data

Note that the first variable included in the model is x_1, years of experience. At the second step, x_3, a dummy variable for the qualitative variable, bonus eligibility or not, is brought into the model. In steps 3, 4, and 5, the variables x_4 (number of employees supervised), x_2 (years of education), and x_5 (corporate assets), respectively, are selected for model inclusion. Minitab stops after five steps because no other independent variables met the criterion for admission into the model. As a default, Minitab uses $\alpha = .15$ in the t-tests conducted. In other words, if the p-value associated with a β coefficient exceeds $\alpha = .15$, the variable is *not* included in the model.

The results of the stepwise regression suggest that we should concentrate on these five independent variables. Models with second-order terms and interactions should be proposed and evaluated to determine the best model for predicting executive salaries.

■ **Now Work Exercise 12.113**

⚠ **RECOMMENDATION** Do *not* use the stepwise regression model as the *final* model for predicting y. Recall that the stepwise procedure tends to perform a large number of t-tests, inflating the overall probability of a Type I error, and does not automatically include higher-order terms (e.g., interactions and squared terms) in the final model. Use stepwise regression as a variable screening tool when there exists a large number of potentially important independent variables. Then begin building models for y using the variables identified by stepwise.

Variable Screening and Model Building

In the previous Statistics in Action Revisited section (p. 687), we used all eight of the independent variables in Table SIA12.1 to fit a first-order model for the cost (y) of a road construction contract awarded using the sealed-bid system. Although the model was deemed statistically useful for predicting y, the standard deviation of the model ($s = 305$ thousand dollars) was probably too large for the model to be practically useful. A more complex model—one involving higher-order terms (interactions and squared terms)—needs to be considered. A complete second-order model involving all eight of the independent variables, however, would require over 100 terms! Consequently, we'll use stepwise regression to select the best subset of independent variables and then form a complete second-order model with just these variables.

Figure SIA12.4 is a Minitab printout of the stepwise regression. You can see that the DOT engineer's cost estimate (DOTEST) is the first variable selected, followed by bid status (STATUS), estimated work days (DAYSEST), and bids to plan holders ratio (BTPRATIO). Recall that Minitab uses a default α level of .15. If we reduce the significance level for entry to $\alpha = .05$, only DOTEST and STATUS are selected because the p-values (highlighted on the printout) for DAYSEST and BTPRATIO are both greater than .05.

```
 Alpha-to-Enter: 0.15  Alpha-to-Remove: 0.15


Response is COST on 8 predictors, with N = 235


Step                1        2        3         4
Constant        20.91   -20.54   -55.22   -212.85

DOTEST         0.9263   0.9308   0.9110    0.9132
T-Value         93.89    95.52    56.86     57.11
P-Value         0.000    0.000    0.000     0.000

STATUS                     166      167       171
T-Value                   3.38     3.40      3.50
P-Value                  0.001    0.001     0.001

DAYSEST                            0.27      0.33
T-Value                            1.55      1.85
P-Value                           0.122     0.065

BTPRATIO                                      241
T-Value                                      1.81
P-Value                                     0.072

S                 313      306      305       304
R-Sq            97.42    97.55    97.57     97.60
R-Sq(adj)       97.41    97.52    97.54     97.56
Mallows C-p      15.2      5.7      5.2       4.0
```

Figure SIA12.4
Minitab stepwise regression for the road cost data

Because bid status is a qualitative variable ($x_2 = 1$ if fixed and 0 if competitive), a complete second-order model for contract cost (y) using DOTEST (x_1) and STATUS (x_2) is given by the equation

$$E(y) = \beta_0 + \beta_1 x_1 + \beta_2 (x_1)^2 + \beta_3 x_2 + \beta_4 x_1 x_2 + \beta_5 (x_1)^2 x_2$$

The Minitab printout for this model is shown in Figure SIA12.5. Note that the global F-test for the model is statistically significant (p-value $= .000$), and the model standard deviation, $s = 296.6$, is smaller than the standard deviation of the first-order model.

Are the second-order terms in the model, $\beta_2(x_1)^2$ and $\beta_5(x_1)^2 x_2$, necessary? If not, we can simplify the model by dropping these curvature terms. The hypothesis of interest is H_0: $\beta_2 = \beta_5 = 0$. To test this subset of β's, we compare the complete second-order model to a model without the curvilinear terms. The reduced model takes the form

$$E(y) = \beta_0 + \beta_1 x_1 + \beta_3 x_2 + \beta_4 x_1 x_2$$

STATISTICS in ACTION REVISITED CONTINUED

```
The regression equation is
COST = - 3.0 + 0.916 DOTEST + 0.000001 DOTEST2 - 36.7 STATUS + 0.324 STA_DOT
       - 0.000036 STA_DOT2

Predictor          Coef      SE Coef       T      P
Constant          -2.98        30.89   -0.10  0.923
DOTEST          0.91553      0.02917   31.39  0.000
DOTEST2      0.00000072   0.00000340    0.21  0.833
STATUS           -36.72        74.77   -0.49  0.624
STA_DOT          0.3242       0.1192    2.72  0.007
STA_DOT2    -0.00003576   0.00002478   -1.44  0.150

S = 296.646   R-Sq = 97.7%   R-Sq(adj) = 97.7%

Analysis of Variance

Source           DF         SS         MS        F      P
Regression        5  866723202  173344640  1969.85  0.000
Residual Error  229   20151771      87999
Total           234  886874973
```

Figure SIA12.5
Minitab regression printout for the complete second-order model of contract cost

The results of this nested model (or partial) F-test are shown at the bottom of the SPSS printout, Figure SIA12.6. The p-value of the test (highlighted on the SPSS printout) is .355. Because this p-value is greater than $\alpha = .05$, there is insufficient evidence to reject H_0—that is, there is no evidence to indicate that the two curvature terms are useful predictors of road construction cost. Consequently, the reduced model is selected as the better predictor of cost.

Model Summary

					Change Statistics				
Model	R	R Square	Adjusted R Square	Std. Error of the Estimate	R Square Change	F Change	df1	df2	Sig. F Change
1	.988[a]	.977	.977	296.69515	.977	3281.312	3	231	.000
2	.989[b]	.977	.977	296.64238	.000	1.041	2	229	.355

a. Predictors: (Constant), STA_DOT, DOTEST, STATUS
b. Predictors: (Constant), STA_DOT, DOTEST, STATUS, DOTEST2, STA_DOT2

Figure SIA12.6
SPSS printout of test to compare the complete second-order model of contract cost to the reduced model

The Minitab printout for the reduced model is shown in Figure SIA12.7. The overall model is statistically useful (p-value = .000 for global F-test), explaining about 98% of the sample variation in contract costs. The model standard deviation, $s = 296.7$, implies that we can predict costs to within about 593 thousand dollars. Also, the t-test for the interaction term, $\beta_4 x_1 x_2$, is significant (p-value = .000), implying that the relationship between contract cost (y) and DOT cost estimate depends on bid status (fixed or competitive).

```
The regression equation is
COST = - 6.4 + 0.921 DOTEST + 28.7 STATUS + 0.163 STA_DOT

Predictor       Coef    SE Coef       T      P
Constant       -6.43      26.21   -0.25  0.806
DOTEST      0.921336   0.009723   94.75  0.000
STATUS         28.67      58.66    0.49  0.625
STA_DOT      0.16328    0.04043    4.04  0.000

S = 296.699   R-Sq = 97.7%   R-Sq(adj) = 97.7%

Analysis of Variance

Source           DF         SS         MS        F      P
Regression        3  866540004  288846668  3281.22  0.000
Residual Error  231   20334968      88030
Total           234  886874973
```

Figure SIA12.7
Minitab regression printout for the reduced model of contract cost

The nature of the interaction is illustrated in the Minitab graph of the least squares prediction equation for the reduced model, Figure SIA12.8. You can see that the rate of increase of contract cost (y) with the DOT engineer's estimate of cost (x_1) is steeper for fixed contracts than for competitive contracts.

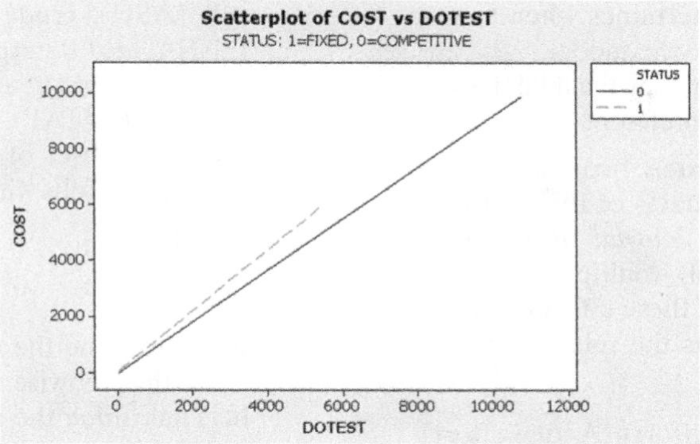

Figure SIA12.8
Minitab plot of least squares prediction equation for the reduced model of contract cost

Exercises 12.111–12.118

Learning the Mechanics

12.111 There are six independent variables, x_1, x_2, x_3, x_4, x_5, and x_6, that might be useful in predicting a response y. A total of $n = 50$ observations is available, and it is decided to employ stepwise regression to help in selecting the independent variables that appear to be useful. The software fits all possible one-variable models of the form

$$E(y) = \beta_0 + \beta_1 x_i$$

where x_i is the ith independent variable, $i = 1, 2, \ldots, 6$. The information in the table is provided from the computer printout.

Independent Variable	$\hat{\beta}_i$	$s_{\hat{\beta}_i}$
x_1	1.6	.42
x_2	−.9	.01
x_3	3.4	1.14
x_4	2.5	2.06
x_5	−4.4	.73
x_6	.3	.35

a. Which independent variable is declared the best one-variable predictor of y? Explain.
b. Would this variable be included in the model at this stage? Explain.
c. Describe the next phase that a stepwise procedure would execute.

Applying the Concepts—Basic

12.112 Teacher pay and pupil performance. In *Economic Policy* (January 2011), researchers from the London School of Economics conducted a cross-country analysis of the relationship between teacher's pay and pupils' performance. Data collected for 39 countries were used to model y = the country's average standardized score of its pupils. The independent variables under consideration were: x_1 = country's total teaching staff as a percentage of the country's labor force, x_2 = percentage of women on country's total teaching staff, x_3 = country's pupil-teacher ratio, x_4 = average teacher's salary after 15 years on staff, x_5 = average teaching hours per year, x_6 = GDP growth of country (%), x_7 = country's educational spending per year, and x_8 = percentile position of country's teachers' salaries after 15 years on staff. Consider a stepwise regression run on the data.
a. What is the form of the model fit in step 1? How many models are fit? How is the "best" independent variable selected in this step?
b. What is the form of the model fit in step 2? How many models are fit? How is the "best" independent variable selected in this step?
c. What is the form of the model fit in step 3? How many models are fit? How is the "best" independent variable selected in this step?
d. The variables x_3, x_4, and x_6 were deemed the best variables for predicting y. How do you recommend the researchers proceed from here? Why?

12.113 Entry-level job preferences. *Benefits Quarterly* (First Quarter, 1995) published a study of entry-level job preferences. A number of independent variables were used to model the job preferences (measured on a 10-point scale) of 164 business school graduates. Suppose stepwise regression is used to build a model for job preference score (y) as a function of the following independent variables:
NW

$$x_1 = \begin{cases} 1 & \text{if flextime position} \\ 0 & \text{if not} \end{cases}$$

$$x_2 = \begin{cases} 1 & \text{if day care support required} \\ 0 & \text{if not} \end{cases}$$

$$x_3 = \begin{cases} 1 & \text{if spousal transfer support required} \\ 0 & \text{if not} \end{cases}$$

x_4 = Number of sick days allowed

$$x_5 = \begin{cases} 1 & \text{if applicant married} \\ 0 & \text{if not} \end{cases}$$

x_6 = Number of children of applicant

$$x_7 = \begin{cases} 1 & \text{if male applicant} \\ 0 & \text{if female applicant} \end{cases}$$

a. How many models are fit to the data in step 1? Give the general form of these models.
b. How many models are fit to the data in step 2? Give the general form of these models.
c. How many models are fit to the data in step 3? Give the general form of these models.
d. Explain how the procedure determines when to stop adding independent variables to the model.
e. Describe two major drawbacks to using the final stepwise model as the best model for job preference score *y*.

12.114 Accuracy of software effort estimates. Periodically, software engineers must provide estimates of their effort in developing new software. In the *Journal of Empirical Software Engineering* (Vol. 9, 2004), multiple regression was used to predict the accuracy of these effort estimates. The dependent variable, defined as the relative error in estimating effort,

$$y = (\text{Actual effort} - \text{Estimated effort})/(\text{Actual effort})$$

was determined for each in a sample of $n = 49$ software development tasks. Eight independent variables were evaluated as potential predictors of relative error using stepwise regression. Each of these was formulated as a dummy variable, as shown in the table.

Company role of estimator:	$x_1 = 1$ if developer, 0 if project leader
Task complexity:	$x_2 = 1$ if low, 0 if medium/high
Contract type:	$x_3 = 1$ if fixed price, 0 if hourly rate
Customer importance:	$x_4 = 1$ if high, 0 if low/medium
Customer priority:	$x_5 = 1$ if time of delivery, 0 if cost or quality
Level of knowledge:	$x_6 = 1$ if high, 0 if low/medium
Participation:	$x_7 = 1$ if estimator participates in work, 0 if not
Previous accuracy:	$x_8 = 1$ if more than 20% accurate, 0 if less than 20% accurate

a. In step 1 of the stepwise regression, how many different one-variable models are fit to the data?
b. In step 1, the variable x_1 is selected as the best one-variable predictor. How is this determined?
c. In step 2 of the stepwise regression, how many different two-variable models (where x_1 is one of the variables) are fit to the data?
d. The only two variables selected for entry into the stepwise regression model were x_1 and x_8. The stepwise regression yielded the following prediction equation:

$$\hat{y} = .12 - .28x_1 + .27x_8$$

Give a practical interpretation of the β estimates multiplied by x_1 and x_8.
e. Why should a researcher be wary of using the model, part **d,** as the final model for predicting effort (y)?

Applying the Concepts—Intermediate

12.115 Diet of ducks bred for broiling. Corn is high in starch content; consequently, it is considered excellent feed for domestic chickens. Does corn possess the same potential in feeding ducks bred for broiling? This was the subject of research published in *Animal Feed Science and Technology* (April 2010). The objective of the study was to establish a prediction model for the true metabolizable energy (TME) of corn regurgitated from ducks. The researchers considered 11 potential predictors of TME: dry matter (DM), crude protein (CP), ether extract (EE), ash (ASH), crude fiber (CF), neutral detergent fiber (NDF), acid detergent fiber (ADF), gross energy (GE), amylose (AM), amylopectin (AP), and amylopectin/amylose (AMAP). Stepwise regression was used to find the best subset of predictors. The final stepwise model yielded the following results:

$$\widehat{TME} = 7.70 + 2.14(\text{AMAP}) + .16(\text{NDF}),\ R^2 = .988,$$
$$s = .07,\ \text{Global } F\ p\text{-value} = .001$$

a. Determine the number of t-tests performed in step 1 of the stepwise regression.
b. Determine the number of t-tests performed in step 2 of the stepwise regression.
c. Give a full interpretation of the final stepwise model regression results.
d. Explain why it is dangerous to use the final stepwise model as the "best" model for predicting TME.
e. Using the independent variables selected by the stepwise routine, write a complete second-order model for TME.
f. Refer to part **e.** How would you determine if the terms in the model that allow for curvature are statistically useful for predicting TME?

12.116 Reality TV and cosmetic surgery. Refer to the *Body Image: An International Journal of Research* (March 2010) study of the influence of reality TV shows on one's desire to undergo cosmetic surgery, Exercise 12.17 (p. 682). Recall that psychologists modeled desire to have cosmetic surgery (y) as a function of gender (x_1), self-esteem (x_2), body satisfaction (x_3), and impression of reality TV (x_4). Suppose you want to determine which subset of these four independent variables is best for predicting one's desire to have cosmetic surgery. Consequently, you will run a stepwise regression.

BDYIMG

a. In step 1 of the stepwise regression, how many t-tests will be performed?
b. In step 2 of the stepwise regression, how many t-tests will be performed?
c. Access the data saved in the file and run the stepwise regression. Which independent variables comprise the best subset of variables for predicting one's desire to have cosmetic surgery?
d. Do you recommend using the resulting stepwise regression model for predicting one's desire to have cosmetic surgery or do you recommend further analysis? Explain your reasoning.

12.117 Bus Rapid Transit study. Bus Rapid Transit (BRT) is a rapidly growing trend in the provision of public transportation in America. The Center for Urban Transportation Research (CUTR) at the University of South Florida conducted a survey of BRT customers in Miami (*Transportation Research Board* Annual Meeting, Jan. 2003). Data on the following variables (all measured on a 5-point scale, where 1 = very unsatisfied and 5 = very satisfied) were collected for a sample of over 500 bus riders: overall satisfaction with BRT (y), safety on bus (x_1), seat availability (x_2), dependability (x_3), travel time (x_4), cost (x_5), information/maps (x_6), convenience of routes (x_7), traffic signals (x_8), safety at bus stops (x_9), hours of service (x_{10}), and frequency of service (x_{11}). CUTR analysts used stepwise regression to model overall satisfaction (y).

a. How many models are fit at step 1 of the stepwise regression?

b. How many models are fit at step 2 of the stepwise regression?

c. How many models are fit at step 11 of the stepwise regression?

d. The stepwise regression selected the following eight variables to include in the model (in order of selection): x_{11}, x_4, x_2, x_7, x_{10}, x_1, x_9, and x_3. Write the equation for $E(y)$ that results from stepwise regression.

e. The model, part **d**, resulted in $R^2 = .677$. Interpret this value.

f. Explain why the CUTR analysts should be cautious in concluding that the best model for $E(y)$ has been found.

12.118 Adverse effects of hot-water runoff. A marine biologist was hired by the EPA to determine whether the hot-water runoff from a particular power plant located near a large gulf is having an adverse effect on the marine life in the area. The biologist's goal is to acquire a prediction equation for the number of marine animals located at certain designated areas, or stations, in the gulf. Based on past experience, the EPA considered the following environmental factors as predictors for the number of animals at a particular station:

x_1 = Temperature of water (TEMP)

x_2 = Salinity of water (SAL)

x_3 = Dissolved oxygen content of water (DO)

x_4 = Turbidity index, a measure of the turbidity of the water (TI)

x_5 = Depth of the water at the station (ST_DEPTH)

x_6 = Total weight of sea grasses in sampled area (TGRSWT)

As a preliminary step in the construction of this model, the biologist used a stepwise regression procedure to identify the most important of these six variables. A total of 716 samples were taken at different stations in the gulf, producing the SPSS printout shown below. (The response measured was y, the logarithm of the number of marine animals found in the sampled area.)

a. According to the SPSS printout, which of the six independent variables should be used in the model? (Use $\alpha = .10$.)

b. Are we able to assume that the marine biologist has identified all the important independent variables for the prediction of y? Why?

c. Using the variables identified in part **a,** write the first-order model with interaction that may be used to predict y.

d. How would the marine biologist determine whether the model specified in part **c** is better than the first-order model?

e. Note the small value of R^2. What action might the biologist take to improve the model?

Variables Entered/Removed[a]

Model	Variables Entered	Variables Removed	Method
1	ST_DEPTH	.	Stepwise (Criteria: Probability-of-F-to-enter <= .050, Probability-of-F-to-remove >= .100).
2	TGRSWT	.	Stepwise (Criteria: Probability-of-F-to-enter <= .050, Probability-of-F-to-remove >= .100).
3	TI	.	Stepwise (Criteria: Probability-of-F-to-enter <= .050, Probability-of-F-to-remove >= .100).

a. Dependent Variable: LOGNUM

Model Summary

Model	R	R Square	Adjusted R Square	Std. Error of the Estimate
1	.329[a]	.122	.121	.7615773
2	.427[b]	.182	.180	.7348470
3	.432[c]	.187	.184	.7348469

a. Predictors: (Constant), ST_DEPTH

b. Predictors: (Constant), ST_DEPTH, TGRSWT

c. Predictors: (Constant), ST_DEPTH, TGRSWT, TI

PART III: MULTIPLE REGRESSION DIAGNOSTICS

12.11 Residual Analysis: Checking the Regression Assumptions

When we apply regression analysis to a set of data, we never know for certain whether the assumptions of Section 12.1 are satisfied. How far can we deviate from the assumptions and still expect regression analysis to yield results that will have the reliability stated in this chapter? How can we detect departures (if they exist) from the assumptions, and what can we do about them? We provide some answers to these questions in this section.

Recall from Section 12.1 that for any given set of values of $x_1, x_2, \ldots, x_k$, we assume that the random error term ε has the following properties:

1. mean equal to 0
2. constant variance (σ^2)
3. normal probability distribution
4. probabilistically independent

It is unlikely that these assumptions are ever satisfied exactly in a practical application of regression analysis. Fortunately, experience has shown that least squares regression analysis produces reliable statistical tests, confidence intervals, and prediction intervals as long as the departures from the assumptions are not too great. In this section, we present some methods for determining whether the data indicate significant departures from the assumptions.

Because the assumptions all concern the random error component, ε, of the model, the first step is to estimate the random error. Because the actual random error associated with a particular value of y is the difference between the actual y value and its unknown mean, we estimate the error by the difference between the actual y-value and the *estimated* mean. This estimated error is called the *regression residual*, or simply the **residual,** and is denoted by $\hat{\varepsilon}$. The actual error ε and residual $\hat{\varepsilon}$ are shown in Figure 12.33.

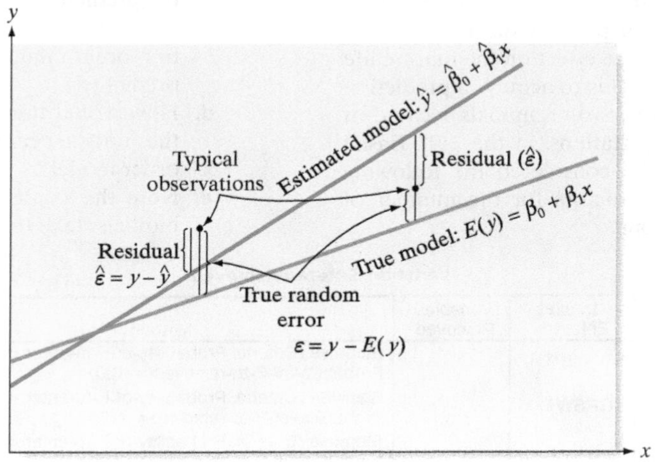

Figure 12.33
Actual random error ε and regression residual $\hat{\varepsilon}$

A **regression residual,** $\hat{\varepsilon}$, is defined as the difference between an observed y value and its corresponding predicted value:

$$\hat{\varepsilon} = (y - \hat{y}) = y - (\hat{\beta}_0 + \hat{\beta}_1 x_1 + \hat{\beta}_2 x_2 + \cdots + \hat{\beta}_k x_k)$$

Because the true mean of y (that is, the true regression model) is not known, the actual random error cannot be calculated. However, because the residual is based on the estimated mean (the least squares regression model), it can be calculated and used to estimate the random error and to check the regression assumptions. Such checks are generally referred to as **residual analyses.** Two useful properties of residuals are given in the next box.

Properties of Regression Residuals

1. The mean of the residuals is equal to 0. This property follows from the fact that the sum of the differences between the observed y values and their least squares predicted $\hat{y}$ values is equal to 0.

$$\sum(\text{Residuals}) = \sum(y - \hat{y}) = 0$$

2. The standard deviation of the residuals is equal to the standard deviation of the fitted regression model, s. This property follows from the fact that the sum of the squared residuals is equal to SSE, which when divided by the error degrees of freedom is equal to the variance of the fitted regression model, s^2. The square root of the variance is both the standard deviation of the residuals and the standard deviation of the regression model.

$$\sum(\text{Residuals})^2 = \sum(y - \hat{y})^2 = \text{SSE}$$

$$s = \sqrt{\frac{\Sigma(\text{Residuals})^2}{n - (k + 1)}} = \sqrt{\frac{\text{SSE}}{n - (k + 1)}}$$

BIOGRAPHY

FRANCIS J. ANSCOMBE (1918–2001)

Anscombe's Data

British citizen Frank Anscombe grew up in a small town near the English Channel. He attended Trinity College in Cambridge, England, on a merit scholarship, graduating with first class honors in mathematics in 1939. He later earned his master's degree in 1943. During World War II, Anscombe worked for the British Ministry of Supply, developing a mathematical solution for aiming antiaircraft rockets at German bombers and buzz bombs. Following the war, Anscombe worked at the Rothamsted Experimental Station, applying statistics to agriculture. There, he formed his appreciation for solving problems with social relevance. During his career as a professor of statistics, Anscombe served on the faculty of Cambridge, Princeton, and Yale universities. He was a pioneer in the application of computers to statistical analysis and was one of the original developers of residual analysis in regression. Anscombe is famous for a paper he wrote in 1973, in which he showed that one regression model could be fit by four very different data sets ("Anscombe's data"). While Anscombe published 50 research articles on statistics, he also had serious interests in classical music, poetry, and art.

The following examples show how a graphical analysis of regression residuals can be used to verify the assumptions associated with the model and to support improvements to the model when the assumptions do not appear to be satisfied. We rely on statistical software to generate the appropriate graphs in the examples and exercises.

Checking Assumption #1: Mean $\varepsilon = 0$

First, we demonstrate how a residual plot can detect a model in which the hypothesized relationship between $E(y)$ and an independent variable x is misspecified. The assumption of mean error of 0 is violated in these types of models.*

Example 12.14

Analyzing Residuals—Electrical Usage Model

Problem Refer to the problem of modeling the relationship between home size (x) and electrical usage (y) in Example 12.7 (p. 698). The data for $n = 15$ homes are repeated in Table 12.6. Minitab printouts for a straight-line model and a quadratic model fitted to the data are shown in Figures 12.34a and 12.34b, respectively. The residuals from these models are highlighted in the printouts. The residuals are then plotted on the vertical axis against the variable x, size of home, on the horizontal axis in Figures 12.35a and 12.35b, respectively.

a. Verify that each residual is equal to the difference between the observed y value and the estimated mean value, $\hat{y}$.

b. Analyze the residual plots.

*For a misspecified model, the hypothesized mean of y, denoted by $E_h(y)$, will not equal the true mean of y, $E(y)$. Because $y = E_h(y) + \varepsilon$, then $\varepsilon = y - E_h(y)$ and $E(\varepsilon) = E[y - E_h(y)] = E(y) - E_h(y) \neq 0$.

Table 12.6 Home Size–Electrical Usage Data

Size of Home, x (sq. ft.)	Monthly Usage, y (kilowatt-hours)
1,290	1,182
1,350	1,172
1,470	1,264
1,600	1,493
1,710	1,571
1,840	1,711
1,980	1,804
2,230	1,840
2,400	1,956
2,710	2,007
2,930	1,984
3,000	1,960
3,210	2,001
3,240	1,928
3,520	1,945

Solution

a. For the straight-line model, the residual is calculated for the first y value as follows:

$$\hat{\varepsilon} = (y - \hat{y}) = 1{,}182 - 1{,}362.2 = -180.2$$

where $\hat{y}$ is the first number in the column labeled **Fit** on the Minitab printout in Figure 12.34a. Similarly, the residual for the first y value using the quadratic model (Figure 12.34b) is

$$\hat{\varepsilon} = 1{,}182 - 1{,}157.2 = 24.8$$

Both residuals agree with the first values given in the column labeled **Residual** in Figures 12.34a and 12.34b, respectively. Although the residuals both correspond to the same observed y value, 1,182, they differ because the predicted mean value changes depending on whether the straight-line model or quadratic model is used. Similar calculations produce the remaining residuals.

Regression Analysis: USAGE versus SIZE

```
The regression equation is
USAGE = 903 + 0.356 SIZE

Predictor       Coef  SE Coef     T      P
Constant       903.0    132.1  6.83  0.000
SIZE         0.35594  0.05477  6.50  0.000

S = 155.251    R-Sq = 76.5%    R-Sq(adj) = 74.7%

Analysis of Variance

Source          DF       SS       MS      F      P
Regression       1  1017803  1017803  42.23  0.000
Residual Error  13   313338    24103
Total           14  1331140

Obs  SIZE   USAGE     Fit  SE Fit  Residual  St Resid
  1  1290  1182.0  1362.2    68.3    -180.2     -1.29
  2  1350  1172.0  1383.5    65.6    -211.5     -1.50
  3  1470  1264.0  1426.2    60.6    -162.2     -1.13
  4  1600  1493.0  1472.5    55.4      20.5      0.14
  5  1710  1571.0  1511.7    51.4      59.3      0.41
  6  1840  1711.0  1557.9    47.3     153.1      1.04
  7  1980  1804.0  1607.8    43.7     196.2      1.32
  8  2230  1840.0  1696.8    40.3     143.2      0.96
  9  2400  1956.0  1757.3    40.5     198.7      1.33
 10  2710  2007.0  1867.6    46.0     139.4      0.94
 11  2930  1984.0  1945.9    52.9      38.1      0.26
 12  3000  1960.0  1970.8    55.5     -10.8     -0.07
 13  3210  2001.0  2045.6    64.0     -44.6     -0.32
 14  3240  1928.0  2056.3    65.3    -128.3     -0.91
 15  3520  1945.0  2155.9    78.0    -210.9     -1.57
```

Figure 12.34a

Minitab printout for straight-line model of electrical usage

Regression Analysis: USAGE versus SIZE, SIZESQ

The regression equation is
USAGE = - 807 + 1.96 SIZE - 0.000340 SIZESQ

Predictor	Coef	SE Coef	T	P
Constant	-806.7	166.9	-4.83	0.000
SIZE	1.9616	0.1525	12.86	0.000
SIZESQ	-0.00034044	0.00003212	-10.60	0.000

S = 50.1998   R-Sq = 97.7%   R-Sq(adj) = 97.3%

Analysis of Variance

Source	DF	SS	MS	F	P
Regression	2	1300900	650450	258.11	0.000
Residual Error	12	30240	2520		
Total	14	1331140			

Obs	SIZE	USAGE	Fit	SE Fit	Residual	St Resid
1	1290	1182.0	1157.2	29.3	24.8	0.61
2	1350	1172.0	1221.0	26.2	-49.0	-1.14
3	1470	1264.0	1341.2	21.2	-77.2	-1.70
4	1600	1493.0	1460.3	18.0	32.7	0.70
5	1710	1571.0	1552.2	17.1	18.8	0.40
6	1840	1711.0	1650.1	17.6	60.9	1.30
7	1980	1804.0	1742.6	19.0	61.4	1.32
8	2230	1840.0	1874.7	21.2	-34.7	-0.76
9	2400	1956.0	1940.2	21.7	15.8	0.35
10	2710	2007.0	2009.0	20.0	-2.0	-0.04
11	2930	1984.0	2018.2	18.4	-34.2	-0.73
12	3000	1960.0	2014.1	18.4	-54.1	-1.16
13	3210	2001.0	1982.1	21.5	18.9	0.42
14	3240	1928.0	1975.1	22.5	-47.1	-1.05
15	3520	1945.0	1880.0	36.2	65.0	1.87

Figure 12.34b
Minitab printout for quadratic model of electrical usage

b. The Minitab plot of the residuals for the straight-line model (Figure 12.35a) reveals a nonrandom pattern. The residuals exhibit a curved shape, with the residuals for the small values of x below the horizontal 0 (mean of the residuals) line, the residuals corresponding to the middle values of x above the 0 line, and the residuals for the largest values of x again below the 0 line. The indication is that the mean value of the random error ε *within* each of these ranges of x (small, medium, large) may not be equal to 0. Such a pattern usually indicates that curvature needs to be added to the model.

When the second-order term is added to the model, the nonrandom pattern disappears. In Figure 12.35b, the residuals appear to be randomly distributed around the 0 line, as expected. Note, too, that the residuals on the quadratic residual plot vary between -75 and 50, compared to between -200 and 200 on the straight-line plot. In fact, $s \approx 50$ for the quadratic model is much smaller than $s \approx 155$ for the straight-line model. The implication is that the quadratic model provides a considerably better model for predicting electrical usage.

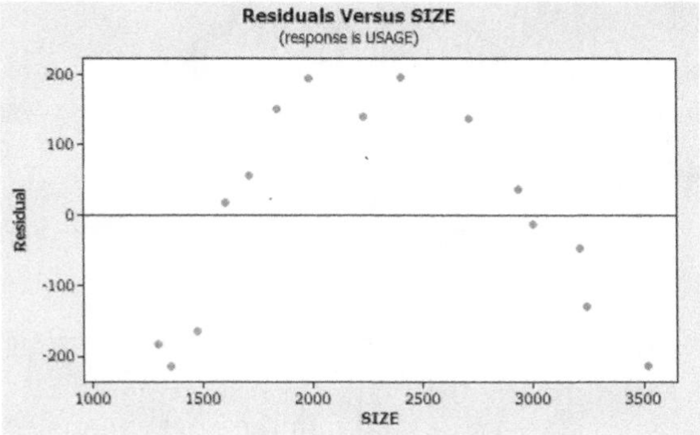

Figure 12.35a
Minitab residual plot for straight-line model of electrical usage

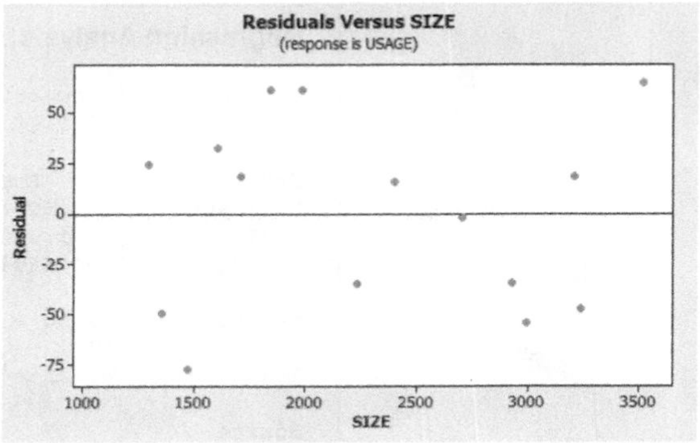

Figure 12.35b
Minitab residual plot for quadratic model of electrical usage

Look Back The residual analysis verifies our conclusions from Example 12.7, where we found the t-test for the quadratic term, $\beta_2 x^2$, to be statistically significant.

■ **Now Work Exercise 12.120a**

Checking Assumption #2: Constant Error Variance

Residual plots can also be used to detect violations of the assumption of constant error variance. For example, a plot of the residuals versus the predicted value $\hat{y}$ may display one of the patterns shown in Figure 12.36. In these figures, the range in values of the residuals increases (or decreases) as $\hat{y}$ increases, thus indicating that the variance of the random error, ε, becomes larger (or smaller) as the estimate of $E(y)$ increases in value. Because $E(y)$ depends on the x values in the model, this implies that the variance of ε is not constant for all settings of the x's.

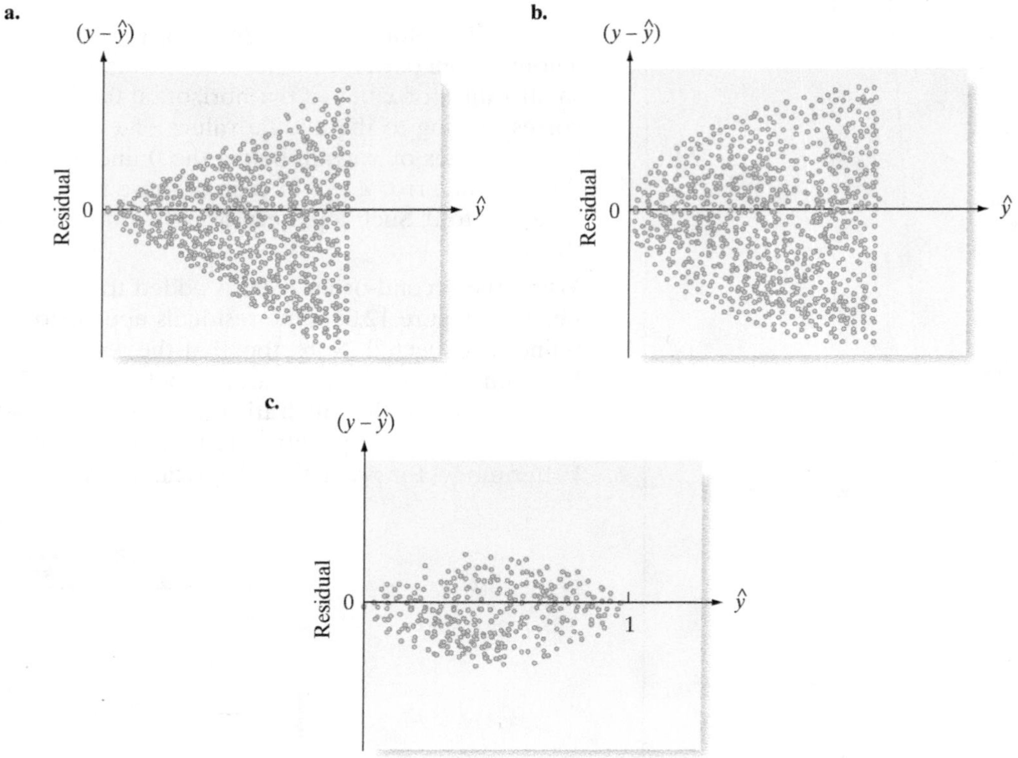

Figure 12.36
Residual plots showing changes in the variance of ε

In the next example, we demonstrate how to use this plot to detect a nonconstant variance and suggest a useful remedy.

Example 12.15

Using Residuals to Check Equal Variances—Social Workers' Salaries

Problem The data in Table 12.7 are the salaries, y, and years of experience, x, for a sample of 50 social workers. The first-order model $E(y) = \beta_0 + \beta_1 x$ was fitted to the data using SPSS. The SPSS printout is shown in Figure 12.37, followed by a plot of the residuals versus $\hat{y}$ in Figure 12.38. Interpret the results. Make model modifications, if necessary.

Solution The SPSS printout, Figure 12.37, suggests that the first-order model provides an adequate fit to the data. The R^2-value indicates that the model explains 78.7% of the sample variation in salaries. The t-value for testing β_1, 13.31, is highly significant (p-value $\approx$ 0) and indicates that the model contributes information for the prediction of y. However, an examination of the residuals plotted against $\hat{y}$ (Figure 12.38) reveals

Table 12.7 Salary Data for Example 12.15

Years of Experience, x	Salary, y	Years of Experience, x	Salary, y	Years of Experience, x	Salary, y
7	$26,075	21	$43,628	28	$99,139
28	79,370	4	16,105	23	52,624
23	65,726	24	65,644	17	50,594
18	41,983	20	63,022	25	53,272
19	62,308	20	47,780	26	65,343
15	41,154	15	38,853	19	46,216
24	53,610	25	66,537	16	54,288
13	33,697	25	67,447	3	20,844
2	22,444	28	64,785	12	32,586
8	32,562	26	61,581	23	71,235
20	43,076	27	70,678	20	36,530
21	56,000	20	51,301	19	52,745
18	58,667	18	39,346	27	67,282
7	22,210	1	24,833	25	80,931
2	20,521	26	65,929	12	32,303
18	49,727	20	41,721	11	38,371
11	33,233	26	82,641		

Data Set: SOCIAL

Model Summary[b]

Model	R	R Square	Adjusted R Square	Std. Error of the Estimate
1	.887[a]	.787	.782	8642.441

a. Predictors: (Constant), ESP
b. Dependent Variable: SALARY

ANOVA[b]

Model		Sum of Squares	df	Mean Square	F	Sig.
1	Regression	1.3E+10	1	1.324E+10	177.257	.000[a]
	Residual	3.6E+09	48	74691793.28		
	Total	1.7E+10	49			

a. Predictors: (Constant), ESP
b. Dependent Variable: SALARY

Coefficients[a]

Model		Unstandardized Coefficients		Standardized Coefficients		
		B	Std. Error	Beta	t	Sig.
1	(Constant)	11368.72	3160.317		3.597	.001
	ESP	2141.381	160.839	.887	13.314	.000

a. Dependent Variable: SALARY

Figure 12.37
SPSS regression printout for first-order model of salary

a potential problem. Note the "cone" shape of the residual variability; the size of the residuals increases as the estimated mean salary increases, implying that the constant variance assumption is violated.

One way to stabilize the variance of ε is to refit the model using a transformation on the dependent variable y. With economic data (e.g., salaries), a useful **variance-stabilizing transformation** is the natural logarithm of y, denoted $\ln(y)$.* We fit the model

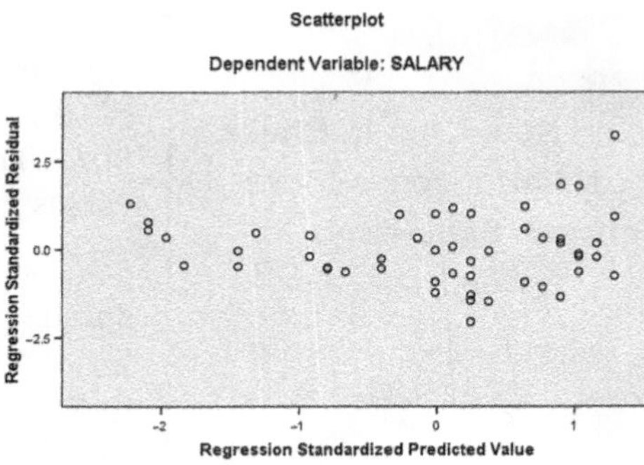

Figure 12.38
SPSS residual plot for first-order model of salary

$$\ln(y) = \beta_0 + \beta_1 x + \varepsilon$$

to the data of Table 12.7. Figure 12.39 shows the SPSS regression analysis printout for the $n = 50$ measurements, while Figure 12.40 shows a plot of the residuals from the log model.

Model Summary[b]

Model	R	R Square	Adjusted R Square	Std. Error of the Estimate
1	.929[a]	.864	.861	.1541127

a. Predictors: (Constant), ESP
b. Dependent Variable: LNSALARY

ANOVA[b]

Model		Sum of Squares	df	Mean Square	F	Sig.
1	Regression	7.212	1	7.212	303.660	.000[a]
	Residual	1.140	48	.024		
	Total	8.352	49			

a. Predictors: (Constant), ESP
b. Dependent Variable: LNSALARY

Coefficients[a]

Model		Unstandardized Coefficients B	Unstandardized Coefficients Std. Error	Standardized Coefficients Beta	t	Sig.
1	(Constant)	9.841	.056		174.631	.000
	ESP	.050	.003	.929	17.426	.000

a. Dependent Variable: LNSALARY

Figure 12.39
SPSS regression printout for model of log salary

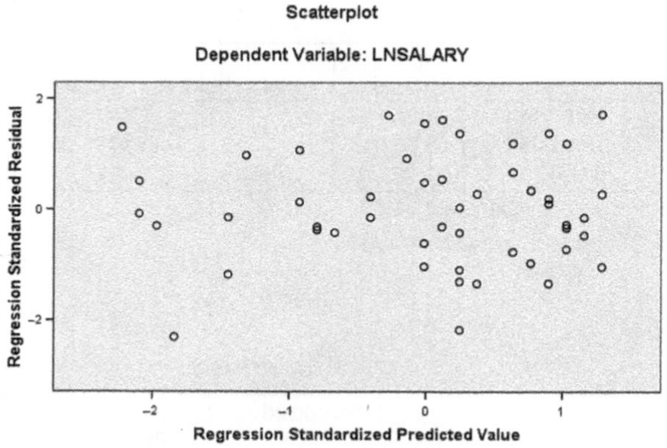

Figure 12.40
SPSS residual plot for model of ln(salary)

*Other variance-stabilizing transformations that are used successfully in practice are $\sqrt{y}$ and $\sin^{-1}\sqrt{y}$. Consult the references for more details on these transformations.

You can see that the logarithmic transformation has stabilized the error variances. Note that the cone shape is gone; there is no apparent tendency of the residual variance to increase as mean salary increases. We therefore are confident that inferences using the ln(y) model are more reliable than those using the untransformed model.

Look Back With transformed models, the analyst should be wary when interpreting model statistics such as $\hat{\beta}_1$ and s. These interpretations must take into account that the dependent variable is not some function of y. For example, the antilogarithm of $\hat{\beta}_1$ in the ln(y) model for salary (y) represents the percentage change in salary for every 1 year increase in experience (x).

■ Now Work Exercise 12.120b

Checking Assumption #3: Errors Normally Distributed

Several graphical methods are available for assessing whether the random error ε has an approximate normal distribution. Recall (Section 4.7) that stem-and-leaf displays, histograms, and normal probability plots are useful for checking whether the data are normally distributed. We illustrate these techniques in an example. But first, we discuss a related problem—using residuals to check for *outliers*.

If the assumption of normally distributed errors is satisfied, then we expect approximately 95% of the residuals to fall within 2 standard deviations of the mean of 0, and almost all of the residuals to lie within 3 standard deviations of the mean of 0. Residuals that are extremely far from 0 and disconnected from the bulk of the other residuals are called **regression outliers** and should receive special attention from the analyst.

A **regression outlier** is a residual that is larger than $3s$ (in absolute value).

Example 12.16

Identifying Outliers—Grandfather Clock Price Model

Problem Refer to Example 12.6 (p. 692) in which we modeled the auction price (y) of a grandfather clock as a function of age (x_1) and number of bidders (x_2). The data for this example are repeated in Table 12.8, with one important difference: The auction price of the clock at the top of the sixth column has been changed from $2,131 to $1,131 (highlighted in Table 12.8). The interaction model

$$E(y) = \beta_0 + \beta_1 x_1 + \beta_2 x_2 + \beta_3 x_1 x_2$$

is again fit to these (modified) data, with the Minitab printout shown in Figure 12.41. The residuals are shown highlighted in the printout and then plotted against the number of bidders, x_2, in Figure 12.42. Analyze the residual plot.

Table 12.8 Altered Auction Price Data

Age, x_1 (years)	Number of Bidders, x_2	Auction Price, y ($)	Age, x_1 (years)	Number of Bidders, x_2	Auction Price, y ($)
127	13	1,235	170	14	1,131
115	12	1,080	182	8	1,550
127	7	845	162	11	1,884
150	9	1,522	184	10	2,041
156	6	1,047	143	6	845
182	11	1,979	159	9	1,483
156	12	1,822	108	14	1,055
132	10	1,253	175	8	1,545
137	9	1,297	108	6	729
113	9	946	179	9	1,792
137	15	1,713	111	15	1,175
117	11	1,024	187	8	1,593
137	8	1,147	111	7	785
153	6	1,092	115	7	744
117	13	1,152	194	5	1,356
126	10	1,336	168	7	1,262

Data Set: CLOCK2

The regression equation is
PRICE = - 513 + 8.17 AGE + 19.9 NUMBIDS + 0.320 AGE_BIDS

Predictor	Coef	SE Coef	T	P
Constant	-512.8	665.9	-0.77	0.448
AGE	8.165	4.585	1.78	0.086
NUMBIDS	19.89	67.44	0.29	0.770
AGE_BIDS	0.3196	0.4790	0.67	0.510

S = 200.598 R-Sq = 72.9% R-Sq(adj) = 70.0%

Analysis of Variance

Source	DF	SS	MS	F	P
Regression	3	3033587	1011196	25.13	0.000
Residual Error	28	1126703	40239		
Total	31	4160290			

Obs	AGE	PRICE	Fit	SE Fit	Residual	St Resid
1	127	1235.0	1310.4	59.3	-75.4	-0.39
2	115	1080.0	1105.9	62.1	-25.9	-0.14
3	127	845.0	947.5	61.1	-102.5	-0.54
4	150	1522.0	1322.5	37.1	199.5	1.01
5	156	1047.0	1179.5	60.3	-132.5	-0.69
6	182	1979.0	1831.9	82.9	147.1	0.81
7	156	1822.0	1598.0	61.9	224.0	1.17
8	132	1253.0	1185.8	39.7	67.2	0.34
9	137	1297.0	1178.9	39.0	118.1	0.60
10	113	946.0	913.9	58.6	32.1	0.17
11	137	1713.0	1561.0	78.4	152.0	0.82
12	117	1024.0	1072.6	53.1	-48.6	-0.25
13	137	1147.0	1115.2	44.3	31.8	0.16
14	153	1092.0	1149.2	59.0	-57.2	-0.30
15	117	1152.0	1187.2	69.7	-35.2	-0.19
16	126	1336.0	1117.6	43.4	218.4	1.12
17	170	1131.0	1914.4	116.7	-783.4	-4.80R
18	182	1550.0	1597.7	62.8	-47.7	-0.25
19	162	1884.0	1598.3	57.0	285.7	1.49
20	184	2041.0	1776.6	70.7	264.4	1.41
21	143	845.0	1048.4	58.9	-203.4	-1.06
22	159	1483.0	1421.8	40.6	61.2	0.31
23	108	1055.0	1130.7	97.9	-75.7	-0.43
24	175	1545.0	1522.7	55.4	22.3	0.12
25	108	729.0	695.5	99.6	33.5	0.19
26	179	1792.0	1642.7	57.6	149.3	0.78
27	111	1175.0	1224.0	107.2	-49.0	-0.29
28	187	1593.0	1651.3	68.6	-58.3	-0.31
29	111	785.0	781.1	80.9	3.9	0.02
30	115	744.0	822.7	75.5	-78.7	-0.42
31	194	1356.0	1480.7	133.6	-124.7	-0.83 X
32	168	1262.0	1374.0	57.7	-112.0	-0.58

R denotes an observation with a large standardized residual.
X denotes an observation whose X value gives it large influence.

Figure 12.41
Minitab regression printout for altered grandfather clock data

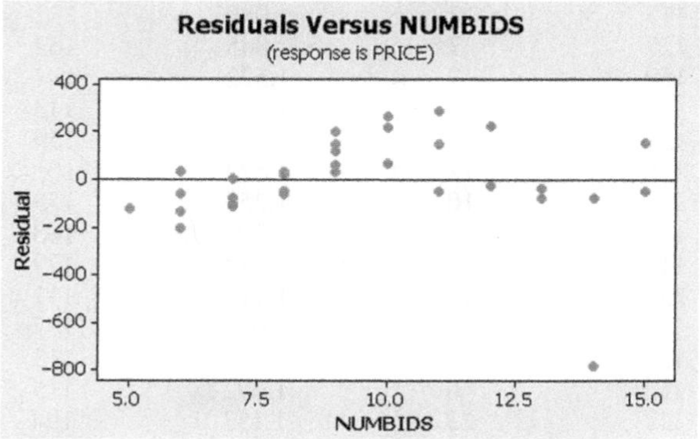

Figure 12.42
Minitab residual plot for altered grandfather clock data

Solution The residual plot dramatically reveals the one altered measurement. Note that one of the two residuals at $x_2 = 14$ bidders falls more than 3 standard deviations below 0. (This observation is highlighted on Figure 12.41.) Note that no other residual falls more than 2 standard deviations from 0.

What do we do with outliers once we identify them? First, we try to determine the cause. Were the data entered into the computer incorrectly? Was the observation recorded incorrectly when the data were collected? If so, we correct the observation and rerun the analysis. Another possibility is that the observation is not representative of the conditions we are trying to model. For example, in this case the low price may be attributable to extreme damage to the clock or to a clock of inferior quality compared to the others. In these cases, we probably would exclude the observation from the analysis. In many cases, you may not be able to determine the cause of the outlier. Even so, you may want to rerun the regression analysis excluding the outlier in order to assess the effect of that observation on the results of the analysis.

Figure 12.43 shows the printout when the outlier observation is excluded from the grandfather clock analysis, and Figure 12.44 shows the new plot of the residuals against the number of bidders. Now only one of the residuals lies beyond 2 standard deviations from 0, and none of them lies beyond 3 standard deviations. Also, the model statistics indicate a much better model without the outlier. Most notably, the s has decreased from 200.6 to 85.83, indicating a model that will provide more precise estimates and predictions (narrower confidence and prediction intervals) for clocks that are similar to those in the reduced sample.

```
The regression equation is
PRICE = 474 - 0.46 AGE - 114 NUMBIDS + 1.48 AGE_BIDS


Predictor      Coef   SE Coef       T      P
Constant      474.0     298.2    1.59  0.124
AGE          -0.465     2.107   -0.22  0.827
NUMBIDS     -114.12     31.23   -3.65  0.001
AGE_BIDS     1.4781    0.2295    6.44  0.000


S = 85.8286    R-Sq = 95.2%    R-Sq(adj) = 94.7%


Analysis of Variance

Source          DF       SS       MS       F      P
Regression       3  3933417  1311139  177.99  0.000
Residual Error  27   198897     7367
Total           30  4132314
```

Figure 12.43
Minitab regression printout when outlier is deleted

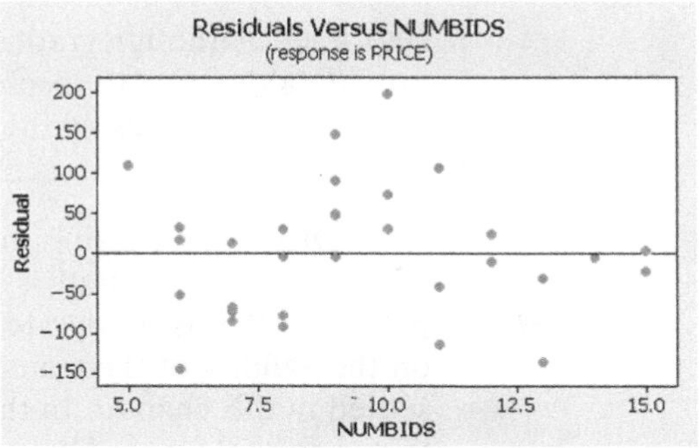

Figure 12.44
Minitab residual plot when outlier is deleted

ETHICS in STATISTICS

Removing observations from a sample data set for the sole purpose of improving the fit of a regression model without investigating whether the observations are outliers or legitimate data points is considered *unethical statististical practice*.

Look Back Remember that if the outlier is removed from the analysis when in fact it belongs to the same population as the rest of the sample, the resulting model may provide misleading estimates and predictions.

■ Now Work Exercise 12.120c

The next example checks the assumption of the normality of the random error component.

Example 12.17

Using Residuals to Check for Normal Errors—Grandfather Clock Prices

Problem Refer to Example 12.16. Analyze the distribution of the residuals in the grandfather clock example, both before and after the outlier residual is removed. Determine whether the assumption of a normally distributed error term is reasonable.

Solution A histogram and normal probability plot for the two sets of residuals are constructed using Minitab and are shown in Figures 12.45 and 12.46. Note that the outlier appears to skew the histogram in Figure 12.45, whereas the histogram in Figure 12.46 appears to be more mound-shaped. Similarly, the pattern of residuals in the normal probability plot in Figure 12.46 (outlier deleted) is more nearly a straight line than the pattern in Figure 12.45 (outlier included). Thus, the normality assumption appears to be more plausible after the outlier is removed.

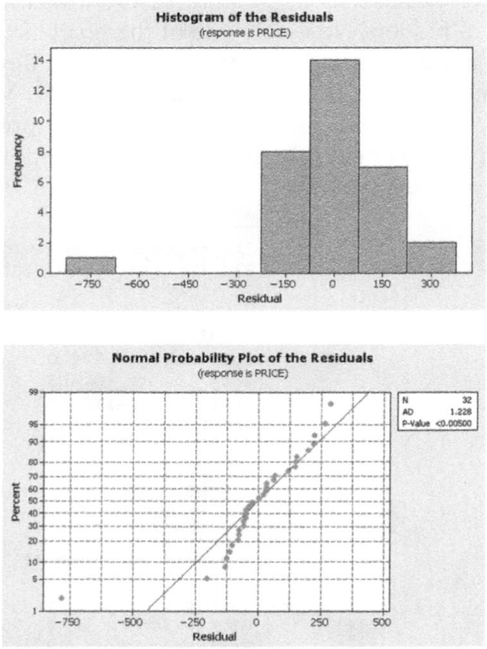

Figure 12.45
Minitab graphs of regression residuals for grandfather clock model (outlier included)

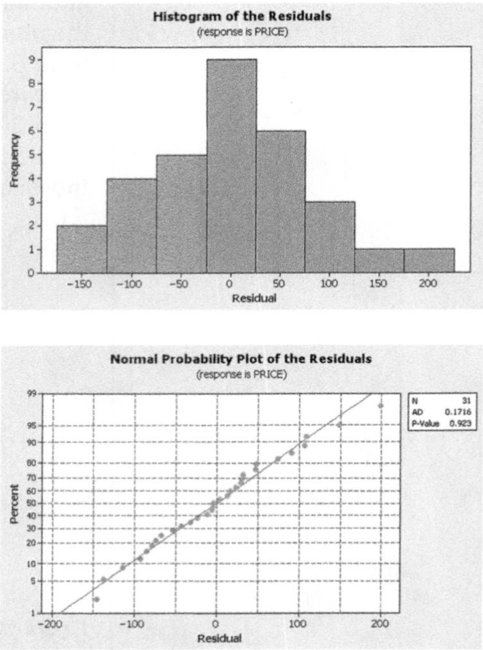

Figure 12.46
Minitab graphs of regression residuals for grandfather clock model (outlier deleted)

Look Back Although graphs do not provide formal statistical tests of normality, they do provide a descriptive display. Consult the references for methods to conduct statistical tests of normality using the residuals.

Now Work Exercise 12.120d

Of the four assumptions in Section 12.1, the assumption that the random error is normally distributed is the least restrictive when we apply regression analysis in practice—that is, moderate departures from a normal distribution have very little effect on the validity of the statistical tests, confidence intervals, and prediction intervals presented in this chapter. In this case, we say that regression analysis is **robust** with respect to nonnormal errors. However, great departures from normality cast doubt on any inferences derived from the regression analysis.

Checking Assumption #4: Errors Independent

The assumption of independent errors is violated when successive errors are correlated. This typically occurs when the data for both the dependent and independent variables are observed sequentially over a period of time—called **time series data.** Time series data have a unique characteristic; the experimental unit represents a unit of time (e.g., a year, a month, a quarter). There are both graphical and formal statistical tests available for checking the assumption of independent regression errors. For example, a simple graph is to plot the residuals against time. If the residuals tend to group alternately into positive and negative clusters (as shown in Figure 12.47), then it is likely that the errors are correlated and the assumption is violated. If correlated errors are detected, one solution is to construct a **time series model** for $E(y)$. These methods are discussed in detail in Chapter 14.

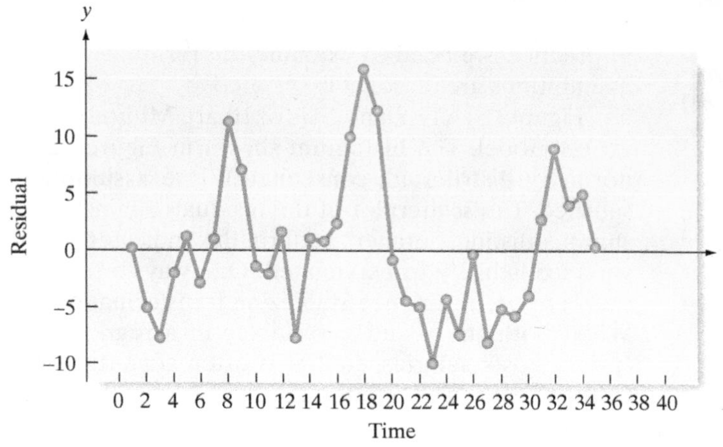

Figure 12.47
Hypothetical residual plot for time series data

Summary

Residual analysis is a useful tool for the regression analyst, not only to check the assumptions but also to provide information about how the model can be improved. A summary of the residual analyses presented in this section to check the assumption that the random error ε is normally distributed with mean 0 and constant variance is presented in the next box.

Steps in a Residual Analysis

1. Check for a misspecified model by plotting the residuals against each of the quantitative independent variables. Analyze each plot, looking for a curvilinear trend. This shape signals the need for a quadratic term in the model. Try a second-order term in the variable against which the residuals are plotted.
2. Examine the residual plots for outliers. Draw lines on the residual plots at 2- and 3-standard-deviation distances below and above the 0 line. Examine residuals outside the 3-standard-deviation lines as potential outliers and check to see that no more than 5% of the residuals exceed the 2-standard-deviation lines. Determine whether each outlier can be explained as an error in data collection or transcription, corresponds to a member of a population different from that of the remainder of the sample, or simply represents an unusual observation. If the observation is determined to be an error, fix it or remove it. Even if you cannot determine the cause, you may want to rerun the regression analysis without the observation to determine its effect on the analysis.
3. Check for nonnormal errors by plotting a frequency distribution of the residuals, using a stem-and-leaf display or a histogram. Check to see if obvious departures from normality exist. Extreme skewness of the frequency distribution may be due to outliers or could indicate the need for a transformation of the dependent variable. (Normalizing transformations are beyond the scope of this book, but you can find information in the references.)
4. Check for unequal error variances by plotting the residuals against the predicted values, $\hat{y}$. If you detect a cone-shaped pattern or some other pattern that indicates that the variance of ε is not constant, refit the model using an appropriate variance-stabilizing transformation on y, such as $\ln(y)$. (Consult the references for other useful variance-stabilizing transformations.)

A Residual Analysis

In the previous Statistics in Action Revisited section (p. 735), we found the interaction model, $E(y) = \beta_0 + \beta_1 x_1 + \beta_3 x_2 + \beta_4 x_1 x_2$, to be both a statistically and practically useful model for predicting the cost (y) of a road construction contract. Recall that the two independent variables are the DOT engineer's estimate of cost (x_1) and bid status, where $x_2 = 1$ if a fixed bid and $x_2 = 0$ if a competitive bid. Before actually using the model in practice, we need to examine the residuals to be sure that the standard regression assumptions are reasonably satisfied.

Figures SIA12.9 and SIA12.10 are Minitab graphs of the residuals from the interaction model. The histogram shown in Figure SIA12.9 appears to be approximately normally distributed; consequently the assumption of normal errors is reasonably satisfied. The scatterplot of the residuals against $\hat{y}$ shown in Figure SIA12.10, however, shows a distinct "funnel" pattern; this indicates that the assumption of a constant error variance is likely to be violated. One way to modify the model to satisfy this assumption is to use a variance-stabilizing transformation (such as the natural log) on cost (y). When both the y and x variables in a regression equation are economic variables (prices, costs, salaries, etc.), it is often advantageous to transform the x variable also. Consequently, we'll modify the model by making a log transform on both cost (y) and DOTEST (x_1).

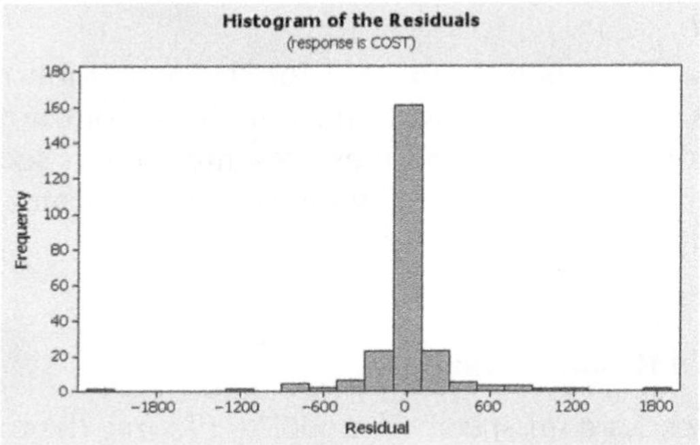

Figure SIA12.9
Minitab histogram of residuals from interaction model for road cost

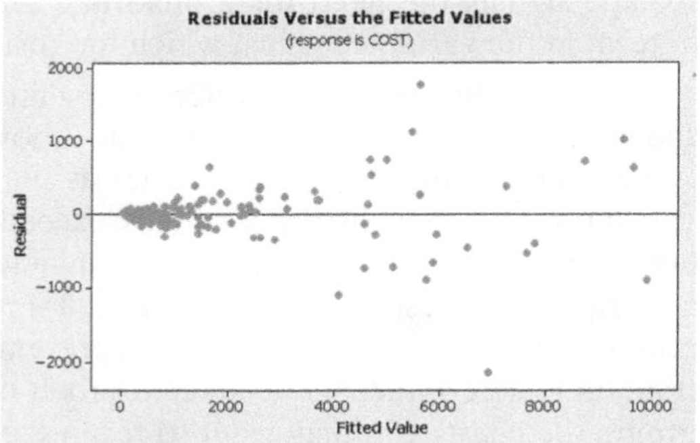

Figure SIA12.10
Minitab plot of residuals versus predicted values from interaction model for road cost

Our modified (log-log) interaction model takes the form

$$E(y^*) = \beta_0 + \beta_1 x_1^* + \beta_2 x_2 + \beta_3 (x_1^*) x_2$$

where $y^* = \ln(\text{COST})$ and $x_1^* = \ln(\text{DOTEST})$. The Minitab printout for this model is shown in Figure SIA12.11, followed by graphs of the residuals in Figures SIA12.12 and SIA12.13. The histogram shown in Figure SIA12.12 is approximately normal, and, more important, the scatterplot of the residuals shown in Figure SIA12.13 has no distinct trend. It appears that the log transformations successfully stabilized the error variance. Note, however, that the t-test for the interaction term in the model (highlighted in Figure SIA12.11) is no longer statistically significant (p-value $= .420$).

Consequently, we will drop the interaction term from the model and use the simpler modified model,

$$E(y^*) = \beta_0 + \beta_1 x_1^* + \beta_2 x_2$$

to predict road construction cost.

```
The regression equation is
LNCOST = - 0.162 + 1.01 LNDOTEST + 0.324 STATUS - 0.0176 STA_LNDOT

Predictor        Coef   SE Coef       T      P
Constant     -0.16188   0.05193   -3.12  0.002
LNDOTEST      1.00780   0.00798  126.23  0.000
STATUS         0.3243    0.1356    2.39  0.018
STA_LNDOT    -0.01762   0.02181   -0.81  0.420

S = 0.154922   R-Sq = 98.8%   R-Sq(adj) = 98.7%

Analysis of Variance

Source           DF      SS      MS        F      P
Regression        3  439.64  146.55  6105.87  0.000
Residual Error  231    5.54    0.02
Total           234  445.18
```

Figure SIA12.11
Minitab regression printout for modified (log-log) model of road construction cost

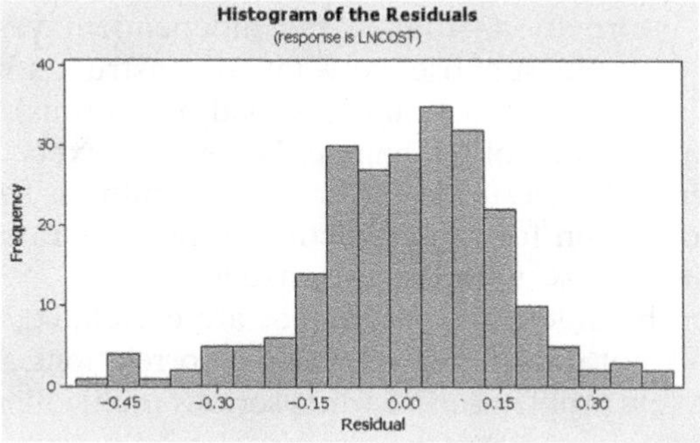

Figure SIA12.12
Minitab histogram of residuals from modified (log-log) model for road construction cost

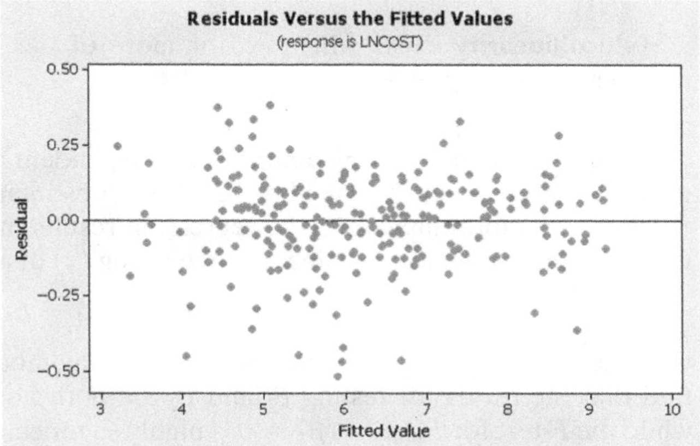

Figure SIA12.13
Minitab plot of residuals versus predicted values from modified (log-log) model for road construction cost

12.12 Some Pitfalls: Estimability, Multicollinearity, and Extrapolation

You should be aware of several potential problems when constructing a prediction model for some response y. A few of the most important are discussed in this final section.

Problem 1: Parameter Estimability

Suppose you want to fit a model relating annual crop yield y to the total expenditure for fertilizer x. We propose the first-order model

$$E(y) = \beta_0 + \beta_1 x$$

Now suppose we have 3 years of data and \$1,000 is spent on fertilizer each year. The data are shown in Figure 12.48. You can see the problem: The parameters of the model cannot be estimated when all the data are concentrated at a single x-value. Recall that it takes two points (x-values) to fit a straight line. Thus, the parameters are not estimable when only one x is observed.

A similar problem would occur if we attempted to fit the quadratic model

$$E(y) = \beta_0 + \beta_1 x + \beta_2 x^2$$

to a set of data for which only one or two different x-values were observed (see Figure 12.49). At least three different x-values must be observed before a quadratic model can be fit to a set of data (that is, before all three parameters are estimable).

In general, the number of levels of observed x*-values must be one more than the order of the polynomial in* x *that you want to fit.*

For controlled experiments, the researcher can select one of the experimental designs in Chapter 9 that will permit estimation of the model parameters. Even when the values of the independent variables cannot be controlled by the researcher, the independent variables are almost always observed at a sufficient number of levels to permit estimation of the model parameters. When the statistical software you use suddenly refuses to fit a model, however, the problem is probably inestimable parameters.

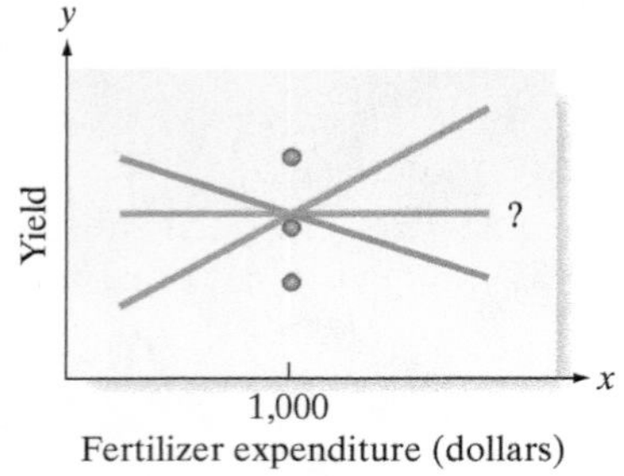

Figure 12.48
Yield and fertilizer expenditure data: Three years

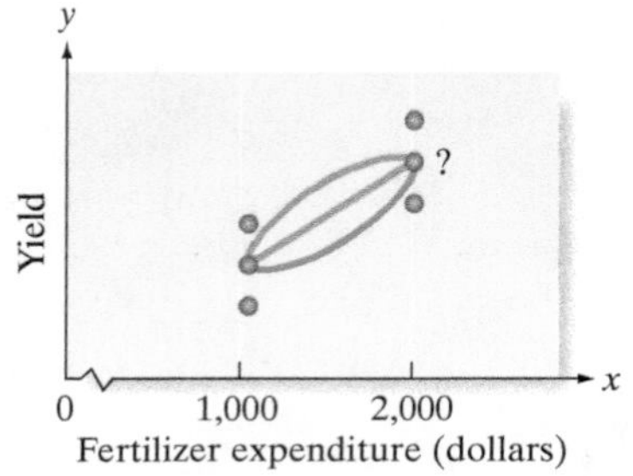

Figure 12.49
Only two x values observed: Quadratic model not estimable

Problem 2: Multicollinearity

Often, two or more of the independent variables used in a regression model contribute redundant information—that is, the independent variables are correlated with each other. For example, suppose we want to construct a model to predict the gas mileage rating of a truck as a function of its load, x_1 (in tons), and the horsepower, x_2 (in foot-pounds per second), of its engine. We would expect heavy loads to require greater horsepower and to result in lower mileage ratings. Thus, although both x_1 and x_2 contribute information for the prediction of mileage rating, y, some of the information is overlapping because x_1 and x_2 are correlated.

When the independent variables are correlated, we say *multicollinearity* exists. In practice, it is not uncommon to observe correlations among the independent variables. However, a few problems arise when serious multicollinearity is present in the regression variables.

> **Multicollinearity** exists when two or more of the independent variables used in regression are correlated.

First, high correlations among the independent variables increase the likelihood of rounding errors in the calculations of the β estimates, standard errors, and so forth. Second, and more important, the regression results may be confusing and misleading. Consider the model for gasoline mileage rating (y) of a truck:

$$E(y) = \beta_0 + \beta_1 x_1 + \beta_2 x_2$$

where x_1 = load and x_2 = horsepower. Fitting the model to a sample data set, we might find that the t-tests for testing β_1 and β_2 are both nonsignificant at the $\alpha = .05$ level, while the F-test for H_0: $\beta_1 = \beta_2 = 0$ is highly significant ($p = .001$). The tests may seem to be contradictory, but really they are not. The t-tests indicate that the contribution of one variable, say x_1 = load, is not significant after the effect of x_2 = horsepower has been accounted for (because x_2 is also in the model). The significant F-test, on the other hand, tells us that at least one of the two variables is making a contribution to the prediction of y (i.e., either β_1 or β_2 or both differ from 0). In fact, both are probably contributing, but the contribution of one overlaps with that of the other.

Multicollinearity can also have an effect on the signs of the parameter estimates. More specifically, a value of β_i may have the opposite sign from what is expected. In the truck gasoline mileage example, we expect heavy loads to result in lower mileage ratings, and we expect higher horsepowers to result in lower mileage ratings; consequently, we expect the signs of both the parameter estimates to be negative. Yet we may actually see a positive value of β_1 and be tempted to claim that heavy loads result in *higher* mileage ratings. This is the danger of interpreting a β coefficient when the independent variables are correlated. Because the variables contribute redundant information, the effect of x_1 = load on y = mileage rating is measured only partially by β_1.

How can you avoid the problems of multicollinearity in regression analysis? One way is to conduct a designed experiment (Chapter 9) so that the levels of the x variables are uncorrelated. Unfortunately, time and cost constraints may prevent you from collecting data in this manner. Consequently, most data are collected observationally. Because observational data frequently consist of correlated independent variables, you will need to recognize when multicollinearity is present and, if necessary, make modifications in the regression analysis.

Several methods are available for detecting multicollinearity in regression. A simple technique is to calculate the coefficient of correlation, r, between each pair of independent variables in the model and use the procedure outlined in Section 11.5 to test for significantly correlated variables. If one or more of the r-values are statistically different from 0, the variables in question are correlated, and a multicollinearity problem may exist.* The degree of multicollinearity will depend on the magnitude of the value of r, as shown in the box.

Using the Correlation Coefficient r to Detect Multicollinearity

Extreme multicollinearity: $|r| \geq .8$

Moderate multicollinearity: $.2 \leq |r| < .8$

Low multicollinearity: $|r| < .2$

Other indications of the presence of multicollinearity include those mentioned above—namely, nonsignificant t-tests for the individual parameter estimates when the F-test for overall model adequacy is significant and estimates with opposite signs from what is expected.†

Detecting Multicollinearity in the Regression Model

1. Significant correlations between pairs of independent variables (see box above)
2. Nonsignificant t-tests for all (or nearly all) of the individual β parameters when the F-test for overall model adequacy is significant
3. Signs opposite from what is expected in the estimated β parameters

Example 12.18

Detecting Multicollinearity—Modeling Carbon Monoxide in Cigarette Smoke

Problem The Federal Trade Commission (FTC) annually ranks varieties of domestic cigarettes according to their tar, nicotine, and carbon monoxide contents. The U.S. Surgeon General considers each of these three substances hazardous to a smoker's health. Past studies have shown that increases in the tar and nicotine contents of a cigarette are accompanied by an increase in the carbon monoxide emitted from the cigarette smoke. Table 12.9 presents data on tar, nicotine, and carbon monoxide contents (in milligrams) and weight (in grams) for a sample of 25 (filter) brands tested in a recent

*Remember that r measures only the pairwise correlation between x-values. Three variables, x_1, x_2, and x_3, may be highly correlated as a group but may not exhibit large pairwise correlations. Thus, multicollinearity may be present even when all pairwise correlations are not significantly different from 0.

†More formal methods for detecting multicollinearity, such as variance-inflation factors (VIFs), are available. Independent variables with a VIF of 10 or above are usually considered to be highly correlated with one or more of the other independent variables in the model. Calculation of VIFs are beyond the scope of this introductory text. Consult the chapter references for a discussion of VIFs and other formal methods of detecting multicollinearity.

year. Suppose we want to model carbon monoxide content, y, as a function of tar content, x_1, nicotine content, x_2, and weight, x_3, using the model

$$E(y) = \beta_0 + \beta_1 x_1 + \beta_2 x_2 + \beta_3 x_3$$

The model is fit to the 25 data points in Table 12.9, and a portion of the Minitab printout is shown in Figure 12.50. Examine the printout. Do you detect any signs of multicollinearity?

Table 12.9 FTC Cigarette Data for Example 12.18

Tar, x_1	Nicotine, x_2	Weight, x_3	Carbon Monoxide, y
14.1	.86	.9853	13.6
16.0	1.06	1.0938	16.6
29.8	2.03	1.1650	23.5
8.0	.67	.9280	10.2
4.1	.40	.9462	5.4
15.0	1.04	.8885	15.0
8.8	.76	1.0267	9.0
12.4	.95	.9225	12.3
16.6	1.12	.9372	16.3
14.9	1.02	.8858	15.4
13.7	1.01	.9643	13.0
15.1	.90	.9316	14.4
7.8	.57	.9705	10.0
11.4	.78	1.1240	10.2
9.0	.74	.8517	9.5
1.0	.13	.7851	1.5
17.0	1.26	.9186	18.5
12.8	1.08	1.0395	12.6
15.8	.96	.9573	17.5
4.5	.42	.9106	4.9
14.5	1.01	1.0070	15.9
7.3	.61	.9806	8.5
8.6	.69	.9693	10.6
15.2	1.02	.9496	13.9
12.0	.82	1.1184	14.9

Source: Federal Trade Commission

Data Set: FTC

Regression Analysis: CO versus TAR, NICOTINE, WEIGHT

```
The regression equation is
CO = 3.20 + 0.963 TAR - 2.63 NICOTINE - 0.13 WEIGHT

Predictor     Coef  SE Coef      T      P
Constant     3.202    3.462   0.93  0.365
TAR         0.9626   0.2422   3.97  0.001
NICOTINE    -2.632    3.901  -0.67  0.507
WEIGHT      -0.130    3.885  -0.03  0.974

S = 1.44573   R-Sq = 91.9%   R-Sq(adj) = 90.7%

Analysis of Variance

Source          DF      SS      MS      F      P
Regression       3  495.26  165.09  78.98  0.000
Residual Error  21   43.89    2.09
```

Correlations: TAR, NICOTINE, WEIGHT

```
              TAR  NICOTINE
NICOTINE    0.977
            0.000

WEIGHT      0.491     0.500
            0.013     0.011

Cell Contents: Pearson correlation
               P-Value
```

Figure 12.50
Minitab printout for model of carbon monoxide content, Example 12.18

Solution First, note that the F-test for overall model utility is highly significant. The test statistic ($F = 78.98$) and observed significance level (p-value $= .000$) are highlighted on the Minitab printout, Figure 12.50. Therefore, at, say $\alpha = .01$, we can conclude that at least one of the parameters—β_1, β_2, or β_3—in the model is nonzero. The t-tests for two of three individual β's, however, are nonsignificant. (The p-values for these tests are highlighted on the printout.) Unless tar (x_1) is the only one of the three variables useful for predicting carbon monoxide content, these results are the first indication of a potential multicollinearity problem.

The negative values for β_2 and β_3 (highlighted on the printout) are a second clue to the presence of multicollinearity. From past studies, the FTC expects carbon monoxide content (y) to increase when either nicotine content (x_2) or weight (x_3) increases—that is, the FTC expects *positive* relationships between y and x_2 and between y and x_3, not negative ones.

All signs indicate that a serious multicollinearity problem exists.

Look Back To confirm our suspicions, we had Minitab produce the coefficient of correlation, r, for each of the three pairs of independent variables in the model. The resulting output is shown (highlighted) at the bottom of Figure 12.50. You can see that tar (x_1) and nicotine (x_2) are highly correlated ($r = .977$), while weight (x_3) is moderately correlated with the other two x's ($r \approx .5$). All three correlations have p-values $\approx .01$ or less; consequently, all three are significantly different from 0 at, say, $\alpha = .05$.

Now Work Exercise 12.119

Once you have detected that multicollinearity exists, there are several alternative measures available for solving the problem. The appropriate measure to take depends on the severity of the multicollinearity and the ultimate goal of the regression analysis.

Some researchers, when confronted with highly correlated independent variables, choose to include only one of the correlated variables in the final model. If you are interested in using the model only for estimation and prediction (step 6), you may decide not to drop any of the independent variables from the model. In the presence of multicollinearity, we have seen that it is dangerous to interpret the individual β parameters. However, confidence intervals for $E(y)$ and prediction intervals for y generally remain unaffected *as long as the values of the x's used to predict* y *follow the same pattern of multicollinearity exhibited in the sample data*—that is, you must take strict care to ensure that the values of the x variables fall within the range of the sample data.

Solutions to Some Problems Created by Multicollinearity in Regression*

1. Drop one or more of the correlated independent variables from the model. One way to decide which variables to keep in the model is to employ stepwise regression (Section 12.10).
2. If you decide to keep all the independent variables in the model,
   a. Avoid making inferences about the individual β parameters based on the t-tests.
   b. Restrict inferences about $E(y)$ and future y values to values of the x's that fall within the range of the sample data.

Problem 3: Prediction Outside the Experimental Region

Many research economists had developed highly technical models to relate the state of the economy to various economic indices and other independent variables. Many of these models were multiple regression models, where, for example, the dependent

*Several other solutions are available. For example, in the case where higher-order regression models are fit, the analyst may want to code the independent variables so that higher-order terms (e.g., x^2) for a particular x variable are not highly correlated with x. One transformation that works is $z = (x - \bar{x})/s$. Other, more sophisticated procedures for addressing multicollinearity (such as *ridge regression*) are beyond the scope of the text. Consult the references at the end of this chapter.

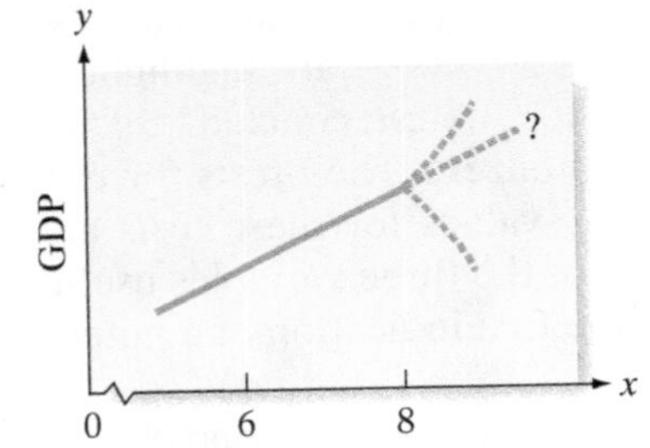

Figure 12.51
Using a regression model outside the experimental region

variable y might be next year's gross domestic product (GDP) and the independent variables might include this year's rate of inflation, this year's consumer price index (CPI), and so on. In other words, the model might be constructed to predict next year's economy using this year's knowledge.

Unfortunately, these models were almost all unsuccessful in predicting the recession in the early 1970s and the late 1990s. What went wrong? One of the problems was that many of the regression models were used to **extrapolate** (i.e., predict y-values of the independent variables that were outside the region in which the model was developed). For example, the inflation rate in the late 1960s, when the models were developed, ranged from 6% to 8%. When the double-digit inflation of the early 1970s became a reality, some researchers attempted to use the same models to predict future growth in GDP. As you can see in Figure 12.51, the model may be very accurate for predicting y when x is in the range of experimentation, but using the model outside that range is a dangerous practice.

Exercises 12.119–12.131

Learning the Mechanics

12.119 Consider fitting the multiple regression model
NW

$$E(y) = \beta_0 + \beta_1 x_1 + \beta_2 x_2 + \beta_3 x_3 + \beta_4 x_4 + \beta_5 x_5$$

A matrix of correlations for all pairs of independent variables is given below. Do you detect a multicollinearity problem? Explain.

	x_1	x_2	x_3	x_4	x_5
x_1	—	.17	.02	−.23	.19
x_2		—	.45	.93	.02
x_3			—	.22	−.01
x_4				—	.86
x_5					—

12.120 Identify the problem(s) in each of the residual plots shown below.
NW

Applying the Concepts—Basic

12.121 State casket sales restrictions. Some states permit only licensed firms to sell funeral goods (e.g., caskets, urns) to the consumer, while other states have no restrictions. States with casket sales restrictions are being challenged in court to lift these monopolistic restrictions. A paper in the *Journal of Law and Economics* (Feb. 2008) used multiple regression to investigate the impact of lifting casket sales restrictions on the cost of a funeral. Data collected for a sample of 1,437 funerals were used to fit the model. A simpler version of the model estimated by the researchers is $E(y) = \beta_0 + \beta_1 x_1 + \beta_2 x_2 + \beta_3 x_1 x_2$, where y is the price (in dollars) of a direct burial, $x_1 = \{1$ if funeral home is in a restricted state, 0 if not$\}$, and $x_2 = \{1$ if price includes a basic wooden casket, 0 if no casket$\}$. The estimated equation (with standard errors in parentheses) is:

$$\hat{y} = 1{,}432 + \underset{(70)}{793x_1} - \underset{(134)}{252x_2} + \underset{(109)}{261x_1x_2}, \quad R^2 = .78$$

a.

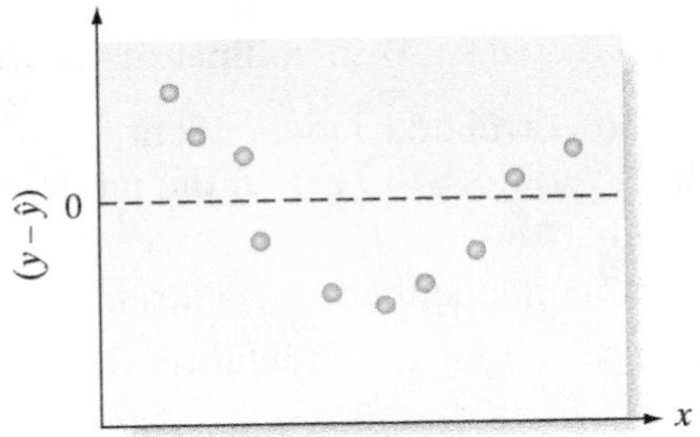

b.

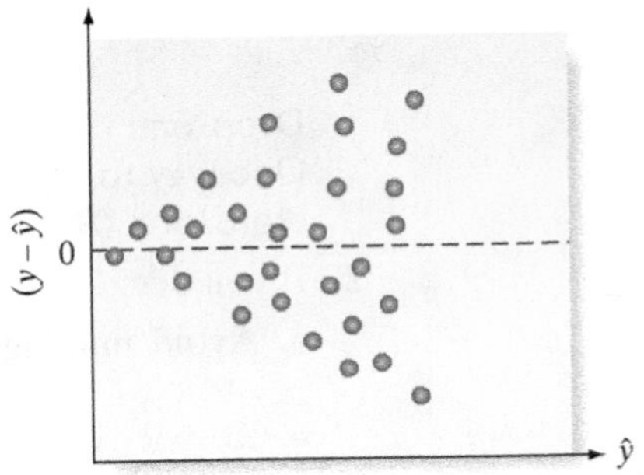

c.

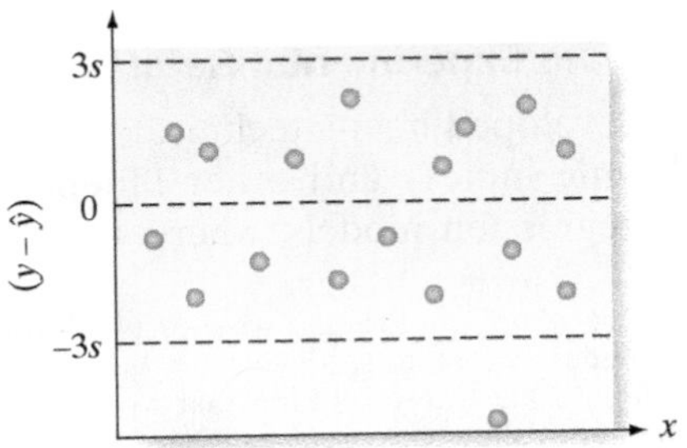

d.

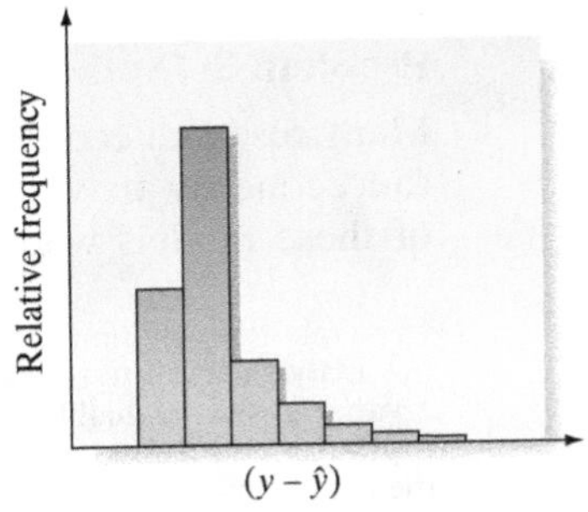

a. Calculate the predicted price of a direct burial with a basic wooden casket at a funeral home in a restricted state.

b. The data include a direct burial funeral with a basic wooden casket at a funeral home in a restricted state that costs $2,200. Assuming the standard deviation of the model is $50, is this data value an outlier?

c. The data also include a direct burial funeral with a basic wooden casket at a funeral home in a restricted state that costs $2,500. Again, assume that the standard deviation of the model is $50. Is this data value an outlier?

12.122 Personality traits and job performance. Refer to the *Journal of Applied Psychology* (Jan. 2011) study of the determinants of task performance, Exercise 12.94 (p. 722). In addition to x_1 = conscientiousness score and x_2 = {1 if highly complex job, 0 if not}, the researchers also used x_3 = emotional stability score, x_4 = organizational citizenship behavior score, and x_5 = counterproductive work behavior score to model y = task performance score. One of their concerns is the level of multicollinearity in the data. Below is a matrix of correlations for all possible pairs of independent variables. Based on this information, do you detect a moderate or high level of multicollinearity? If so, what are your recommendations?

	x_1	x_2	x_3	x_4
Conscientiousness (x_1)				
Job complexity (x_2)	.13			
Emotional stability (x_3)	.62	.14		
Organizational citizenship (x_4)	.24	.03	.24	
Counterproductive work (x_5)	−.23	−.02	−.25	−.62

12.123 Women in top management. Refer to the *Journal of Organizational Culture, Communications and Conflict* (July 2007) study on women in upper management positions at U.S. firms, Exercise 11.67 (p. 639). Monthly data (n = 252 months) were collected for several variables in an attempt to model the number of females in managerial positions (y). The independent variables included the number of females with a college degree (x_1), the number of female high school graduates with no college degree (x_2), the number of males in managerial positions (x_3), the number of males with a college degree (x_4), and the number of male high school graduates with no college degree (x_5). The correlations provided in Exercise 11.67 are given in each part. Determine which of the correlations results in a potential multicollinearity problem for the regression analysis.

a. The correlation relating number of females in managerial positions and number of females with a college degree: r = .983.

b. The correlation relating number of females in managerial positions and number of female high school graduates with no college degree: r = .074.

c. The correlation relating number of males in managerial positions and number of males with a college degree: r = .722.

d. The correlation relating number of males in managerial positions and number of male high school graduates with no college degree: r = .528.

12.124 Factors identifying urban counties. The *Professional Geographer* (Feb. 2000) published a study of urban and rural counties in the western United States. Six independent variables—total county population (x_1), population density (x_2), population concentration (x_3), population growth (x_4), proportion of county land in farms (x_5), and 5-year change in agricultural land base (x_6)—were used to model the urban/rural rating (y) of a county, where rating was recorded on a scale of 1 (most rural) to 10 (most urban). Prior to running the multiple regression analysis, the researchers were concerned about possible multicollinearity in the data. Below is a correlation matrix for data collected on n = 256 counties.

Independent Variable	x_1	x_2	x_3	x_4	x_5
x_1: Total population					
x_2: Population density	.20				
x_3: Population concentration	.45	.43			
x_4: Population growth	−.05	−.14	−.01		
x_5: Farm land	−.16	−.15	−.07	−.20	
x_6: Agricultural change	−.12	−.12	−.22	−.06	−.06

Source: Based on Berry, K. A., et al. "Interpreting what is rural and urban for western U.S. counties," *Professional Geographer*, Vol. 52, No. 1, Feb. 2000, pp. 93–105 (Table 2).

a. Based on the correlation matrix, is there any evidence of extreme multicollinearity?

b. The first-order model with all six independent variables was fit, and the results are shown in the next table. Based on the reported tests, is there any evidence of extreme multicollinearity?

Independent Variable	β Estimate	p-value
x_1: Total population	0.110	0.045
x_2: Population density	0.065	0.230
x_3: Population concentration	0.540	0.000
x_4: Population growth	−0.009	0.860
x_5: Farm land	−0.150	0.003
x_6: Agricultural change	−0.027	0.580
Overall model: $R^2 = .44$	$R_a^2 = .43$ $F = 32.47$	p-value $< .001$

Source: Berry, K. A., et al. "Interpreting what is rural and urban for western U.S. counties," *Professional Geographer*, Vol. 52, No. 1, Feb. 2000 (Table 2).

12.125 Accuracy of software effort estimates. Refer to the *Journal of Empirical Software Engineering* (Vol. 9, 2004) study of the accuracy of new software effort estimates, Exercise 12.114 (p. 738). Recall that stepwise regression was used to develop a model for the relative error in estimating effort (y) as a function of company role of estimator (x_1 = 1 if developer, 0 if project leader) and previous accuracy (x_8 = 1 if more than 20% accurate, 0 if less than 20% accurate). The stepwise regression yielded the prediction equation $\hat{y} = .12 - .28x_1 + .27x_8$. The researcher is concerned that the sign of the estimated β multiplied by x_1 is the opposite from what is expected. (The researcher expects a project leader to have a smaller relative error of estimation than a developer.) Give at least one reason why this phenomenon occurred.

Applying the Concepts—Basic

12.126 Reality TV and cosmetic surgery. Refer to the *Body Image: An International Journal of Research* (March 2010) study of the influence of reality TV shows on one's desire to undergo cosmetic surgery, Exercise 12.17 (p. 682). Simulated data for the study is saved in the file. In Exercise 12.17, you fit the first-order model, $E(y) = \beta_0 + \beta_1x_1 + \beta_2x_2 + \beta_3x_3 + \beta_4x_4$, where y = desire to have cosmetic surgery, x_1 is a dummy variable for gender, x_2 = level of self-esteem, x_3 = level of body satisfaction, and x_4 = impression of reality TV.

BDYIMG

a. Check the data for multicollinearity. If you detect multicollinearity, what modifications to the model do you recommend?

b. Conduct a complete residual analysis for the model. Do you detect any violations of the assumptions? If so, what modifications to the model do you recommend?

12.127 Arsenic in groundwater. Refer to the *Environmental Science & Technology* (Jan. 2005) study of the reliability of a commercial kit to test for arsenic in groundwater, Exercise 12.16 (p. 682). Recall that you fit a first-order model for arsenic level (y) as a function of latitude (x_1), longitude (x_2), and depth (x_3) to data saved in the file. Conduct a residual analysis of the data. Based on the results, comment on each of the following:

WELLS

a. assumption of mean error = 0

b. assumption of constant error variance

c. outliers

d. assumption of normally distributed errors

e. multicollinearity

12.128 Contamination from a plant's discharge. Refer to the U.S. Army Corps of Engineers data on fish contaminated from the toxic discharges of a chemical plant located on the banks of the Tennessee River in Alabama. In Exercise 12.18 (p. 683), you fit the first-order model, $E(y) = \beta_0 + \beta_1x_1 + \beta_2x_2 + \beta_3x_3$, where y = DDT level in captured fish, x_1 = miles captured upstream, x_2 = fish length, and x_3 = fish weight. Conduct a complete residual analysis for the model. Do you recommend any model modifications be made? Explain.

DDT

12.129 Failure times of silicon wafer microchips. Refer to the National Semiconductor study of manufactured silicon wafer integrated circuit chips, Exercise 12.63 (p. 706). Recall that the failure times of the microchips (in hours) was determined at different solder temperatures (degrees Celsius). The data are repeated in the table in the next column.

WAFER

a. Fit the straight-line model $E(y) = \beta_0 + \beta_1x$ to the data, where y = failure time and x = solder temperature.

b. Compute the residual for a microchip manufactured at a temperature of 149°C.

c. Plot the residuals against solder temperature (x). Do you detect a trend?

Temperature (°C)	Time to Failure (hours)
165	200
162	200
164	1,200
158	500
158	600
159	750
156	1,200
157	1,500
152	500
147	500
149	1,100
149	1,150
142	3,500
142	3,600
143	3,650
133	4,200
132	4,800
132	5,000
134	5,200
134	5,400
125	8,300
123	9,700

Source: Gee, S., and Nguyen, L. "Mean time to failure in wafer level-CSP packages with SnPb and SnAgCu solder bmps," International Wafer Level Packaging Conference, San Jose, CA, Nov. 3–4, 2005 (adapted from Figure 7).

d. In Exercise 12.63c, you determined that failure time (y) and solder temperature (x) were curvilinearly related. Does the residual plot, part c, support this conclusion?

12.130 Cooling method for gas turbines. Refer to the *Journal of Engineering for Gas Turbines and Power* (Jan. 2005) study of a high-pressure inlet fogging method for a gas turbine engine, Exercise 12.103 (p. 729). Now consider the interaction model for heat rate (y) of a gas turbine as a function of cycle speed (x_1) and cycle pressure ratio (x_2), $E(y) = \beta_0 + \beta_1x_1 + \beta_2x_2 + \beta_3x_1x_2$. Use the data saved in the file to conduct a complete residual analysis for the model. Do you recommend making model modifications?

GASTRB

12.131 Agreeableness, gender, and wages. Refer to the *Journal of Personality and Social Psychology* (Feb. 2012) study of on-the-job agreeableness and wages, Exercise 12.107 (p. 730). Recall that the researchers modeled mean income, $E(y)$, as a function of both agreeableness score (x_1) and a dummy variable for gender (x_2 = 1 if male, 0 if female). Use the data saved in the file to analyze the residuals of the model,

WAGAP

$$E(y) = \beta_0 + \beta_1x_1 + \beta_2(x_1)^2 + \beta_3x_2$$

What model modifications, if any, do you recommend?

Chapter Notes

Key Terms

Key Formulas

$s^2 = \text{MSE} = \dfrac{\text{SSE}}{n - (k+1)}$	Estimator of σ^2 for a model with k independent variables
$t = \dfrac{\hat{\beta}_i}{s_{\hat{\beta}_i}}$	Test statistic for testing H_0: β_i
$\hat{\beta}_i \pm (t_{\alpha/2})s_{\hat{\beta}_i}$, where $t_{\alpha/2}$ depends on $n - (k+1)$ df	$100(1-\alpha)\%$ confidence interval for β_i
$R^2 = \dfrac{\text{SS}_{yy} - \text{SSE}}{\text{SS}_{yy}}$	Multiple coefficient of determination
$R_a^2 = 1 - \left[\dfrac{(n-1)}{n-(k+1)}\right](1-R^2)$	Adjusted multiple coefficient of determination
$F = \dfrac{\text{MS (Model)}}{\text{MSE}} = \dfrac{R^2/k}{(1-R^2)/[n-(k+1)]}$	Test statistic for testing H_0: $\beta_1 = \beta_2 = \cdots = \beta_k = 0$
$F = \dfrac{(\text{SSE}_\text{R} - \text{SSE}_\text{C})/\text{number of } \beta\text{'s tested}}{\text{MSE}_\text{C}}$	Test statistic for comparing reduced and complete models
$y - \hat{y}$	Regression residual

Key Symbols

x_1^2	Quadratic form for a quantitative x
x_1x_2	Interaction term
MSE	Mean square for error (estimates σ^2)
$\hat{\varepsilon}$	Estimated random error (residual)
SSE_R	Sum of squared errors, reduced model
SSE_C	Sum of squared errors, complete model
MSE_C	Mean squared error, complete model
$\ln(y)$	Natural logarithm of dependent variable

Key Ideas

Multiple regression variables

y = **Dependent** variable (quantitative)

$x_1, x_2, \ldots, x_k$ are **independent** variables (quantitative or qualitative)

First-order model in k quantitative x's

$$E(y) = \beta_0 + \beta_1x_1 + \beta_2x_2 + \cdots + \beta_kx_k$$

Each β_i represents the change in $E(y)$ for every 1-unit increase in x_i, holding all other x's fixed.

Interaction model in 2 quantitative x's

$E(y) = \beta_0 + \beta_1x_1 + \beta_2x_2 + \beta_3x_1x_2$

$(\beta_1 + \beta_3x_2)$ represents the change in $E(y)$ for every 1-unit increase in x_1, for fixed value of x_2

$(\beta_2 + \beta_3x_1)$ represents the change in $E(y)$ for every 1-unit increase in x_2, for fixed value of x_1

Quadratic model in 1 quantitative x

$E(y) = \beta_0 + \beta_1x + \beta_2x^2$

β_2 represents the rate of curvature in $E(y)$ for x

($\beta_2 > 0$ implies *upward* curvature)

($\beta_2 < 0$ implies *downward* curvature)

Complete second-order model in 2 quantitative x's

$E(y) = \beta_0 + \beta_1x_1 + \beta_2x_2 + \beta_3x_1x_2 + \beta_4x_1^2 + \beta_5x_2^2$

β_4 represents the rate of curvature in $E(y)$ for x_1, holding x_2 fixed

β_5 represents the rate of curvature in $E(y)$ for x_2, holding x_1 fixed

Dummy variable model for 1 qualitative x

$E(y) = \beta_0 + \beta_1x_1 + \beta_2x_2 + \cdots + \beta_{k-1}x_{k-1}$

$x_1 = \{1 \text{ if level 1, 0 if not}\}$

$x_2 = \{1 \text{ if level 2, 0 if not}\}$

$x_{k-1} = \{1 \text{ if level } k-1\text{, 0 if not}\}$

$\beta_0 = E(y)$ for level k (base level) $= \mu_k$

$\beta_1 = \mu_1 - \mu_k$

$\beta_2 = \mu_2 - \mu_k$

Complete second-order model in 1 quantitative x and 1 qualitative x (two levels, A and B)

$$E(y) = \beta_0 + \beta_1x_1 + \beta_2x_1^2 + \beta_3x_2 + \beta_4x_1x_2 + \beta_5x_1^2x_2$$

$$x_2 = \{1 \text{ if level A, 0 if level B}\}$$

Adjusted coefficient of determination, R_a^2

Cannot be "forced" to 1 by adding independent variables to the model.

Interaction between x_1 and x_2

Implies that the relationship between y and one x depends on the other x.

Parsimonious model
A model with a small number of β parameters.

Recommendation for Assessing Model Adequacy
1. Conduct global F-test; if significant, then:
2. Conduct t-tests on only the most important β's (*interaction* or *squared terms*)
3. Interpret value of $2s$
4. Interpret value of R^2_a

Recommendation for Testing Individual β's
1. If *curvature* (x^2) deemed important, do not conduct test for first-order (x) term in the model.
2. If *interaction* (x_1x_2) deemed important, do not conduct tests for first-order terms (x_1 and x_2) in the model.

Extrapolation
Occurs when you predict y for values of x's that are outside of range of sample data.

Nested models
Are models where one model (the *complete model*) contains all the terms of another model (the *reduced model*) plus at least one additional term.

Multicollinearity
Occurs when two or more x's are correlated.
Indicators of multicollinearity:
1. Highly correlated x's
2. Significant global F-test, but all t-tests nonsignificant
3. Signs on β's opposite from expected

Problems with Using Stepwise Regression Model as the "Final" Model
1. *Extremely large number of* t*-tests* inflate overall probability of at least one Type I error.
2. *No higher-order terms* (interactions or squared terms) are included in the model.

Analysis of Residuals

1. Detect **misspecified model:** *plot residuals vs. quantitative x* (look for trends, e.g., curvilinear trend)
2. Detect **nonconstant error variance:** *plot residuals vs.* $\hat{y}$ (look for patterns, e.g., cone shape)
3. Detect **nonnormal errors:** *histogram, stem-leaf, or normal probability plot of residuals* (look for strong departures from normality)
4. Identify **outliers:** *residuals greater than 3s in absolute value* (investigate outliers before deleting)

Guide to Multiple Regression

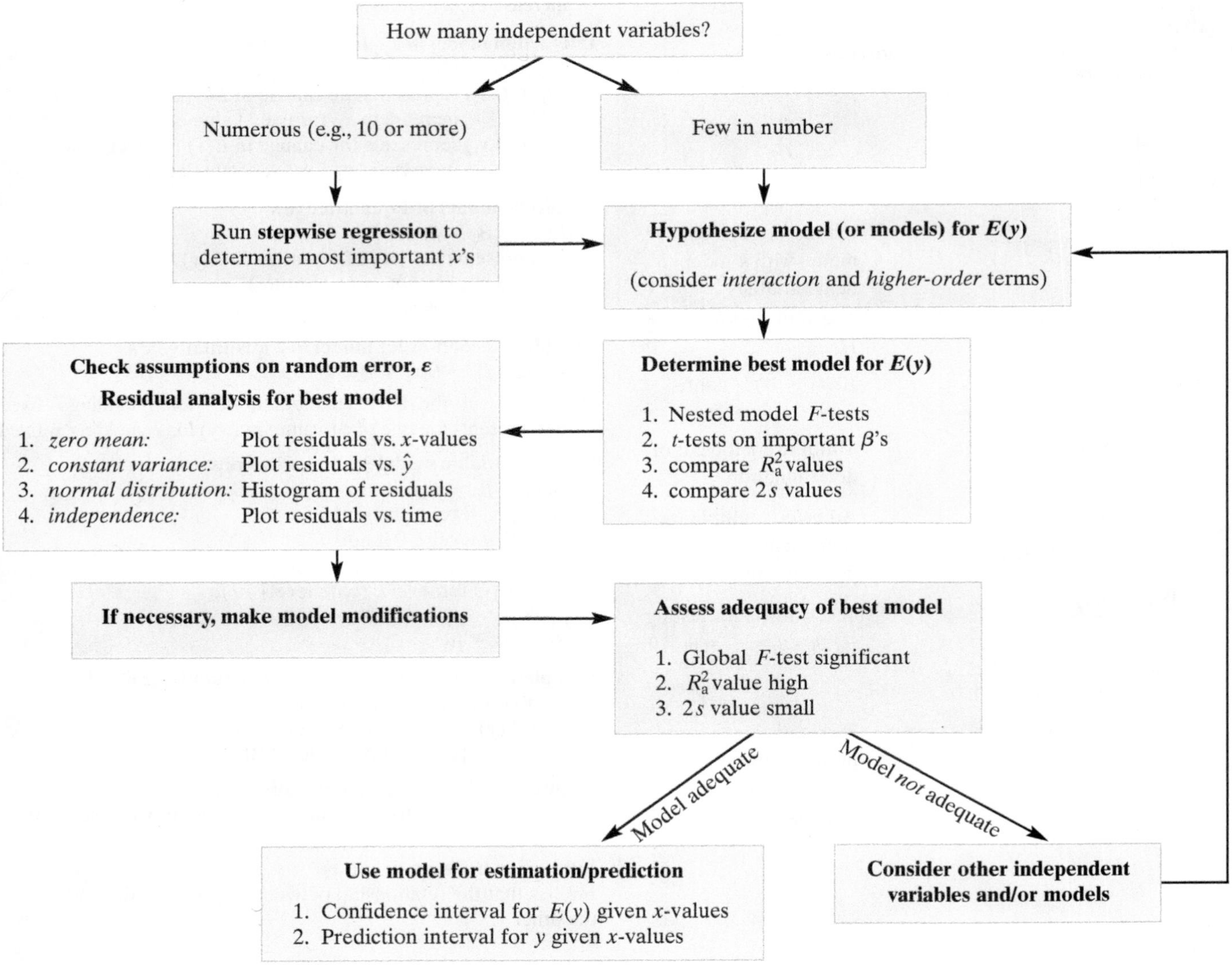

Supplementary Exercises 12.132–12.170

Learning the Mechanics

12.132 Suppose you have developed a regression model to explain the relationship between y and x_1, x_2, and x_3. The ranges of the variables you observed were as follows: $10 \le y \le 100$, $5 \le x_1 \le 55$, $.5 \le x_2 \le 1$, and $1{,}000 \le x_3 \le 2{,}000$. Will the error of prediction be smaller when you use the least squares equation to predict y when $x_1 = 30$, $x_2 = .6$, and $x_3 = 1{,}300$, or when $x_1 = 60$, $x_2 = .4$, and $x_3 = 900$? Why?

12.133 When a multiple regression model is used for estimating the mean of the dependent variable and for predicting a new value of y, which will be narrower—the confidence interval for the mean or the prediction interval for the new y value? Why?

12.134 Suppose you fit the model

$$y = \beta_0 + \beta_1 x_1 + \beta_2 x_1^2 + \beta_3 x_2 + \beta_4 x_1 x_2 + \varepsilon$$

to $n = 25$ data points with the following results:

$$\hat{\beta}_0 = 1.26 \quad \hat{\beta}_1 = -2.43 \quad \hat{\beta}_2 = .05 \quad \hat{\beta}_3 = .62 \quad \hat{\beta}_4 = 1.81$$

$$s_{\hat{\beta}_1} = 1.21 \quad s_{\hat{\beta}_2} = .16 \quad s_{\hat{\beta}_3} = .26 \quad s_{\hat{\beta}_4} = 1.49$$

$$\text{SSE} = .41 \quad R^2 = .83$$

a. Is there sufficient evidence to conclude that at least one of the parameters β_1, β_2, β_3, or β_4 is nonzero? Test using $\alpha = .05$.
b. Test H_0: $\beta_1 = 0$ against H_a: $\beta_1 < 0$. Use $\alpha = .05$.
c. Test H_0: $\beta_2 = 0$ against H_a: $\beta_2 > 0$. Use $\alpha = .05$.
d. Test H_0: $\beta_3 = 0$ against H_a: $\beta_3 \neq 0$. Use $\alpha = .05$.

12.135 Suppose you used Minitab to fit the model

$$y = \beta_0 + \beta_1 x_1 + \beta_2 x_2 + \varepsilon$$

to $n = 15$ data points and obtained the printout shown below.

```
The regression equation is
Y  = 90.1 - 1.84 X1 + .285 X2

Predictor      Coef   SE Coef       T      P
Constant      90.10     23.10    3.90  0.002
X1           -1.836     0.367   -5.01  0.001
X2            0.285     0.231    1.24  0.465

S = 10.68       R-Sq = 91.6%     R-Sq(adj)  = 90.2%

Analysis of Variance

Source           DF        SS        MS        F       P
Regression        2     14801      7400    64.91   0.001
Residual Error   12      1364       114
Total            14     16165
```

a. What is the least squares prediction equation?
b. Find R^2 and interpret its value.
c. Is there sufficient evidence to indicate that the model is useful for predicting y? Conduct an F-test using $\alpha = .05$.
d. Test the null hypothesis H_0: $\beta_1 = 0$ against the alternative hypothesis H_a: $\beta_1 \neq 0$. Test using $\alpha = .05$. Draw the appropriate conclusions.
e. Find the standard deviation of the regression model and interpret it.

12.136 The first-order model $E(y) = \beta_0 + \beta_1 x_1$ was fit to $n = 19$ data points. A residual plot for the model is provided below. Is the need for a quadratic term in the model evident from the residual plot? Explain.

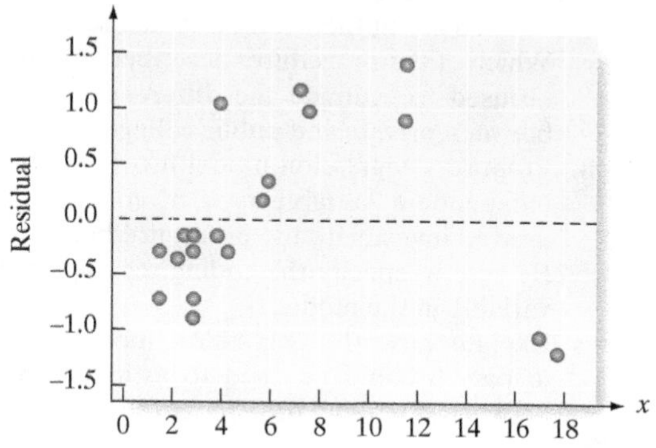

12.137 Write a model relating $E(y)$ to one qualitative independent variable that is at four levels. Define all the terms in your model.

12.138 It is desired to relate $E(y)$ to a quantitative variable x_1 and a qualitative variable at three levels.
a. Write a first-order model.
b. Write a model that will graph as three different second-order curves—one for each level of the qualitative variable.

12.139 Explain why stepwise regression is used. What is its value in the model-building process?

12.140 Consider relating $E(y)$ to two quantitative independent variables x_1 and x_2.
a. Write a first-order model for $E(y)$.
b. Write a complete second-order model for $E(y)$.

12.141 To model the relationship between y, a dependent variable, and x, an independent variable, a researcher has taken one measurement on y at each of three different x values. Drawing on his mathematical expertise, the researcher realizes that he can fit the second-order model

$$E(y) = \beta_0 + \beta_1 x + \beta_2 x^2$$

and it will pass exactly through all three points, yielding SSE = 0. The researcher, delighted with the excellent fit of the model, eagerly sets out to use it to make inferences. What problems will he encounter in attempting to make inferences?

12.142 Suppose you fit the regression model

$$E(y) = \beta_0 + \beta_1 x_1 + \beta_2 x_2 + \beta_3 x_2^2 + \beta_4 x_1 x_2 + \beta_5 x_1 x_2^2$$

to $n = 35$ data points and wish to test the null hypothesis H_0: $\beta_4 = \beta_5 = 0$.
a. State the alternative hypothesis.
b. Explain in detail how to compute the F-statistic needed to test the null hypothesis.

c. What are the numerator and denominator degrees of freedom associated with the F-statistic in part **b**?
d. Give the rejection region for the test if $\alpha = .05$.

Applying the Concepts—Basic

12.143 Comparing private and public college tuition. According to the *Chronicle of Higher Education Almanac,* 4-year private colleges charge, on average, five times as much for tuition and fees than 4-year public colleges. In order to estimate the true difference in the mean amounts charged for an academic year, random samples of 40 private colleges and 40 public colleges were contacted and questioned about their tuition structures.
a. Which of the procedures described in Chapter 8 could be used to estimate the difference in mean charges between private and public colleges?
b. Propose a regression model involving the qualitative independent variable type of college that could be used to investigate the difference between the means. Be sure to specify the coding scheme for the dummy variable in the model.
c. Explain how the regression model you developed in part **b** could be used to estimate the difference between the population means.

12.144 GPAs of business students. Research scientists at the Educational Testing Service (ETS) used multiple regression analysis to model y, the final grade point average (GPA) of business and management doctoral students. A list of the potential independent variables measured for each doctoral student in the study follows:
(1) Quantitative Graduate Management Aptitude Test (GMAT) score
(2) Verbal GMAT score
(3) Undergraduate GPA
(4) First-year graduate GPA
(5) Student cohort (i.e., year in which student entered doctoral program: year 1, year 3, or year 5)
a. Identify the variables as quantitative or qualitative.
b. For each quantitative variable, give your opinion on whether the variable is positively or negatively related to final GPA.
c. For each of the qualitative variables, set up the appropriate dummy variable.
d. Write a first-order, main effects model relating final GPA, y, to the five independent variables.
e. Interpret the β's in the model, part **d**.
f. Write a first-order model for final GPA, y, that allows for a different slope for each student cohort.
g. For each quantitative independent variable in the model, part **f**, give the slope of the line (in terms of the β's) for the year 1 cohort.

12.145 Comparing two orange juice extractors. The Florida Citrus Commission is interested in evaluating the performance of two orange juice extractors, brand A and brand B. It is believed that the size of the fruit used in the test may influence the juice yield (amount of juice per pound of oranges) obtained by the extractors. The commission wants to develop a regression model relating the mean juice yield $E(y)$ to the type of orange juice extractor (brand A or brand B) and the size of orange (diameter), x_1.
a. Identify the independent variables as qualitative or quantitative.
b. Write a model that describes the relationship between $E(y)$ and size of orange as two parallel lines, one for each brand of extractor.
c. Modify the model of part **b** to permit the slopes of the two lines to differ.
d. Sketch typical response lines for the model of part **b.** Do the same for the model of part **c.** Carefully label your graphs.
e. Specify the null and alternative hypotheses you would use to determine whether the model in part **c** provides more information for predicting yield than does the model in part **b.**
f. Explain how you would obtain the quantities necessary to compute the F-statistic that would be used in testing the hypotheses you described in part **e.**

12.146 Global warming and foreign investments. Scientists believe that a major cause of global warming is higher levels of carbon dioxide (CO_2) in the atmosphere. In the *Journal of World-Systems Research* (Summer 2003), sociologists examined the impact of foreign investment dependence on CO_2 emissions in $n = 66$ developing countries. In particular, the researchers modeled the level of CO_2 emissions in 1996 based on foreign investments made 16 years earlier and several other independent variables. The variables and the model results are listed in the table below.

a. Interpret the value of R^2.
b. Use the value of R^2 to test the null hypothesis, H_0: $\beta_1 = \beta_2 = \cdots = \beta_7 = 0$, at $\alpha = .01$.

Results for Exercise 12.146

y = ln(level of CO_2 emissions in 1996)	β Estimate	t-value	p-value
x_1 = ln(foreign investments in 1980)	.79	2.52	< .05
x_2 = gross domestic investment in 1980	.01	.13	> .10
x_3 = trade exports in 1980	−.02	−1.66	> .10
x_4 = ln(GNP in 1980)	−.44	−.97	> .10
x_5 = agricultural production in 1980	−.03	−.66	> .10
x_6 = 1 if African country, 0 if not	−1.19	−1.52	> .10
x_7 = ln(level of CO_2 emissions in 1980)	.56	3.35	< .001
$R^2 = .31$			

Source: Based on Grimes, P., & Kentor, J. "Exporting the greenhouse: Foreign capital penetration and CO_2 emissions 1980–1996," *Journal of World-Systems Research,* Vol. IX, No. 2, Summer 2003 (Table 1).

Correlation matrix for Exercise 12.147

Independent Variable	x_2	x_3	x_4	x_5	x_6	x_7 = ln(level of CO_2 emissions in 1980)
x_1 = ln(foreign investments in 1980)	.13	.57	.30	−.38	.14	−.14
x_2 = gross domestic investment in 1980		.49	.36	−.47	−.14	.25
x_3 = trade exports in 1980			.43	−.47	−.06	−.07
x_4 = ln(GNP in 1980)				−.84	−.53	.42
x_5 = agricultural production in 1980					.45	−.50
x_6 = 1 if African country, 0 if not						−.47

Source: Grimes, P., & Kentor, J. "Exporting the greenhouse: Foreign capital penetration and CO_2 emissions 1980–1996," *Journal of World-Systems Research,* Vol. IX, No. 2, Summer 2003 (Appendix B).

c. What null hypothesis would you test to determine if foreign investments in 1980 is a statistically useful predictor of CO_2 emissions in 1996?

d. Conduct the test, part **c,** at $\alpha = .05$.

12.147 Global warming and foreign investments (cont'd). Refer to Exercise 12.146. A matrix giving the correlation (r) for each pair of independent variables is shown above. Identify the independent variables that are highly correlated. What problems may result from including these highly correlated variables in the regression model?

12.148 Accuracy of software effort estimates. Refer to the *Journal of Empirical Software Engineering* (Vol. 9, 2004) study of the accuracy of software effort estimates, Exercise 12.73 (p. 712). Recall that the dependent variable (y) is measured as relative error of the effort estimate of a software development task. A total of eight independent variables were evaluated as potential predictors of relative error. Each of these was formulated as a dummy variable, as shown in the table below.

a. The eight independent variables were entered into a stepwise regression, and the following two variables were selected for entry into the model: x_1 and x_8. Write the main effects model for $E(y)$ as a function of these two variables.

b. The stepwise regression yielded the following prediction equation:

$$\hat{y} = .12 - .28x_1 + .27x_8$$

Give a practical interpretation of the β estimates multiplied by x_1 and x_8.

c. The researcher is concerned that the sign of $\hat{\beta}_1$ in the model is the opposite from what is expected. (The researcher expects a project leader to have a smaller relative error of estimation than a developer.) Give at least one reason why this phenomenon occurred.

Company role of estimator:	x_1 = 1 if developer, 0 if project leader
Task complexity:	x_2 = 1 if low, 0 if medium/high
Contract type:	x_3 = 1 if fixed price, 0 if hourly rate
Customer importance:	x_4 = 1 if high, 0 if low/medium
Customer priority:	x_5 = 1 if time of delivery, 0 if cost or quality
Level of knowledge:	x_6 = 1 if high, 0 if low/medium
Participation:	x_7 = 1 if estimator participates in work, 0 if not
Previous accuracy:	x_8 = 1 if more than 20% accurate, 0 if less than 20% accurate

12.149 Urban population estimation using satellite images. Can the population of an urban area be estimated without taking a census? In *Geographical Analysis* (January, 2007) geography professors at the University of Wisconsin–Milwaukee and Ohio State University demonstrated the use of satellite image maps for estimating urban population. A portion of Columbus, Ohio, was partitioned into $n = 125$ census block groups, and satellite imagery was obtained. For each census block, the following variables were measured: population density (y), proportion of block with low-density residential areas (x_1), and proportion of block with high-density residential areas (x_2). A first-order model for y was fit to the data with the following results:

$$\hat{y} = -.0304 + 2.006x_1 + 5.006x_2,\ R^2 = .686$$

a. Give a practical interpretation of each β estimate in the model.

b. Give a practical interpretation of the coefficient of determination, R^2.

c. State H_0 and H_a for a test of overall model adequacy.

d. Refer to part **c.** Compute the value of the test statistic.

e. Refer to parts **c** and **d.** Make the appropriate conclusion at $\alpha = .01$.

12.150 Trust in e-retailers. Electronic commerce (or "e-commerce") describes the use of electronic networks to simplify a business operation. With e-commerce, retailers now can advertise and sell their products easily over the Web. In *Internet Research: Electronic Networking Applications and Policy* (Vol. 11, 2001), Canadian researchers investigated the factors that impact the level of trust in Web e-retailers. Five quantitative independent variables were used to model level of trust (y):

x_1 = ease of navigation on the Web site

x_2 = consistency of the Web site

x_3 = ease of learning the Web interface

x_4 = perception of the interface design

x_5 = level of support available to the user

a. Write a first-order model for level of trust as a function of the five independent variables.

b. The model, part **a,** was fit to data collected for $n = 66$ visitors to e-retailers' Web sites and yielded a coefficient of determination of $R^2 = .58$. Interpret this result.

c. Compute the F-statistic used to test the global utility of the model.

d. Using $\alpha = .10$, give the appropriate conclusion for the test, part **c.**

12.151 Prototyping new software. To meet the increasing demand for new software products, many systems development experts have adopted a prototyping methodology. The effects of prototyping on the system development life cycle (SDLC) was investigated in the *Journal of Computer Information Systems* (Spring 1993). A survey of 500 randomly selected corporate-level MIS managers was conducted. Three potential independent variables were (1) *importance* of prototyping to each phase of the SDLC; (2) degree of *support* prototyping provides for the SDLC; and (3) degree to which prototyping *replaces* each phase of the SDLC. The table below gives the pairwise correlations of the three variables in the survey data for one particular phase of the SDLC. Use this information to assess the degree of multicollinearity in the survey data. Would you recommend using all three independent variables in a regression analysis? Explain.

Variable Pairs	Correlation Coefficient, r
Importance–Replace	.2682
Importance–Support	.6991
Replace–Support	−.0531

Source: Hardgrave, B. C., Doke, E. R., & Swanson, N. E. "Prototyping effects of the system development life cycle: An empirical study," *Journal of Computer Information Systems,* Vol. 33, No. 3, Spring 1993, p. 16 (Table 1). Copyright © 1993 by IACIS. Reprinted by permission of the author.

12.152 A CEO's impact on corporate profits. Can a corporation's annual profit be predicted from information about the company's CEO? Each year *Forbes* publishes data on company profit (in \$ millions), CEO's annual income (in \$ thousands), and percentage of the company's stock owned by the CEO. Consider a model relating company profit (y) to CEO income (x_1) and stock percentage (x_2). Explain what it means to say that "CEO income x_1 and stock percentage x_2 interact to affect company profit y."

12.153 "Sun safety" study. Numerous "sun safety" products exist on the market to prevent excessive exposure to solar radiation. But many people do not practice "sun safety" or recognize the effectiveness of these products. A group of University of Arizona researchers examined the feasibility of educating preschool (4- to 5-year-old) children about sun safety (*American Journal of Public Health,* July 1995). A sample of 122 preschool children was divided into two groups, the control group and the intervention group. Children in the intervention group received a *Be Sun Safe* curriculum in preschool, while the control group did not. All children were tested for their knowledge, comprehension, and application of sun safety at two points in time: prior to the sun safety curriculum (pretest, x_1) and 7 weeks following the curriculum (posttest, y).

a. Write a first-order model for mean posttest score, $E(y)$, as a function of pretest score, x_1, and group. Assume that no interaction exists between pretest score and group.

b. For the model, part **a,** show that the slope of the line relating posttest score to pretest score is the same for both groups of children.

c. Repeat part **a** but assume that pretest score and group interact.

d. For the model, part **c,** show that the slope of the line relating posttest score to pretest score differs for the two groups of children.

Applying the Concepts—Intermediate

12.154 Promotion of supermarket vegetables. A supermarket chain is interested in exploring the relationship between the sales of its store-brand canned vegetables (y), the amount spent on promotion of the vegetables in local newspapers (x_1), and the amount of shelf space allocated to the brand (x_2). One of the chain's supermarkets was randomly selected, and over a 20-week period x_1 and x_2 were varied, as reported in the table.

CANVEG

Week	Sales (\$)	Advertising Expenditures (\$)	Shelf Space (sq. ft.)
1	2,010	201	75
2	1,850	205	50
3	2,400	355	75
4	1,575	208	30
5	3,550	590	75
6	2,015	397	50
7	3,908	820	75
8	1,870	400	30
9	4,877	997	75
10	2,190	515	30
11	5,005	996	75
12	2,500	625	50
13	3,005	860	50
14	3,480	1,012	50
15	5,500	1,135	75
16	1,995	635	30
17	2,390	837	30
18	4,390	1,200	50
19	2,785	990	30
20	2,989	1,205	30

a. Fit the following model to the data:

$$y = \beta_0 + \beta_1 x_1 + \beta_2 x_2 + \beta_3 x_1 x_2 + \varepsilon$$

b. Conduct an F-test to investigate the overall usefulness of this model. Use $\alpha = .05$.

c. Test for the presence of interaction between advertising expenditures and shelf space. Use $\alpha = .05$.

d. Explain what it means to say that advertising expenditures and shelf space interact.

e. Explain how you could be misled by using a first-order model instead of an interaction model to explain how advertising expenditures and shelf space influence sales.

f. Based on the type of data collected, comment on the assumption of independent errors.

12.155 Yield strength of steel alloy. Industrial engineers at the University of Florida used regression modeling as a tool to reduce the time and cost associated with developing new metallic alloys (*Modelling and Simulation in Materials Science and Engineering,* Vol. 13, 2005). To illustrate, the engineers built a regression model for the tensile yield strength (y) of a new steel alloy.

The potentially important predictors of yield strength are listed in the accompanying table.

x_1 = Carbon amount (% weight)
x_2 = Manganese amount (% weight)
x_3 = Chromium amount (% weight)
x_4 = Nickel amount (% weight)
x_5 = Molybdenum amount (% weight)
x_6 = Copper amount (% weight)
x_7 = Nitrogen amount (% weight)
x_8 = Vanadium amount (% weight)
x_9 = Plate thickness (millimeters)
x_{10} = Solution treating (milliliters)
x_{11} = Aging temperature (degrees, Celsius)

a. The engineers discovered that the variable Nickel (x_4) was highly correlated with the other potential independent variables. Consequently, Nickel was dropped from the model. Do you agree with this decision? Explain.

b. The engineers used stepwise regression on the remaining 10 potential independent variables in order to search for a parsimonious set of predictor variables. Do you agree with this decision? Explain.

c. The stepwise regression selected the following independent variables: x_1 = Carbon, x_2 = Manganese, x_3 = Chromium, x_5 = Molybdenum, x_6 = Copper, x_8 = Vanadium, x_9 = Plate thickness, x_{10} = Solution treating, and x_{11} = Aging temperature. All these variables were statistically significant in the stepwise model, with $R^2 = .94$. Consequently, the engineers used the estimated stepwise model to predict yield strength. Do you agree with this decision? Explain.

12.156 Optimizing semiconductor material processing. Fluorocarbon plasmas are used in the production of semiconductor materials. In the *Journal of Applied Physics* (Dec. 1, 2000), electrical engineers at Nagoya University (Japan) studied the kinetics of fluorocarbon plasmas in order to optimize material processing. In one portion of the study, the surface production rate of fluorocarbon radicals emitted from the production process was measured at various points in time (in milliseconds) after the radio frequency power was turned off. The data are given in the next table. Consider a model relating surface production rate (y) to time (x).

RADCAL

Rate	Time	Rate	Time
1.00	0.1	0.00	1.7
0.80	0.3	−0.10	1.9
0.40	0.5	−0.15	2.1
0.20	0.7	−0.05	2.3
0.05	0.9	−0.13	2.5
0.00	1.1	−0.08	2.7
−0.05	1.3	0.00	2.9
−0.02	1.5		

Source: Takizawa, K., et al. "Characteristics of C_3 radicals in high-density C_4F_8 plasmas studied by laser-induced fluorescence spectroscopy," *Journal of Applied Physics,* Vol. 88, No. 11, Dec. 1, 2000 (Figure 7). Copyright © 2000 by American Institute of Physics. Reprinted with permission.

a. Graph the data in a scatterplot. What trend do you observe?

b. Fit a quadratic model to the data. Give the least squares prediction equation.

c. Is there sufficient evidence of upward curvature in the relationship between surface production rate and time after turnoff? Use $\alpha = .05$.

12.157 Modeling peak-hour roadway traffic. Traffic forecasters at the Minnesota Department of Transportation (MDOT) use regression analysis to estimate weekday peak-hour traffic volumes on existing and proposed roadways. In particular, they model y, the peak-hour volume (typically, the volume between 7:00 and 8:00 A.M.), as a function of x_1, the road's total volume for the day. For one project involving the redesign of a section of Interstate 494, the forecasters collected $n = 72$ observations of peak-hour traffic volume and 24-hour weekday traffic volume using electronic sensors that count vehicles. The data are saved in the file. (The first and last five observations are listed in the table.)

MNDOT

Observation Number	Peak-Hour Volume	24-Hour Volume	I-35
1	1,990.94	20,070	0
2	1,989.63	21,234	0
3	1,986.96	20,633	0
4	1,986.96	20,676	0
5	1,983.78	19,818	0
⋮	⋮	⋮	
68	2,147.93	22,948	1
69	2,147.85	23,551	1
70	2,144.23	21,637	1
71	2,142.41	23,543	1
72	2,137.39	22,594	1

Source: Traffic and Commodities Studies Section, Minnesota Department of Transportation, St. Paul, Minnesota.

a. Construct a scatterplot for the data, plotting peak-hour volume y against 24-hour volume x_1. Note the isolated group of observations at the top of the scatterplot. Investigators discovered that all of these data points were collected at the intersection of Interstate 35W and 46th Street. (These are observations 55–72 in the table.) While all other locations in the sample were three-lane highways, this location was unique in that the highway widens to four lanes just north of the electronic sensor. Consequently, the forecasters decided to include a dummy variable to account for a difference between the I-35W location and all other locations.

b. Knowing that peak-hour traffic volumes have a theoretical upper bound, the forecasters hypothesized that a second-order model should be used to explain the variation in y. Propose a complete second-order model for $E(y)$ as a function of 24-hour volume x_1 and the dummy variable for location.

c. Using an available statistical software package, fit the model of part **b** to the data. Interpret the results. Specifically, is the curvilinear relationship between peak-hour volume and 24-hour volume different at the two locations?

d. Conduct a residual analysis of the model, part **b.** Evaluate the assumptions of normality and constant error variance and determine whether any outliers exist.

12.158 Improving Math SAT scores. Refer to the *Chance* (Winter 2001) study of students who paid a private tutor (or coach) to help them improve their Scholastic Assessment Test (SAT) scores, Exercise 2.88 (p. 86). Multiple regression was used to estimate the effect of coaching on SAT–Mathematics scores. Data on 3,492 students (573 of whom were coached) were used to fit the model, $E(y) = \beta_0 + \beta_1 x_1 + \beta_2 x_2$, where y = SAT–Math score, x_1 = score on PSAT, and x_2 = {1 if student was coached, 0 if not}.

a. The fitted model had an adjusted R^2 value of .76. Interpret this result.

b. The estimate of β_2 in the model was 19, with a standard error of 3. Use this information to form a 95% confidence interval for β_2. Interpret the interval.

c. Based on the interval, part **b,** what can you say about the effect of coaching on SAT–Math scores?

d. As an alternative model, the researcher added several "control" variables, including dummy variables for student ethnicity (x_3, x_4, and x_5), a socioeconomic status index variable (x_6), two variables that measured high school performance (x_7 and x_8), the number of math courses taken in high school (x_9), and the overall GPA for the math courses (x_{10}). Write the hypothesized equation for $E(y)$ for the alternative model.

e. Give the null hypothesis for a nested model F-test comparing the initial and alternative models.

f. The nested model F-test, part **e,** was statistically significant at $\alpha = .05$. Practically interpret this result.

g. The alternative model, part **d,** resulted in $R_a^2 = .79$, $\hat{\beta}_2 = 14$, and $s_{\hat{\beta}_2} = 3$. Interpret the value of R_a^2.

h. Refer to part **g.** Find and interpret a 95% confidence interval for β_2.

i. The researcher concluded that "the estimated effect of SAT coaching decreases from the baseline model when control variables are added to the model." Do you agree? Justify your answer.

j. As a modification to the model of part **d,** the researcher added all possible interactions between the coaching variable (x_2) and the other independent variables in the model. Write the equation for $E(y)$ for this modified model.

k. Give the null hypothesis for comparing the models, parts **d** and **j.** How would you perform this test?

12.159 Impact of advertising on market share. The audience for a product's advertising can be divided into four segments according to the degree of exposure received as a result of the advertising. These segments are groups of consumers who receive very high (VH), high (H), medium (M), or low (L) exposure to the advertising. A company is interested in exploring whether its advertising effort affects its product's market share. Accordingly, the company identifies 24 sample groups of consumers who have been exposed to its advertising, six groups at each exposure level. Then, the company determines its product's market share within each group.

MKTSHR

Market Share within Group	Exposure Level	Market Share within Group	Exposure Level
10.1	L	12.2	H
10.3	L	12.1	H
10.0	L	11.8	H
10.3	L	12.6	H
10.2	L	11.9	H
10.5	L	12.9	H
10.6	M	10.7	VH
11.0	M	10.8	VH
11.2	M	11.0	VH
10.9	M	10.5	VH
10.8	M	10.8	VH
11.0	M	10.6	VH

a. Write a regression model that expresses the company's market share as a function of advertising exposure level. Define all terms in your model and list any assumptions you make about them.

b. Did you include interaction terms in your model? Why or why not?

c. The data in the table above were obtained by the company. Fit the model in part **a** to the data.

d. Is there evidence to suggest that the firm's expected market share differs for different levels of advertising exposure? Test using $\alpha = .05$.

12.160 Downtime of a production process. An operations manager is interested in modeling $E(y)$, the expected length of time per month (in hours) that a machine will be shut down for repairs, as a function of the type of machine (001 or 002) and the age of the machine (in years). The manager has proposed the following model:

REPAIR

$$E(y) = \beta_0 + \beta_1 x_1 + \beta_2 x_1^2 + \beta_3 x_2$$

where

x_1 = Age of machine

x_2 = 1 if machine type 001, 0 if machine type 002

The following data were obtained for $n = 20$ machine breakdowns.

Downtime (hours per month)	Machine Age, x_1 (years)	Machine Type	x_2
10	1.0	001	1
20	2.0	001	1
30	2.7	001	1
40	4.1	001	1
9	1.2	001	1
25	2.5	001	1
19	1.9	001	1
41	5.0	001	1
22	2.1	001	1
12	1.1	001	1
10	2.0	002	0
20	4.0	002	0
30	5.0	002	0
44	8.0	002	0
9	2.4	002	0
25	5.1	002	0
20	3.5	002	0
42	7.0	002	0
20	4.0	002	0
13	2.1	002	0

a. Use the data (saved in the file) to estimate the parameters of this model.

b. Do these data provide sufficient evidence to conclude that the second-order term (x_1^2) in the model proposed by the operations manager is necessary? Test using $\alpha = .05$.

c. Test the null hypothesis that $\beta_1 = \beta_2 = 0$ using $\alpha = .10$. Interpret the results of the test in the context of the problem.

12.161 Forecasting daily admission of a water park. To determine whether extra personnel are needed for the day, the owners of a water adventure park would like to find a model that would allow them to predict the day's attendance each morning before opening based on the day of the week and weather conditions. The model is of the form

$$E(y) = \beta_0 + \beta_1 x_1 + \beta_2 x_2 + \beta_3 x_3$$

where

$$y = \text{Daily admission}$$

$$x_1 = \begin{cases} 1 & \text{if weekend} \\ 0 & \text{otherwise} \end{cases} \quad \text{(dummy variable)}$$

$$x_2 = \begin{cases} 1 & \text{if sunny} \\ 0 & \text{if overcast} \end{cases} \quad \text{(dummy variable)}$$

$$x_3 = \text{predicted daily high temperature (°F)}$$

These data were recorded for a random sample of 30 days, and a regression model was fitted to the data. The least squares analysis produced the following results:

$$\hat{y} = -105 + 25x_1 + 100x_2 + 10x_3$$

with

$$s_{\hat{\beta}_1} = 10 \quad s_{\hat{\beta}_2} = 30 \quad s_{\hat{\beta}_3} = 4 \quad R^2 = .65$$

a. Interpret the estimated model coefficients.

b. Is there sufficient evidence to conclude that this model is useful for the prediction of daily attendance? Use $\alpha = .05$.

c. Is there sufficient evidence to conclude that the mean attendance increases on weekends? Use $\alpha = .10$.

d. Use the model to predict the attendance on a sunny weekday with a predicted high temperature of 95°F.

e. Suppose the 90% prediction interval for part **d** is (645, 1,245). Interpret this interval.

12.162 Forecasting daily admission of a water park (cont'd). Refer to Exercise 12.161. The owners of the water adventure park are advised that the prediction model could probably be improved if interaction terms were added. In particular, it is thought that the *rate* at which mean attendance increases as predicted high temperature increases will be greater on weekends than on weekdays. The following model is therefore proposed:

$$E(y) = \beta_0 + \beta_1 x_1 + \beta_2 x_2 + \beta_3 x_3 + \beta_4 x_1 x_3$$

The same 30 days of data used in Exercise 12.161 are again used to obtain the least squares model

$$\hat{y} = 250 - 700x_1 + 100x_2 + 5x_3 + 15x_1x_3$$

with

$$s_{\hat{\beta}_4} = 3.0 \quad R^2 = .96$$

a. Graph the predicted day's attendance, y, against the day's predicted high temperature, x_3, for a sunny weekday and for a sunny weekend day. Plot both on the same graph for x_3 between 70°F and 100°F. Note the increase in slope for the weekend day. Interpret this.

b. Do the data indicate that the interaction term is a useful addition to the model? Use $\alpha = .05$.

c. Use this model to predict the attendance for a sunny weekday with a predicted high temperature of 95°F.

d. Suppose the 90% prediction interval for part **c** is (800, 850). Compare this result with the prediction interval for the model without interaction in Exercise 12.161, part **e.** Do the relative widths of the confidence intervals support or refute your conclusion about the utility of the interaction term (part **b**)?

e. The owners, noting that the coefficient $\hat{\beta}_1 = -700$, conclude the model is ridiculous because it seems to imply that the mean attendance will be 700 less on weekends than on weekdays. Explain why this is *not* the case.

12.163 Sale prices of apartments. APTS A Minneapolis, Minnesota, real estate appraiser used regression analysis to explore the relationship between the sale prices of apartment buildings and various characteristics of the buildings. The file contains data for a random sample of 25 apartment buildings. *Note:* Physical condition of each apartment building is coded E (excellent), G (good), or F (fair). Data for selected observations are shown in the table below.

Data for Exercise 12.163 (selected observations)

Code No.	Sale Price, y (\$)	No. of Apartments, x_1	Age of Structure, x_2 (years)	Lot Size, x_3 (sq. ft.)	No. of On-Site Parking Spaces, x_4	Gross Building Area, x_5 (sq. ft.)	Condition of Apartment Building
0229	90,300	4	82	4,635	0	4,266	F
0094	384,000	20	13	17,798	0	14,391	G
0043	157,500	5	66	5,913	0	6,615	G
0079	676,200	26	64	7,750	6	34,144	E
0134	165,000	5	55	5,150	0	6,120	G
⋮	⋮	⋮	⋮	⋮	⋮	⋮	⋮
0019	93,600	4	82	6,864	0	3,840	F
0074	110,000	4	50	4,510	0	3,092	G
0057	573,200	14	10	11,192	0	23,704	E
0104	79,300	4	82	7,425	0	3,876	F
0024	272,000	5	82	7,500	0	9,542	E

Source: Robinson Appraisal Co., Inc., Mankato, Minnesota.

a. Write a model that describes the relationship between sale price and number of apartment units as three parallel lines, one for each level of physical condition. Besure to specify the dummy variable coding scheme you use.

b. Plot y against x_1 (number of apartment units) for all buildings in excellent condition. On the same graph, plot y against x_1 for all buildings in good condition. Do this again for all buildings in fair condition. Does it appear that the model you specified in part **a** is appropriate? Explain.

c. Fit the model from part **a** to the data. Report the least squares prediction equation for each of the three building condition levels.

d. Plot the three prediction equations of part **c** on a scatterplot of the data.

e. Do the data provide sufficient evidence to conclude that the relationship between sale price and number of units differs depending on the physical condition of the apartments? Test using $\alpha = .05$.

f. Check the data set for multicollinearity. How does this impact your choice of independent variables to use in a model for sale price?

g. Conduct a complete residual analysis for the model to check the assumptions on ε.

12.164 Light output of a bulb. A firm that has developed a new type of lightbulb is interested in evaluating its performance in order to decide whether to market it. It is known that the light output of the bulb depends on the cleanliness of its surface area and the length of time the bulb has been in operation. Use the data in the next table and the procedures you learned in this chapter to build a regression model that relates drop in light output to bulb surface cleanliness and length of operation. Be sure to conduct a residual analysis also.

LTBULB

Drop in Light Output (% original output)	Bulb Surface (C = clean) (D = dirty)	Length of Operation (hours)
0	C	0
16	C	400
22	C	800
27	C	1,200
32	C	1,600
36	C	2,000
38	C	2,400
0	D	0
4	D	400
6	D	800
8	D	1,200
9	D	1,600
11	D	2,000
12	D	2,400

12.165 Forecasting a job applicant's merit rating. A large research and development firm rates the performance of each member of its technical staff on a scale of 0 to 100, and this merit rating is used to determine the size of the person's pay raise for the coming year. The firm's personnel department is interested in developing a regression model to help them forecast the merit rating that an applicant for a technical position will receive after being employed 3 years. The firm proposes to use the following second-order model to forecast the merit ratings of applicants who have just completed their graduate studies and have no prior related job experience:

$$E(y) = \beta_0 + \beta_1x_1 + \beta_2x_2 + \beta_3x_1x_2 + \beta_4x_1^2 + \beta_5x_2^2$$

where

y = Applicant's merit rating after 3 years
x_1 = Applicant's GPA in graduate school
x_2 = Applicant's total score (verbal plus quantitative) on the Graduate Record Examination (GRE)

The model, fit to data collected for a random sample of $n = 40$ employees, resulted in SSE = 1,830.44 and SS(model) = 4,911.5. The reduced model $E(y) = \beta_0 + \beta_1x_1 + \beta_2x_2$ is also fit to the same data, resulting in SSE = 3,197.16.

a. Identify the appropriate null and alternative hypotheses to test whether the complete (second-order) model contributes information for the prediction of y.

b. Conduct the test of hypothesis given in part **a.** Test using $\alpha = .05$. Interpret the results in the context of this problem.

c. Identify the appropriate null and alternative hypotheses to test whether the complete model contributes more information than the reduced (first-order) model for the prediction of y.

d. Conduct the test of hypothesis given in part **c.** Test using $\alpha = .05$. Interpret the results in the context of this problem.

e. Which model, if either, would you use to predict y? Explain.

12.166 Household food consumption. The data in the table on the next page were collected for a random sample of 26 households in Washington, D.C. An economist wants to relate household food consumption, y, to household income, x_1, and household size, x_2, with the first-order model

DCFOOD

$$E(y) = \beta_0 + \beta_1x_1 + \beta_2x_2$$

a. Fit the model to the data. Do you detect any signs of multicollinearity in the data? Explain.

b. Is there visual evidence (from a residual plot) that a second-order model may be more appropriate for predicting household food consumption? Explain.

c. Comment on the assumption of constant error variance, using a residual plot. Does it appear to be satisfied?

d. Are there any outliers in the data? If so, identify them.

e. Based on a graph of the residuals, does the assumption of normal errors appear to be reasonably satisfied? Explain.

12.167 State casket sales restrictions. Refer to the *Journal of Law and Economics* (Feb. 2008) study of the impact of lifting casket sales restrictions on the cost of a funeral, Exercise 12.121 (p. 758). Recall that data collected for a sample of 1,437 funerals were used to fit the model, $E(y) = \beta_0 + \beta_1x_1 + \beta_2x_2 + \beta_3x_1x_2$, where y is the price (in dollars) of a direct burial, x_1 = {1 if funeral home is

Data for Exercise 12.166

Household	Food Consumption ($1,000s)	Income ($1,000s)	Household Size	Household	Food Consumption ($1,000s)	Income ($1,000s)	Household Size
1	4.2	41.1	4	14	4.1	95.2	2
2	3.4	30.5	2	15	5.5	45.6	9
3	4.8	52.3	4	16	4.5	78.5	3
4	2.9	28.9	1	17	5.0	20.5	5
5	3.5	36.5	2	18	4.5	31.6	4
6	4.0	29.8	4	19	2.8	39.9	1
7	3.6	44.3	3	20	3.9	38.6	3
8	4.2	38.1	4	21	3.6	30.2	2
9	5.1	92.0	5	22	4.6	48.7	5
10	2.7	36.0	1	23	3.8	21.2	3
11	4.0	76.9	3	24	4.5	24.3	7
12	2.7	69.9	1	25	4.0	26.9	5
13	5.5	43.1	7	26	7.5	7.3	5

in a restricted state, 0 if not}, and x_2 = {1 if price includes a basic wooden casket, 0 if no casket}. The estimated equation (with standard errors in parentheses) is:

$$\hat{y} = 1{,}432 + 793x_1 - 252x_2 + 261x_1x_2, R^2 = .78$$

$$(70) \quad (134) \quad (109)$$

a. Interpret the reported value of R^2.

b. Use the value of R^2 to compute the F-statistic for testing the overall adequacy of the model. Test at $\alpha = .05$.

c. Compute the predicted price of a direct burial with a basic wooden casket for a funeral home in a restrictive state.

d. Estimate the difference between the mean price of a direct burial with a basic wooden casket and the mean price of a burial with no casket for a funeral home in a restrictive state.

e. Estimate the difference between the mean price of a direct burial with a basic wooden casket and the mean price of a burial with no casket for a funeral home in a nonrestrictive state.

f. Is there sufficient evidence to indicate that the difference between the mean price of a direct burial with a basic wooden casket and the mean price of a burial with no casket depends on whether the funeral home is in a restrictive state? Test using $\alpha = .05$.

Applying the Concepts—Advanced

12.168 Modeling monthly collision claims. A medium-sized automobile insurance company is interested in developing a regression model to help predict the monthly collision claims of its policyholders. A company analyst has proposed modeling monthly collision claims (y) in the middle Atlantic states as a function of the percentage of claims by drivers under age 30 (x_1) and the average daily temperature during the month (x_2). She believes that as the percentage of claims by drivers under age 30 increases, claims will rise because younger drivers are usually involved in more serious accidents than older drivers. She also believes that claims will rise as the average daily temperature decreases because lower temperatures are associated with icy, hazardous driving conditions. In order to develop a preliminary model, data were collected for the state of New Jersey over a 3-year period. The data are saved in the file. (The first and last five observations are listed in the table below.)

CLAIMS

a. Use a statistical software package to fit the complete second-order model

$$E(y) = \beta_0 + \beta_1x_1 + \beta_2x_2 + \beta_3x_1x_2 + \beta_4x_1^2 + \beta_5x_2^2$$

b. Test the hypothesis H_0: $\beta_4 = \beta_5 = 0$ using $\alpha = .05$. Interpret the results in practical terms.

c. Do the results support the analysts' beliefs? Explain. (You may need to conduct further tests of hypotheses to answer this question.)

Data for Exercise 12.168 (first and last 5 months)

Month	Monthly Collision Claims, y ($)	Percentage of Monthly Claimants under the Age of 30, x_1	Newark, N.J., Average Daily Temperature during the Month, x_2 (°F)
1	116,250	50.0	31.5
2	217,180	60.8	33.0
3	43,436	45.1	45.0
4	159,265	56.4	53.9
5	130,308	53.3	63.9
⋮	⋮	⋮	⋮
44	136,528	53.1	76.6
45	193,608	59.8	68.6
46	38,722	45.6	62.4
47	212,309	63.9	50.0
48	118,796	52.3	42.3

Sources: New Jersey Department of Insurance; *Weather of U.S. Cities,* 4th ed., Gale Research Inc., Detroit, 1992.

12.169 Developing a model for college GPA. Many colleges and universities develop regression models for predicting the GPA of incoming freshmen. This predicted GPA can then be used to make admission decisions. Although most models use many independent variables to predict GPA, we will illustrate by choosing two variables:

ADMIT

x_1 = Verbal score on college entrance examination (percentile)

x_2 = Mathematics score on college entrance examination (percentile)

The file contains data on these variables for a random sample of 40 freshmen at one college. (Selected observations are shown in the table.) Use the data to develop a useful prediction equation for college freshman GPA (y). Be sure to conduct a residual analysis for the model.

Verbal, x_1	Mathematics, x_2	GPA, y
81	87	3.49
68	99	2.89
57	86	2.73
100	49	1.54
54	83	2.56
⋮	⋮	⋮
74	67	2.83
87	93	3.84
90	65	3.01
81	76	3.33
84	69	3.06

Critical Thinking Challenge

12.170 IQs and *The Bell Curve*. *The Bell Curve* (Free Press, 1994), written by Richard Herrnstein and Charles Murray (H&M), is a controversial book about race, genes, IQ, and economic mobility. The book heavily employs statistics and statistical methodology in an attempt to support the authors' positions on the relationships among these variables and their social consequences. The main theme of *The Bell Curve* can be summarized as follows:

(1) Measured intelligence (IQ) is largely genetically inherited.

(2) IQ is correlated positively with a variety of socioeconomic status success measures, such as prestigious job, high annual income, and high educational attainment.

(3) From 1 and 2, it follows that socioeconomic successes are largely genetically caused and therefore resistant to educational and environmental interventions (such as affirmative action).

The statistical methodology (regression) employed by the authors and the inferences derived from the statistics were critiqued in *Chance* (Summer 1995) and *The Journal of the American Statistical Association* (Dec. 1995). The following are just a few of the problems with H&M's use of regression that are identified:

Problem 1 H&M consistently use a trio of independent variables—IQ, socioeconomic status, and age—in a series of first-order models designed to predict dependent social outcome variables such as income and unemployment. (Only on a single occasion are interaction terms incorporated.) Consider, for example, the model

$$E(y) = \beta_0 + \beta_1 x_1 + \beta_2 x_2 + \beta_3 x_3$$

where y = income, x_1 = IQ, x_2 = socioeconomic status, and x_3 = age. H&M employ t-tests on the individual β parameters to assess the importance of the independent variables. As with most of the models considered in *The Bell Curve*, the estimate of β_1 in the income model is positive and statistically significant at $\alpha = .05$, and the associated t-value is larger (in absolute value) than the t-values associated with the other independent variables. Consequently, *H&M claim that IQ is a better predictor of income than the other two independent variables.* No attempt was made to determine whether the model was properly specified or whether the model provides an adequate fit to the data.

Problem 2 In an appendix, the authors describe multiple regression as a "mathematical procedure that yields coefficients for each of [the independent variables], indicating how much of a change in [the dependent variable] can be anticipated for a given change in any particular [independent] variable, with all the others held constant." Armed with this information and the fact that the estimate of β_1 in the model above is positive, *H&M infer that a high IQ necessarily implies (or causes) a high income, and a low IQ inevitably leads to a low income.* (Cause-and-effect inferences like this are made repeatedly throughout the book.)

Problem 3 The title of the book refers to the normal distribution and its well-known "bell-shaped" curve. There is a misconception among the general public that scores on intelligence tests (IQ) are normally distributed. In fact, most IQ scores have distributions that are decidedly skewed. Traditionally, psychologists and psychometricians have transformed these scores so that the resulting numbers have a precise normal distribution. H&M make a special point to do this. Consequently, *the measure of IQ used in all the regression models is normalized (i.e., transformed so that the resulting distribution is normal), despite the fact that regression methodology does not require predictor (independent) variables to be normally distributed.*

Problem 4 A variable that is not used as a predictor of social outcome in any of the models in *The Bell Curve* is level of education. H&M purposely omit education from the models, arguing that IQ causes education, not the other way around. Other researchers who have examined H&M's data report that *when education is included as an independent variable in the model, the effect of IQ on the dependent variable (say, income) is diminished.*

a. Comment on each of the problems identified. Why do each of these problems cast a shadow on the inferences made by the authors?

b. Using the variables specified in the model above, describe how you would conduct the multiple regression analysis. (Propose a more complex model and describe the appropriate model tests, including a residual analysis.)

Activity 12.1 *Insurance Premiums:* Collecting Data for Several Variables

Premiums for life insurance, health insurance, homeowners insurance, and car insurance are based on more than one factor. In this activity, you will consider factors that influence the price that an individual pays for insurance and how you might collect data that would be useful in studying insurance premiums. You may wish to look over statements from your own insurance policies to determine how much coverage you have and how much it costs you.

1. Suppose that you host an independent Web site that provides information about insurance coverage and costs. You would like to add a feature to your site where a person answers a few simple questions in order to receive an estimate of what that person should expect to pay for insurance with a major carrier. Pick one type of insurance and determine what five questions you would most like to ask the person in order to prepare an estimate.
2. Use your five questions from Exercise 1 to define five independent variables. What is the dependent variable in this situation? What would a first-order model for this situation look like?
3. The estimates provided on your Web site will be based on a random sample of policies recently purchased through major carriers. Because insurance rates change frequently, your Web site will need to be frequently updated through new samples. Design a sampling method that can easily be repeated as needed. Be specific as to how you will identify people who have recently purchased policies, how you will choose your sample, what data you will gather, and what method you will use to gather the data.
4. Once the data are collected, describe how you will organize them and use them to complete the model in Exercise 3.

Activity 12.2 Collecting Data and Fitting a Multiple Regression Model

Note: The use of statistical software is required for this project. This is a continuation of the Activity section in Chapter 11, in which you selected three independent variables as predictors of a dependent variable of your choice and obtained at least 25 data values. Now, by means of an available software package, fit the multiple regression model

$$y = \beta_0 + \beta_1 x_1 + \beta_2 x_2 + \beta_3 x_3 + \varepsilon$$

where

y = Dependent variable you chose

x_1 = First independent variable you chose

x_2 = Second independent variable you chose

x_3 = Third independent variable you chose

1. Compare the coefficients $\hat{\beta}_1$, $\hat{\beta}_2$, and $\hat{\beta}_3$ with their corresponding slope coefficients in the Activity of Chapter 11, where you fit three separate straight-line models. How do you account for the differences?
2. Calculate the coefficient of determination, R^2, and conduct the *F*-test of the null hypothesis H_0: $\beta_1 = \beta_2 = \beta_3 = 0$. What is your conclusion?
3. Check the data for multicollinearity. If multicollinearity exists, how sould you proceed?
4. Now increase your list of 3 variables to include approximately 10 that you think would be useful in predicting the dependent variable. With the aid of statistical software, employ a stepwise regression program to choose the important variables among those you have listed. To test your intuition, list the variables in the order you think they will be selected before you conduct the analysis. How does your list compare with the stepwise regression results?
5. After the group of 10 variables has been narrowed to a smaller group of variables by the stepwise analysis, try to improve the model by including interactions and quadratic terms. Be sure to consider the meaning of each interaction or quadratic term before adding it to the model. (A quick sketch can be very helpful.) See if you can systematically construct a useful model for prediction. If you have a large data set, you might want to hold out the last observations to test the predictive ability of your model after it is constructed. (As noted in Section 12.10, using the same data to construct *and* to evaluate predictive ability can lead to invalid statistical tests and a false sense of security.)

References

Barnett, V., & Lewis, T. *Outliers in Statistical Data*. New York: Wiley, 1978.

Belsley, D. A., Kuh, E., & Welsch, R. E. *Regression Diagnostics: Identifying Influential Data and Sources of Collinearity*. New York: Wiley, 1980.

Chatterjee, S., & Price, B. *Regression Analysis by Example*, 2nd ed. New York: Wiley, 1991.

Draper, N., & Smith, H. *Applied Regression Analysis*, 2nd ed. New York: Wiley, 1981.

Graybill, F. *Theory and Application of the Linear Model*. North Scituate, Mass.: Duxbury, 1976.

Kutner, M., Nachtsheim, C., Neter, J., & Li, W. *Applied Linear Statistical Models*, 5th ed. New York: McGraw. Hill/Irwin, 2005.

Mendenhall, W. *Introduction to Linear Models and the Design and Analysis of Experiments*. Belmont, Calif.: Wadsworth, 1968.

Mendenhall, W., & Sincich, T. *A Second Course in Statistics: Regression Analysis*, 7th ed. Upper Saddle River, N.J.: Prentice Hall, 2011.

Mosteller, F., & Tukey, J. W. *Data Analysis and Regression: A Second Course in Statistics*. Reading, Mass.: Addison-Wesley, 1977.

Rousseeuw, P. J., & Leroy, A. M. *Robust Regression and Outlier Detection*. New York: Wiley, 1987.

Weisberg, S. *Applied Linear Regression*, 2nd ed. New York: Wiley, 1985.

USING TECHNOLOGY Technology images shown here are taken from SPSS Statistics Professional 20.0, Minitab 16, XLSTAT for Pearson, and Excel 2010.

Note: Automated commands for generating combinations and permutations are not available in SPSS.

SPSS: Multiple Regression

Step 1 Access the SPSS spreadsheet file that contains the dependent and independent variables.

Step 2 Click on the "Analyze" button on the SPSS menu bar and then click on "Regression" and "Linear," as shown in Figure 12.S.1. The resulting dialog box appears as shown in Figure 12.S.2.

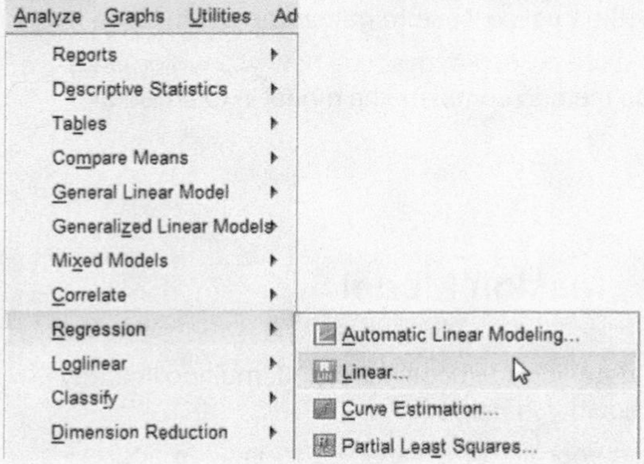

Figure 12.S.1 SPSS menu options for regression

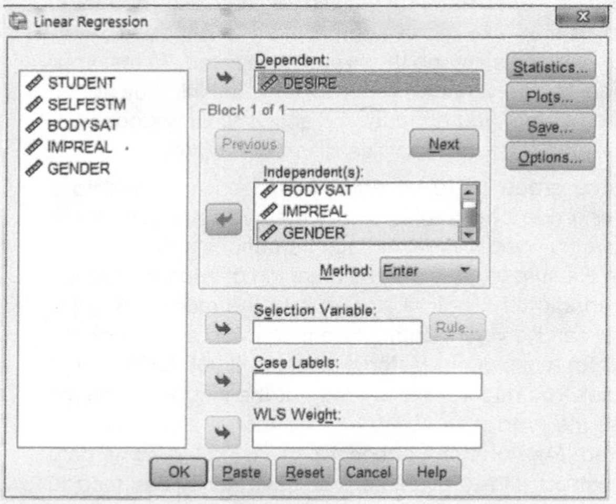

Figure 12.S.2 SPSS linear regression dialog box

Step 3 Specify the dependent variable in the "Dependent" box and the independent variables in the "Independent(s)" box. [*Note:* If your model includes interaction and/or squared terms, you must create and add these higher-order variables to the SPSS spreadsheet file *prior* to running a regression analysis. You can do this by clicking the "Transform" button on the SPSS main menu and selecting the "Compute" option.]

Step 4 To perform a standard regression analysis, select "Enter" in the "Method" box. To perform a stepwise regression analysis, select "Stepwise" in the "Method" box.

Step 5 To perform a nested model F-test for additional model terms, click the "Next" button and enter the terms you want to test in the "Independent(s)" box. [*Note:* These terms, plus the terms you entered initially, form the complete model for the nested F-test.] Next, click the "Statistics" button and select "R squared change." Click "Continue" to return to the main SPSS regression dialog box.

Step 6 To produce confidence intervals for the model parameters, click the "Statistics" button and check the appropriate menu items in the resulting menu list (see Figure 12.S.3).

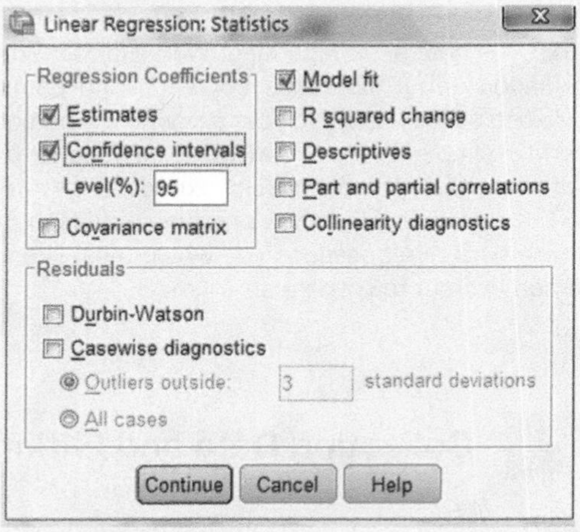

Figure 12.S.3 SPSS linear regression save options

Step 7 To obtain prediction intervals for y and confidence intervals for $E(y)$, click the "Save" button and check the appropriate items in the resulting menu list. (The prediction intervals will be added as new columns to the SPSS data spreadsheet.)

Step 8 Residual plots are obtained by clicking the "Plots" button and making the appropriate selections on the resulting menu (see Figure 12.S.4).

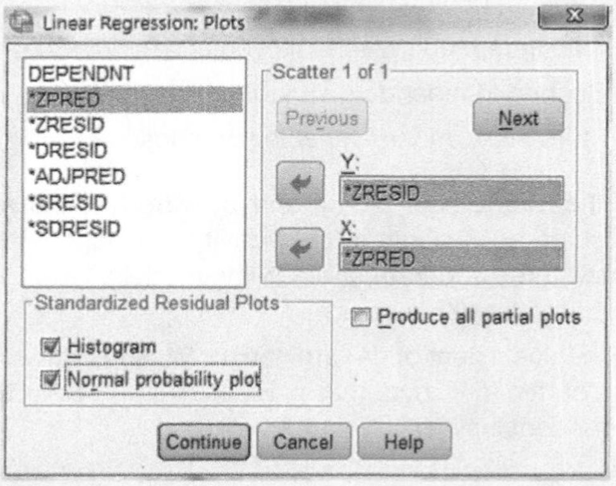

Figure 12.S.4 SPSS linear regression plots options

Step 9 To return to the main Regression dialog box from any of these optional screens, click "Continue." Click "OK" on the Regression dialog box to view the multiple regression results.

Minitab: Multiple Regression

Multiple Regression

Step 1 Access the Minitab worksheet file that contains the dependent and independent variables.

Step 2 Click on the "Stat" button on the Minitab menu bar and then click on "Regression" and "Regression" again, as shown in Figure 12.M.1.

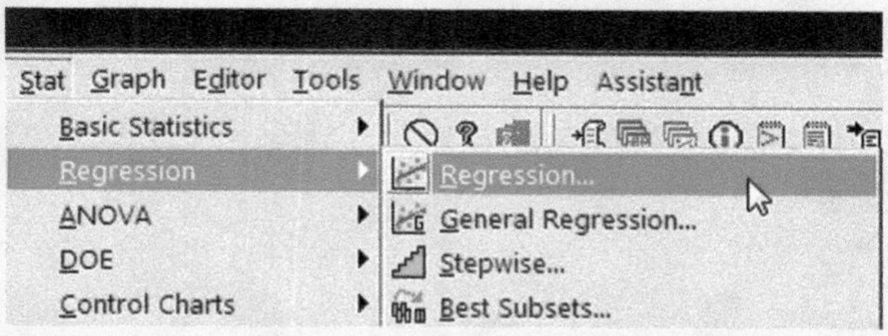

Figure 12.M.1 Minitab menu options for regression

Step 3 The resulting dialog box appears as shown in Figure 12.M.2. Specify the dependent variable in the "Response" box and the independent variables in the "Predictors" box. [*Note*: If your model includes interaction and/or squared terms, you must create and add these higher-order variables to the Minitab worksheet *prior* to running a regression analysis. You can do this by clicking the "Calc" button on the Minitab main menu and selecting the "Calculator" option.]

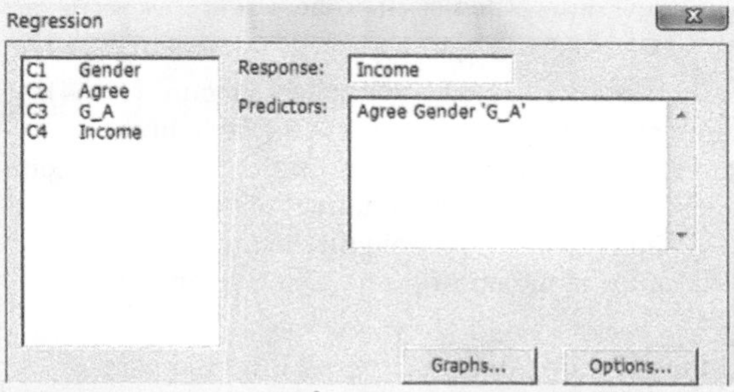

Figure 12.M.2 Minitab regression dialog box

Step 4 To produce prediction intervals for y and confidence intervals for $E(y)$, click the "Options" button and then enter the values of the x's in the appropriate box on the resulting menu list (see Figure 12.M.3).

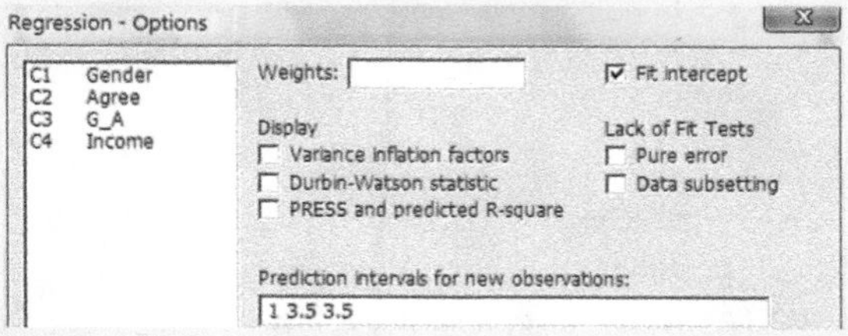

Figure 12.M.3 Minitab regression options

Step 5 Residual plots are obtained by clicking the "Graphs" button and making the appropriate selections on the resulting menu (see Figure 12.M.4).

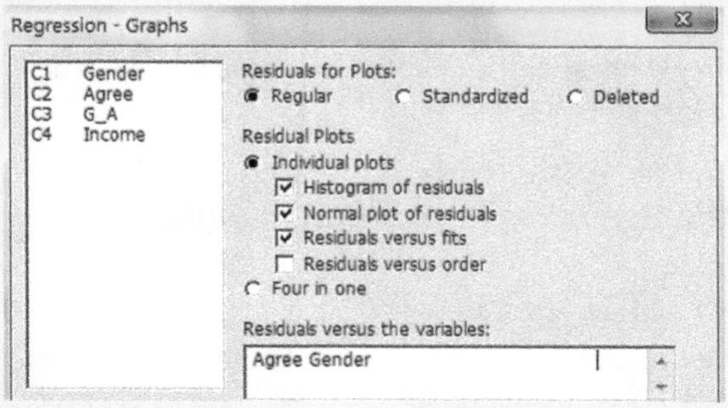

Figure 12.M.4 Minitab regression graphs options

Step 6 To return to the main Regression dialog box from any of these optional screens, click "OK."

Step 7 When you have made all your selections, click "OK" on the main Regression dialog box to produce the Minitab multiple regression printout.

Stepwise Regression

Step 1 Click on the "Stat" button on the main menu bar; then click on "Regression" and click on "Stepwise" (see Figure 12.M.1). The resulting dialog box appears like the one in Figure 12.M.2.

Step 2 Specify the dependent variable in the "Response" box and the independent variables in the stepwise model in the "Predictors" box.

Step 3 As an option, you can select the value of α to use in the analysis by clicking on the "Methods" button and specifying the value. (The default is $\alpha = .15$.)

Step 4 Click "OK" to view the stepwise regression results.

Excel: Multiple Regression

Multiple Regression in Excel

Step 1 Access the Excel worksheet file that contains the dependent and independent variables. [*Note:* If your model includes interaction and/or squared terms, you must create and add these higher-order variables to the Excel worksheet *prior* to running a regression analysis.]

Step 2 Click "Data" from the Excel menu bar and then select "Data Analysis." The resulting menu is shown in Figure 12.E.1.

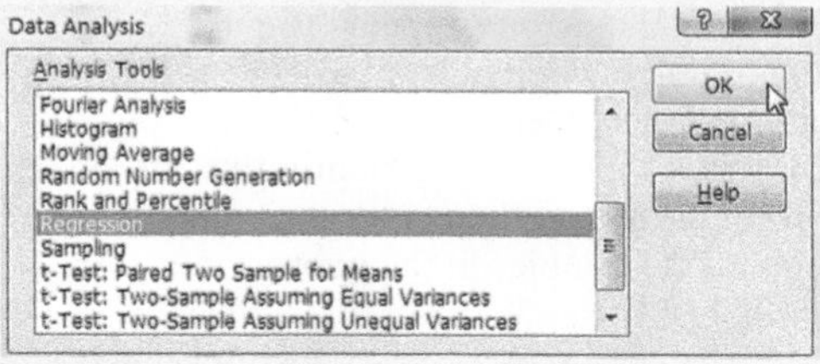

Figure 12.E.1 Excel data analysis menu options for regression

Step 3 Select "Regression" from the drop-down menu and then click "OK." The resulting dialog box is shown in Figure 12.E.2.

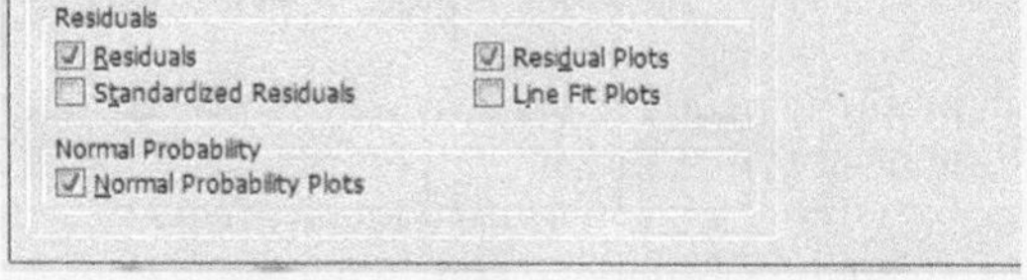

Figure 12.E.2 Excel regression dialog box

Step 4 Specify the cell ranges for the y and x variables in the "Input" area of the Multiple Regression dialog box. [*Note:* The x variables must be in adjacent columns on the Excel worksheet.]

Step 5 Select the confidence level for confidence intervals for the model parameters.

Step 6 To produce graphs of the regression residual, select the "Residual Plots" and "Normal probability plots" options.

Step 7 After making all your selections, click "OK" to produce the multiple regression results.

Multiple Regression with Excel/XLSTAT

Step 1 Within XLSTAT, open the Excel spreadsheet with the data for the dependent and independent variables.

Step 2 Click the "XLSTAT" button on the Excel main menu bar, select "Modeling data," then click "Linear regression," as shown in Figure 12.E.3.

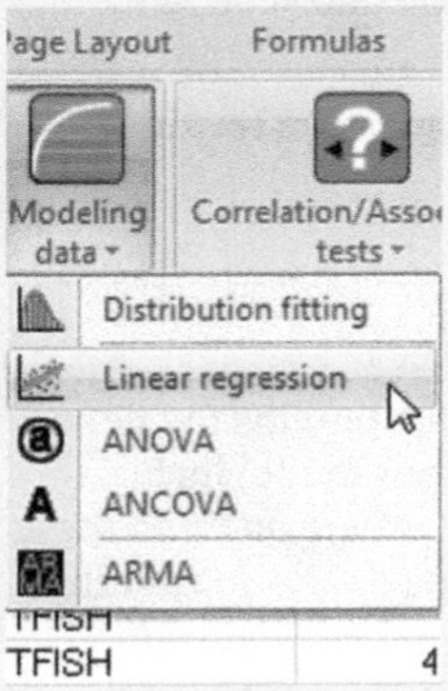

Figure 12.E.3 XLSTAT menu options for multiple regression

Step 3 When the resulting dialog box appears (Figure 12.E.4), enter the column containing the dependent variable in the "Y / Dependent variables" box. Depending on the type of independent variables, check either the "Quantitative" or "Qualitative" option (or both) and then enter the columns containing the independent variables in the appropriate "X / Explanatory variables" boxes.

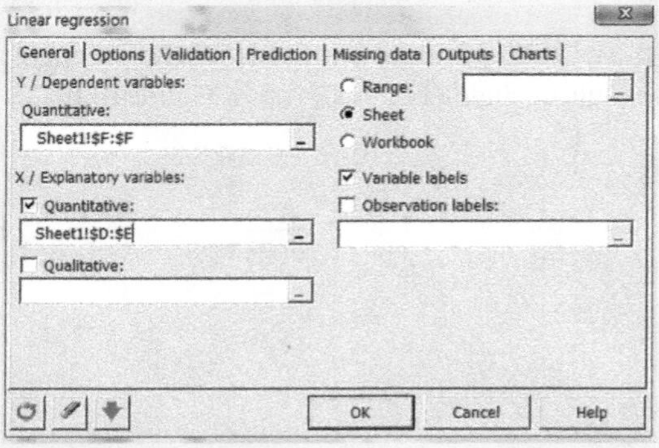

Figure 12.E.4 XLSTAT dialog box for linear regression

Step 4 To obtain prediction/confidence intervals, select the "Prediction" tab, then enter the column with the values of the independent variables for which you want to make predictions in the "X / Explanatory variables" and "Quantitative" or "Qualitative" boxes, as shown in Figure 12.E.5.

Step 5 Click "OK," then "Continue" to display the test results.

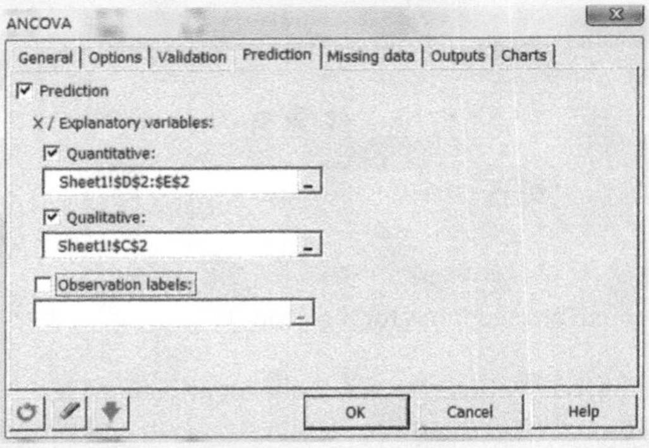

Figure 12.E.5 XLSTAT dialog box for predictions

Stepwise Regression with Excel/XLSTAT

Step 1 Within XLSTAT, open the Excel spreadsheet with the data for the dependent and independent variables.

Step 2 Click the "XLSTAT" button on the Excel main menu bar, select "Modeling data," then click "Linear regression," as shown in Figure 12.E.3.

Step 3 When the resulting dialog box appears (Figure 12.E.4), enter the column containing the dependent variable in the "Y / Dependent variables" box. Depending on the type of independent variables, check either the "Quantitative" or "Qualitative" option (or both) and then enter the columns containing the independent variables in the appropriate "X / Explanatory variables" boxes.

Step 4 Select the "Options" tab, then check the "Stepwise" option under "Model selection," as shown in Figure 12.E.6.

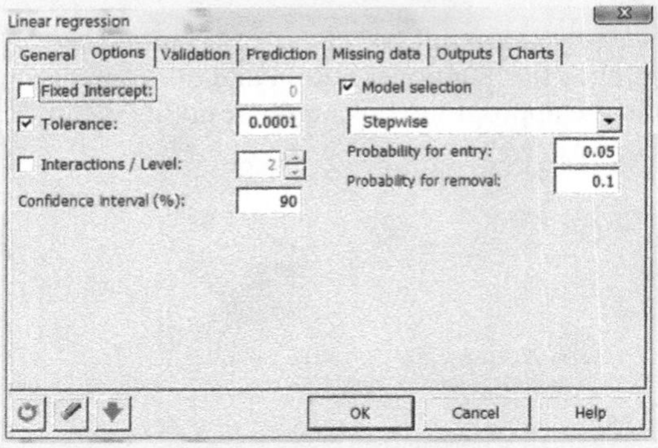

Figure 12.E.6 XLSTAT regression options dialog box

Step 5 Click "OK," then "Continue" to display the stepwise results.

TI-84 Graphing Calculator: Multiple Regression

Note: Only simple linear and quadratic regression models can be fit using the TI-84 graphing calculator.

Quadratic Regression

I. Finding the Quadratic Regression Equation

Step 1 *Enter the data*

- Press **STAT** and select **1:Edit**

  Note: If the list already contains data, clear the old data. Use the up **ARROW** to highlight "**L1**" or "**L2.**"

- Press **CLEAR ENTER**
- Use the **ARROW** and **ENTER** keys to enter the data set into **L1** and **L2**

Step 2 *Find the quadratic regression equation*

- Press **STAT** and highlight **CALC**
- Press **5** for **QuadReg**
- Press **ENTER**
- The screen will show the values for a, b, and c in the equation
- If the diagnostics are on, the screen will also give the value for $\mathbf{r^2}$
- To turn the diagnostics feature on:
- Press **2nd 0** for **CATALOG**
- Press the **ALPHA** key and $\mathbf{x^{-1}}$ for **D**
- Press the down **ARROW** until **DiagnosticsOn** is highlighted
- Press **ENTER** twice

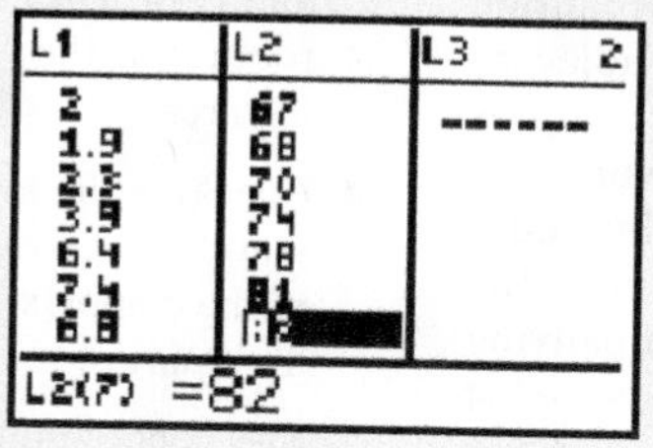

II. Graphing the Quadratic Curve with the Scatterplot

Step 1 *Enter the data as shown in part I above*

Step 2 *Set up the data plot*

- Press **Y** = and **CLEAR** all functions from the Y registers
- Press **2nd Y** = for **STAT PLOT**
- Press **1** for **Plot1**
- Set the cursor so that **ON** is flashing and press **ENTER**
- For **Type,** use the **ARROW** and **ENTER** keys to highlight and select the scatterplot (first icon in the first row)
- For **Xlist,** choose the column containing the *x*-data
- For **Freq,** choose the column containing the *y*-data

Step 3 *Find the regression equation and store the equation in Y1*

- Press **STAT** and highlight **CALC**
- Press **5** for **QuadReg** (*Note:* Don't press ENTER here because you want to store the regression equation in Y1)
- Press **VARS**
- Use the right **ARROW** to highlight **Y-VARS**
- Press **ENTER** to select **1:Function**
- Press **ENTER** to select **1:Y1**
- Press **ENTER**

Step 4 *View the scatterplot and regression line*

- Press **ZOOM** and then press **9** to select **9:ZoomStat**

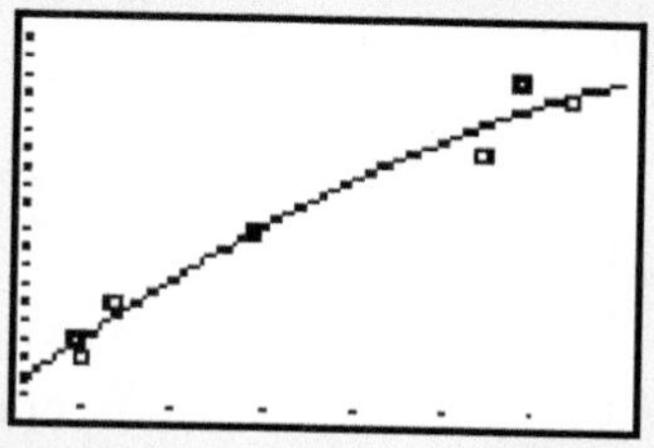

Plotting Residuals

When computing a regression equation on the TI-84, the residuals are automatically computed and saved to a list called **RESID. RESID** can be found under the **LIST menu** (**2nd STAT**).

Step 1 *Enter the data*

- Press **STAT** and select **1:Edit**
- *Note:* If the list already contains data, clear the old data. Use the up **ARROW** to highlight "**L1**" or "**L2.**"
- Press **CLEAR ENTER**
- Use the **ARROW** and **ENTER** keys to enter the data set into **L1** and **L2**

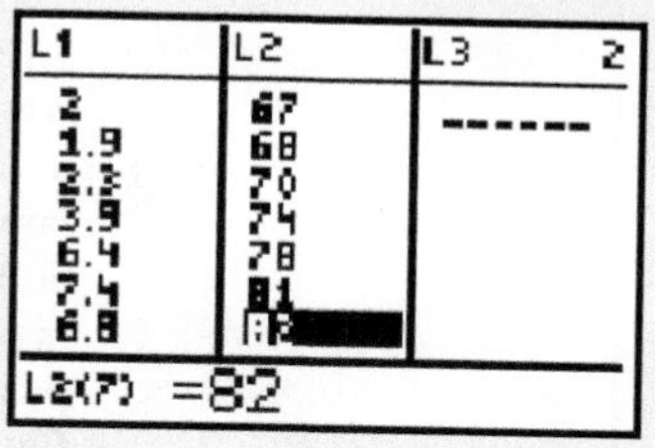

Step 2 *Compute the regression equation*

- Press **STAT** and highlight **CALC**
- Press **4** for **LinReg**(**ax** + **b**)
- Press **ENTER**

Step 3 *Set up the data plot*

- Press **Y**= and **CLEAR** all functions from the Y registers
- Press **2nd Y** = for **STAT-PLOT**
- Press **1** for **Plot1**
- Set the cursor so that **ON** is flashing and press **ENTER**
- For **Type,** use the **ARROW** and **ENTER** keys to highlight and select the scatterplot (first icon in the first row).
- Move the cursor to **Xlist** and choose the column containing the *x*-data
- Move the cursor to **Ylist** and press **2nd STAT** for **LIST**
- Use the down **ARROW** to highlight the listname **RESID** and press **ENTER**

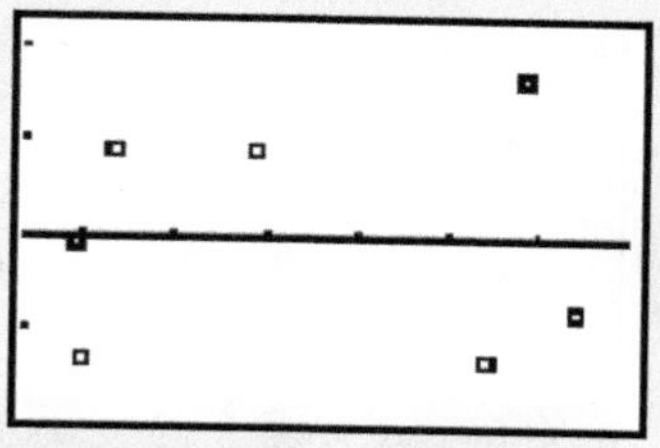

Step 4 *View the scatterplot of the residuals*

- Press **ZOOM 9** for **ZoomStat**

The Condo Sales Case

This case involves an investigation of the factors that affect the sale price of oceanside condominium units. It represents an extension of an analysis of the same data by Herman Kelting. Although condo sale prices have increased dramatically over the past 20 years, the relationship between these factors and sale price remains about the same. Consequently, the data provide valuable insight into today's condominium sales market.

The sales data were obtained for a new oceanside condominium complex consisting of two adjacent and connected eight-floor buildings. The complex contains 200 units of equal size (approximately 500 square feet each). The locations of the buildings relative to the ocean, the swimming pool, the parking lot, etc., are shown in the accompanying figure. There are several features of the complex that you should note:

1. The units facing south, called *ocean view*, face the beach and ocean. In addition, units in building 1 have a good view of the pool. Units to the rear of the building, called *bay-view*, face the parking lot and an area of land that ultimately borders a bay. The view from the upper floors of these units is primarily of wooded, sandy terrain. The bay is very distant and barely visible.
2. The only elevator in the complex is located at the east end of building 1, as are the office and the game room. People moving to or from the higher floor units in building 2 would likely use the elevator and move through the passages to their units. Thus, units on the higher floors and at a greater distance from the elevator would be less convenient; they would require greater effort in moving baggage, groceries, and so on and would be farther away from the game room, the office, and the swimming pool. These units also possess an advantage: there would be the least amount of traffic through the hallways in the area and hence they are the most private.
3. Lower-floor oceanside units are most suited to active people; they open onto the beach, ocean, and pool. They are within easy reach of the game room, and they are easily reached from the parking area.
4. Checking the layout of the condominium complex, you discover that some of the units in the center of the complex, units ending in numbers 11 and 14, have part of their view blocked.
5. The condominium complex was completed at the time of the 1975 recession; sales were slow, and the developer was forced to sell most of the units at auction approximately 18 months after opening. Consequently, the auction data are completely buyer specified and hence consumer oriented in contrast to most other real estate sales data that are, to a high degree, seller and broker specified.
6. Many unsold units in the complex were furnished by the developer and rented prior to the auction. Consequently, some of the units bid on and sold at auction had furniture, others did not.

This condominium complex is obviously unique. For example, the single elevator located at one end of the complex produces a remarkably high level of both inconvenience and privacy for the people occupying units on the top floors in building 2. Consequently, the developer is unsure of how the height of the unit (floor number), distance of the unit from the elevator, presence or absence of an ocean view, etc., affect the prices of the units sold at auction. To investigate these relationships, the following data (saved in the data file) were recorded for each of the 106 units sold at the auction:

1. *Sale price.* Measured in hundreds of dollars (adjusted for inflation).
2. *Floor height.* The floor location of the unit; the variable levels are 1, 2, . . . , 8.
3. *Distance from elevator.* This distance, measured along the length of the complex, is expressed in number of condominium units. An additional two units of distance was added to the units in building 2 to account for the walking distance in the connecting area between the two buildings. Thus, the distance of unit 105 from the elevator would be 3, and the distance between unit 113 and the elevator would be 9. The variable levels are 1, 2, . . . , 15.
4. *View of ocean.* The presence or absence of an ocean view is recorded for each unit and specified

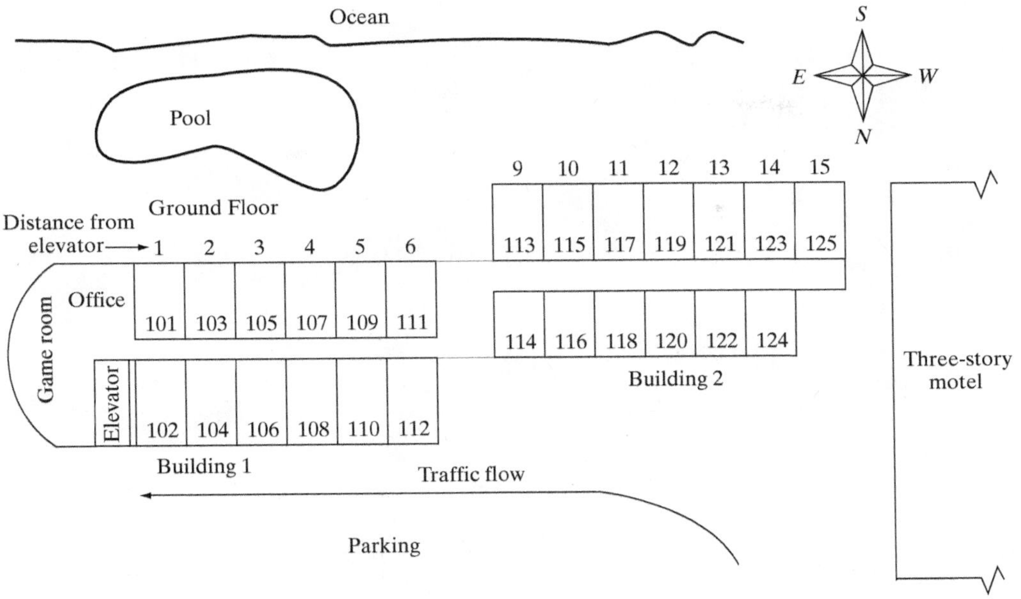

Figure C5.1 Layout of condominium complex

with a dummy variable (1 if the unit possesses an ocean view and 0 if not). Note that units not possessing an ocean view face the parking lot.

5. *End unit.* We expect the partial reduction of view of end units on the ocean side (numbers ending in 11) to reduce their sale price. The ocean view of these end units is partially blocked by building 2. This qualitative variable is also specified with a dummy variable (1 if the unit has a unit number ending in 11 and 0 if not).
6. *Furniture.* The presence or absence of furniture is recorded for each unit and is represented with a single dummy variable (1 if the unit was furnished and 0 if not).

Your objective for this case is to build a regression model that accurately predicts the sale price of a condominium unit sold at auction. Prepare a professional document that presents the results of your analysis. Include graphs that demonstrate how each of the independent variables in your model affects auction price. A layout of the data file is described below.

Variable	Type
PRICE	QN
FLOOR	QN
DISTANCE	QN
VIEW	QL
ENDUNIT	QL
FURNISH	QL

(Number of Observations: 106) *Data Set:* CONDO

13

CONTENTS

Where We've Been

- Presented methods for making inferences about populations based on sample data (Chapters 6–10) using confidence intervals and tests of hypotheses
- Presented methods for modeling the relationships between variables (Chapters 11–12) using regression analysis

Where We're Going

- Return to an examination of processes, i.e., actions/operations that transform inputs to outputs (13.1)
- Describe methods for improving processes and the quality of the output they produce (13.2)
- Present control charts for monitoring a process mean (13.3, 13.4)
- Present control charts for monitoring process variation (13.5)
- Present control charts for monitoring proportion defectives (13.6)
- Introduce some advanced methods for improving quality (13.7, 13.8)

Methods for Quality Improvement *Statistical Process Control*

STATISTICS in ACTION Testing Jet Fuel Additive for Safety

The American Society of Testing and Materials (ASTM) International provides standards and guidelines for materials, products, systems, and services. The Federal Aviation Administration (FAA) has a huge conglomerate of testing requirements for jet fuel safety that are spelled out in ASTM methods. This Statistics in Action involves an engineering firm that is developing a new method of surfactant detection in jet fuel.

Surfactants (surface active agents) are basically soaps that can form due to acids in the fuel but are more commonly caused by contamination from other products, such as engine cleaning additives. Although the surfactants do not directly cause problems, they reduce the ability of coalescing filters to remove water. Water in jet fuel carries bacteria that are deposited in tanks and engine components, causing major corrosion and engine damage.

The standard test for surfactants (described in ASTM Rule D-3948) is to use a miniature filter (Filter-A) with a pumping mechanism (Pump-A). A water/fuel mixture is pumped through the filter at a specific rate, and the amount of water that passes through the filter is detected with an optical transmittance test. Test measurements will typically yield a result between 80 and 85.

In an attempt to improve the precision of the surfactant test, the engineering firm compared the standard test (Pump-A with Filter-A) to three other pumping mechanism and filter option combinations—Pump-A with Filter-B, Pump-B with Filter-A, and Pump-B with Filter-B. Each day, a routine batch of jet fuel was created by adding 0.4 ppm of a surfactant solution. Twelve samples of the fuel were randomly selected and randomly divided into four groups of three samples each. The three samples in a group were tested for surfactants using one of the four pump/filter combinations. Consequently, each day there were three test results for each

STATISTICS in ACTION CONTINUED

pump/filter method. This pattern of sampling continued for over 100 days. The test measurements are saved in four **JET** files. (Data for the first 5 days of the sampling experiment are listed in Table SIA13.1).

The firm wants to monitor the results of the surfactant tests and determine if one of the test methods yields the most stable process. In the Statistics in Action Revisited sections listed, we show how to analyze the data using methods for quality and process control.

Table SIA13.1 Selected Data in the JET Files

Weekday	Month	Day	Sample	Pump-B Filter-A	Pump-A Filter-A	Pump-B Filter-B	Pump-A Filter-B
Tue	May	9	1	76	84	85	85
			2	81	91	84	84
			3	81	86	84	88
Wed	May	10	1	84	92	87	92
			2	81	93	82	95
			3	86	94	85	90
Thu	May	11	1	83	94	82	90
			2	82	96	85	87
			3	79	92	84	81
Fri	May	12	1	81	96	81	90
			2	84	91	82	91
			3	83	96	88	92
Mon	May	15	1	80	90	87	94
			2	88	92	85	94
			3	87	91	86	84

Data Sets: JETA-A, JETA-B, JETB-A, JETB-B

STATISTICS in ACTION REVISITED

▫ Monitoring the Process Mean **(p. 13-27)**
▫ Monitoring the Process Variation **(p. 13-38)**

Over the last several decades, U.S. firms have been seriously challenged by products (e.g., automobiles, electronics, cell phones) of superior quality from overseas, particularly from Japan. To meet this competitive challenge, more and more U.S. firms—both manufacturing and service firms—have quality-improvement initiatives of their own. Many of these firms stress **total quality management** (TQM) (i.e., the management of quality in all phases and aspects of their business, from the design of their products to production, distribution, sales, and service).

Broadly speaking, TQM is concerned with (1) finding out what it is that the customer wants, (2) translating those wants into a product or service design, and (3) producing a product or service that meets or exceeds the specifications of the design. In this chapter, we focus primarily on the third of these three areas and its major problem—product and service variation.

Variation is inherent in the output of all production and service processes. No two parts produced by a given machine are the same; no two transactions performed by a given bank teller are the same. Why is this a problem? With variation in output comes variation in the quality of the product or service. If this variation is unacceptable to customers, sales are lost, profits suffer, and the firm may not survive.

The existence of this ever-present variation has made statistical methods and statistical training vitally important to industry. In Sections 13.2–13.8 we present some of the tools and methods currently employed by firms worldwide to monitor and reduce product and service variation. But first, we provide a brief introduction to quality, processes, and systems—three key components of TQM.

13.1 Quality, Processes, and Systems

Quality

Before describing various tools and methods that can be used to monitor and improve the quality of products and services, we need to consider what is meant by the term *quality*. Quality can be defined from several different perspectives. To the engineers and scientists who design products, quality typically refers to the amount of some ingredient or attribute possessed by the product. For example, high-quality ice cream contains a large amount of butterfat. To managers, engineers, and workers involved in the production of a product (or the delivery of a service), quality usually means conformance to requirements, or the degree to which the product or service conforms to its design specifications. For example, in order to fit properly, the cap of a particular molded plastic bottle must be between 1.0000 inch and 1.0015 inches in diameter. Caps that do not conform to this requirement are considered to be of inferior quality.

Although quality can be defined from the perspective of either the designers or the producers of a product, in the final analysis both definitions should be derived from the needs and preferences of the *user* of the product or service. A firm that produces goods that no one wants to purchase cannot stay in business. We define *quality* accordingly.

> The **quality** of a good or service is indicated by the extent to which it satisfies the needs and preferences of its users.

To produce a high-quality product, it is necessary to study the needs and wants of consumers. What product characteristics are consumers looking for? What is it that influences users' perceptions of quality? This is the kind of knowledge that firms need in order to develop and deliver high-quality goods and services. The basic elements of quality are summarized in the eight dimensions shown in the box.

The Eight Dimensions of Quality*

1. **Performance:** The primary operating characteristics of the product. For an automobile, these would include acceleration, handling, smoothness of ride, gas mileage, and so forth.
2. **Features:** The "bells and whistles" that supplement the product's basic functions. Examples include CD players and digital clocks on cars and the frequent-flyer mileage and free drinks offered by airlines.
3. **Reliability:** Reflects the probability that the product will operate properly within a given period of time.
4. **Conformance:** The extent or degree to which a product meets preestablished standards. This is reflected in, for example, a pharmaceutical manufacturer's concern that the plastic bottles it orders for its drugs have caps that are between 1.0000 and 1.0015 inches in diameter, as specified in the order.
5. **Durability:** The life of the product. If repair is possible, durability relates to the length of time a product can be used before replacement is judged to be preferable to continued repair.
6. **Serviceability:** The ease of repair, speed of repair, and competence and courtesy of the repair staff.
7. **Aesthetics:** How a product looks, feels, sounds, smells, or tastes.
8. **Other perceptions that influence judgments of quality:** Such factors as a firm's reputation and the images of the firm and its products that are created through advertising.

**Source:* Based on "The Multiple Dimensions of Quality" from MANAGING QUALITY by David A. Garvin.

To design and produce products of high quality, it is necessary to translate the characteristics described in the box into product attributes that can be built into the product by the manufacturer—that is, user preferences must be interpreted in terms of product variables over which the manufacturer has control. For example, in considering the performance characteristics of a particular brand of wooden pencil, users may indicate a preference for being able to use the pencil for longer periods between sharpenings. The manufacturer may translate this performance characteristic into one or more measurable physical characteristics such as wood hardness, lead hardness, and lead composition. Besides being used to design high-quality products, such variables are used in the process of monitoring and improving quality during production.

Processes

Much of this textbook focuses on methods for using sample data drawn from a population to learn about that population. In this chapter and Chapter 14 (on your CD), however, our attention is not on populations but on processes—such as manufacturing processes—and the output that they generate. In general, a process is defined as follows:

> A **process** is a series of actions or operations that transforms inputs to outputs. A process produces output over time.

In this chapter, we focus on organizational processes—those associated with organizations such as businesses and governments. Perhaps the best example is a manufacturing process, which consists of a series of operations, performed by people and machines, whereby inputs such as raw materials and parts are converted into finished products (the outputs). Examples include automobile assembly lines, oil refineries, and steel mills. Figure 13.1 presents a general description of a process and its inputs.

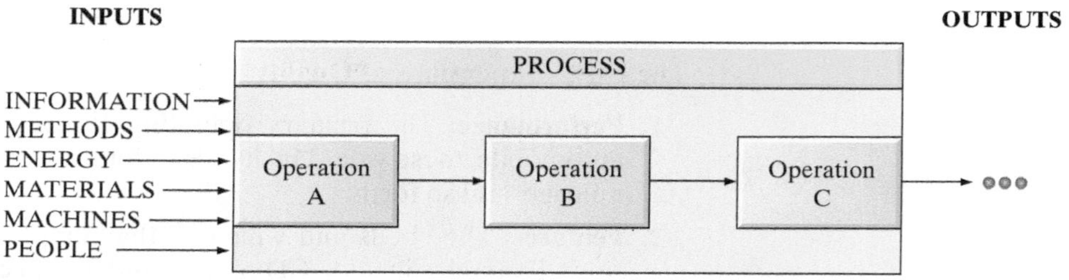

Figure 13.1
Graphical depiction of a process and its inputs

It is useful to think of processes as *adding value* to the inputs of the process. Manufacturing processes, for example, are designed so that the value of the outputs to potential customers exceeds the value of the inputs—otherwise the firm would have no demand for its products and would not survive.

Systems

To understand what causes variation in process output and how processes and their output can be improved, we must understand the role that processes play in *systems.*

> A **system** is a collection or arrangement of interacting processes that has an ongoing purpose or mission. A system receives inputs from its environment, transforms those inputs to outputs, and delivers them to its environment. In order to survive, a system uses feedback (i.e., information) from its environment to understand and adapt to changes in its environment.

Figure 13.2 presents a model of a basic system. As an example of a system, consider a manufacturing company. It has a collection of interacting processes—marketing research, engineering, purchasing, receiving, production, sales, distribution, billing, and so on.

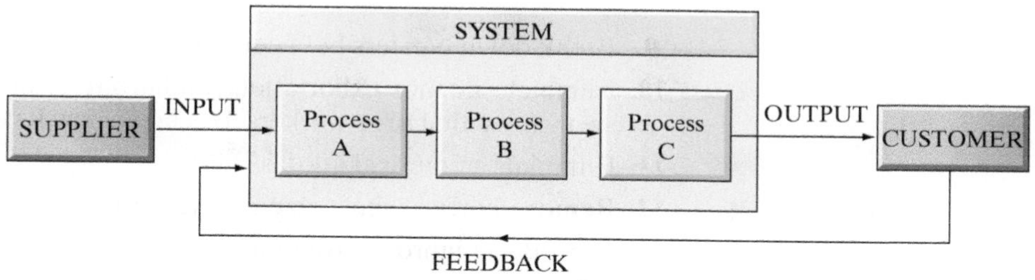

Figure 13.2
Model of a basic system

Its mission is to make money for its owners, to provide high-quality working conditions for its employees, and to stay in business. The firm receives raw materials and parts (inputs) from outside vendors that, through its production processes, it transforms to finished goods (outputs). The finished goods are distributed to its customers. Through its marketing research, the firm "listens" to (receives feedback from) its customers and potential customers in order to change or adapt its processes and products to meet (or exceed) the needs, preferences, and expectations of the marketplace.

Because systems are collections of processes, the various types of system inputs are the same as those listed in Figure 13.1 for processes. System outputs are products or services. These outputs may be physical objects made, assembled, repaired, or moved by the system; or they may be symbolical, such as information, ideas, or knowledge. For example, a brokerage house supplies customers with information about stocks and bonds and the markets where they are traded.

Two important points about systems and the output of their processes are as follows: (1) No two items produced by a process are the same; (2) variability is an inherent characteristic of the output of all processes. This is illustrated in Figure 13.3. No two cars produced by the same assembly line are the same: No two windshields are the same; no two wheels are the same; no two tires are the same; no two hubcaps are the same. The same thing can be said for processes that deliver services. Consider the services offered at the teller windows of a bank to two customers waiting in two lines. Will they wait in line the same amount of time? Will they be serviced by tellers with the same degree of expertise and with the same personalities? Assuming the customers' transactions are the same, will they take the same amount of time to execute? The answer to all these questions is no.

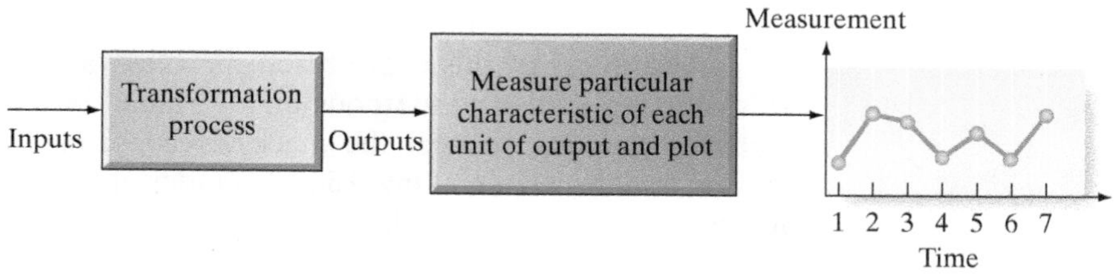

Figure 13.3
Output variation

Deming's 14 Points: Guidelines for Quality Improvement

1. Create constancy of purpose toward improvement of product and service, with the aim to become competitive, to stay in business, and to provide jobs.
2. Adopt the new philosophy.
3. Cease dependence on inspection to achieve quality.
4. End the practice of awarding business on the basis of price tag.
5. Improve constantly and forever the system of production and service, to improve quality and productivity, and thus constantly decrease costs.
6. Institute training.
7. Institute leadership.
8. Drive out fear, so that everyone may work effectively for the company.

9. Break down barriers between departments.
10. Eliminate slogans, exhortations, and arbitrary numerical goals and targets for the workforce that urge workers to achieve new levels of productivity and quality.
11. Eliminate numerical quotas.
12. Remove barriers that rob employees of their pride of workmanship.
13. Institute a vigorous program of education and self-improvement.
14. Take action to accomplish the transformation.

BIOGRAPHY

W. EDWARDS DEMING (1900–1993)

Deming's 14 Points

Born in Sioux City, Iowa, Ed Deming was raised on an Iowa farm until age 7, when his family moved to Wyoming. Because his parents emphasized the importance of education, Deming enrolled at the University of Wyoming in 1917, graduating 4 years later with a degree in electrical engineering. He eventually earned his PhD in mathematical physics from Yale University in 1928. Deming worked for both the U.S. Department of Agriculture and the Census Bureau before becoming a statistics professor at New York University and Columbia University. While studying under W. A. Shewhart (see Biography, p. 13-14) in the 1930s, Deming become interested in the application of statistics to quality and process improvement for industry. He is probably most famous for his "14 Points for Management" (see preceding box)—guidelines that transform the organizational climate to one in which process-management efforts can flourish. In 1950, the Japanese Union of Scientists and Engineers invited Deming to present a series of lectures on these ideas. His expertise and advice on quality-control methods helped to revolutionize Japan's industry, leading to the Japanese economic boom in the twentieth century. (The *Deming Prize* is awarded every year to the corporation with the greatest accomplishment in quality improvement in the world.)

In general, variation in output is caused by the six factors listed below.

The Six Major Sources of Process Variation

1. People
2. Machines
3. Materials
4. Methods
5. Measurement
6. Environment

Awareness of this ever-present process variation has made training in statistical thinking and statistical methods highly valued by industry. Recall (Chapter 1) that by **statistical thinking** we mean the knack of recognizing variation and exploiting it in problem solving and decision making. The remainder of this chapter is devoted to statistical tools for monitoring process variation.

13.2 Statistical Control

For the rest of this chapter, we turn our attention to **control charts**—graphical devices used for monitoring process variation, identifying when to take action to improve the process, and assisting in diagnosing the causes of process variation. Control charts, developed by Walter Shewhart of Bell Laboratories in the mid-1920s, are the tool of choice for continuously monitoring processes. Before we go into the details of control chart construction and use, however, it is important that you have a fuller understanding of **process variation.** To this end, we discuss patterns of variation in this section.

As discussed in Chapter 2, the proper graphical method for describing the variation of process output is a *time series plot*, sometimes called a **run chart.** Recall that in a time series plot, the measurements of interest are plotted against time or are plotted in the order in which the measurements were made, as in Figure 13.4. Whenever you face the task of analyzing data that were generated over time, your first reaction should be

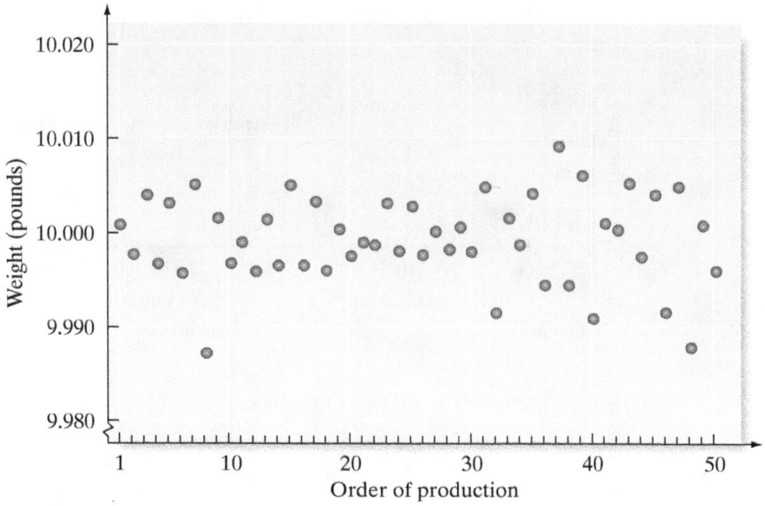

Figure 13.4
Time series plot of fill weights for 50 consecutively produced gallon cans of paint

to plot them. The human eye is one of our most sensitive statistical instruments. Take advantage of that sensitivity by plotting the data and allowing your eyes to seek out patterns in the data.

Let's begin thinking about process variation by examining the plot in Figure 13.4 more closely. The measurements, taken from a paint manufacturing process, are the weights of 50 one-gallon cans of paint that were consecutively filled by the same filling head (nozzle). The weights were plotted in the order of production. Do you detect any systematic, persistent patterns in the sequence of weights? For example, do the weights tend to drift steadily upward or downward over time? Do they oscillate—high, then low, then high, then low, and so on?

To assist your visual examination of this or any other time series plot, Roberts (1991) recommends enhancing the basic plot in two ways. First, compute (or simply estimate) the mean of the set of 50 weights and draw a horizontal line on the graph at the level of the mean. This **centerline** gives you a point of reference in searching for patterns in the data. Second, using straight lines, connect each of the plotted weights in the order in which they were produced. This helps display the sequence of the measurements. Both enhancements are shown in Figure 13.5.

Now do you see a pattern in the data? Successive points alternate up and down, high then low, in an **oscillating sequence.** In this case, the points alternate above and below the centerline. This pattern was caused by a valve in the paint-filling machine that tended to stick in a partially closed position every other time it operated.

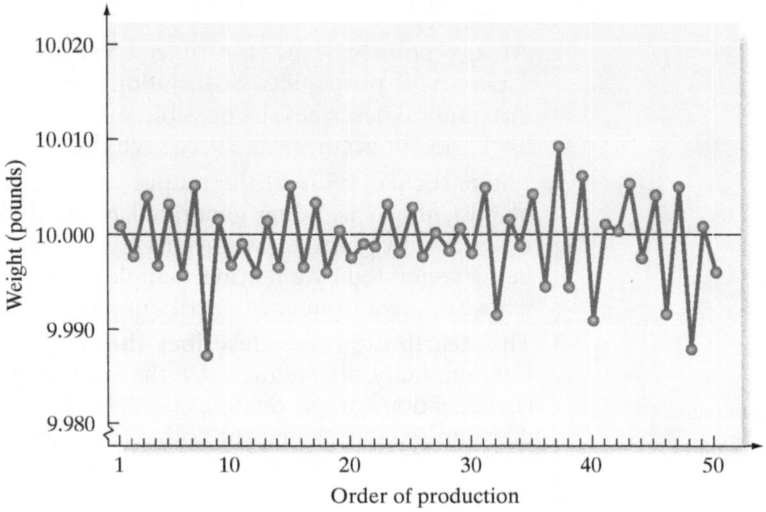

Figure 13.5
An enhanced version of the paint fill time series

Other patterns of process variation are shown in Figure 13.6. We discuss several of them later.

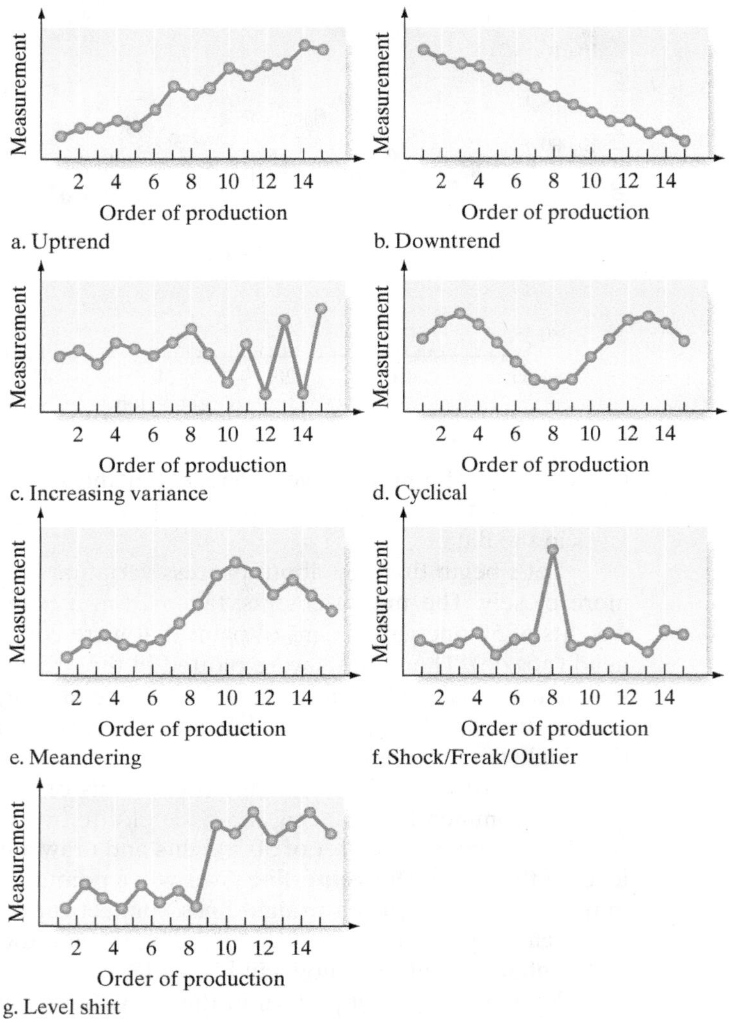

Figure 13.6
Patterns of process variation: Some examples

In trying to describe process variation and diagnose its causes, it helps to think of the sequence of measurements of the output variable (e.g., weight, length, number of defects) as having been generated in the following way:

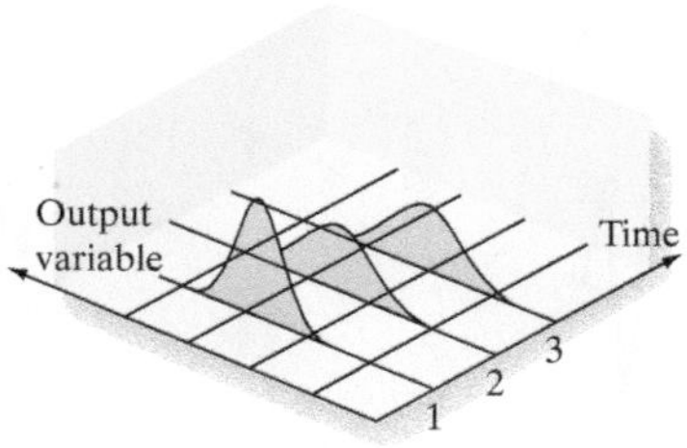

Figure 13.7
Distributions describing one output variable at three points in time

1. At any point in time, the output variable of interest can be described by a particular probability distribution (or relative frequency distribution). This distribution describes the possible values that the variable can assume and their likelihood of occurrence. Three such distributions are shown in Figure 13.7.
2. The particular value of the output variable that is realized at a given time can be thought of as being generated or produced according to the distribution described in point 1. (Alternatively, the realized value can be thought of as being generated by a random sample of size $n = 1$ from a population of values whose relative frequency distribution is that of point 1.)
3. The distribution that describes the output variable may change over time. For simplicity, we characterize the changes as being of three types: the mean (i.e., location) of the distribution may change; the variance (i.e., shape) of the distribution may change; or both. This is illustrated in Figure 13.8.

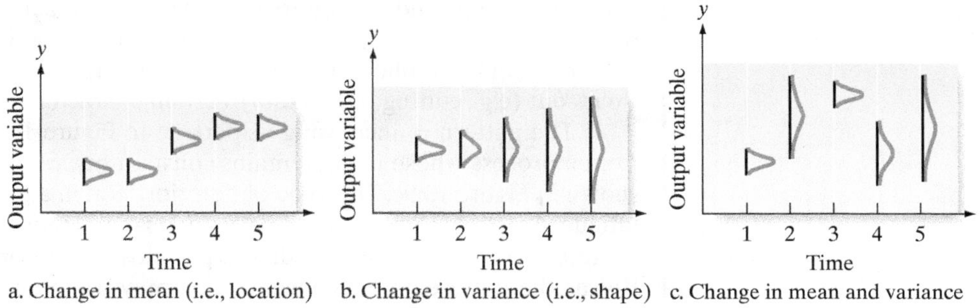

Figure 13.8
Types of changes in output variables

In general, when the output variable's distribution changes over time, we refer to this as a change in the *process*. Thus, if the mean shifts to a higher level, we say that the process mean has shifted. Accordingly, we sometimes refer to the distribution of the output variable as simply the **distribution of the process,** or the **output distribution of the process.**

Example 13.1

Models of Process Variation Patterns

Problem Reconsider the patterns of variation in Figure 13.6. These patterns are modeled in Figure 13.9. Interpret each graph.

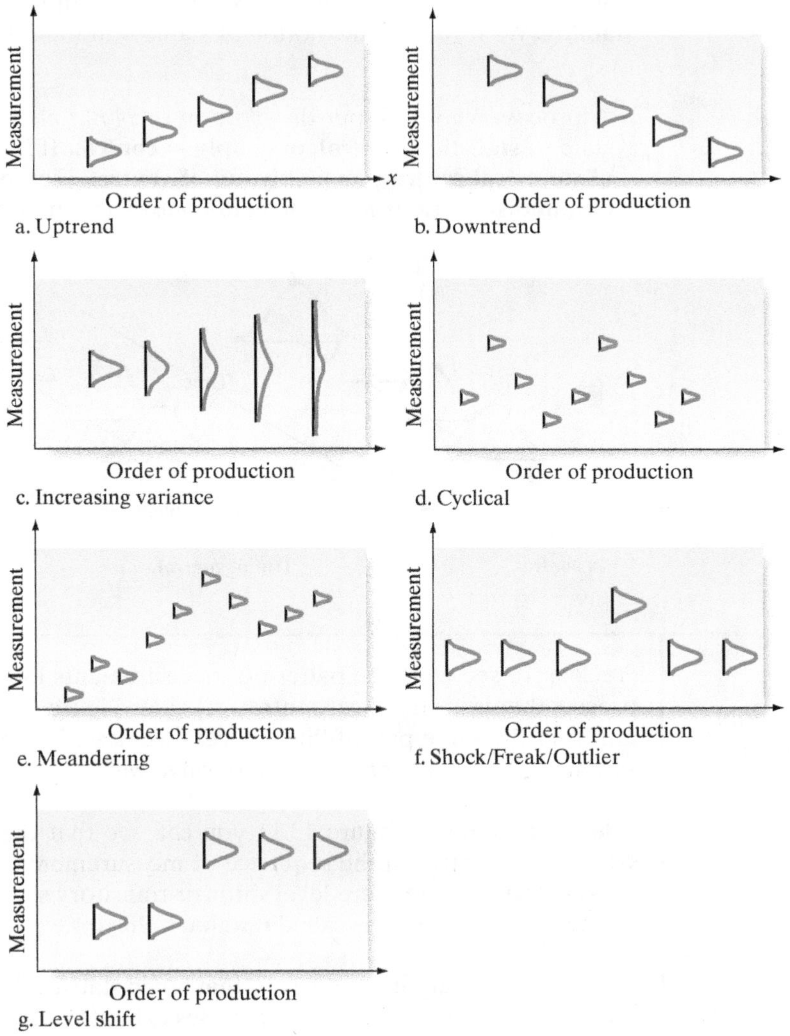

Figure 13.9
Patterns of process variation described by changing distributions

Solution The uptrend of Figure 13.6a can be characterized as resulting from a process whose mean is gradually shifting upward over time, as in Figure 13.9a. Gradual shifts like this are a common phenomenon in manufacturing processes. For example, as a machine wears out (e.g., cutting blades dull), certain characteristics of its output gradually change.

The pattern of increasing dispersion in Figure 13.6c can be thought of as resulting from a process whose mean remains constant but whose variance increases over time, as shown in Figure 13.9c. This type of deterioration in a process may be the result of worker fatigue. At the beginning of a shift, workers—whether they be typists, machine operators, waiters, or managers—are fresh and pay close attention to every item that they process. But as the day wears on, concentration may wane and the workers may become more and more careless or more easily distracted. As a result, some items receive more attention than other items, causing the variance of the workers' output to increase.

The sudden shift in the level of the measurements in Figure 13.6g can be thought of as resulting from a process whose mean suddenly increases but whose variance remains constant, as shown in Figure 13.9g. This type of pattern may be caused by such things as a change in the quality of raw materials used in the process or bringing a new machine or new operator into the process.

Look Back All the relative frequency distributions shown in Figure 13.9 appear to be mound-shaped and symmetric (i.e., normally distributed). In reality, one or more of the distributions are likely to be nonnormal.

One thing that the patterns in Example 13.1 have in common is that the distribution of the output variable *changes over time*. In such cases, we say the process lacks **stability.** We formalize the notion of stability in the following definition.

A process whose output distribution does *not* change over time is said to be in a state of **statistical control,** or simply **in control.** If it does change, it is said to be **out of statistical control,** or simply **out of control.** Figure 13.10 illustrates a sequence of output distributions for both an in-control and an out-of-control process.

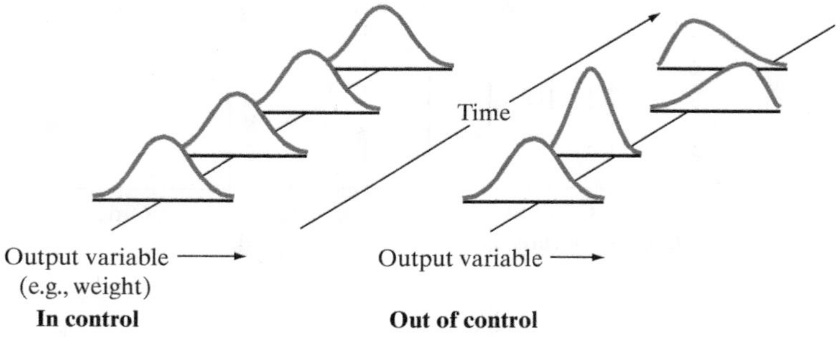

Figure 13.10
Comparison of in-control and out-of-control processes

Example 13.2

A Process "In Statistical Control"—Filling Paint Cans

Problem To see what the pattern of measurements looks like on a time series plot for a process that is in statistical control, consider Figure 13.11 (on the next page). These data are from the same paint-filling process we described earlier, but the sequence of measurements was made *after* the faulty valve was replaced. Interpret the graph.

Solution Examining Figure 13.11 you can see that there are no discernible persistent, systematic patterns in the sequence of measurements such as those in Figures 13.5 and 13.6a–13.6e. Nor are there level shifts or transitory shocks as in Figures 13.6f–13.6g. This "patternless" behavior is called **random behavior.**

Look Back The output of processes that are in statistical control exhibits random behavior. Thus, even the output of stable processes exhibits variation.

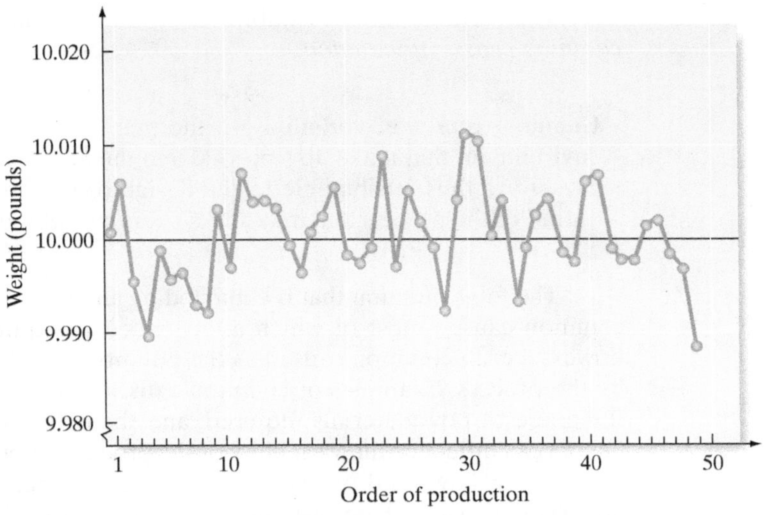

Figure 13.11
Time series plot of 50 consecutive paint can fills collected after replacing faulty valve

If a process is in control and remains in control, its future will be like its past. Accordingly, the process is predictable, in the sense that its output will stay within certain limits. This cannot be said about an out-of-control process. As illustrated in Figure 13.12, with most out-of-control processes, you have no idea what the future pattern of output from the process may look like.* You simply do not know what to expect from the process. Consequently, a business that operates out-of-control processes runs the risk of (1) providing inferior-quality products and services to its internal customers (people within the organization who use the outputs of the processes) and (2) selling inferior products and services to its external customers. In short, it risks losing its customers and threatens its own survival.

One of the fundamental goals of process management is to identify out-of-control processes, to take actions to bring them into statistical control, and to keep them in a state of statistical control. The series of activities used to attain this goal is referred to as *statistical process control.*

The process of monitoring and eliminating variation in order to *keep* a process in a state of statistical control or to *bring* a process into statistical control is called **statistical process control (SPC).**

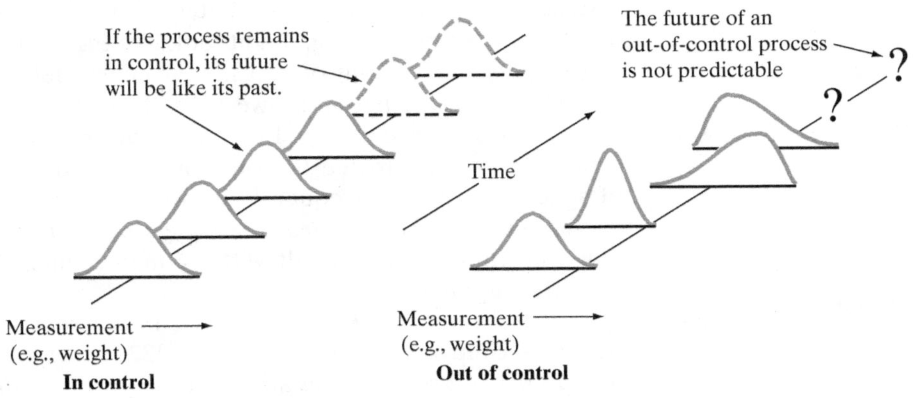

Figure 13.12
In-control processes are predictable; out-of-control processes are not

*The output variables of in-control processes may follow approximately normal distributions, as in Figures 13.10 and 13.12, or they may not. But any in-control process will follow the *same* distribution over time. Do not misinterpret the use of normal distributions in many figures in this chapter as indicating that all in-control processes follow normal distributions.

The variation that is exhibited by processes that are in control is said to be due to *common causes of variation.*

Common causes of variation are the methods, materials, machines, personnel, and environment that make up a process and the inputs required by the process. Common causes are thus attributable to the design of the process. Common causes affect all output of the process and may affect everyone who participates in the process.

The total variation that is exhibited by an in-control process is due to many different common causes, most of which affect process output in very minor ways. In general, however, each common cause has the potential to affect every unit of output produced by the process. Examples of common causes include the lighting in a factory or office, the grade of raw materials required, and the extent of worker training. Each of these factors can influence the variability of the process output. Poor lighting can cause workers to overlook flaws and defects that they might otherwise catch. Inconsistencies in raw materials can cause inconsistencies in the quality of the finished product. The extent of the training provided to workers can affect their level of expertise and, as a result, the quality of the products and services for which they are responsible.

Because common causes are, in effect, designed into a process, the level of variation that results from common causes is viewed as being representative of the capability of the process. If that level is too great (i.e., if the quality of the output varies too much), the process must be redesigned (or modified) to eliminate one or more common causes of variation. Because process redesign is the responsibility of management, the *elimination of common causes of variation is typically the responsibility of management*, not the workers.

Processes that are out of control exhibit variation that is the result of both common causes and *special causes of variation.*

Special causes of variation (sometimes called **assignable causes**) are events or actions that are not part of the process design. Typically, they are transient, fleeting events that affect only local areas or operations within the process (e.g., a single worker, machine, or batch of materials) for a brief period of time. Occasionally, however, such events may have a persistent or recurrent effect on the process.

Examples of special causes of variation include a worker accidentally setting the controls of a machine improperly, a worker becoming ill on the job and continuing to work, a particular machine slipping out of adjustment, and a negligent supplier shipping a batch of inferior raw materials to the process.

In the latter case, the pattern of output variation may look like Figure 13.6f. If instead of shipping just one bad batch the supplier continued to send inferior materials, the pattern of variation might look like Figure 13.6g. The output of a machine that is gradually slipping out of adjustment might yield a pattern like Figure 13.6a, 13.6b, or 13.6c. All these patterns owe part of their variation to common causes and part to the noted special causes. In general, we treat any pattern of variation other than a random pattern as due to both common and special causes.* Because the effects of special causes are frequently localized within a process, *special causes can often be diagnosed and eliminated by workers or their immediate supervisor.* Occasionally, however, they must be dealt with by management, as in the case of a negligent or deceitful supplier.

It is important to recognize that **most processes are not naturally in a state of statistical control.** As Deming (1986, p. 322) observed, *"Stability [i.e., statistical control] is seldom a natural state. It is an achievement, the result of eliminating special causes one by one...leaving only the random variation of a stable process"* (italics added).

*For certain processes (e.g., those affected by seasonal factors), a persistent systematic pattern—such as the cyclical pattern of Figure 13.6d—is an inherent characteristic. In these special cases, some analysts treat the cause of the systematic variation as a common cause. This type of analysis is beyond the scope of this text. We refer the interested reader to Alwan and Roberts (1988).

Process improvement first requires the identification, diagnosis, and removal of special causes of variation. Removing all special causes puts the process in a state of statistical control. Further improvement of the process then requires the identification, diagnosis, and removal of common causes of variation. The effects on the process of the removal of special and common causes of variation are illustrated in Figure 13.13.

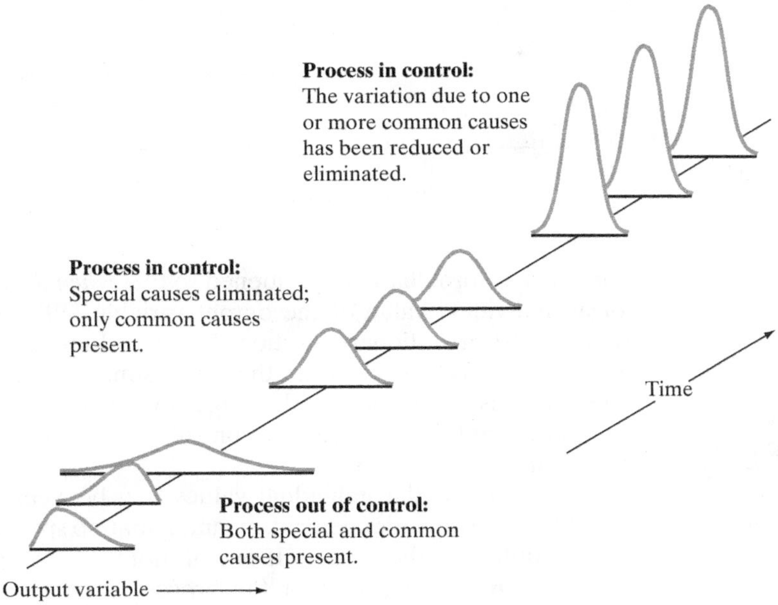

Figure 13.13
The effects of eliminating causes of variation

In the remainder of this chapter, we introduce you to some of the methods of statistical process control. In particular, we address how control charts help us determine whether a given process is in control.

13.3 The Logic of Control Charts

We use control charts to help us differentiate between process variation due to common causes and special causes—that is, we use them to determine whether a process is under statistical control (only common causes present) or not (both common and special causes present). Being able to differentiate means knowing when to take action to find and remove special causes and when to leave the process alone. If you take actions to remove special causes that do not exist—that is called *tampering with the process*—you may actually end up increasing the variation of the process and, thereby, hurting the quality of the output.

In general, control charts are useful for evaluating the past performance of a process and for monitoring its current performance. We can use them to determine whether a process was in control during, say, the past 2 weeks or to determine whether the process is remaining under control from hour to hour or minute to minute. In the latter case, our goal is the swiftest detection and removal of any special causes of variation that might arise. Keep in mind that **the primary goal of quality-improvement activities is variance reduction.**

In this chapter, we show you how to construct and use control charts for both quantitative and qualitative quality variables. Important quantitative variables include such things as weight, width, and time. An important qualitative variable is product status: defective or nondefective.

An example of a control chart is shown in Figure 13.14. A control chart is simply a time series plot of the individual measurements of a quality variable (i.e., an output variable), to which a centerline and two other horizontal lines called **control limits** have been added. The centerline represents the mean of the process (i.e., the mean of the quality variable) *when the process is in a state of statistical control.* The **upper control limit** and

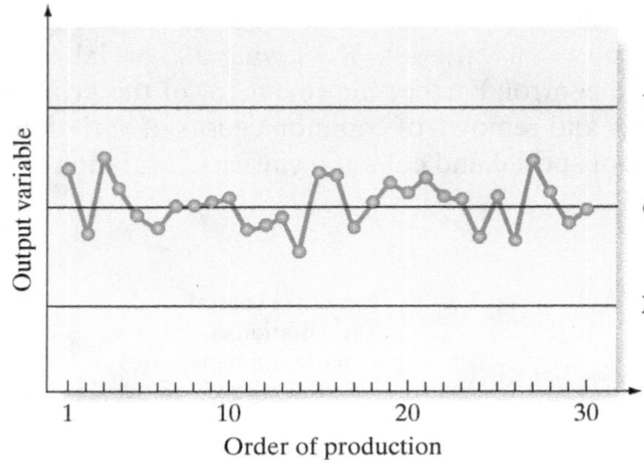

Figure 13.14
A control chart

BIOGRAPHY

WALTER A. SHEWHART (1891–1967)
Shewhart Charts

Illinois native Walter Shewhart earned his bachelor's degree from the University of Illinois, followed by his PhD in physics from the University of California in 1917. A short time later, Shewhart joined Bell Laboratories in New Jersey as an engineer, where he spent the majority of his career. Shewhart also served as a statistical consultant for the U.S. War Department, the United Nations, and the Indian government, as well as teaching at several prominent American universities. Shewhart's most important contribution to both statistics and industry was the development of the statistical control of quality. He first proposed the idea of a control chart in 1924—a procedure commonly called the "Shewhart procedure" or "Shewhart chart." While at Bell Laboratories, Shewhart taught and worked with statistics icon W. Edwards Deming. Shewhart's monumental work, *Economic Control of Quality of Manufactured Product*, published in 1931, is regarded as a complete and thorough exposition of the basic principles of quality control; consequently, he is regarded as the father of statistical quality control.

the **lower control limit** are positioned so that *when the process is in control*, the probability of an individual value of the output variable falling outside the control limits is very small. Most practitioners position the control limits a distance of 3 standard deviations from the centerline (i.e., from the process mean) and refer to them as **3-sigma limits.** If the process is in control and following a normal distribution, the probability of an individual measurement falling outside the control limits is .0027 (less than 3 chances in 1,000). This is shown in Figure 13.15.

As long as the individual values stay between the control limits, the process is considered to be under control, meaning that no special causes of variation are influencing the output of the process. If one or more values fall outside the control limits, either a **rare event** has occurred or the process is out of control. Following the rare-event approach to inference described earlier in the text, such a result is interpreted as evidence that the process is out of control, and actions should be taken to eliminate the special causes of variation that exist.

Other evidence to indicate that the process is out of control may be present on the control chart. For example, if we observe any of the patterns of variation shown in Figure 13.6, we can conclude the process is out of control *even if all the points fall between the control limits*. In general, any persistent, systematic variation pattern (i.e., any nonrandom pattern) is interpreted as evidence that the process is out of control. We discuss this in detail in the next section.

In Chapter 7, we described how to make inferences about populations using hypothesis-testing techniques. What we do in this section should seem quite similar. Although our focus now is on making inferences about a *process* rather than a *population*, we are again testing hypotheses. In this case, we test

H_0: Process is under control.

H_a: Process is out of control.

Each time we plot a new point and see whether it falls inside or outside the control limits, we are running a two-sided hypothesis test. The control limits function as the critical values for the test.

What we learned in Chapter 7 about the types of errors that we might make in running a hypothesis test holds true in using control charts as well. Any time we reject the hypothesis that the process is under control and conclude that the process is out of control, we run the risk of making a Type I error (rejecting the null hypothesis when the null is true). Any time we conclude (or behave as if we conclude) that the process is in control, we run the risk of a Type II error (accepting the null hypothesis when the alternative is true). There is nothing magical or mystical

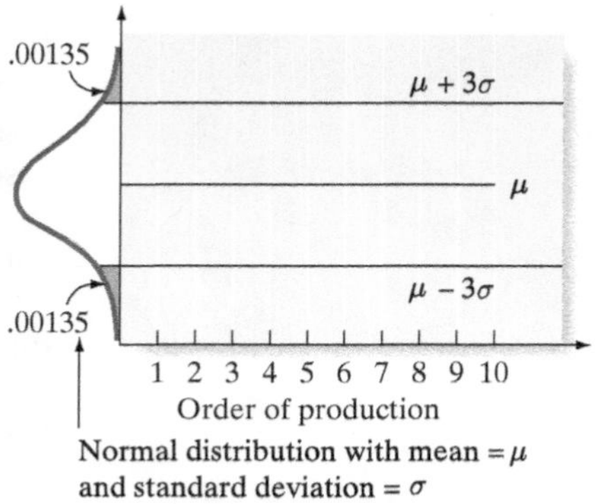

Figure 13.15
The probability of observing a measurement beyond the control limits when the process is in control

about control charts. Just as in any hypothesis test, the conclusion suggested by a control chart may be wrong.

One of the main reasons that 3-sigma control limits are used (rather than 2-sigma or 1-sigma limits, for example) is the small Type I error probability associated with their use. The probability we noted previously of an individual measurement falling outside the control limits—.0027—is a Type I error probability. Because we interpret a sample point that falls beyond the limits as a signal that the process is out of control, the use of 3-sigma limits yields very few signals that are "false alarms."

To make these ideas more concrete, we will construct and interpret a control chart for the paint-filling process discussed in Section 13.2. Our intention is simply to help you better understand the logic of control charts. Structured, step-by-step descriptions of how to construct control charts will be given in later sections.

Example 13.3

Control Chart for Individual Measurements—Filling Paint Cans

Problem The sample measurements from the paint-filling process, presented in Table 13.1, were previously plotted in Figure 13.11. Find the mean and standard deviation of the sample and use these values to construct a control chart for the individual measurements. What does the control chart imply about the behavior of the process?

Table 13.1 Fill Weights of 50 Consecutively Produced Cans of Paint

Order	Weight	Order	Weight	Order	Weight	Order	Weight	Order	Weight
1	10.0008	11	9.9957	21	9.9977	31	10.0107	41	10.0054
2	10.0062	12	10.0076	22	9.9968	32	10.0102	42	10.0061
3	9.9948	13	10.0036	23	9.9982	33	9.9995	43	9.9978
4	9.9893	14	10.0037	24	10.0092	34	10.0038	44	9.9969
5	9.9994	15	10.0029	25	9.9964	35	9.9925	45	9.9969
6	9.9953	16	9.9995	26	10.0053	36	9.9983	46	10.0006
7	9.9963	17	9.9956	27	10.0012	37	10.0018	47	10.0011
8	9.9925	18	10.0005	28	9.9988	38	10.0038	48	9.9973
9	9.9914	19	10.0020	29	9.9914	39	9.9974	49	9.9958
10	10.0035	20	10.0053	30	10.0036	40	9.9966	50	9.9873

Data Set: CAN50

Solution An Excel/XLSTAT printout with descriptive statistics for the data is shown in Figure 13.16. The sample mean and standard deviation (highlighted on the printout) are $\bar{x} = 10$ and $s = .005$. Although these are estimates, in using and interpreting control charts, we treat them *as if* they were the actual mean μ and standard deviation σ of the in-control process. This is standard practice in control charting.

Descriptive statistics (Quantitative data):

Statistic	FillWt
No. of observations	50
Minimum	9.9873
Maximum	10.0107
Range	0.0234
1st Quartile	9.9965
Median	9.9995
3rd Quartile	10.0036
Mean	10.000
Variance (n-1)	0.000028
Standard deviation (n-1)	0.00527

Figure 13.16
Excel/XLSTAT summary statistics for 50 fill weights

The centerline of the control chart, representing the process mean, is drawn so that it intersects the vertical axis at $\bar{x} = 10$, as shown in Figure 13.17. The upper control limit (UCL) is drawn at a distance of $3s = 3(.005) = .015$ above the centerline, i.e., at $\bar{x} + 3s = 10 + .015 = 10.015$. The lower control limit (LCL) is $3s = .015$ below the

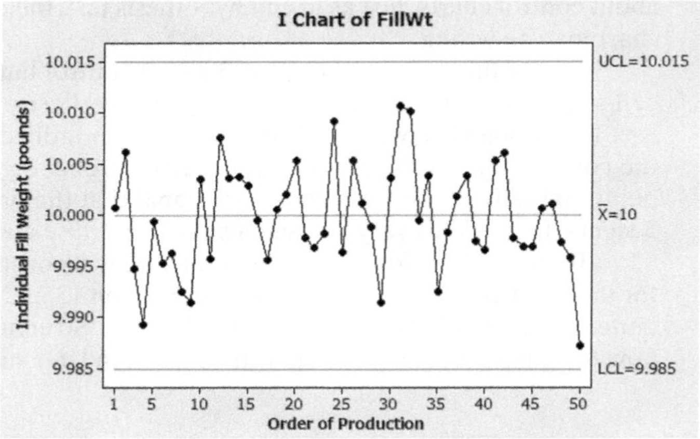

Figure 13.17
Minitab control chart of 50 consecutive fill weights

centerline, i.e., at $\bar{x} - 3s = 10 - .015 = 9.985$. Then the 50 sample weights are plotted on the chart in the order that they were generated by the paint-filling process.

As can be seen in Figure 13.17, all the weight measurements fall within the control limits. Further, there do not appear to be any systematic, nonrandom patterns in the data such as displayed in Figures 13.5 and 13.6. Accordingly, we are unable to conclude that the process is out of control—that is, we are unable to reject the null hypothesis that the process is in control. However, instead of using this formal hypothesis-testing language in interpreting control chart results, we prefer simply to say that the data suggest or indicate that the process is in control. We do this, however, with the full understanding that the probability of a Type II error is generally unknown in control chart applications and that we might be wrong in our conclusion.

Look Back What we are really saying when we conclude that the process is in control is that *the data indicate that it is better to behave as if the process were under control than to tamper with the process.*

We have portrayed the control chart hypothesis test as testing "in control" versus "out of control." Another way to look at it is this: When we compare the weight of an *individual* can of paint to the control limits in Example 13.3, we are conducting the following two-tailed hypothesis test:

$$H_0: \mu = 10$$
$$H_0: \mu \neq 10$$

where 10 is the centerline of the control chart. The control limits delineate the two rejection regions for this test. Accordingly, with each weight measurement that we plot and compare to the control limits, we are testing whether the process mean (the mean fill weight) has changed. Thus, what the control chart is monitoring is the mean of the process. **The control chart leads us to accept or reject statistical control on the basis of whether the mean of the process has changed or not.** This type of process instability is illustrated in the left graph in Figure 13.8. In the paint-filling process example, the process mean apparently has remained constant over the period in which the sample weights were collected.

Other types of control charts—one of which we will describe in Section 13.5—help us determine whether the *variance* of the process has changed, as in the center and right graphs of Figure 13.8.

The control chart we have just described is called an **individuals chart,** or an ***x*-chart.** The term *individuals* refers to the fact that the chart uses individual measurements to monitor the process—that is, measurements taken from individual units of process output. This is in contrast to plotting sample means on the control chart—for example, as we do in the next section.

Students sometimes confuse control limits with product *specification limits.* We have already explained control limits, which are a function of the natural variability of the process. Assuming we always use 3-sigma limits, the position of the control limits is a function of the size of σ, the process standard deviation.

Specification limits are boundary points that define the acceptable values for an output variable (i.e., for a quality characteristic) of a particular product or service. They are determined by customers, management, and product designers. Specification limits may be two-sided, with upper and lower limits, or one-sided, with either an upper or a lower limit.

Process output that falls inside the specification limits is said to **conform to specifications.** Otherwise it is said to be **nonconforming.**

Unlike control limits, specification limits are not often dependent on the process in any way. A customer of the paint-filling process may specify that all cans contain no more than 10.005 pounds of paint and no less than 9.995 pounds. These are specification limits. The customer has reasons for these specifications but may have no idea whether the supplier's process can meet them. Both the customer's specification limits and the control limits of the supplier's paint-filling process are shown in Figure 13.18. Do you think the customer will be satisfied with the quality of the product received? We don't. Although some cans are within the specification limits, most are not, as indicated by the shaded region on the figure.

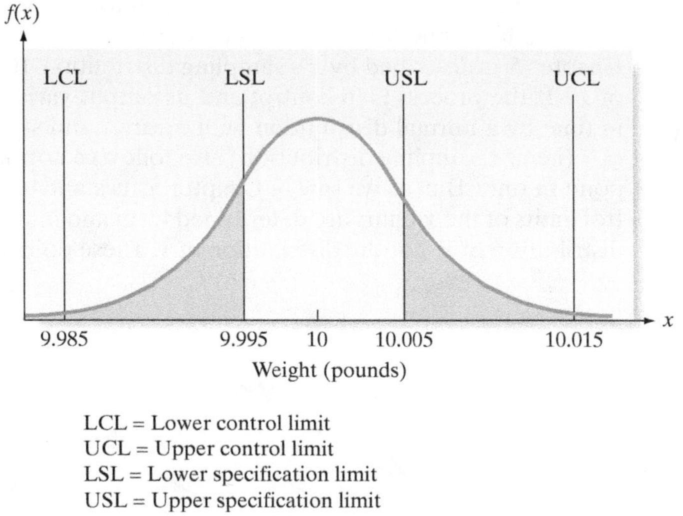

Figure 13.18
Comparison of control limits and specification limits

13.4 A Control Chart for Monitoring the Mean of a Process: The $\bar{x}$-Chart

In the previous section, we introduced you to the logic of control charts by focusing on a chart that reflected the variation in individual measurements of process output. We used the chart to determine whether the process mean had shifted. The control chart we present in this section—the **$\bar{x}$-chart**—is also used to detect changes in the process mean, but it does so by monitoring the variation in the mean of samples that have been drawn from the process—that is, instead of plotting individual measurements on the control chart, in this case we plot sample means. Because of the additional information reflected in sample means (because each sample mean is calculated from n individual measurements), the $\bar{x}$-chart is more sensitive than the individuals chart for detecting changes in the process mean.

In practice, the $\bar{x}$-chart is rarely used alone. It is typically used in conjunction with a chart that monitors the variation of the process, usually a chart called an R-chart. The $\bar{x}$- and R-charts are the most widely used control charts in industry. Used in concert, these charts make it possible to determine whether a process has gone out of control because the variation has changed or because the mean has changed. We present the R-chart in the next section, at the end of which we discuss their simultaneous use.

For now, we focus only on the $\bar{x}$-chart. **Consequently, we assume throughout this section that the process variation is stable.**

Figure 13.19 is an example of an $\bar{x}$-chart. As with the individuals chart, the centerline represents the mean of the process, and the upper and lower control limits are positioned a distance of 3 standard deviations from the mean. However, because the chart is tracking sample means rather than individual measurements, the relevant standard deviation is the standard deviation of $\bar{x}$ not σ, the standard deviation of the output variable.

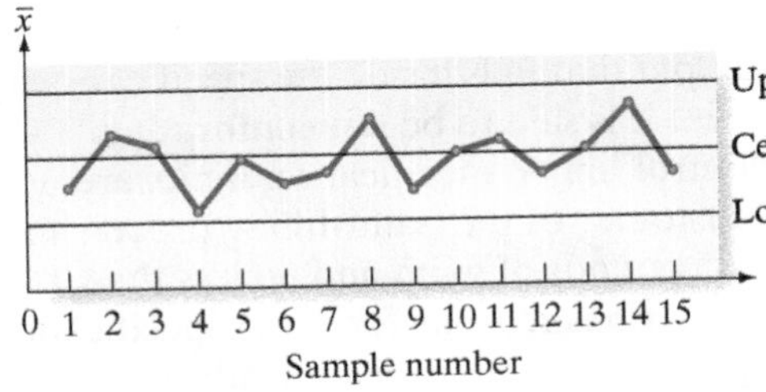

Figure 13.19
$\bar{x}$-chart

If the process were in statistical control, the sequence of $\bar{x}$'s plotted on the chart would exhibit random behavior between the control limits. Only if a rare event occurred or if the process went out of control would a sample mean fall beyond the control limits.

To better understand the justification for having control limits that involve $\sigma_{\bar{x}}$, consider the following. The $\bar{x}$-chart is concerned with the variation in $\bar{x}$, which, as we saw in Chapter 5, is described by $\bar{x}$'s sampling distribution. But what is the sampling distribution of $\bar{x}$? If the process is in control and its output variable x is characterized at each point in time by a normal distribution with mean μ and standard deviation σ, the distribution of $\bar{x}$ (i.e., $\bar{x}$'s sampling distribution) also follows a normal distribution with mean μ at each point in time. But, as we saw in Chapter 5, its standard deviation is $\sigma_{\bar{x}} = \sigma/\sqrt{n}$. The control limits of the $\bar{x}$-chart are determined from and interpreted with respect to the sampling distribution of $\bar{x}$, not the distribution of x. These points are illustrated in Figure 13.20.*

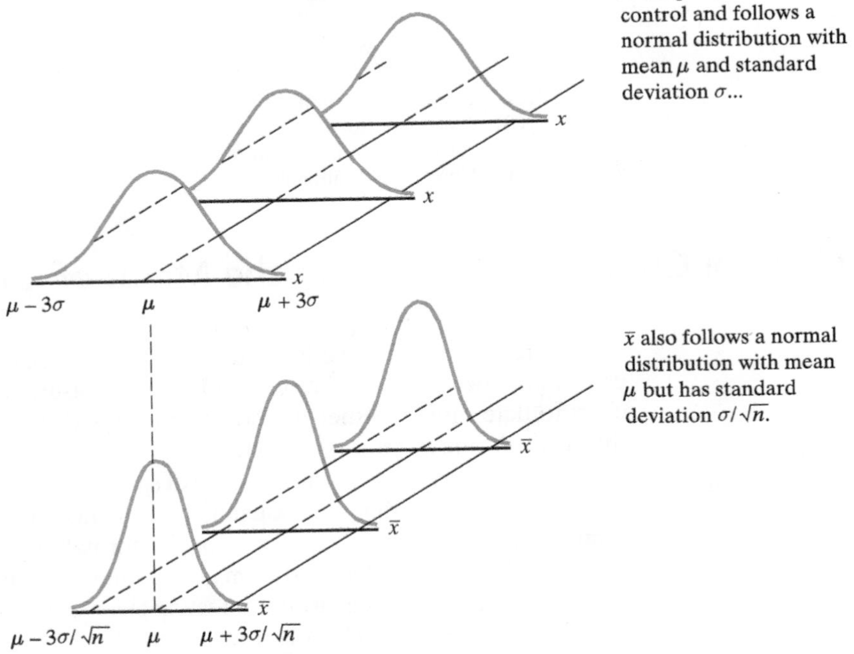

Figure 13.20
The sampling distribution of $\bar{x}$

*The sampling distribution of $\bar{x}$ can also be approximated using the Central Limit Theorem (Chapter 5)—that is, when the process is under control and $\bar{x}$ is to be computed from a large sample from the process ($n \geq 30$), the sampling distribution will be approximately normally distributed with the mean μ and standard deviation $\sigma/\sqrt{n}$. Even for samples as small as 4 or 5, the sampling distribution of $\bar{x}$ will be approximately normal as long as the distribution of x is reasonably symmetric and roughly bell shaped.

In order to construct an $\bar{x}$-chart, you should have at least 20 samples of n items each, where $n \geq 2$. This will provide sufficient data to obtain reasonably good estimates of the mean and variance of the process. The centerline, which represents the mean of the process, is determined as follows:

$$\textit{Centerline: } \bar{\bar{x}} = \frac{\bar{x}_1 + \bar{x}_2 + \cdots + \bar{x}_k}{k}$$

where k is the number of samples of size n from which the chart is to be constructed and $\bar{x}_i$ is the sample mean of the ith sample. Thus $\bar{\bar{x}}$ is an estimator of μ.

The control limits are positioned as follows:

$$\textit{Upper control limit: } \bar{\bar{x}} + \frac{3\sigma}{\sqrt{n}}$$

$$\textit{Lower control limit: } \bar{\bar{x}} - \frac{3\sigma}{\sqrt{n}}$$

Because σ, the process standard deviation, is virtually always unknown, it must be estimated. This can be done in several ways. One approach involves calculating the standard deviations for each of the k samples and averaging them. Another involves using the sample standard deviation s from a large sample that was generated while the process was believed to be in control. We employ a third approach, however—the one favored by industry. It has been shown to be as effective as the other approaches for sample sizes of $n = 10$ or less, the sizes most often used in industry.

This approach uses the ranges of the k samples to estimate the process standard deviation, σ. Recall from Chapter 2 that the range, R, of a sample is the difference between the maximum and minimum measurements in the sample. It can be shown that dividing the mean of the k ranges, $\bar{R}$, by the constant d_2 obtains an unbiased estimator for σ. [For details, see Ryan (2011).] The estimator, denoted by $\hat{\sigma}$, is calculated as follows:

$$\hat{\sigma} = \frac{\bar{R}}{d_2} = \frac{R_1 + R_2 + \cdots + R_k}{k}\left(\frac{1}{d_2}\right)$$

where R_i is the range of the ith sample and d_2 is a constant that depends on the sample size. Values of d_2 for samples of size $n = 2$ to $n = 25$ can be found in Table IX in Appendix D.

Substituting $\hat{\sigma}$ for σ in the formulas for the upper control limit (UCL) and the lower control limit (LCL), we get

$$\text{UCL: } \bar{\bar{x}} + \frac{3\left(\frac{\bar{R}}{d_2}\right)}{\sqrt{n}} \qquad \text{LCL: } \bar{\bar{x}} - \frac{3\left(\frac{\bar{R}}{d_2}\right)}{\sqrt{n}}$$

Notice that $(\bar{R}/d_2)/\sqrt{n}$ is an estimator of $\sigma_{\bar{x}}$. The calculation of these limits can be simplified by creating the constant

$$A_2 = \frac{3}{d_2\sqrt{n}}$$

Then the control limits can be expressed as

$$\text{UCL: } \bar{\bar{x}} + A_2\bar{R}$$

$$\text{LCL: } \bar{\bar{x}} - A_2\bar{R}$$

where the values for A_2 for samples of size $n = 2$ to $n = 25$ can be found in Table IX in Appendix D.

The degree of sensitivity of the $\bar{x}$-chart to changes in the process mean depends on two decisions that must be made in constructing the chart.

The Two Most Important Decisions in Constructing an $\bar{x}$-Chart

1. The sample size, *n*, must be determined.
2. The frequency with which samples are to be drawn from the process must be determined (e.g., once an hour, once each shift, or once a day).

In order to quickly detect process change, we try to choose samples in such a way that the change in the process mean occurs *between* samples, not *within* samples (i.e., not during the period when a sample is being drawn). In this way, every measurement in the sample before the change will be unaffected by the change, and every measurement in the sample following the change will be affected. The result is that the $\bar{x}$ computed from the latter sample should be substantially different from that of the former sample—a signal that something has happened to the process mean.

Samples whose size and frequency have been designed to make it likely that process changes will occur between, rather than within, the samples are referred to as **rational subgroups.**

Rational Subgrouping Strategy

The samples (rational subgroups) should be chosen in a manner that

1. Gives the maximum chance for the *measurements* in each sample to be similar (i.e., to be affected by the same sources of variation)
2. Gives the maximum chance for the *samples* to differ (i.e., to be affected by at least one different source of variation)

The following example illustrates the concept of *rational subgrouping.*

Example 13.4

Selecting Rational Subgroups

Problem An operations manager suspects that the quality of the output in a manufacturing process may differ from shift to shift because of the preponderance of newly hired workers on the night shift. The manager wants to be able to detect such differences quickly, using an $\bar{x}$-chart. Develop a rational subgrouping strategy for the manager.

Solution Because the process may differ from shift to shift, it is logical to construct the control chart with samples that are drawn *within* each shift. None of the samples should span shifts—that is, no sample should contain, say, the last three items produced by shift 1 and the first two items produced by shift 2. In this way, the measurements in each sample would be similar, but the $\bar{x}$'s would reflect differences between shifts.

The secret to designing an effective $\bar{x}$-chart is to anticipate the *types of special causes of variation* that might affect the process mean. Then purposeful rational subgrouping can be employed to construct a chart that is sensitive to the anticipated cause or causes of variation.

The preceding discussion and example focused primarily on the timing or frequency of samples. Concerning the size of the samples, practitioners typically work with samples of size $n = 4$ to $n = 10$ consecutively produced items. Using small samples of consecutively produced items helps to ensure that the measurements in each sample will be similar (i.e., affected by the same causes of variation).

Constructing an $\bar{x}$-Chart: A Summary

1. Using a rational subgrouping strategy, collect at least 20 samples (subgroups), each of size $n \geq 2$.
2. Calculate the mean and range for each sample.

3. Calculate the mean of the sample means, $\bar{\bar{x}}$, and the mean of the sample ranges, $\bar{R}$:

$$\bar{\bar{x}} = \frac{\bar{x}_1 + \bar{x}_2 + \cdots + \bar{x}_k}{k} \qquad \bar{R} = \frac{R_1 + R_2 + \cdots + R_k}{k}$$

where

k = number of samples (i.e., subgroups)
$\bar{x}_i$ = sample mean for the ith sample
R_i = range of the ith sample

4. Plot the centerline and control limits:

Centerline: $\bar{\bar{x}}$
Upper control limit: $\bar{\bar{x}} + A_2\bar{R}$
Lower control limit: $\bar{\bar{x}} - A_2\bar{R}$

where A_2 is a constant that depends on n. Its values are given in Table IX in Appendix D, for samples of size $n = 2$ to $n = 25$.

5. Plot the k sample means on the control chart in the order that the samples were produced by the process.

Note: Most quality-control analysts use available statistical software to perform the calculations and generate the $\bar{x}$-chart.

When interpreting a control chart, it is convenient to think of the chart as consisting of six zones, as shown in Figure 13.21. Each zone is 1 standard deviation wide. The two zones within 1 standard deviation of the centerline are called **C zones;** the regions between 1 and 2 standard deviations from the centerline are called **B zones;** and the regions between 2 and 3 standard deviations from the centerline are called **A zones.** The box describes how to construct the *zone boundaries* for an $\bar{x}$-chart.

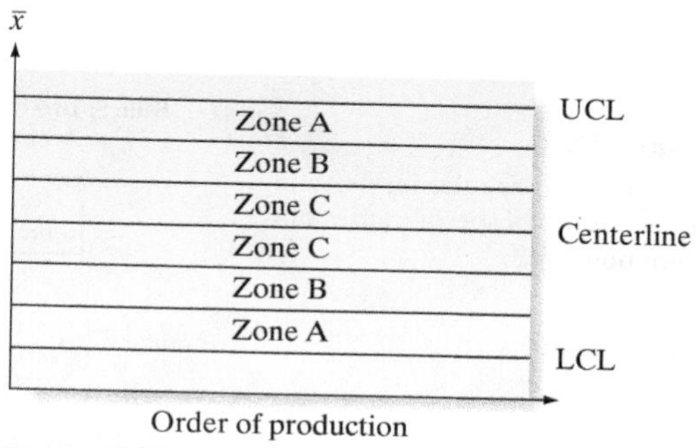

Figure 13.21
The zones of a control chart

Constructing Zone Boundaries for an $\bar{x}$-Chart

The zone boundaries can be constructed in either of the following ways:

1. Using the 3-sigma control limits:

Lower and Upper A–B boundaries: $\bar{\bar{x}} \pm \frac{2}{3}(A_2\bar{R})$
Lower and Upper B–C boundaries: $\bar{\bar{x}} \pm \frac{1}{3}(A_2\bar{R})$

2. Using the estimated standard deviation of $\bar{x}$, $(\bar{R}/d_2)/\sqrt{n}$:

$$\textit{Lower and Upper A–B boundaries: } \bar{\bar{x}} \pm 2\left[\frac{\left(\frac{\bar{R}}{d_2}\right)}{\sqrt{n}}\right]$$

$$\textit{Lower and Upper B–C boundaries: } \bar{\bar{x}} \pm \left[\frac{\left(\frac{\bar{R}}{d_2}\right)}{\sqrt{n}}\right]$$

Note: Again, statistical software programs that automatically find the zone boundaries for the control chart are available.

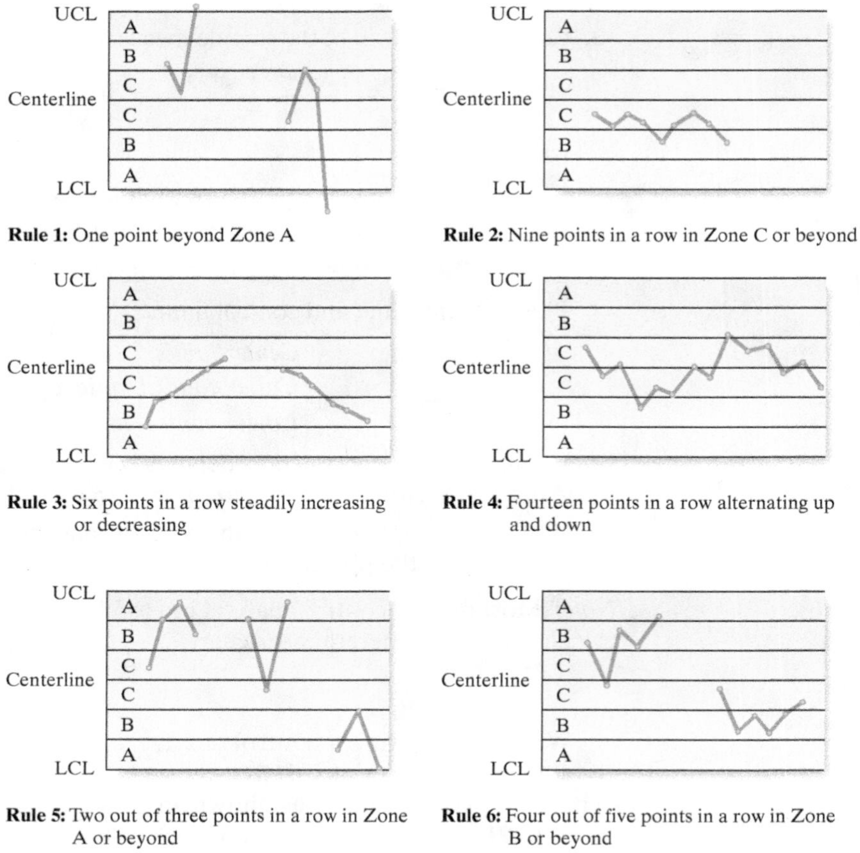

Rules 1, 2, 5, and 6 should be applied separately to the upper and lower halves of the control chart. Rules 3 and 4 should be applied to the whole chart.

Figure 13.22
Pattern-analysis rules for detecting the presence of special causes of variation

Practitioners use six simple rules that are based on these zones to help determine when a process is out of control. The six rules are summarized in Figure 13.22. They are referred to as **pattern-analysis rules.**

Rule 1 is the familiar point-beyond-the-control-limit rule that we have mentioned several times. The other rules all help to determine when the process is out of control *even though all the plotted points fall within the control limits*—that is, the other rules help to identify nonrandom patterns of variation that have not yet broken through the control limits (or may never break through).

All the patterns shown in Figure 13.22 are *rare events* under the assumption that the process is under control. We demonstrate this notion in the next example.

Example 13.5 Probabilities for Pattern-Analysis Rules

Problem Assume a process is under control and the data follow a normal distribution with mean μ and standard deviation σ.

a. What is the probability that an individual data point (x) will fall above upper Zone A? In upper Zone A? In upper Zone B? In upper Zone C?

b. Use these probabilities to evaluate the chance of an individual data point violating Rule 1.

c. Use these probabilities to evaluate the chance of an individual data point violating Rule 5.

Solution

a. Zone A is defined as the region that is between 2 and 3 standard deviations above (or below) the mean. (See Figure 13.21.) Because the data are normally distributed, we use the standard normal table (Table II in Appendix D) to find

$$P(x \text{ falls above upper Zone A}) = P(x > \mu + 3\sigma) = P(z > 3) = .5 - .4987 = .0013$$

$$P(x \text{ falls in upper Zone A}) = P(\mu + 2\sigma < x < \mu + 3\sigma) = P(2 < z < 3)$$
$$= .4987 - .4772 = .0125$$

Now, Zone B is defined as the region that is between 1 and 2 standard deviations above (or below) the mean and Zone C as the region that is between 0 and 1 standard deviation above (or below) the mean. Thus, we have

$$P(x \text{ falls in upper Zone B}) = P(\mu + \sigma < x < \mu + 2\sigma) = P(1 < z < 2)$$
$$= .4772 - .3413 = .1359$$
$$P(x \text{ falls in upper Zone C}) = P(\mu < x < \mu + \sigma) = P(0 < z < 1) = .3413$$

b. An individual data point violates Rule 1 if it falls beyond Zone A. Thus, we desire the probability

$$P(x \text{ falls beyond Zone A}) = P(x \text{ falls above upper Zone A}) + P(x \text{ falls below lower Zone A})$$

Because the normal distribution is symmetric, the two probabilities in the expression above are the same. Consequently, we have

$$P(x \text{ falls beyond Zone A}) = .0013 + .0013 = .0026$$

Thus, the probability of observing a point beyond the control limits (Rule 1) is only .0026. This is clearly a rare event.

c. Rule 5 is violated if two out of three points in succession fall in (say, upper) Zone A or beyond. For one point, the probability of this event is

$$P(x \text{ falls in or above upper Zone A}) = P(x \text{ falls in upper Zone A}) + P(x \text{ falls above Zone} A) = .0215 + .0013 = .0228$$

Now we use the binomial distribution (Chapter 4) to find the probability of observing 2 out of 3 points in or beyond Zone A. The binomial probability of 2 successes in 3 trials when the probability of success is .0228 is

$$\binom{3}{2}(.0228)^2(.9972) = .0016$$

Again, if this occurs, it is clearly a rare event.

■ Now Work Exercise 13.18a

In general, when the process is in control and normally distributed, the probability of any one of these rules *incorrectly* signaling the presence of special causes of variation is less than .005, or 5 chances in 1,000. If all of the first four rules are applied, the overall probability of a false signal is about .01. If all six of the rules are applied, the overall probability of a false signal rises to .02, or 2 chances in 100. These three probabilities can be thought of as Type I error probabilities. Each indicates the probability of incorrectly rejecting the null hypothesis that the process is in a state of statistical control.

Explanation of the possible causes of these nonrandom patterns is beyond the scope of this text. We refer the interested reader to AT&T's *Statistical Quality Control Handbook* (1956).

We use these rules again in the next section when we interpret the R-chart.

Interpreting an $\bar{x}$-Chart

1. The **process is out of control** if one or more sample means fall beyond the control limits or if any of the other five patterns of variation of Figure 13.22 are observed. Such signals are an indication that one or more special causes of variation are affecting the process mean. We must identify and eliminate them to bring the process into control.

2. The **process is treated as being in control** if none of the previously noted out-of-control signals are observed. Processes that are in control should not be tampered with. However, if the level of variation is unacceptably high, common causes of variation should be identified and eliminated.

Assumption: The variation of the process is stable. (If it were not, the control limits of the $\bar{x}$-chart would be meaningless because they are a function of the process variation. The *R*-chart, presented in the next section, is used to investigate this assumption.)

In theory, the centerline and control limits should be developed using samples that were collected during a period in which the process was in control. Otherwise, they will not be representative of the variation of the process (or, in the present case, the variation of $\bar{x}$) when the process is in control. However, we will not know whether the process is in control until after we have constructed a control chart. Consequently, when a control chart is first constructed, the centerline and control limits are treated as **trial values.** If the chart indicates that the process was in control during the period when the sample data were collected, then the centerline and control limits become "official" (i.e., no longer treated as trial values). It is then appropriate to extend the control limits and the centerline to the right and to use the chart to monitor future process output.

However, if in applying the pattern-analysis rules of Figure 13.22 it is determined that the process was out of control while the sample data were being collected, the trial values (i.e., the trial chart) should, in general, not be used to monitor the process. The points on the control chart that indicate that the process is out of control should be investigated to see if any special causes of variation can be identified. A graphical method that can be used to facilitate this investigation—a *cause-and-effect diagram*—is described in Section 13.7. If special causes of variation are found, (1) they should be eliminated; (2) any points on the chart determined to have been influenced by the special causes—whether inside or outside the control limits—should be discarded; and (3) *new* trial centerline and control limits should be calculated from the remaining data. However, the new trial limits may still indicate that the process is out of control. If so, repeat these three steps until all points fall within the control limits.

If special causes cannot be found and eliminated, the severity of the out-of-control indications should be evaluated and a judgment made as to whether (1) the out-of-control points should be discarded anyway and new trial limits constructed, (2) the original trial limits are good enough to be made official, or (3) new sample data should be collected to construct new trial limits.

Example 13.6

Creating and Interpreting an $\bar{x}$-Chart—Paint-Filling Process

Problem Let's return to the paint-filling process described in Sections 13.2 and 13.3. Suppose instead of sampling 50 consecutive gallons of paint from the filling process to develop a control chart, it was decided to sample five consecutive cans once each hour for the next 25 hours. The sample data are presented in an Excel worksheet, Figure 13.23. This sampling strategy (rational subgrouping) was selected because several times a month the filling head in question becomes clogged. When that happens, the head dispenses less and less paint over the course of the day. However, the pattern of decrease is so irregular that minute-to-minute or even half-hour-to-half-hour changes are difficult to detect.

a. Explain the logic behind the rational subgrouping strategy that was used.

b. Construct an $\bar{x}$-chart for the process using the data in Figure 13.23.

c. What does the chart suggest about the stability of the filling process (whether the process is in or out of statistical control)?

d. Should the control limits be used to monitor future process output?

Solution

a. The samples are far enough apart in time to detect hour-to-hour shifts or changes in the mean amount of paint dispensed, but the individual measurements that make up each sample are close enough together in time to ensure that the process has

	A	B	C	D	E	F	G	H	I
1	Sample	Weight1	Weight2	Weight3	Weight4	Weight5		Mean	Range
2	1	10.0042	9.9981	10.001	9.9964	10.0001		9.99996	0.0078
3	2	9.995	9.9986	9.9948	10.003	9.9938		9.99704	0.0092
4	3	10.0028	9.9998	10.0086	9.9949	9.998		10.00082	0.0137
5	4	9.9952	9.9923	10.0034	9.9965	10.0026		9.998	0.0111
6	5	9.9997	9.9883	9.9975	10.0078	9.9891		9.99648	0.0195
7	6	9.9987	10.0027	10.0001	10.0027	10.0029		10.00142	0.0042
8	7	10.0004	10.0023	10.0024	9.9992	10.0135		10.00356	0.0143
9	8	10.0013	9.9938	10.0017	10.0089	10.0001		10.00116	0.0151
10	9	10.0103	10.0009	9.9969	10.0103	9.9986		10.0034	0.0134
11	10	9.998	9.9954	9.9941	9.9958	9.9963		9.99592	0.0039
12	11	10.0013	10.0033	9.9943	9.9949	9.9999		9.99874	0.009
13	12	9.9986	9.999	10.0009	9.9947	10.0008		9.9988	0.0062
14	13	10.0089	10.0056	9.9976	9.9997	9.9922		10.0008	0.0167
15	14	9.9971	10.0015	9.9962	10.0038	10.0022		10.00016	0.0076
16	15	9.9949	10.0011	10.0043	9.9988	9.9919		9.9982	0.0124
17	16	9.9951	9.9957	10.0094	10.004	9.9974		10.00032	0.0143
18	17	10.0015	10.0026	10.0032	9.9971	10.0019		10.00126	0.0061
19	18	9.9983	10.0019	9.9978	9.9997	10.0029		10.00012	0.0051
20	19	9.9977	9.9963	9.9981	9.9968	10.0009		9.99796	0.0046
21	20	10.0078	10.0004	9.9966	10.0051	10.0007		10.00212	0.0112
22	21	9.9963	9.999	10.0037	9.9936	9.9962		9.99776	0.0101
23	22	9.9999	10.0022	10.0057	10.0026	10.0032		10.00272	0.0058
24	23	9.9998	10.0002	9.9978	9.9966	10.006		10.00008	0.0094
25	24	10.0031	10.0078	9.9988	10.0032	9.9944		10.00146	0.0134
26	25	9.9993	9.9978	9.9964	10.0032	10.0041		10.00016	0.0077
27									
28							Averages	9.999937	0.010072
29									

Data Set: CAN125

Figure 13.23
Excel worksheet with 25 samples of $n = 5$ from paint-filling process

changed little, if at all, during the time the individual measurements were made. Overall, the rational subgrouping employed affords the opportunity for process changes to occur between samples and therefore show up on the control chart as differences between the sample means.

b. Twenty-five samples ($k = 25$ subgroups), each containing $n = 5$ cans of paint, were collected from the process. The first step after collecting the data is to calculate the 25 sample means and sample ranges needed to construct the $\bar{x}$-chart. The mean and range of the first sample are

$$\bar{x} = \frac{10.0042 + 9.9981 + 10.0010 + 9.9964 + 10.0001}{5} = 9.99996$$

$$R = 10.0042 - 9.9964 = .0078$$

All 25 means and ranges were computed using Excel and are displayed in Figure 13.23. Next, we use Excel to calculate the mean of the sample means and the mean of the sample ranges:

$$\bar{\bar{x}} = \frac{9.99996 + 9.99704 + \cdots + 10.00016}{25} = 9.99994$$

$$\bar{R} = \frac{.0078 + .0092 + \cdots + .0077}{25} = .010072$$

These values are highlighted on Figure 13.23. Now, the centerline of the chart is positioned at $\bar{\bar{x}} = 9.9999$. To determine the control limits, we need the constant A_2, which can be found in Table IX in Appendix D. For $n = 5$, $A_2 = .577$. Then,

$$\text{UCL: } \bar{\bar{x}} + A_2\bar{R} = 9.99994 + .577(.010072) = 10.00575$$

$$\text{LCL: } \bar{\bar{x}} - A_2\bar{R} = 9.99994 - .577(.010072) = 9.99413$$

After positioning the control limits on the chart, we plot the 25 sample means in the order of sampling and connect the points with straight lines. The resulting trial $\bar{x}$-chart, shown in Figure 13.24, is produced using Minitab.

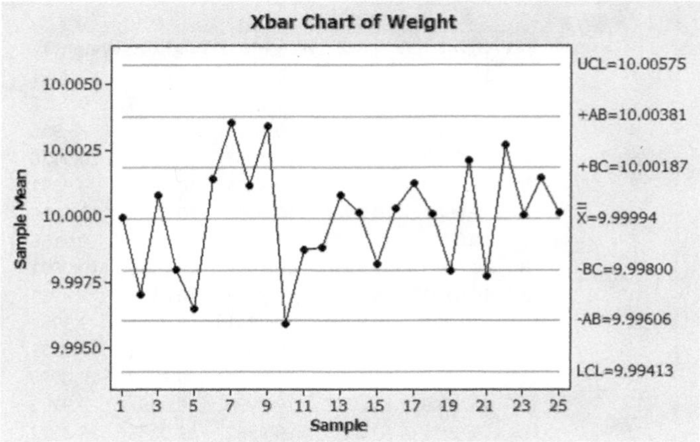

Figure 13.24
Minitab $\bar{x}$-chart for paint-filling process

c. To check the stability of the process, we use the six pattern-analysis rules for detecting special causes of variation, which were presented in Figure 13.22. To apply most of these rules requires identifying the A, B, and C zones of the control chart. These are indicated (with annotations) in Figure 13.24. We describe how they were constructed below.

The boundary between the A and B zones is 2 standard deviations from the centerline, and the boundary between the B and C zones is 1 standard deviation from the centerline. Thus, using $A_2\bar{R}$ and the 3-sigma limits previously calculated, we locate the A, B, and C zones above the centerline:

$$\text{A–B boundary} = \bar{\bar{x}} + \tfrac{2}{3}(A_2\bar{R}) = 9.99994 + \tfrac{2}{3}(.577)(.010072) = 10.00381$$
$$\text{B–C boundary} = \bar{\bar{x}} + \tfrac{1}{3}(A_2\bar{R}) = 9.99994 + \tfrac{1}{3}(.577)(.010072) = 10.00187$$

Similarly, the zones below the centerline are located:

$$\text{A–B boundary} = \bar{\bar{x}} - \tfrac{2}{3}(A_2\bar{R}) = 9.99606$$
$$\text{B–C boundary} = \bar{\bar{x}} - \tfrac{1}{3}(A_2\bar{R}) = 9.99800$$

A careful comparison of the six pattern-analysis rules with the sequence of sample means yields no out-of-control signals. All points are inside the control limits, and there appear to be no nonrandom patterns within the control limits—that is, we can find no evidence of a shift in the process mean. Accordingly, we conclude that the process is in control.

d. Because the process was found to be in control during the period in which the samples were drawn, the trial control limits constructed in part **b** can be considered official. They should be extended to the right and used to monitor future process output.

Look Back Most statistical software (like Minitab) will automatically calculate and plot the sample means and control limits. No hand calculations are needed to create an $\bar{x}$-chart.

■ Now Work Exercise 13.7

Example 13.7

Monitoring Future Output with an $\bar{x}$-Chart—Paint-Filling Process

Problem Ten new samples of size $n = 5$ were drawn from the paint-filling process of the previous example. The sample data, including sample means and ranges, are shown in the Excel worksheet, Figure 13.25. Investigate whether the process remained in control during the period in which the new sample data were collected.

Solution We begin by simply extending the control limits, centerline, and zone boundaries of the control chart in Figure 13.24 to the right. Next, beginning with sample number 26, we plot the 10 new sample means on the control chart and connect them with straight lines. This extended version of the control chart, produced using Minitab, is shown in Figure 13.26.

Figure 13.25
Excel worksheet with 10 additional samples of $n = 5$ from paint-filling process

	A	B	C	D	E	F	G	H	I
1	Sample	Weight1	Weight2	Weight3	Weight4	Weight5		Mean	Range
2	26	10.0019	9.9981	9.9952	9.9976	9.9999		9.99854	0.0067
3	27	10.0041	9.9982	10.0028	10.004	9.9971		10.00124	0.007
4	28	9.9999	9.9974	10.0078	9.9971	9.9923		9.9989	0.0155
5	29	9.9982	10.0002	9.9916	10.004	9.9916		9.99712	0.0124
6	30	9.9933	9.9963	9.9955	9.9993	9.9905		9.99498	0.0088
7	31	9.9915	9.9984	10.0053	9.9888	9.9876		9.99432	0.0177
8	32	9.9912	9.997	9.9961	9.9879	9.997		9.99384	0.0091
9	33	9.9942	9.996	9.9975	10.0019	9.9912		9.99616	0.0107
10	34	9.9949	9.9967	9.9936	9.9941	10.0071		9.99728	0.0135
11	35	9.9943	9.9969	9.9937	9.9912	10.0053		9.99628	0.0141

Data Set: CANNEW

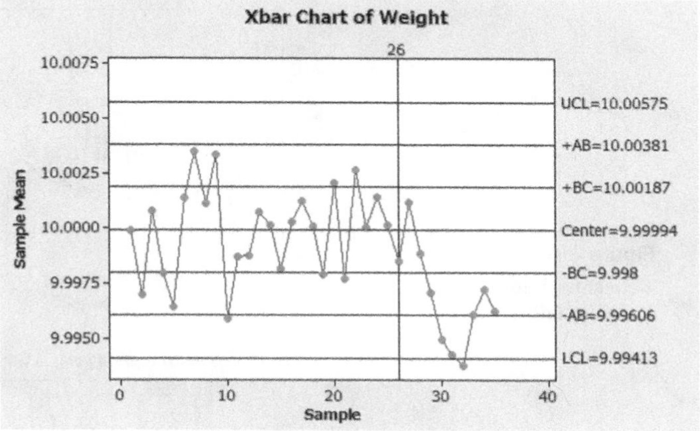

Figure 13.26
Minitab extended $\bar{x}$-chart for paint-filling process

Now that the control chart has been prepared, we apply the six pattern-analysis rules for detecting special causes of variation (Figure 13.22) to the new sequence of sample means. First, notice that the mean for sample 32 falls below the lower control limit (Rule 1). Also, notice that six points in a row steadily decrease (samples 27–32). Rule 3 says that if we observe six points in a row steadily increasing or decreasing, that is an indication of the presence of special causes of variation. Notice that if you apply the rules from left to right along the sequence of sample means, the decreasing pattern also triggers signals from Rules 5 (samples 29–31) and 6 (samples 28–32). These signals lead us to conclude that the process has gone out of control.

Look Back Apparently, the filling head began to clog about the time that either sample 26 or 27 was drawn from the process. As a result, the mean of the process (the mean fill weight dispensed by the process) began to decline.

Now Work Exercise 13.8

Monitoring the Process Mean

The engineering firm that tests for surfactants in jet fuel additive is experimenting with different pump and filter combinations—Pump-A with Filter-A (the standard test), Pump-A with Filter-B, Pump-B with Filter-A, and Pump-B with Filter-B. To monitor the test results, three fuel samples were tested each day by each of the four methods, for a period of over 100 consecutive days. A "safe" surfactant additive measurement should range between 80 and 90, and this range represents the specification limits of the process.

We analyzed the data in the **JET** files using Minitab. Treating the three samples collected on the same day as a rational subgroup, four Minitab $\bar{x}$-charts are produced (one for each pump/filter method) in Figures SIA13.1a–d. As an option, Minitab will highlight (in red) any sample means that match any of the six pattern-analysis rules for

STATISTICS in ACTION REVISITED CONTINUED

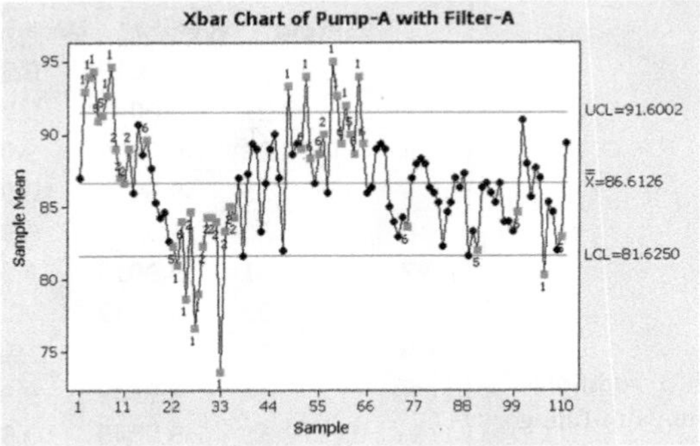

Figure SIA13.1a
$\bar{x}$-chart for Pump-A with Filter-A (standard) method

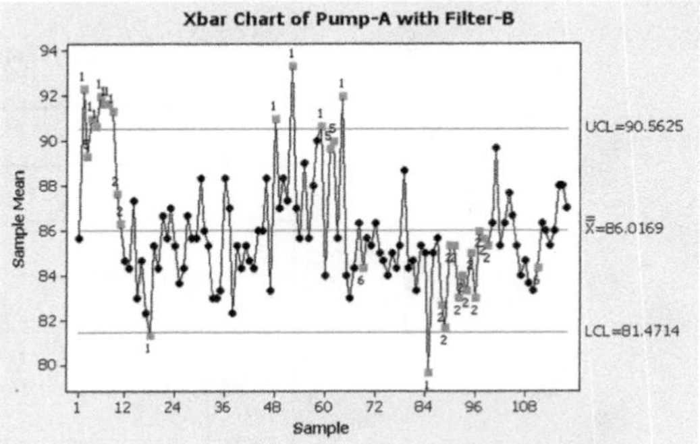

Figure SIA13.1b
$\bar{x}$-chart for Pump-A with Filter-B method

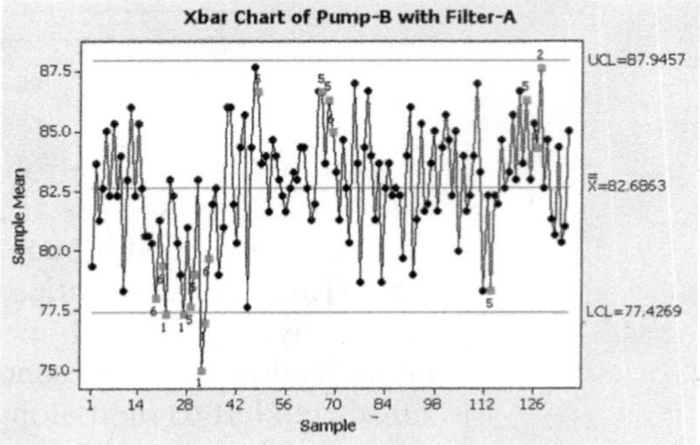

Figure SIA13.1c
$\bar{x}$-chart for Pump-B with Filter-A method

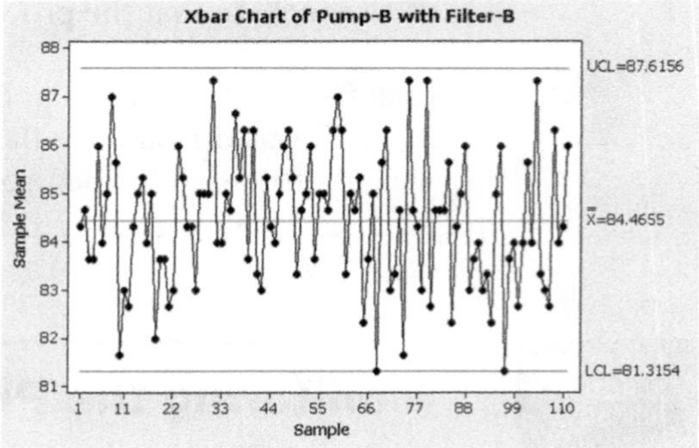

Figure SIA13.1d
$\bar{x}$-chart for Pump-B with Filter-B method

detecting special causes of variation. The number of the rule that is violated is shown above (or below) the sample mean on the chart.

You can see that only one of the process means is "in control"—the mean for the Pump-B with Filter-B test method—as shown in Figure SIA13.1d There is at least one pattern-analysis rule violated in each of the other three $\bar{x}$-charts. Also, each sample mean for Pump-B/Filter-B falls within the specification limits (80%–90%). In contrast, the other injection methods have several means that fall outside the specification limits of the process. Of the three nonstandard surfactant test methods, the Pump-B/Filter-B method appears to have the most promise. This analysis helped the company to focus on perfecting this method of surfactant testing in jet fuel.

Exercises 13.1–13.21

Learning the Mechanics

13.1 What is a control chart? Describe its use.

13.2 Explain why rational subgrouping should be used in constructing control charts.

13.3 When a control chart is first constructed, why are the centerline and control limits treated as trial values?

13.4 Which process parameter is an $\bar{x}$-chart used to monitor?

13.5 Even if all the points on an $\bar{x}$-chart fall between the control limits, the process may be out of control. Explain.

13.6 What must be true about the variation of a process before an $\bar{x}$-chart is used to monitor the mean of the process? Why?

13.7 NW Use the six pattern-analysis rules described in Figure 13.22 to determine whether the process being monitored with the $\bar{x}$-chart shown below is out of statistical control.

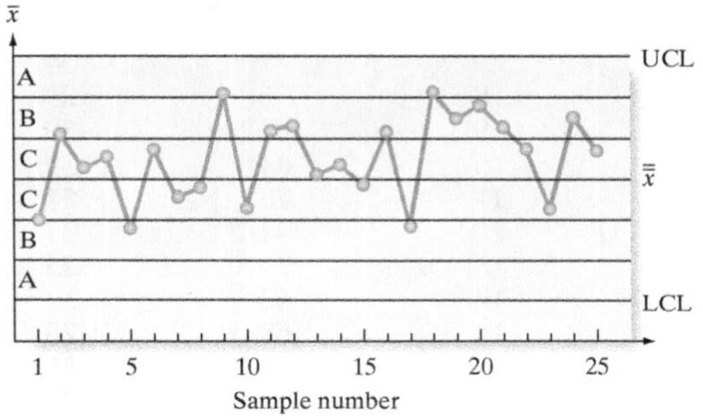

13.8 NW Consider the next $\bar{x}$-chart shown.

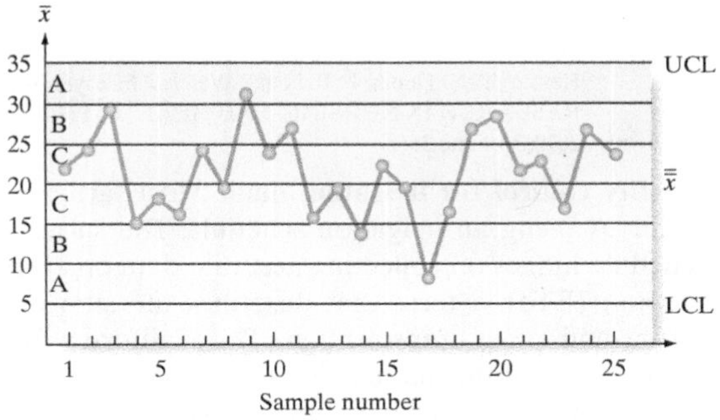

a. Is the process affected by special causes of variation only, common causes of variation only, or both? Explain.

b. The means for the next five samples in the process are 27, 29, 32, 36, and 34. Plot these points on an extended $\bar{x}$-chart. What does the pattern suggest about the process?

13.9 Use Table IX in Appendix D to find the value of A_2 for each of the following sample sizes.

a. $n = 3$

b. $n = 10$

c. $n = 22$

13.10 Twenty-five consecutive samples of size $n = 5$ were collected to construct an $\bar{x}$-chart. The sample means and ranges for the data are shown in the next table.
L13010

a. Calculate the mean of the sample means, $\bar{\bar{x}}$, and the mean of the sample ranges, $\bar{R}$.

b. Calculate and plot the centerline and the upper and lower control limits for the $\bar{x}$-chart.

Sample	$\bar{x}$	R	Sample	$\bar{x}$	R
1	80.2	7.2	14	83.1	10.2
2	79.1	9.0	15	79.6	7.8
3	83.2	4.7	16	80.0	6.1
4	81.0	5.6	17	83.2	8.4
5	77.6	10.1	18	75.9	9.9
6	81.7	8.6	19	78.1	6.0
7	80.4	4.4	20	81.4	7.4
8	77.5	6.2	21	81.7	10.4
9	79.8	7.9	22	80.9	9.1
10	85.3	7.1	23	78.4	7.3
11	77.7	9.8	24	79.6	8.0
12	82.3	10.7	25	81.6	7.6
13	79.5	9.2			

c. Calculate and plot the A, B, and C zone boundaries of the $\bar{x}$-chart.

d. Plot the 25 sample means on the $\bar{x}$-chart and use the six pattern-analysis rules to determine whether the process is under statistical control.

13.11 The data in the following table were collected for the purpose of constructing an $\bar{x}$-chart.

L13011 **a.** Calculate $\bar{x}$ and R for each sample.

b. Calculate $\bar{\bar{x}}$ and $\bar{R}$.

c. Calculate and plot the centerline and the upper and lower control limits for the $\bar{x}$-chart.

d. Calculate and plot the A, B, and C zone boundaries of the $\bar{x}$-chart.

e. Plot the 20 sample means on the $\bar{x}$-chart. Is the process in control? Justify your answer.

Sample	Measurements			
1	19.4	19.7	20.6	21.2
2	18.7	18.4	21.2	20.7
3	20.2	18.8	22.6	20.1
4	19.6	21.2	18.7	19.4
5	20.4	20.9	22.3	18.6
6	17.3	22.3	20.3	19.7
7	21.8	17.6	22.8	23.1
8	20.9	17.4	19.5	20.7
9	18.1	18.3	20.6	20.4
10	22.6	21.4	18.5	19.7
11	22.7	21.2	21.5	19.5
12	20.1	20.6	21.0	20.2
13	19.7	18.6	21.2	19.1
14	18.6	21.7	17.7	18.3
15	18.2	20.4	19.8	19.2
16	18.9	20.7	23.2	20.0
17	20.5	19.7	21.4	17.8
18	21.0	18.7	19.9	21.2
19	20.5	19.6	19.8	21.8
20	20.6	16.9	22.4	19.7

Applying the Concepts—Basic

13.12 Detecting gender-related employment disparities. In the *Federal Reserve Bank of Atlanta, Working Paper Series* (Oct. 2008), researchers presented a novel approach to identifying firms that discriminate against women. The researchers used the Equal Employment Opportunity

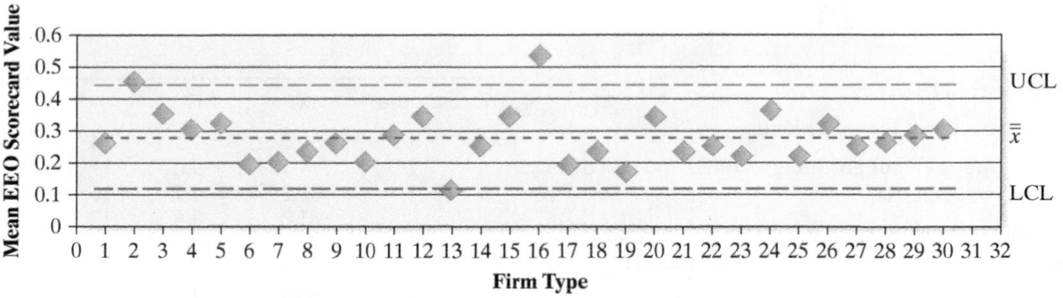

(EEOC) Systematic Gender Disparity Scorecard as a measure of the degree to which a firm complies with EEOC guidelines for eliminating gender bias. (EEOC Scorecard values range from 0 to 1, with larger values indicating a greater gender disparity.) In a hypothetical example, a sample of firms was selected for each of 30 different types of firms in the service industry (e.g., food service, financial services, oil and gas service, etc.). The mean scorecard values for the 30 firm types are plotted in the $\bar{x}$-chart shown above. The centerline and upper and lower control limits are shown on the chart.

a. Identify the rational subgroups used to construct the chart.

b. Identify the key variable plotted on the chart.

c. What are the approximate values of $\bar{\bar{x}}$, UCL, and LCL?

d. What conclusions can you draw from the chart? Are there any firm types that should concern the EEOC? Why?

13.13 Pain levels of ICU patients. Various interventions are available for nurses to help relieve patients' pain (e.g., heat/cold applications, breathing exercises, massage). The journal *Research in Nursing & Health* (Vol. 35, 2012) demonstrated the utility of statistical process control in determining the effectiveness of a pain intervention. The researchers presented the following illustration. Pain levels (measured on a 100-point scale) were recorded for a sample of 10 intensive care unit (ICU) patients 24 hours postsurgery each week for 20 consecutive weeks. The next table provides the means and ranges for each of the 20 weeks. To establish that the pain management process is "in control," an $\bar{x}$-chart is constructed.

ICU

a. Compute the value of the centerline for the $\bar{x}$-chart.

b. Compute the value of $\bar{R}$.

c. Compute the UCL and LCL for the $\bar{x}$-chart.

d. Plot the means for the 20 weeks on the $\bar{x}$-chart. Is the pain management process "in control"?

e. After the 20th week, a pain intervention occurred in the ICU. The goal of the intervention was to reduce the average pain level of ICU patients. To determine if the intervention was effective, the sampling of ICU patients was continued for 8 more consecutive weeks. The mean pain levels of these patients were (in order): 71, 72, 69, 67, 66, 65, 64, and 62. Plot these means on the $\bar{x}$-chart.

f. Apply pattern-analysis rules to the extended $\bar{x}$-chart, part **e**. Do you detect a shift in the mean pain level of the patients following the intervention? Explain.

Data for Exercise 13.13

Week	$\bar{x}$	Range
1	65	28
2	75	41
3	72	31
4	69	35
5	73	35
6	63	33
7	77	34
8	75	29
9	69	30
10	64	39
11	70	34
12	74	37
13	73	25
14	62	33
15	68	28
16	75	35
17	72	29
18	70	32
19	62	33
20	72	29

Source: Based on "Statistical Process Control in Nursing Research" by Denise F. Polit and Wendy Chaboyer from RESEARCH IN NURSING AND HEALTH, February 2012, Volume 35(1).

13.14 Quality control for irrigation data. Most farmers budget water by using an irrigation schedule. The success of the schedule hinges on collecting accurate data on *evapotranspiration* (ETo), a term that describes the sum of evaporation and plant transpiration. The California Irrigation Management Information System (CIMIS) collects daily weather data (e.g., air temperature, wind speed, and vapor pressure) used to estimate ETo and supplies this information to farmers. Researchers at CIMIS demonstrated the use of quality-control charts to monitor daily ETo measurements (*IV International Symposium on Irrigation of Horticultural Crops*, Dec. 31, 2004). Daily minimum air temperatures (°C) collected hourly during the month of May at the Davis CIMIS station yielded the following summary statistics (where five measurements are collected each hour): $\bar{\bar{x}} = 10.16°$ and $\bar{R} = 14.87°$.

a. Use the information provided to find the lower and upper control limits for an $\bar{x}$-chart.

b. Suppose that one day in May the mean air temperature at the Davis CIMIS station was recorded as $\bar{x} = 20.3°$. How should the manager of the station respond to this observation?

13.15 CPU of a computer chip. The central processing unit (CPU) of a microcomputer is a computer chip containing millions of transistors. Connecting the transistors are slender circuit paths only .5 to .85 micrometer wide. A manufacturer of CPU chips knows that if the circuit paths are not .5–.85 micrometer wide, a variety of problems will arise in the chips' performance. The manufacturer sampled four CPU chips six times a day (every 90 minutes from 8:00 A.M. until 4:30 P.M.) for 5 consecutive days and measured the circuit path widths. These data and Minitab were used to construct the $\bar{x}$-chart shown below.

a. Assuming that $\bar{R} = .335$, calculate the chart's upper and lower control limits, the upper and lower A–B boundaries, and the upper and lower B–C boundaries.

b. What does the chart suggest about the stability of the process used to put circuit paths on the CPU chip? Justify your answer.

c. Should the control limits be used to monitor future process output? Explain.

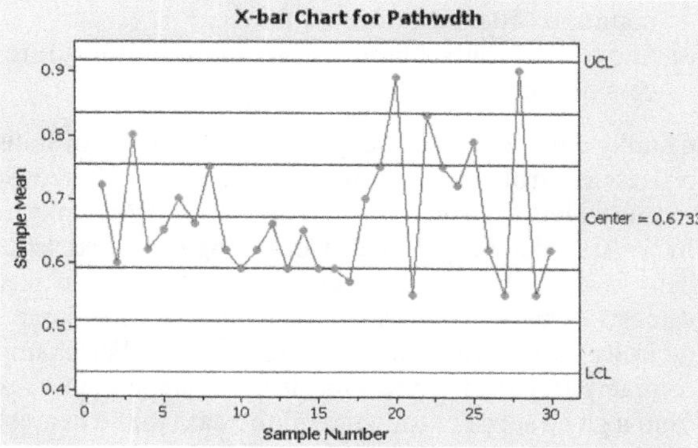

13.16 Cereal box manufacturing. A machine at K-Company fills boxes with bran flakes cereal. The target weight for the filled boxes is 24 ounces. The company would like to use an $\bar{x}$-chart to monitor the performance of the machine. To develop the control chart, the company decides to sample and weigh five boxes of cereal each day (at 8:00 and 11:00 A.M. and 2:00, 5:00, and 8:00 P.M.) for 20 consecutive days. The data are summarized in the SPSS printout below.

CEREAL

a. Construct an $\bar{x}$-chart from the summary statistics.

b. What does the chart suggest about the stability of the filling process (whether the process is in or out of statistical control)? Justify your answer.

Case Summaries[a]

	DAY	MEANWT	RANGEWT
1	1	24.05	.22
2	2	23.96	.12
3	3	23.99	.32
4	4	24.02	.16
5	5	23.95	.26
6	6	24.01	.25
7	7	23.97	.17
8	8	23.98	.12
9	9	23.95	.28
10	10	24.00	.07
11	11	24.01	.21
12	12	24.02	.16
13	13	24.06	.16
14	14	23.96	.15
15	15	24.03	.12
16	16	24.03	.18
17	17	23.97	.19
18	18	24.00	.21
19	19	24.02	.13
20	20	23.97	.15

a. Limited to first 100 cases.

c. Should the control limits be used to monitor future process output? Explain.

d. Two shifts of workers run the filling operation. Each day the second shift takes over at 3:00 P.M. Will the rational subgrouping strategy used by K-Company facilitate or hinder the identification of process variation caused by differences in the two shifts? Explain.

Applying the Concepts—Intermediate

13.17 Improving public health waiting times. Statistical process control was utilized in an effort to improve the service delivery at a Women, Infants, and Children (WIC) health clinic in Minnesota (*American Journal of Public Health,* Sep. 2009). The health department sampled patients for 10 consecutive days and recorded each patient's lobby waiting time (in minutes). The mean lobby waiting times were (in order): 25.5, 16.5, 22.5, 18, 13, 10.5, 14, 4.5, 12.5, and 14 minutes. These means were plotted in an $\bar{x}$-chart to monitor the waiting time process.

WIC1, WIC2

a. Compute the value of the centerline for the $\bar{x}$-chart.

b. Critical boundaries for the $\bar{x}$-chart are listed as follows: UCL = 31.5, Upper A-B = 26, Upper B-C = 20.5, Lower B-C = 9.5, Lower A-B = 4, LCL = 0. Plot the 10 means in an $\bar{x}$-chart; include the critical boundaries on the chart.

c. Refer to part **b.** Apply pattern-analysis rules to the chart. Do you detect the presence of any special causes of variation?

d. After a 3-month time period, during which the clinic implemented new procedures, the health department conducted a second sampling of patients over 14 consecutive days. The mean lobby waiting times for these 14 days were (in order): 11.5, 12.5, 14.5, 11, 12.5, 11.5, 13.5, 11.5, 7.5, 13.5, 7, 10.5, 13.5, and 2 minutes. Critical $\bar{x}$-chart boundaries for the new data are listed as follows: UCL = 21.5, Upper A-B = 18, Upper B-C = 14.5, Lower B-C = 7.5, Lower A-B = 4, LCL = .5. Construct an $\bar{x}$-chart for the new data. Do you detect the presence of any special causes of variation?

e. Place the two $\bar{x}$-charts side by side. The health department concluded that a process shift occurred after the clinic implemented its new procedures. Do you agree?

13.18 Selecting the best wafer-slicing machine. Silicon wafer slicing is a critical step in the production of semiconductor devices (e.g., diodes, solar cells, transistors). Yuanpei (China) University researchers used control charts to aid in selecting the best silicon wafer-slicing machine (*Computers & Industrial Engineering,* Vol. 52, 2007). Samples of $n = 2$ wafers were sliced each hour for 67 consecutive hours and bow measurements (a measure of precision) were recorded. The resulting $\bar{x}$-chart for one of the machines tested revealed that the cutting process was out of control on the 19th, 40th, and 59th hours. For each of these 3 hours, the mean bow measurement fell above the upper control limit. Assume the mean bow measurements are normally distributed.

NW **a.** If the process is in control, what is the probability that a mean bow measurement for a randomly selected hour will fall above the upper control limit?

b. If the process is in control, what is the probability that 3 of 67 mean bow measurements fall above the upper control limit?

13.19 Detecting under-reported emissions. The Environmental Protection Agency (EPA) regulates the level of carbon dioxide (CO_2) emissions. Periodically these emissions

CO2

Data for Exercise 13.19

Daily Average CO_2 Measurements for 30 Consecutive Days

1	*2*	*3*	*4*	*5*	*6*	*7*	*8*	*9*	*10*	*11*	*12*	*13*	*14*	*15*
12.9	13.2	13.4	13.3	13.1	13.2	13.1	13.0	12.5	12.5	12.7	12.8	12.7	12.9	12.0
16	*17*	*18*	*19*	*20*	*21*	*22*	*23*	*24*	*25*	*26*	*27*	*28*	*29*	*30*
12.9	12.8	12.7	13.2	13.2	13.3	13.0	13.0	13.2	13.2	13.4	13.1	13.3	13.4	13.4

measurements are under-reported due to leakage or faulty equipment. Such problems are often detected only by an expensive test (RATA) that is typically conducted only once per year. Just recently, the EPA began applying an automated control chart methodology to detect under-measurement of emissions data (*EPRI CEM Users Group Conference*, Nashville, TN, May 13, 2008). Each day, the EPA collects emissions data by measuring CO_2 concentration for each of 6 randomly selected hours. The daily average CO_2 levels for each of 30 days are shown in the table above. The EPA considers these values to truly represent emissions levels because the RATA test was recently performed and showed no problems with under-reporting. The lower and upper control limits for the averages were established as LCL = 12.26 and UCL = 13.76.

a. Construct a control chart for the daily average CO_2 levels.

b. Based on the control chart, describe the behavior of the measurement process.

c. The following average CO_2 levels were determined for a later 10-day period: 12.7, 12.1, 12.0, 12.0, 11.8, 11.7, 11.6, 11.7, 11.8, 11.7. Make an inference about the potential under-reporting of the emissions data for this 10-day period.

13.20 Military aircraft bolts. A precision parts manufacturer produces bolts for use in military aircraft. Ideally, the bolts should be 37 centimeters in length. The company sampled four consecutively produced bolts each hour on the hour for 25 consecutive hours and measured them using a computerized precision instrument. The data are presented in the table below.

BOLTS

Hour	Bolt Lengths (centimeters)			
1	37.03	37.08	36.90	36.88
2	36.96	37.04	36.85	36.98
3	37.16	37.11	36.99	37.01
4	37.20	37.06	37.02	36.98
5	36.81	36.97	36.91	37.10
6	37.13	36.96	37.01	36.89
7	37.07	36.94	36.99	37.00
8	37.01	36.91	36.98	37.12
9	37.17	37.03	36.90	37.01
10	36.91	36.99	36.87	37.11
11	36.88	37.10	37.07	37.03
12	37.06	36.98	36.90	36.99
13	36.91	37.22	37.12	37.03
14	37.08	37.07	37.10	37.04
15	37.03	37.04	36.89	37.01
16	36.95	36.98	36.90	36.99
17	36.97	36.94	37.14	37.10
18	37.11	37.04	36.98	36.91
19	36.88	36.99	37.01	36.94
20	36.90	37.15	37.09	37.00
21	37.01	36.96	37.05	36.96
22	37.09	36.95	36.93	37.12
23	37.00	37.02	36.95	37.04
24	36.99	37.07	36.90	37.02
25	37.10	37.03	37.01	36.90

a. What process is the manufacturer interested in monitoring?

b. Construct an $\bar{x}$-chart from the data.

c. Does the chart suggest that special causes of variation are present? Justify your answer.

d. Provide an example of a special cause of variation that could potentially affect this process. Do the same for a common cause of variation.

e. Should the control limits be used to monitor future process output? Explain.

13.21 Chunky data. BPI Consulting, a leading provider of statistical process control software and training in the United States, recently alerted its clients to problems with "chunky" data. In an April 2007 report, BPI Consulting identified "chunky" data as data that result when the range between possible values of the variable of interest becomes too large. This typically occurs when the data are rounded. For example, a company monitoring the time it takes shipments to arrive from a given supplier rounded off the data to the nearest day. To show the effect of chunky data on a control chart, BPI Consulting considered a process with a quality characteristic that averages about 100. Data on the quality characteristic for a random sample of three observations collected each hour for 40 consecutive hours are given in the table below. (*Note:* BPI Consulting cautions its clients that out-of-control data points in this example were actually due to the measurement process and not to an "out-of-control" process.)

CHUNKY

a. Show that the process is "in control," according to Rule 1, by constructing an $\bar{x}$-chart for the data.

b. Round each measurement in the data set to a whole number and then form an $\bar{x}$-chart for the rounded data. What do you observe?

Sample	Quality Levels			Sample	Quality Levels		
1	99.69	99.73	99.81	21	99.43	99.63	100.08
2	98.67	99.47	100.20	22	100.04	99.71	100.40
3	99.93	99.97	100.22	23	101.08	99.84	99.93
4	100.58	99.40	101.08	24	99.98	99.50	100.25
5	99.28	99.48	99.10	25	101.18	100.79	99.56
6	99.06	99.61	99.85	26	99.24	99.90	100.03
7	99.81	99.78	99.53	27	99.41	99.18	99.39
8	99.78	100.10	99.27	28	100.84	100.47	100.48
9	99.76	100.83	101.02	29	99.31	100.15	101.08
10	100.20	100.24	99.85	30	99.65	100.05	100.12
11	99.12	99.74	100.04	31	100.24	101.01	100.71
12	101.58	100.54	100.53	32	99.08	99.73	99.61
13	101.51	100.52	100.50	33	100.30	100.02	99.31
14	100.27	100.77	100.48	34	100.38	100.76	100.37
15	100.43	100.67	100.53	35	100.48	99.96	99.72
16	101.08	100.54	99.89	36	99.98	100.30	99.07
17	99.63	100.77	99.86	37	100.25	99.58	101.27
18	99.29	99.49	99.37	38	100.49	100.16	100.86
19	99.89	100.75	100.73	39	100.44	100.53	99.84
20	100.54	101.51	100.54	40	99.45	99.41	99.27

13.5 A Control Chart for Monitoring the Variation of a Process: The *R*-Chart

Recall from Section 13.2 that a process may be out of statistical control because its mean or variance or both are changing over time (see Figure 13.8). The $\bar{x}$-chart of the previous section is used to detect changes in the process mean. The control chart we present in this section—the ***R*-chart**—is used to detect changes in process variation.

The primary difference between the $\bar{x}$-chart and the R-chart is that instead of plotting *sample means* and monitoring their variation, we plot and monitor the variation of *sample ranges*. Changes in the behavior of the sample range signal changes in the variation of the process.

We could also monitor process variation by plotting *sample standard deviations*—that is, we could calculate s for each sample (i.e., each subgroup) and plot them on a control chart known as an ***s*-chart.** In this chapter, however, we focus on just the R-chart because (1) when using samples of size 9 or less, the s-chart and the R-chart reflect about the same information, and (2) the R-chart is used much more widely by practitioners than is the s-chart (primarily because the sample range is easier to calculate and interpret than the sample standard deviation). For more information about s-charts, see the references at the end of the chapter.

The underlying logic and basic form of the R-chart are similar to those of the $\bar{x}$-chart. In monitoring $\bar{x}$, we use the standard deviation of $\bar{x}$ to develop 3-sigma control limits. Now, because we want to be able to determine when R takes on unusually large or small values, we use the standard deviation of R, or σ_R, to construct 3-sigma control limits. The centerline of the $\bar{x}$-chart represents the process mean μ or, equivalently, the mean of the sampling distribution of $\bar{x}$, $\mu_{\bar{x}}$. Similarly, the centerline of the R-chart represents μ_R, the mean of the sampling distribution of R. These points are illustrated in the R-chart of Figure 13.27.

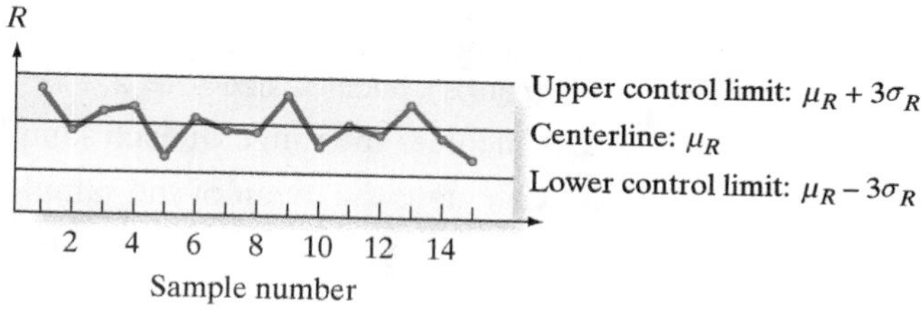

Figure 13.27
R-chart

As with the $\bar{x}$-chart, you should have at least 20 samples of n items each ($n \geq 2$) to construct an R-chart. This will provide sufficient data to obtain reasonably good estimates of μ_R and σ_R. Rational subgrouping is again used for determining sample size and frequency of sampling.

The centerline of the R-chart is positioned as follows:

$$\textit{Centerline: } \bar{R} = \frac{R_1 + R_2 + \cdots + R_k}{k}$$

where k is the number of samples of size n and R_i is the range of the ith sample. $\bar{R}$ is an estimate of μ_R.

In order to construct the control limits, we need an estimator of σ_R. The estimator recommended by Montgomery (2009) and Ryan (2011) is

$$\hat{\sigma}_R = d_3\left(\frac{\bar{R}}{d_2}\right)$$

where d_2 and d_3 are constants whose values depend on the sample size, n. Values for d_2 and d_3 for samples of size $n = 2$ to $n = 25$ are given in Table IX in Appendix D.

The control limits are positioned as follows:

$$\textit{Upper control limit: } \overline{R} + 3\hat{\sigma}_R = \overline{R} + 3d_3\left(\frac{\overline{R}}{d_2}\right)$$

$$\textit{Lower control limit: } \overline{R} - 3\hat{\sigma}_R = \overline{R} - 3d_3\left(\frac{\overline{R}}{d_2}\right)$$

Notice that $\overline{R}$ appears twice in each control limit. Accordingly, we can simplify the calculation of these limits by factoring out $\overline{R}$:

$$\text{UCL: } \overline{R}\left(1 + \frac{3d_3}{d_2}\right) = \overline{R}D_4 \qquad \text{LCL: } \overline{R}\left(1 - \frac{3d_3}{d_2}\right) = \overline{R}D_3$$

where

$$D_4 = \left(1 + \frac{3d_3}{d_2}\right) \qquad D_3 = \left(1 - \frac{3d_3}{d_2}\right)$$

The values for D_3 and D_4 have been tabulated for samples of size $n = 2$ to $n = 25$ and can be found in Table IX in Appendix D.

For samples of size $n = 2$ through $n = 6$, D_3 is negative, and the lower control limit falls below zero. Because the sample range cannot take on negative values, such a control limit is meaningless. Thus, when $n \leq 6$, the R-chart contains only one control limit, the upper control limit.

Although D_3 is actually negative for $n \leq 6$, the values reported in Table IX in Appendix D are all zeros. This has been done to discourage the inappropriate construction of negative lower control limits. If the lower control limit is calculated using $D_3 = 0$, you obtain $D_3\overline{R} = 0$. This should be interpreted as indicating that the R-chart has no lower 3-sigma control limit.

Constructing an *R*-Chart: A Summary

1. Using a rational subgrouping strategy, collect at least 20 samples (i.e., subgroups), each of size $n \geq 2$.
2. Calculate the range of each sample.
3. Calculate the mean of the sample ranges, $\overline{R}$:

$$\overline{R} = \frac{R_1 + R_2 + \cdots + R_k}{k}$$

where

$k =$ The number of samples (i.e., subgroups)

$R_i =$ The range of the ith sample

4. Plot the centerline and control limits:

Centerline: $\overline{R}$

Upper control limit: $\overline{R}D_4$

Lower control limit: $\overline{R}D_3$

where D_3 and D_4 are constants that depend on n. Their values can be found in Table IX in Appendix D. When $n \leq 6$, $D_3 = 0$, indicating that the control chart does not have a lower control limit.

5. Plot the k sample ranges on the control chart in the order that the samples were produced by the process.

We interpret the completed R-chart in basically the same way as we did the $\overline{x}$-chart. We look for indications that the process is out of control. Those indications include points that fall outside the control limits as well as any nonrandom patterns of variation that appear between the control limits. To help spot nonrandom behavior, we include the A, B, and C zones (described in the previous section) on the R-chart. The next box describes how to construct the zone boundaries for the R-chart. It requires only Rules 1 through 4 of Figure 13.22; Rules 5 and 6 are based on the assumption that the statistic plotted on the control chart follows a normal (or nearly normal) distribution, whereas R's distribution is skewed to the right.*

Constructing Zone Boundaries for an R-Chart

The simplest method of construction uses the estimator of the standard deviation of R, which is $\hat{\sigma}_R = d_3(\overline{R}/d_2)$:

$$\textit{Upper A–B boundary: } \overline{R} + 2d_3\left(\frac{\overline{R}}{d_2}\right)$$

$$\textit{Lower A–B boundary: } \overline{R} - 2d_3\left(\frac{\overline{R}}{d_2}\right)$$

$$\textit{Upper B–C boundary: } \overline{R} + d_3\left(\frac{\overline{R}}{d_2}\right)$$

$$\textit{Lower B–C boundary: } \overline{R} - d_3\left(\frac{\overline{R}}{d_2}\right)$$

Note: Whenever $n \le 6$, the R-chart has no lower 3-sigma control limit. However, the lower A–B and B–C boundaries can still be plotted if they are nonnegative.

Interpreting an R-Chart

1. The **process is out of control** if one or more sample ranges fall beyond the control limits (Rule 1) or if any of the three patterns of variation described by Rules 2, 3, and 4 (Figure 13.22) are observed. Such signals indicate that one or more special causes of variation are influencing the *variation* of the process. These causes should be identified and eliminated to bring the process into control.
2. The **process is treated as being in control** if none of the noted out-of-control signals are observed. Processes that are in control should not be tampered with. However, if the level of variation is unacceptably high, common causes of variation should be identified and eliminated.

As with the $\bar{x}$-chart, the centerline and control limits should be developed using samples that were collected during a period in which the process was in control. Accordingly, when an R-chart is first constructed, the centerline and the control limits are treated as *trial values* (see Section 13.4) and are modified, if necessary, before being extended to the right and used to monitor future process output.

Example 13.8

Creating and Interpreting an R-Chart—Paint-Filling Process

Problem Refer to Example 13.6 and the paint-filling process. Recall that five paint cans were sampled each hour for 25 consecutive hours, and the can weights (oz.) were measured.

a. Construct an R-chart for the paint-filling process.

b. What does the chart indicate about the stability of the filling process during the time when the data were collected?

c. Is it appropriate to use the control limits constructed in part **a** to monitor future process output?

*Some authors (e.g., Kane, 1989) apply all six pattern-analysis rules as long as $n \ge 4$.

Solution

a. The first step after collecting the data is to calculate the range of each sample. These ranges were computed using Excel in Example 13.6 and are shown on the Excel spreadsheet, Figure 13.23 (p. 13-25). Next, calculate the mean of the ranges, $\overline{R}$. From Example 13.6, we have $\overline{R} = .010072$.

The centerline of the chart is positioned at $\overline{R} = .010072$. To determine the control limits, we need the constants D_3 and D_4, which can be found in Table IX in Appendix D. For $n = 5$, $D_3 = 0$ and $D_4 = 2.114$. Because $D_3 = 0$, the lower 3-sigma control limit is negative and is not included on the chart. The upper control limit is calculated as follows:

$$\text{UCL: } \overline{R}D_4 = (.010072)(2.114) = .02130$$

After positioning the upper control limit on the chart, we plot the 25 sample ranges in the order of sampling and connect the points with straight lines. The resulting trial R-chart, produced using Minitab, is shown in Figure 13.28.

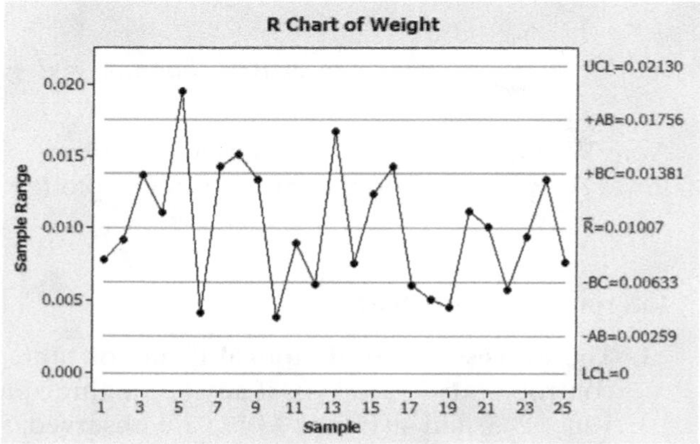

Figure 13.28
Minitab R-chart for paint-filling process

b. To facilitate our examination of the R-chart, we plot the four zone boundaries. Recall that, in general, the A–B boundaries are positioned 2 standard deviations from the centerline and the B–C boundaries are 1 standard deviation from the centerline. In the case of the R-chart, we use the estimated standard deviation of R, $\hat{\sigma}_R = d_3(\overline{R}/d_2)$, and calculate the boundaries:

$$\textit{Upper A–B boundary: } \overline{R} + 2d_3\left(\frac{\overline{R}}{d_2}\right) = .01755$$

$$\textit{Lower A–B boundary: } \overline{R} - 2d_3\left(\frac{\overline{R}}{d_2}\right) = .00259$$

$$\textit{Upper B–C boundary: } \overline{R} + d_3\left(\frac{\overline{R}}{d_2}\right) = .01381$$

$$\textit{Lower B–C boundary: } \overline{R} - d_3\left(\frac{\overline{R}}{d_2}\right) = .00633$$

where (from Table IX in Appendix D) for $n = 5$, $d_2 = 2.326$ and $d_3 = .864$. Notice in Figure 13.28 that the lower A zone is slightly narrower than the upper A zone. This occurs because the lower 3-sigma control limit (the usual lower boundary of the lower A zone) is negative.

All the plotted R values fall below the upper control limit. This is one indication that the process is under control (i.e., is stable). However, we must also look for patterns of points that would be unlikely to occur if the process were in control. To assist us with this process, we use pattern-analysis Rules 1–4 (Figure 13.22). None of the rules signal the presence of special causes of variation. Accordingly, we conclude that it is reasonable to treat the process—in particular, the variation of the process—as being under control during the period in question. Apparently, no significant special causes of variation are influencing the variation of the process.

c. Yes. Because the variation of the process appears to be in control during the period when the sample data were collected, the control limits appropriately characterize the variation in R that would be expected when the process is in a state of statistical control.

■ **Now Work Exercise 13.25**

In practice, the $\bar{x}$-chart and the R-chart are not used in isolation, as our presentation so far might suggest. Rather, they are used together to monitor the mean (i.e., the location) of the process and the variation of the process simultaneously. In fact, many practitioners plot them on the same piece of paper.

One important reason for dealing with them as a unit is that the control limits of the $\bar{x}$-chart are a function of R—that is, the control limits depend on the variation of the process. (Recall that the control limits are $\bar{\bar{x}} \pm A_2\bar{R}$.) Thus, if the process variation is out of control, the control limits of the $\bar{x}$-chart have little meaning. This is because when the process variation is changing (as in the rightmost graphs of Figure 13.8), any single estimate of the variation (such as $\bar{R}$ or s) is not representative of the process. Accordingly, **the appropriate procedure is to first construct and then interpret the *R*-chart. If it indicates that the process variation is in control, then it makes sense to construct and interpret the $\bar{x}$-chart.**

Figure 13.29 is reprinted from Kaoru Ishikawa's classic text on quality-improvement methods, *Guide to Quality Control* (1986). It illustrates how particular changes in a process over time may be reflected in $\bar{x}$- and R-charts. At the top of the figure, running across the page, is a series of probability distributions A, B, and C that describe the process (i.e., the output variable) at different points in time. In practice, we never have this information. For this example, however, Ishikawa worked with a known process (i.e., with its given probabilistic characterization) to illustrate how sample data from a known process might behave.

The control limits for both charts were constructed from $k = 25$ samples of size $n = 5$. These data were generated by Distribution A. The 25 sample means and ranges were plotted on the $\bar{x}$- and R-charts, respectively. Because the distribution did not change over this period of time, it follows from the definition of statistical control that the process was under control. If you did not know this—as would be the case in practice—what would you conclude from looking at the control charts? (Remember, always interpret the R-chart before the $\bar{x}$-chart.) Both charts indicate that the process is under control. Accordingly, the control limits are made official and can be used to monitor future output, as is done next.

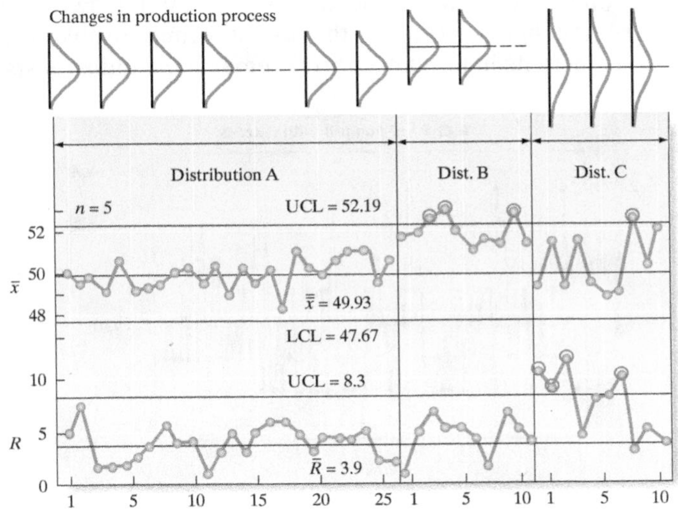

Figure 13.29
Combined $\bar{x}$- and R-chart
Source: Based on GUIDE TO QUALITY CONTROL by Kaoru Ishikawa.

Toward the middle of the figure, the process changes. The mean shifts to a higher level. Now the output variable is described by Distribution B. The process is out of control. Ten new samples of size 5 are sampled from the process. Because the variation of the process has not changed, the R-chart should indicate that the variation remains stable. This is, in fact, the case. All points fall below the upper control limit. As we would hope, it is the $\bar{x}$-chart that reacts to the change in the mean of the process.

Then the process changes again (Distribution C). This time the mean shifts back to its original position, but the variation of the process increases. The process is still out of control but this time for a different reason. Checking the R-chart first, we see that it has reacted as we would hope. It has detected the increase in the variation. Given this R-chart finding, the control limits of the $\bar{x}$-chart become inappropriate (as described before), and we would not use them. Notice, however, how the sample means react to the increased variation in the process. This increased variation in $\bar{x}$ is consistent with what we know about the variance of $\bar{x}$. It is directly proportional to the variance of the process, $\sigma_{\bar{x}}^2 = \sigma^2/n$.

Keep in mind that what Ishikawa did in this example is exactly the opposite of what we do in practice. In practice, we use sample data and control charts to make inferences about changes in unknown process distributions. Here, for the purpose of helping you to understand and interpret control charts, known process distributions were changed to see what would happen to the control charts.

Monitoring the Process Variation

Recall (p. 13-27) that the engineering firm discovered that tests for surfactants in jet fuel additive using Pump-B with Filter-B yielded an "in-control" process mean. However, as discussed in this section, the variation of the process should be checked first, before interpreting the $\bar{x}$-chart. Figure SIA13.2 is a Minitab R-chart for the test results using Pump-B with Filter-B. As an option, we again instructed Minitab to highlight (in red) any sample ranges that match any of the four pattern-analysis rules for detecting special causes of variation given in this section. (If a rule is violated, the rule number will be shown next to the sample range on the chart.)

Figure SIA13.2 shows that the process variation is "in control"—none of the pattern-analysis rules for ranges are matched. Now that we've established the stability of the process variance, the $\bar{x}$-chart of Figure SIA13.1d can be meaningfully interpreted. Together, the $\bar{x}$-chart and R-chart helped the engineering firm establish the Pump-B with Filter-B surfactant test method as a viable alternative to the standard test, one that appears to have no special causes of variation present and with more precision than the standard.

[*Note:* Extensive testing done with the Navy concluded that the improved precision of the "new" surfactant test was valid. However, the new test was unable to detect several light surfactants that can still cause problems in jet engines. The original test for surfactants in jet fuel additive remains the industry standard.]

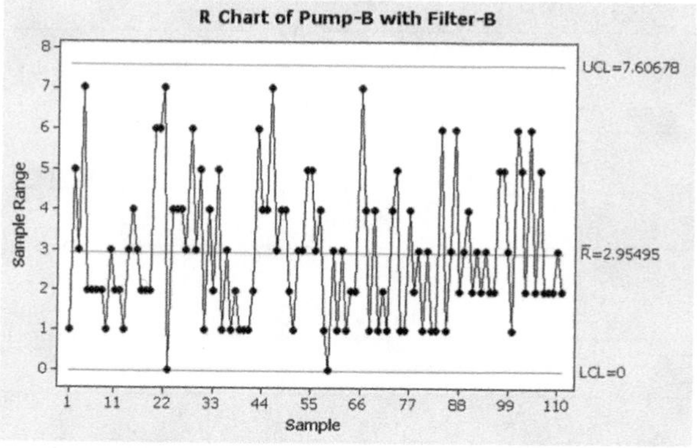

Figure SIA13.2
R-chart for Pump-B with Filter-B method

Exercises 13.22–13.36

Learning the Mechanics

13.22 What characteristic of a process is an *R*-chart designed to monitor?

13.23 In practice, $\bar{x}$- and *R*-charts are used together to monitor a process. However, the *R*-chart should be interpreted before the $\bar{x}$-chart. Why?

13.24 Use Table IX in Appendix D to find the values of D_3 and D_4 for each of the following sample sizes.

a. $n = 4$
b. $n = 12$
c. $n = 24$

13.25 Construct and interpret an *R*-chart for the data in Exercise 13.10 (p. 13-29).
NW

a. Calculate and plot the upper control limit and, if appropriate, the lower control limit.
b. Calculate and plot the A, B, and C zone boundaries on the *R*-chart.
c. Plot the sample ranges on the *R*-chart and use pattern-analysis Rules 1–4 of Figure 13.22 to determine whether the process is under statistical control.

13.26 Construct and interpret an *R*-chart for the data in Exercise 13.11 (p. 13-29).

a. Calculate and plot the upper control limit and, if appropriate, the lower control limit.
b. Calculate and plot the A, B, and C zone boundaries on the *R*-chart.
c. Plot the sample ranges on the *R*-chart and determine whether the process is in control.

13.27 Construct and interpret an *R*-chart and an $\bar{x}$-chart from the sample data shown below. Remember to interpret the *R*-chart *before* the $\bar{x}$-chart.
L13027

Applying the Concepts—Basic

13.28 Detecting gender-related employment disparities. Refer to the *Federal Reserve Bank of Atlanta, Working Paper Series* (Oct. 2008) study of gender-related employment disparities, Exercise 13.12 (p. 13-29). Recall that the researchers used the Equal Employment Opportunity (EEOC) Systematic Gender Disparity Scorecard as a measure of the degree to which a firm complies with EEOC guidelines for eliminating gender bias. An *R*-chart for the data obtained by sampling firms for each of 30 different service industry firm types is shown below. The centerline and upper and lower control limits are shown on the chart.

a. What are the approximate values of $\bar{R}$, UCL, and LCL?
b. What conclusions can you draw from the chart? Are there any firm types that should concern the EEOC? Why?

Data for Exercise 13.27

Sample	Measurements							$\bar{x}$	*R*
	1	2	3	4	5	6	7		
1	20.1	19.0	20.9	22.2	18.9	18.1	21.3	20.07	4.1
2	19.0	17.9	21.2	20.4	20.0	22.3	21.5	20.33	4.4
3	22.6	21.4	21.4	22.1	19.2	20.6	18.7	20.86	3.9
4	18.1	20.8	17.8	19.6	19.8	21.7	20.0	19.69	3.9
5	22.6	19.1	21.4	21.8	18.4	18.0	19.5	20.11	4.6
6	19.1	19.0	22.3	21.5	17.8	19.2	19.4	19.76	4.5
7	17.1	19.4	18.6	20.9	21.8	21.0	19.8	19.80	4.7
8	20.2	22.4	22.0	19.6	19.6	20.0	18.5	20.33	3.9
9	21.9	24.1	23.1	22.8	25.6	24.2	25.2	23.84	3.7
10	25.1	24.3	26.0	23.1	25.8	27.0	26.5	25.40	3.9
11	25.8	29.2	28.5	29.1	27.8	29.0	28.0	28.20	3.4
12	28.2	27.5	29.3	30.7	27.6	28.0	27.0	28.33	3.7
13	28.2	28.6	28.1	26.0	30.0	28.5	28.3	28.24	4.0
14	22.1	21.4	23.3	20.5	19.8	20.5	19.0	20.94	4.3
15	18.5	19.2	18.0	20.1	22.0	20.2	19.5	19.64	4.0
16	21.4	20.3	22.0	19.2	18.0	17.9	19.5	19.76	4.1
17	18.4	16.5	18.1	19.2	17.5	20.9	19.6	18.60	4.4
18	20.1	19.8	22.3	22.5	21.8	22.7	23.0	21.74	3.2
19	20.0	17.5	21.0	18.2	19.5	17.2	18.1	18.79	3.8
20	22.3	18.2	21.5	19.0	19.4	20.5	20.0	20.13	4.1

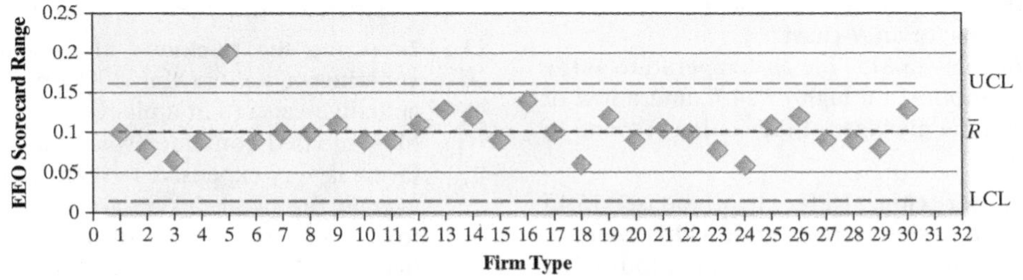

Control chart for Exercise 13.28

13.29 Pain levels of ICU patients. Refer to the *Research in Nursing & Health* (Vol. 35, 2012) study of the effectiveness of a pain intervention, Exercise 13.13 (p. 13-30). Recall that pain levels (measured on a 100-point scale) were recorded for a sample of 10 ICU patients 24 hours post surgery each week for 20 consecutive weeks. The data are repeated in the accompanying table. Now, you want to check process variation using an *R*-chart

ICU

- **a.** Compute the centerline for the chart.
- **b.** Compute the UCL and LCL for the *R*-chart.
- **c.** Plot the ranges for the 20 weeks on the *R*-chart. Does the variation of the pain management process appear to be "in control"?
- **d.** Recall that after the 20th week, a pain intervention occurred in the ICU. The ranges of the pain levels for the samples of patients over the next 8 consecutive weeks were (in order): 22, 29, 16, 15, 23, 19, 30, and 32. Plot these ranges on the *R*-chart.
- **e.** Apply pattern-analysis rules to the extended *R*-chart, part **d.** What do you observe?

Week	$\bar{x}$	Range
1	65	28
2	75	41
3	72	31
4	69	35
5	73	35
6	63	33
7	77	34
8	75	29
9	69	30
10	64	39
11	70	34
12	74	37
13	73	25
14	62	33
15	68	28
16	75	35
17	72	29
18	70	32
19	62	33
20	72	29

Source: Based on "Statistical Process Control in Nursing Research" by Denise F. Polit and Wendy Chaboyer from RESEARCH IN NURSING AND HEALTH, February 2012, Volume 35(1).

13.30 Quality control for irrigation data. Refer to Exercise 13.14 (p. 13-30) and the monitoring of irrigation data by the CIMIS. Recall that daily minimum air temperatures (°C) collected hourly during the month of May at the Davis CIMIS station yielded the following summary statistics (where five measurements are collected each hour): $\bar{\bar{x}} = 10.16°$ and $\bar{R} = 14.87°$.

- **a.** Use the information provided to find the lower and upper control limits for an *R*-chart.
- **b.** Suppose that one day in May the air temperature at the Davis CIMIS station had a high of 24.7° and a low of 2.2°. How should the manager of the station respond to this observation?

13.31 CPU of a computer chip. Refer to Exercise 13.15 (p. 13-30), where the desired circuit path widths were .5 to .85 micro-meter. The manufacturer sampled four CPU chips six times a day (every 90 minutes from 8:00 a.m. until 4:30 p.m.) for 5 consecutive days. The path widths were measuredand used to construct the accompanying Minitab *R*-chart.

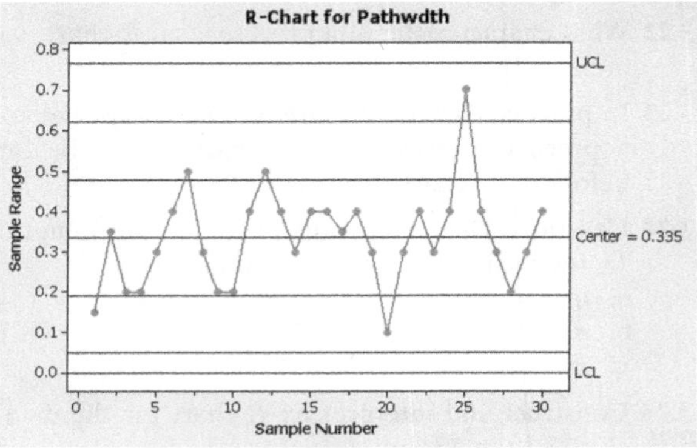

- **a.** Calculate the chart's upper and lower control limits.
- **b.** What does the *R*-chart suggest about the presence of special causes of variation during the time when the data were collected?
- **c.** Should the control limit(s) be used to monitor future process output? Explain.
- **d.** How many different *R* values are plotted on the control chart? Notice how most of the *R* values fall along three horizontal lines. What could cause such a pattern?

Applying the Concepts—Intermediate

13.32 Cola bottle filling process. A soft-drink bottling company is interested in monitoring the amount of cola injected into 16-ounce bottles by a particular filling head. The process is entirely automated and operates 24 hours a day. At 6:00 a.m. and 6:00 p.m. each day, a new dispenser of carbon dioxide capable of producing 20,000 gallons of cola is hooked up to the filling machine. To monitor the process using control charts, the company decided to sample five consecutive bottles of cola each hour beginning at 6:15 A.M. (i.e., 6:15 A.M., 7:15 A.M., 8:15 A.M., etc.). The data for the first day are saved in the file. An SPSS descriptive statistics printout for the data is shown on the next page.

COLA

- **a.** Will the rational subgrouping strategy that was used enable the company to detect variation in fill caused by differences in the carbon dioxide dispensers? Explain.
- **b.** Construct an *R*-chart from the data.
- **c.** What does the *R*-chart indicate about the stability of the filling process during the time when the data were collected? Justify your answer.
- **d.** Should the control limit(s) be used to monitor future process output? Explain.
- **e.** Given your answer to part **c,** should an $\bar{x}$-chart be constructed from the given data? Explain.

13.33 Lowering the thickness of an expensive blow-molded container. *Quality* (Mar. 2009) presented a problem that actually occurred at a plant that produces a high-volume, blow-molded container with multiple layers. One of the layers is very expensive to manufacture. The quality manager at the plant desires to lower the average thickness for the expensive layer of material and still meet specifications. To estimate the actual thickness for this layer, the manager measured the thickness for one container

BLWMLD

SPSS output for Exercise 13.32

Descriptive Statistics for 25 Cola Samples

	Count	Mean	Minimum	Maximum	Range
1	5	16.01	15.98	16.03	.05
2	5	16.00	15.97	16.03	.06
3	5	16.01	15.98	16.04	.06
4	5	16.00	15.98	16.03	.05
5	5	16.01	15.97	16.04	.07
6	5	16.01	15.97	16.04	.07
7	5	16.00	15.96	16.05	.09
8	5	16.01	15.97	16.05	.08
9	5	15.99	15.95	16.03	.08
10	5	16.01	15.95	16.06	.11
11	5	16.00	15.93	16.07	.14
12	5	16.02	15.94	16.08	.14
13	5	15.99	15.96	16.01	.05
14	5	16.00	15.98	16.02	.04
15	5	16.00	15.98	16.03	.05
16	5	16.00	15.97	16.02	.05
17	5	16.01	15.99	16.05	.06
18	5	16.01	15.98	16.04	.06
19	5	15.98	15.96	16.01	.05
20	5	16.01	15.96	16.04	.08
21	5	16.01	15.97	16.05	.08
22	5	16.01	15.95	16.07	.12
23	5	16.02	15.95	16.07	.12
24	5	15.99	15.93	16.08	.15

from each of two cavities every 2 hours for 2 consecutive days. The data (in millimeters) are shown in the following tables.

a. Construct an *R*-chart for the data.

b. Construct an $\bar{x}$-chart for the data.

c. Based on the control charts in parts **a** and **b,** comment on the current behavior of the manufacturing process. As part of your answer, give an estimate of the true average thickness of the expensive layer.

Day 1

Time	7A.M.	9A.M.	11A.M.	1P.M.	3P.M.	5P.M.	7P.M.	9P.M.
Thickness	.167	.241	.204	.221	.255	.224	.216	.235
(mm)	.232	.203	.214	.190	.207	.238	.210	.210
Average	.1995	.2220	.2090	.2055	.2310	.2310	.2310	.2225
Range	.065	.038	.010	.031	.048	.014	.006	.025

Day 2

Time	7A.M.	9A.M.	11A.M.	1P.M.	3P.M.	5P.M.	7P.M.	9P.M.
Thickness	.223	.202	.258	.243	.248	.192	.208	.223
(mm)	.216	.215	.228	.221	.252	.221	.245	.224
Average	.2195	.2085	.2430	.2320	.2500	.2065	.2265	.2235
Range	.007	.013	.030	.022	.004	.029	.037	.001

13.34 Replacement times for lost ATM cards. In an effort to reduce customer dissatisfaction with delays in replacing lost automated teller machine (ATM) cards, some retail banks monitor the time required to replace a lost ATM card. Called *replacement cycle time,* it is the elapsed time from when the customer contacts the bank about the loss until the customer receives a new card (*Management Science,* Sept. 1999). A particular retail bank monitors replacement cycle time for the first five requests each week for replacement cards. Variation in cycle times is monitored using an *R*-chart. Data for 20 weeks are presented below.

ATM

Week	Replacement Cycle Time (in days)				
1	7	10	6	6	10
2	7	12	8	8	6
3	7	8	7	11	6
4	8	8	12	11	12
5	3	8	4	7	7
6	6	10	11	5	7
7	5	12	11	8	7
8	7	12	8	7	6
9	8	10	12	10	5
10	12	8	6	6	8
11	10	9	9	5	4
12	3	10	7	6	8
13	9	9	8	7	2
14	7	10	18	20	8
15	8	18	15	18	21
16	10	22	16	8	7
17	3	18	4	8	12
18	11	7	8	17	19
19	10	8	19	20	25
20	6	3	18	18	7

a. Construct an *R*-chart for these data.

b. What does the *R*-chart suggest about the presence of special causes of variation in the process?

c. Should the control limits of your *R*-chart be used to monitor future replacement cycle times? Explain.

d. Given your conclusion in part **b** and the pattern displayed on the *R*-chart, discuss the possible future impact on the performance of the bank.

13.35 Chunky data. Refer to Exercise 13.21 (p. 13-32) and the hourly data collected by BPI consulting. Recall that the data are saved in the file.

CHUNKY

a. Construct an R-chart for the data. Is the process variation in control?

b. Round each measurement in the data set to a whole number, like in Exercise 13.21b. Form an R-chart for the rounded data. What do you observe?

Applying the Concepts—Advanced

13.36 Precision of scale weight measurements. The *Journal of Quality Technology* (July 1998) published an article examining the effects of the precision of measurement on the R-chart. The authors presented data from a British nutrition company that fills containers labeled "500 grams" with a powdered dietary supplement. Once every 15 minutes, five containers are sampled from the filling process, and the fill weight is measured. The table to the right lists the measurements for 25 consecutive samples made with a scale that is accurate to .5 gram, followed by the table below, which gives measurements for the same samples made with a scale that is accurate to only 2.5 grams. Throughout the time period over which the samples were drawn, it is known that the filling process was in statistical control with mean 500 grams and standard deviation 1 gram.

FILL1
FILL2

a. Construct an R-chart for the data that is accurate to .5 gram. Is the process under statistical control? Explain.

b. Given your answer to part **a,** is it appropriate to construct an $\bar{x}$-chart for the data? Explain.

c. Construct an R-chart for the data that is accurate to only 2.5 grams. What does it suggest about the stability of the filling process?

d. Based on your answers to parts **a** and **c,** discuss the importance of the accuracy of measurement instruments in evaluating the stability of production processes.

First table for Exercise 13.36

Sample	Fill Weights Accurate to .5 Gram					Range
1	500.5	499.5	502.0	501.0	500.5	2.5
2	500.5	499.5	500.0	499.0	500.0	1.5
3	498.5	499.0	500.0	499.5	500.0	1.5
4	500.5	499.5	499.0	499.0	500.5	1.5
5	500.0	501.0	500.5	500.5	500.0	1.0
6	501.0	498.5	500.0	501.5	500.5	3.0
7	499.5	500.0	499.0	501.0	499.5	2.0
8	498.5	498.0	500.0	500.5	500.5	2.5
9	498.0	499.0	502.0	501.0	501.5	4.0
10	499.0	499.5	499.5	500.0	499.5	1.0
11	502.5	499.5	501.0	501.5	502.0	3.0
12	501.5	501.5	500.0	500.0	501.0	1.5
13	498.5	499.5	501.0	500.5	498.5	2.5
14	499.5	498.0	500.0	499.5	498.5	2.0
15	501.0	500.0	498.0	500.5	500.0	3.0
16	502.5	501.5	502.0	500.5	500.5	2.0
17	499.5	500.5	500.0	499.5	499.5	1.0
18	499.0	498.5	498.0	500.0	498.0	2.0
19	499.0	498.0	500.5	501.0	501.0	3.0
20	501.5	499.5	500.0	500.5	502.0	2.5
21	501.0	500.5	502.0	502.5	502.5	2.0
22	501.5	502.5	502.5	501.5	502.0	1.0
23	499.5	502.0	500.0	500.5	502.0	2.5
24	498.5	499.0	499.0	500.5	500.0	2.0
25	500.0	499.5	498.5	500.0	500.5	2.0

Second table for Exercise 13.36

Sample	Fill Weights Accurate to 2.5 Grams					Range
1	500.0	500.0	502.5	500.0	500.0	2.5
2	500.0	500.0	500.0	500.0	500.0	0.0
3	500.0	500.0	500.0	500.0	500.0	0.0
4	497.5	500.0	497.5	497.5	500.0	2.5
5	500.0	500.0	500.0	500.0	500.0	0.0
6	502.5	500.0	497.5	500.0	500.0	5.0
7	500.0	500.0	502.5	502.5	500.0	2.5
8	497.5	500.0	500.0	497.5	500.0	2.5
9	500.0	500.0	497.5	500.0	502.5	5.0
10	500.0	500.0	500.0	500.0	500.0	0.0
11	500.0	505.0	502.5	500.0	500.0	5.0
12	500.0	500.0	500.0	500.0	500.0	0.0
13	500.0	500.0	497.5	500.0	500.0	2.5
14	500.0	500.0	500.0	500.0	500.0	0.0
15	502.5	502.5	502.5	500.0	502.5	2.5
16	500.0	500.0	500.0	500.0	500.0	0.0
17	497.5	497.5	497.5	497.5	497.5	0.0
18	500.0	500.0	500.0	500.0	500.0	0.0
19	495.0	497.5	500.0	500.0	500.0	5.0
20	500.0	502.5	500.0	500.0	502.5	2.5
21	500.0	500.0	500.0	500.0	500.0	0.0
22	500.0	500.0	500.0	500.0	500.0	0.0
23	500.0	500.0	500.0	500.0	500.0	0.0
24	497.5	497.5	500.0	497.5	497.5	2.5
25	500.0	500.0	497.5	500.0	500.0	2.5

Source: "The effects on the R-chart of precision of measurement" by A. Tricker, E. Coates, and E. Okell, in JOURNAL OF QUALITY TECHNOLOGY, July 1998, Volume 30(3).

13.6 A Control Chart for Monitoring the Proportion of Defectives Generated by a Process: The *p*-Chart

Among the dozens of different control charts that have been proposed by researchers and practitioners, the $\bar{x}$- and R-charts are, by far, the most popular for use in monitoring *quantitative* output variables, such as time, length, and weight. Among the charts developed for use with *qualitative* output variables, the chart we introduce in this section is the most popular. Called the ***p*-chart,** it is used when the output variable is categorical (i.e., measured on a nominal scale). With the *p*-chart, the proportion, *p*, of units produced by the process that belong to a particular category (e.g., defective or nondefective; successful or unsuccessful; early, on-time, or late) can be monitored.

The *p*-chart is typically used to monitor the proportion of defective units produced by a process (i.e., the proportion of units that do not conform to specification). This proportion is used to characterize a process in the same sense that the mean and variance are used to characterize a process when the output variable is quantitative. Examples of process proportions that are monitored in industry include the proportion of billing errors made by credit card companies, the proportion of nonfunctional semiconductor chips produced, and the proportion of checks that a bank's magnetic ink character-recognition system is unable to read.

As is the case for the mean and variance, the process proportion can change over time. For example, it can drift upward or downward or jump to a new level. In such cases, the process is out of control. **As long as the process proportion remains constant, the process is in a state of statistical control.**

As with the other control charts presented in this chapter, the *p*-chart has a centerline and control limits that are determined from sample data. After *k* samples of size *n* are drawn from the process, each unit is classified (e.g., defective or nondefective), the proportion of defective units in each sample—$\hat{p}$—is calculated, the centerline and control limits are determined using this information, and the sample proportions are plotted on the *p*-chart. It is the variation in the $\hat{p}$'s over time that we monitor and interpret. Changes in the behavior of the $\hat{p}$'s signal changes in the process proportion, *p*.

The *p*-chart is based on the assumption that the number of defectives observed in each sample is a binomial random variable. What we have called the process proportion is really the binomial probability, *p*. (We discussed binomial random variables in Chapter 4.) When the process is in a state of statistical control, *p* remains constant over time. Variation in $\hat{p}$—as displayed on a *p*-chart—is used to judge whether *p* is stable.

To determine the centerline and control limits for the *p*-chart, we need to know $\hat{p}$'s sampling distribution. We described the sampling distribution of $\hat{p}$ in Section 5.4. Recall that

$$\hat{p} = \frac{\text{Number of defective items in the sample}}{\text{Number of items in the sample}} = \frac{x}{n}$$

$$\mu_{\hat{p}} = p$$

$$\sigma_{\hat{p}} = \sqrt{\frac{p(1-p)}{n}}$$

and that for large samples, $\hat{p}$ is approximately normally distributed. Thus, if *p* were known, the centerline would be *p* and the 3-sigma control limits would be $p \pm 3\sqrt{p(1-p)/n}$. However, because *p* is unknown, it must be estimated from the sample data. The appropriate estimator is $\bar{p}$, the overall proportion of defective units in the *nk* units sampled:

$$\bar{p} = \frac{\text{Total number of defective units in all } k \text{ samples}}{\text{Total number of units sampled}}$$

To calculate the control limits of the *p*-chart, substitute $\bar{p}$ for *p* in the preceding expression for the control limits, as illustrated in Figure 13.30.

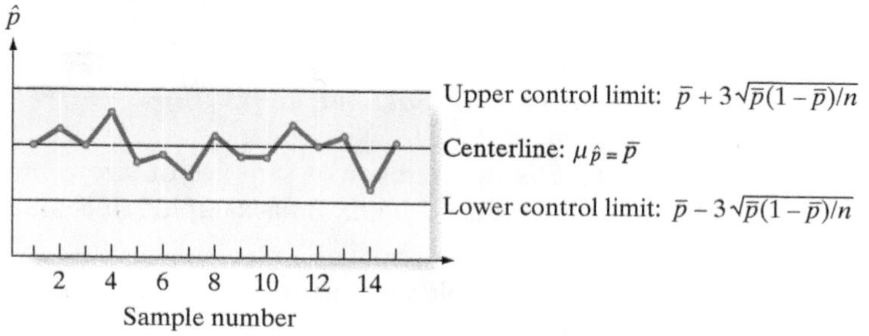

Figure 13.30
p-Chart

In constructing a p-chart, it is advisable to use a much larger sample size than is typically used for $\bar{x}$- and R-charts. Most processes that are monitored in industry have relatively small process proportions, often less than .05 (i.e., less than 5% of output is nonconforming). In those cases, if a small sample size is used, say $n = 5$, samples drawn from the process would likely not contain any nonconforming output. As a result, most, if not all, $\hat{p}$'s would equal zero.

We present a rule of thumb that can be used to determine a sample size large enough to avoid this problem. This rule will also help protect against ending up with a negative lower control limit, a situation that frequently occurs when both p and n are small. See Montgomery (2009) or Duncan (1986) for further details.

Sample-Size Determination for Monitoring a Process Proportion

Choose n such that $n > \dfrac{9(1 - p_0)}{p_0}$

where

n = Sample size

p_0 = An estimate (perhaps judgmental) of the process proportion p

For example, if p is thought to be about .05, the rule indicates that samples of at least size 171 should be used in constructing the p-chart:

$$n > \frac{9(1 - .05)}{.05} = 171$$

In the next three boxes, we summarize how to construct a p-chart and its zone boundaries and how to interpret a p-chart.

Constructing a p-Chart: A Summary

1. Using a rational subgrouping strategy, collect at least 20 samples, each of size
$$n > \frac{9(1 - p_0)}{p_0}$$
where p_0 is an estimate of p, the proportion defective (i.e., nonconforming) produced by the process. p_0 can be determined from sample data (i.e., $\hat{p}$) or may be based on expert opinion.
2. For each sample, calculate $\hat{p}$, the proportion of defective units in the sample:
$$\hat{p} = \frac{\text{Number of defective items in the sample}}{\text{Number of items in the sample}}$$
3. Plot the centerline and control limits:
$$\textit{Centerline: } \bar{p} = \frac{\text{Total number of defective units in all } k \text{ samples}}{\text{Total number of units in all } k \text{ samples}}$$
$$\textit{Upper control limit: } \bar{p} + 3\sqrt{\frac{\bar{p}(1 - \bar{p})}{n}}$$
$$\textit{Lower control limit: } \bar{p} - 3\sqrt{\frac{\bar{p}(1 - \bar{p})}{n}}$$
where k is the number of samples of size n and $\bar{p}$ is the overall proportion of defective units in the nk units sampled. $\bar{p}$ is an estimate of the unknown process proportion p.
4. Plot the k sample proportions on the control chart in the order that the samples were produced by the process.

As with the $\bar{x}$- and R-charts, the centerline and control limits should be developed using samples that were collected during a period in which the process was in control. Accordingly, when a p-chart is first constructed, the centerline and the control limits should be treated as *trial values* (see Section 13.4) and, if necessary, modified before being extended to the right on the control chart and used to monitor future process output.

Constructing Zone Boundaries for a p-Chart

$$\textit{Upper A–B boundary: } \bar{p} + 2\sqrt{\frac{\bar{p}(1-\bar{p})}{n}}$$

$$\textit{Lower A–B boundary: } \bar{p} - 2\sqrt{\frac{\bar{p}(1-\bar{p})}{n}}$$

$$\textit{Upper B–C boundary: } \bar{p} + \sqrt{\frac{\bar{p}(1-\bar{p})}{n}}$$

$$\textit{Lower B–C boundary: } \bar{p} - \sqrt{\frac{\bar{p}(1-\bar{p})}{n}}$$

Note: When the lower control limit is negative, it should not be plotted on the control chart. However, the lower zone boundaries can still be plotted if they are nonnegative.

Interpreting a p-Chart

1. The **process is out of control** if one or more sample proportions fall beyond the control limits (Rule 1) or if any of the three patterns of variation described by Rules 2, 3, and 4 (Figure 13.22) are observed. Such signals indicate that one or more special causes of variation are influencing the process proportion, p. These causes should be identified and eliminated in order to bring the process into control.
2. The **process is treated as being in control** if none of the above noted out-of-control signals are observed. Processes that are in control should not be tampered with. However, if the level of variation is unacceptably high, common causes of variation should be identified and eliminated.

Example 13.9

Creating and Interpreting a p-Chart—Order Assembly Process

Problem A manufacturer of auto parts is interested in implementing statistical process control in several areas within its warehouse operation. The manufacturer wants to begin with the order assembly process. Too frequently, orders received by customers contain the wrong items or too few items.

For each order received, parts are picked from storage bins in the warehouse, labeled, and placed on a conveyor belt system. Because the bins are spread over a 3-acre area, items that are part of the same order may be placed on different spurs of the conveyor belt system. Near the end of the belt system, all spurs converge and a worker sorts the items according to the order they belong to. That information is contained on the labels that were placed on the items by the pickers.

The workers have identified three errors that cause shipments to be improperly assembled: (1) pickers pick from the wrong bin, (2) pickers mislabel items, and (3) the sorter makes an error.

The firm's quality manager has implemented a sampling program in which 90 assembled orders are sampled each day and checked for accuracy. An assembled order is considered nonconforming (defective) if it differs in any way from the order placed by the customer. To date, 25 samples have been evaluated. The resulting data are shown in the Excel spreadsheet, Figure 13.31.

a. Construct a p-chart for the order assembly operation.

b. What does the chart indicate about the stability of the process?

c. Is it appropriate to use the control limits and centerline constructed in part **a** to monitor future process output?

	A	B	C	D
1	Sample	Size (n)	Defective Orders	Sample Proportion
2	1	90	12	0.133333333
3	2	90	6	0.066666667
4	3	90	11	0.122222222
5	4	90	8	0.088888889
6	5	90	13	0.144444444
7	6	90	14	0.155555556
8	7	90	12	0.133333333
9	8	90	6	0.066666667
10	9	90	10	0.111111111
11	10	90	13	0.144444444
12	11	90	12	0.133333333
13	12	90	24	0.266666667
14	13	90	23	0.255555556
15	14	90	22	0.244444444
16	15	90	8	0.088888889
17	16	90	3	0.033333333
18	17	90	11	0.122222222
19	18	90	14	0.155555556
20	19	90	5	0.055555556
21	20	90	12	0.133333333
22	21	90	18	0.2
23	22	90	12	0.133333333
24	23	90	13	0.144444444
25	24	90	4	0.044444444
26	25	90	6	0.066666667
27				
28	Totals	2250	292	0.129777778

Data Set: WAREHS

Figure 13.31
Excel worksheet with 25 samples of size $n = 90$ from warehouse order assembly process

Solution

a. The first step in constructing the p-chart after collecting the sample data is to calculate the sample proportion for each sample. For the first sample,

$$\hat{p} = \frac{\text{Number of defective items in the sample}}{\text{Number of items in the sample}} = \frac{12}{90} = .13333$$

All the sample proportions are computed using Excel and are displayed in Figure 13.31. Next, calculate the proportion of defective items in the total number of items sampled:

$$\overline{p} = \frac{\text{Total number of defective items}}{\text{Total number of items sampled}} = \frac{292}{2,250} = .12978$$

This value is also computed using Excel (and highlighted on Figure 13.31.) The centerline is positioned at $\overline{p}$, and $\overline{p}$ is used to calculate the control limits:

$$\overline{p} \pm 3\sqrt{\frac{\overline{p}(1-\overline{p})}{n}} = .12978 \pm 3\sqrt{\frac{.12978(1-.12978)}{90}}$$

$$= .12978 \pm .10627$$

UCL: .23605

LCL: .02351

After plotting the centerline and the control limits, plot the 25 sample proportions in the order of sampling and connect the points with straight lines. The completed control chart, obtained using Minitab, is shown in Figure 13.32.

b. To assist our examination of the control chart, we add the 1-and 2-standard-deviation zone boundaries. The boundaries are located by substituting $\overline{p} = .12978$ into the following formulas:

$$\textit{Upper A–B boundary: } \overline{p} + 2\sqrt{\frac{\overline{p}(1-\overline{p})}{n}} = .20063$$

$$\textit{Lower A–B boundary: } \overline{p} - 2\sqrt{\frac{\overline{p}(1-\overline{p})}{n}} = .05893$$

$$\textit{Upper B–C boundary: } \bar{p} + \sqrt{\frac{\bar{p}(1-\bar{p})}{n}} = .16521$$

$$\textit{Lower B–C boundary: } \bar{p} - \sqrt{\frac{\bar{p}(1-\bar{p})}{n}} = .09435$$

Note that three of the sample proportions fall above the upper control limit (Rule 1); thus, there is strong evidence that the process is out of control. None of the nonrandom patterns of Rules 2, 3, and 4 (Figure 13.22) are evident. The process proportion appears to have increased dramatically somewhere around sample 12.

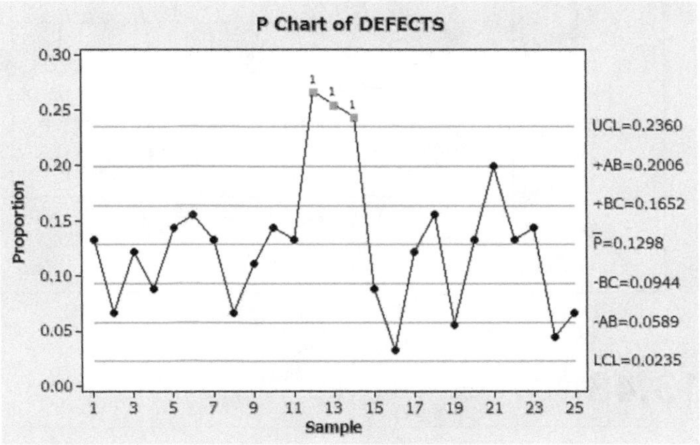

Figure 13.32
Minitab p-chart for warehouse order assembly process

c. Because the process was apparently out of control during the period in which sample data were collected to build the control chart, it is not appropriate to continue using the chart. The control limits and centerline are not representative of the process when it is in control. The chart must be revised before it is used to monitor future output.

In this case, the three out-of-control points were investigated, and it was discovered that they occurred on days when a temporary sorter was working in place of the regular sorter. Actions were taken to ensure that in the future, better-trained temporary sorters would be available.

Because the special cause of the observed variation was identified and eliminated, all sample data from the 3 days the temporary sorter was working were dropped from the data set, and the centerline and control limits were recalculated:

$$\textit{Centerline: } \bar{p} = \frac{223}{1{,}980} = .11263$$

$$\textit{Control limits: } \bar{p} \pm 3\sqrt{\frac{\bar{p}(1-\bar{p})}{n}} = .11263 \pm 3\sqrt{\frac{.11263(.88737)}{90}}$$

$$= .11263 \pm .09997$$

UCL: .21259 LCL: .01266

The revised zones are calculated by substituting $\bar{p} = .11263$ in the following formulas:

$$\textit{Upper A–B boundary: } \bar{p} + 2\sqrt{\frac{\bar{p}(1-\bar{p})}{n}} = .17927$$

$$\textit{Upper B–C boundary: } \bar{p} + \sqrt{\frac{\bar{p}(1-\bar{p})}{n}} = .14595$$

$$\textit{Lower A–B boundary: } \bar{p} - 2\sqrt{\frac{\bar{p}(1-\bar{p})}{n}} = .04598$$

$$\textit{Lower B–C boundary: } \bar{p} - \sqrt{\frac{\bar{p}(1-\bar{p})}{n}} = .07931$$

The revised control chart appears in Figure 13.33. Notice that now all sample proportions fall within the control limits. These limits can now be treated as official, extended to the right on the chart, and used to monitor future orders.

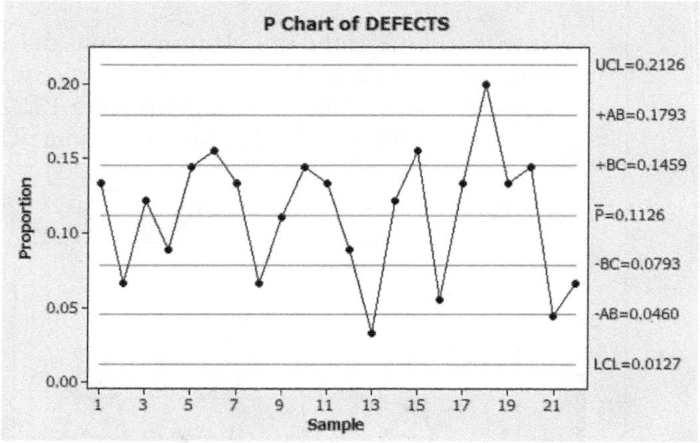

Figure 13.33
Revised Minitab p-chart for warehouse order assembly process

■ **Now Work Exercise 13.41**

Exercises 13.37–13.48

Learning the Mechanics

13.37 What characteristic of a process is a p-chart designed to monitor?

13.38 In each of the following cases, use the sample size formula to determine a sample size large enough to avoid constructing a p-chart with a negative lower control limit.
a. $p_0 = .01$ **b.** $p_0 = .05$ **c.** $p_0 = .10$ **d.** $p_0 = .20$

13.39 The proportion of defective items generated by a manufacturing process is believed to be 8%. In constructing a p-chart for the process, determine how large the sample size should be to avoid ending up with a negative lower control limit.

13.40 To construct a p-chart for a manufacturing process, 25 samples of size 200 were drawn from the process. The number of defectives in each sample is listed in time order in the table that follows.
L13040

Defectives												
16	14	9	11	15	8	12	16	17	13	15	10	9
12	14	11	8	7	12	15	9	16	13	11	10	

a. Calculate the proportion defective in each sample.
b. Calculate and plot $\bar{p}$ and the upper and lower control limits for the p-chart.
c. Calculate and plot the A, B, and C zone boundaries on the p-chart.
d. Plot the sample proportions on the p-chart and connect them with straight lines.
e. Use pattern-analysis Rules 1–4 for detecting the presence of special causes of variation (Figure 13.22) to determine whether the process is out of control.

13.41 To construct a p-chart, 20 samples of size 150 were drawn from a process. The proportion of defective items found in each of the samples is listed in the next table.
NW
L13041

Sample	Proportion Defective	Sample	Proportion Defective
1	.03	11	.07
2	.05	12	.04
3	.10	13	.06
4	.02	14	.05
5	.08	15	.07
6	.09	16	.06
7	.08	17	.07
8	.05	18	.02
9	.07	19	.05
10	.06	20	.03

a. Calculate and plot the centerline and the upper and lower control limits for the p-chart.
b. Calculate and plot the A, B, and C zone boundaries on the p-chart.
c. Plot the sample proportions on the p-chart.
d. Is the process under control? Explain.
e. Should the control limits and centerline of part **a** be used to monitor future process output? Explain.

Applying the Concepts—Basic

13.42 Rental car call center study. A worldwide rental car company receives about 10,000 calls per month at its European call center. These calls typically involve customer issues with the level of service or the billing/invoice process. In an effort to reduce the proportion of issues that are not resolved on the customer's first call, management conducted a thorough study of the call center's procedures. The results were published in the *International Journal of Productivity and Performance Management* (Vol. 59, 2010). After making major changes at the call center, management constructed a p-chart to monitor the process improvements. Assume that 18 calls to the center were sampled each day for 60 consecutive days. The article reported that the proportion of all calls in the sample that had unresolved issues at the end of the call was .107. (This was a major improvement over the previous unresolved-first-call rate of .845.)

a. What is the centerline for the *p*-chart?

b. Compute the lower and upper control limits for the *p*-chart.

c. When the proportions of daily calls that resulted in unresolved issues are plotted on the *p*-chart, all fall within the LCL and UCL boundaries. What does this imply about the process?

13.43 Monitoring surgery complications. An article on the use of control charts for monitoring the proportion of post operative complications at a large hospital was published in the *International Journal for Quality in Health Care* (Oct. 2010). A random sample of surgical procedures was selected each month for 30 consecutive months, and the number of procedures with postoperative complications was recorded. The data are listed in the accompanying table.

POSTOP

a. Identify the attribute of interest to the hospital.

b. What are the rational subgroups for this study?

c. Find the value of $\bar{p}$ for use in a *p*-chart.

d. Compute the proportion of post-op complications in each month.

e. Compute the critical boundaries for the *p*-chart (i.e., UCL, LCL, Upper A–B boundary, etc.).

f. Construct a *p*-chart for the data.

g. Interpret the chart. Does the process appear to be in control? Explain.

Month	Complications	Procedures Sampled
1	14	105
2	12	97
3	10	115
4	12	100
5	9	95
6	7	111
7	9	68
8	11	47
9	9	83
10	12	108
11	10	115
12	7	94
13	12	107
14	9	99
15	15	105
16	13	110
17	7	97
18	10	105
19	8	71
20	5	48
21	12	95
22	9	110
23	7	103
24	9	95
25	15	105
26	12	100
27	8	116
28	2	110
29	9	105
30	10	120
Totals	294	2,939

Source: "The P-Control Chart: A tool for Care Improvement" by A. Duclos and N. Voirin, in INTERNATIONAL JOURNAL FOR QUALITY IN HEALTH CARE, Volume 22(5). Copyright © 2010 by Oxford University Press. Reprinted with permission.

13.44 Defective micron chips. A manufacturer produces micron chips for personal computers. From past experience, the production manager believes that 1% of the chips are defective. The company collected a sample of the first 1,000 chips manufactured after 4:00 P.M. every other day for a month. The chips were analyzed for defects; then these data and Minitab were used to construct the *p*-chart shown here.

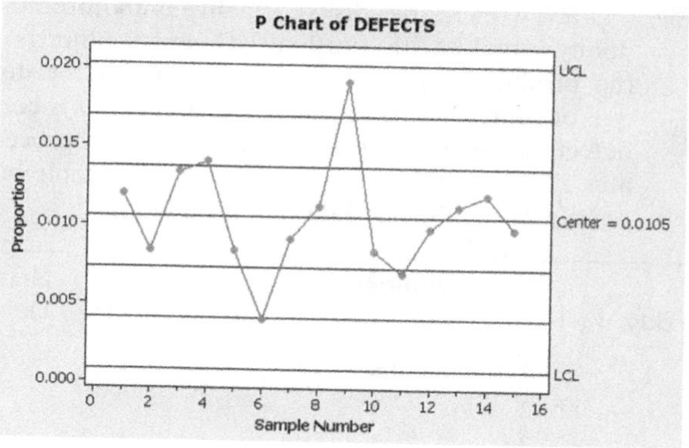

a. From a statistical perspective, is a sample size of 1,000 adequate for constructing the *p*-chart? Explain.

b. Calculate the chart's upper and lower control limits.

c. What does the *p*-chart suggest about the presence of special causes during the time when the data were collected?

d. Critique the rational subgrouping strategy used by the disk manufacturer.

Applying the Concepts—Intermediate

13.45 Monitoring newspaper typesetters. Accurate typesetting is crucial to the production of high-quality newspapers. The editor of the Morristown *Daily Tribune*, a weekly publication with a circulation of 27,000, has instituted a process for monitoring the performance of typesetters. Each week 100 paragraphs of the paper are randomly sampled and read for accuracy. The number of paragraphs with errors is recorded in the following table for each of the last 30 weeks.

TYPSET

Week	Paragraphs with Errors	Week	Paragraphs with Errors
1	2	16	2
2	4	17	3
3	10	18	7
4	4	19	3
5	1	20	2
6	1	21	3
7	13	22	7
8	9	23	4
9	11	24	3
10	0	25	2
11	3	26	2
12	4	27	0
13	2	28	1
14	2	29	3
15	8	30	4

Source: QUANTITATIVE ANALYSIS FOR MANAGEMENT, 6th ed., by Jerry Kinard and Brian Kinard. Copyright © 1997 by Prentice Hall, Upper Saddle Creek, NJ. Reprinted with permission of the author.

a. Construct a p-chart for the process.
b. Is the process under statistical control? Explain.
c. Should the control limits of part **a** be used to monitor future process output? Explain.
d. Suggest two methods that could be used to facilitate the diagnosis of causes of process variation.

13.46 Quality of rewritable CDs. A Japanese compact disc (CD) manufacturer has a daily production rate of about 20,000 CD-RW (rewritable disks). Quality is monitored by randomly sampling 200 finished CDs every other hour from the production process and testing them for defects. If one or more defects are discovered, the CD is considered defective and is destroyed. The production process operates 20 hours per day, 7 days a week. The table below reports data for the last 3 days of production.

CDRW

Day	Hour	Number of Defectives	Day	Hour	Number of Defectives
1	1	13		6	3
	2	5		7	1
	3	2		8	2
	4	3		9	3
	5	2		10	1
	6	3	3	1	9
	7	1		2	5
	8	2		3	2
	9	1		4	1
	10	1		5	3
2	1	11		6	2
	2	6		7	4
	3	2		8	2
	4	3		9	1
	5	1		10	1

a. Construct a p-chart for the CD-RW production process.
b. What does it indicate about the stability of the process? Explain.
c. What advice can you give the manufacturer to assist them in their search for the special cause(s) of variation that is plaguing the process?

13.47 Leaky process pumps. *Quality* (Feb. 2008) presented a problem that actually occurred at a company that produces process pumps for a variety of industries. The company recently introduced a new pump model and immediately began receiving customer complaints about "leaky pumps." There were no complaints about the old pump model. For each of the first 13 weeks of production of the new pump, quality-control inspectors tested 500 randomly selected pumps for leaks. The results of the leak tests are summarized by week in the accompanying table. Construct an appropriate control chart for the data. What does the chart indicate about the stability of the process?

PUMPS

Week	Number Tested	Number with Leaks
1	500	36
2	500	28
3	500	24
4	500	26
5	500	20
6	500	56
7	500	26
8	500	28
9	500	31
10	500	26
11	500	34
12	500	26
13	500	32

13.48 Rubber company tire tests. Goodstone Tire & Rubber Company is interested in monitoring the proportion of defective tires generated by the production process at its Akron, Ohio, production plant. The company's chief engineer believes that the proportion is about 7%. Because the tires are destroyed during the testing process, the company would like to keep the number of tires tested to a minimum. However, the engineer would also like to use a p-chart with a positive lower control limit. A positive lower control limit makes it possible to determine when the process has generated an unusually small proportion of defectives. Such an occurrence is good news and would signal the engineer to look for causes of the superior performance. That information can be used to improve the production process. Using the sample size formula, the chief engineer recommended that the company randomly sample and test 120 tires from each day's production. To date, 20 samples have been taken. The data are presented below.

RUBBER

Sample	Sample Size	Defectives
1	120	11
2	120	5
3	120	4
4	120	8
5	120	10
6	120	13
7	120	9
8	120	8
9	120	10
10	120	11
11	120	10
12	120	12
13	120	8
14	120	6
15	120	10
16	120	5
17	120	10
18	120	10
19	120	3
20	120	8

a. Use the sample size formula to show how the chief engineer arrived at the recommended sample size of 120.
b. Construct a p-chart for the tire production process.
c. What does the chart indicate about the stability of the process? Explain.
d. Is it appropriate to use the control limits to monitor future process output? Explain.
e. Is the p-chart you constructed in part **b** capable of signaling hour-to-hour changes in p? Explain.

13.7 Diagnosing the Causes of Variation

SPC consists of three major activities or phases: (1) monitoring process variation, (2) diagnosing causes of variation, and (3) eliminating those causes. A more detailed description of SPC is shown in Figure 13.34, which depicts SPC as a quality- improvement cycle. In the monitoring phase, statistical signals from the process are evaluated in order to uncover opportunities to improve the process. This is the phase we have dealt with in Sections 13.3–13.6. We turn our attention now to the diagnosis phase.

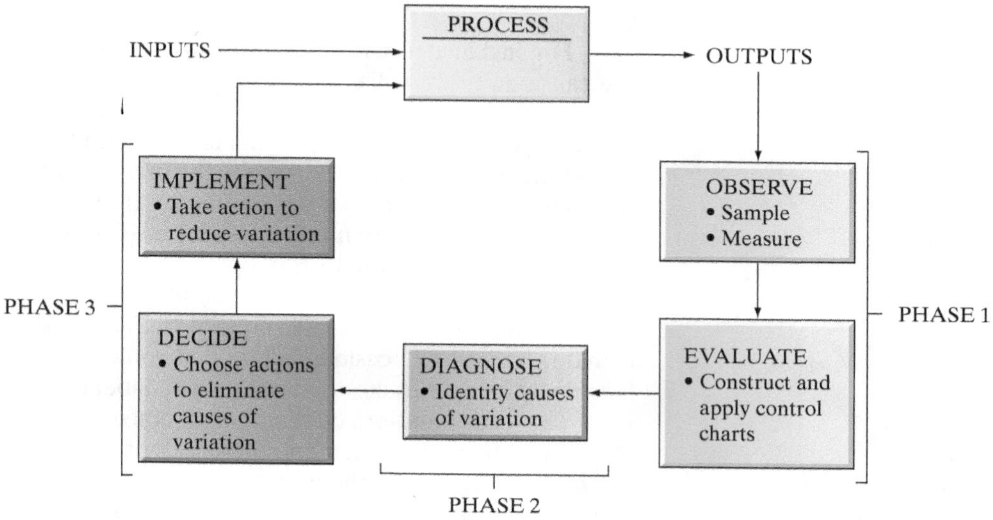

Figure 13.34
SPC viewed as a quality-improvement cycle

The diagnosis phase is the critical link in the SPC improvement cycle. The monitoring phase simply identifies *whether* problems exist; the diagnosis phase identifies *what* the problems are. If the monitoring phase detected the presence of special causes of variation (i.e., an out-of-control signal was observed on a control chart), the diagnosis phase is concerned with tracking down the underlying cause or causes. If no special causes were detected in the monitoring phase (i.e., the process is under statistical control) and further improvement in the process is desired, the diagnosis phase concentrates on uncovering common causes of variation.

It is important to recognize that the achievement of process improvement requires more than the application of statistical tools such as control charts. This is particularly evident in the diagnosis phase. The diagnosis of causes of variation requires expert knowledge about the process in question. Just as you would go to a physician to diagnose a pain in your back, you would turn to people who work in the process or to engineers or analysts with process expertise to help you diagnose the causes of process variation.

Several methods have been developed for assisting process experts with process diagnosis, including *flowcharting* and the simple but powerful graphical tool called *Pareto analysis* (Chapter 2). Another graphical method, the **cause-and-effect diagram,** is described in this section. (A fourth methodology, *experimental design,* is the topic of Chapter 9.)

The cause-and-effect diagram was developed by Kaoru Ishikawa of the University of Tokyo in 1943. As a result, it is also known as an *Ishikawa diagram.* The cause-and-effect diagram facilitates the construction of causal chains that explain the occurrence of events, problems, or conditions. It is often constructed through brainstorming sessions involving a small group of process experts. It has been employed for decades by Japanese firms but was not widely applied in the United States until the mid-1980s.

The basic framework of the cause-and-effect diagram is shown in Figure 13.35. In the right-hand box in the figure, we record the effect whose cause(s) we want to diagnose.

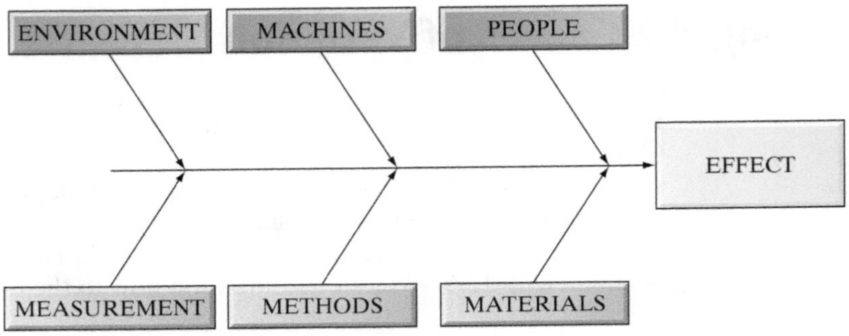

Figure 13.35
The basic framework for a cause-and-effect diagram

For instance, GOAL/QPC (a Massachusetts-based TQM consulting group) used the cause-and-effect diagram in Figure 13.36 to demonstrate why pizzas are delivered late on Fridays and Saturdays. As a second example, Figure 13.37 displays the reasons for high variation in the fill weights of 20-pound bags of dry dog food.

Examining Figure 13.35, we see the branches of the cause-and-effect diagram, which represent the major factors that influence the process and that could be responsible for the effect. These are often taken to be the six universal sources of process variation that we described in Section 13.1: people, machines, materials, methods, measurement, and environment. Notice that in the examples of Figures 13.36 and 13.37, these categories were tailored to fit the process in question. The set of categories must be broad enough to include virtually all possible factors that could influence the process. It is less important how many categories are used or how you label the categories.

The cause-and-effect diagram is constructed using effect-to-cause reasoning—that is, you begin by specifying the effect of interest and then move backward to identify *potential* causes of the effect. After a potential cause has been identified, you treat it as an effect and try to find its cause, and so forth. The result is a **causal chain.** A completed cause-and-effect diagram typically contains many causal chains. These chains help us to track down causes whose eradication will reduce, improve, or eliminate the effect in question.

After setting up the basic framework for the cause-and-effect diagram and recording the effect of interest in the box on the right, you construct the causal chains, proceeding backward from general potential causes to increasingly specific causes. Begin by choosing one of the universal cause categories—say, people—and asking, "What factors related to people could cause the effect in question?" In the pizza delivery example of Figure 13.36, two factors were identified: (1) drivers not showing up for work and (2) drivers getting lost. Each of these causes is written on a twig of the People branch. Next, each cause is treated as an effect and an attempt is made to identify its cause—that is,

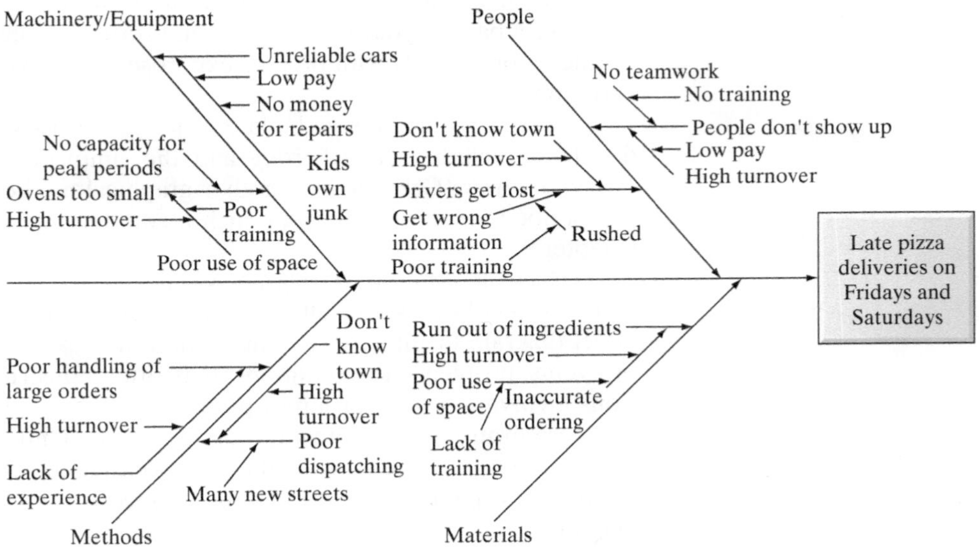

Figure 13.36
Cause-and-effect diagram for late pizza deliveries
Source: "Cause-and-effect diagram for late pizza deliveries," from THE MEMORY JOGGER II, pg 38. Copyright © 2010 by Goal/QPC. Reprinted with permission.

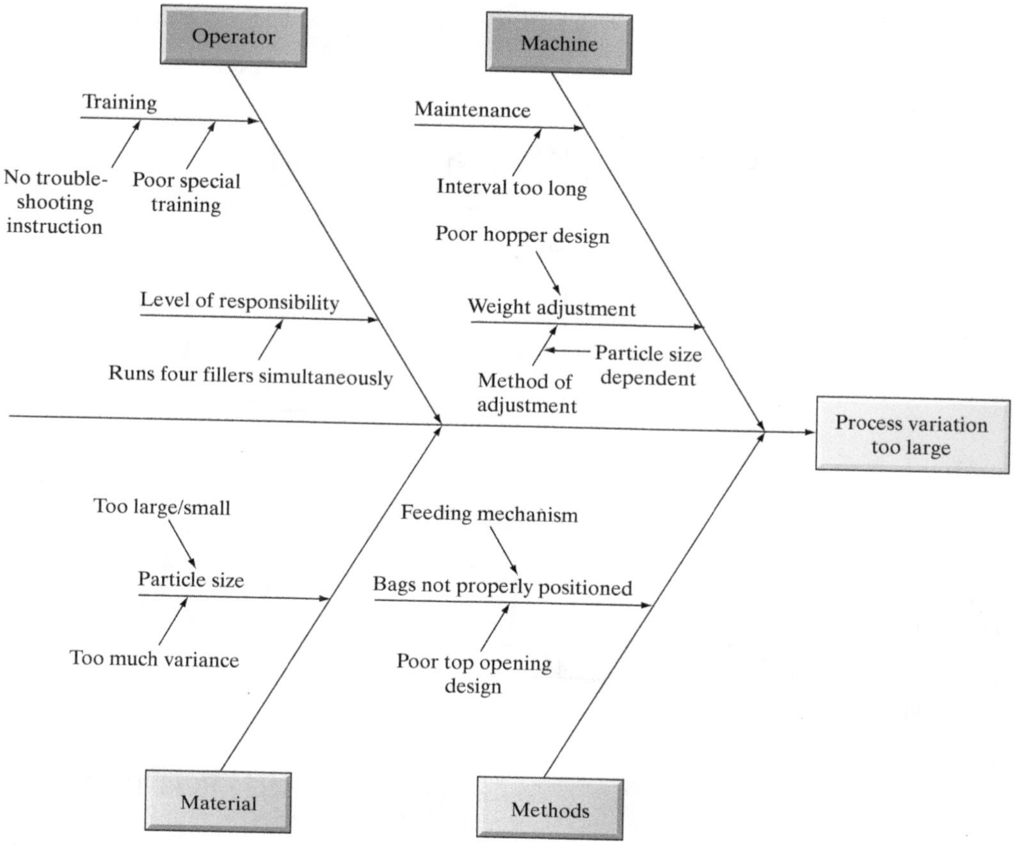

Figure 13.37

Cause-and-effect diagram for the filling process for 20-pound bags of dog food

Source: CONTEMPORARY CONCEPTS AND METHODS, 1st Ed., by Richard E. Devor, Change Tsong-How. Copyright © 1992 by Pearson Education, Inc., Upper Saddle River, NJ. Reprinted with permission.

we look for subcauses. For example, driver absenteeism was blamed on (1) high turnover and (2) no teamwork. The high turnover, in turn, was blamed on low pay, while lack of teamwork was blamed on insufficient training. Thus, the "No show" twig has both a "High turnover" twig and a "No teamwork" twig attached to it; and each of these twigs has a cause twig attached. Multiple causal chains like this should be constructed for each branch of the cause-and-effect diagram.

Once completed, the various causal chains of the cause-and-effect diagram must be evaluated (often subjectively) to identify one or more factors thought most likely to be causes of the effect in question. Then actions can be chosen and implemented (see Figure 13.34) to eliminate the causes and improve the process.

Besides facilitating process diagnosis, cause-and-effect diagrams serve to document the causal factors that may potentially affect a process and to communicate that information to others in the organization. The cause-and-effect diagram is a very flexible tool that can be applied in a variety of situations. It can be used as a formal part of the SPC improvement cycle, as suggested above, or simply as a means of investigating the causes of organizational problems, events, or conditions. It can also help select the appropriate process variables to monitor with control charts.

13.8 Capability Analysis

In the previous four sections, we pointed out that if a process were in statistical control, but the level of variation was unacceptably high, common causes of variation should be identified and eliminated. This was illustrated in Figure 13.13. Here, we describe a methodology that can be used to help determine when such variation is unacceptably high. The methodology is called **capability analysis.** As we have seen, the achievement of process stability is vitally important to process improvement efforts. But it is not an end in itself. A process may be in control but still not be capable of producing output that is acceptable to customers.

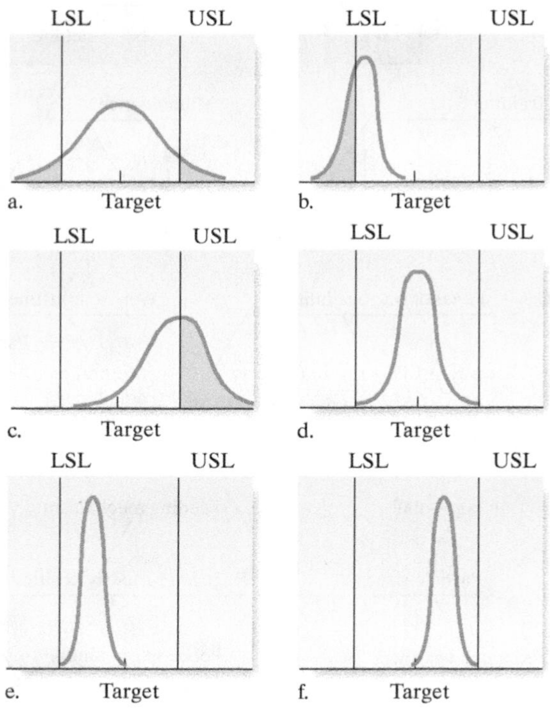

Figure 13.38
Output distributions of six different in-control processes, where LSL = lower specification limit and USL = upper specification limit

To see this, consider Figure 13.38. The figure displays six different in-control processes. Recall that if a process is under statistical control, its output distribution does not change over time, and the process can be characterized by a single probability distribution, as in each of the panels of the figure. The upper and lower specification limits (USL and LSL) for the output of each of the six processes are also indicated on each panel, as is the target value for the output variable. Recall that the specification limits are boundary points that define the acceptable values for an output variable.

The processes of panels a, b, and c produce a high percentage of items that are outside the specification limits. None of these processes is *capable* of satisfying its customers. In panel a, the process is centered on the target value, but the variation due to common causes is too high. In panel b, the variation is low relative to the width of the specification limits, but the process is off-center. In panel **c,** both problems exist: the variation is too high and the process is off-center. Thus, bringing a process into statistical control is not sufficient to guarantee the capability of the process.

All three processes in panels d, e, and f are capable. In each case, the process distribution fits comfortably between the specification limits. Virtually all of the individual items produced by these processes would be acceptable. However, any significant tightening of the specification limits—whether by customers or internal managers or engineers—would result in the production of unacceptable output and necessitate the initiation of process improvement activities to restore the processes' capability. Further, even though a process is capable, continuous improvement of a process requires constant improvement of its capability.

When a process is known to be in control, the most direct way to assess its capability is to construct a frequency distribution (e.g., dot plot, histogram, or stem-and-leaf display) for a large sample of individual measurements (usually 50 or more) from the process. Then, add the specification limits and the target value for the output variable on the graph. This is called a **capability analysis diagram.** It is a simple visual tool for assessing process capability.

The Minitab printout shown in Figure 13.39 is a capability analysis diagram for the paint-filling process found to be under statistical control in Examples 13.1 and 13.2. You can see that the process is roughly centered on the target of 10 pounds of paint, but a large number of paint cans fall outside the specification limits. This tells us that the process is not capable of satisfying customer requirements.

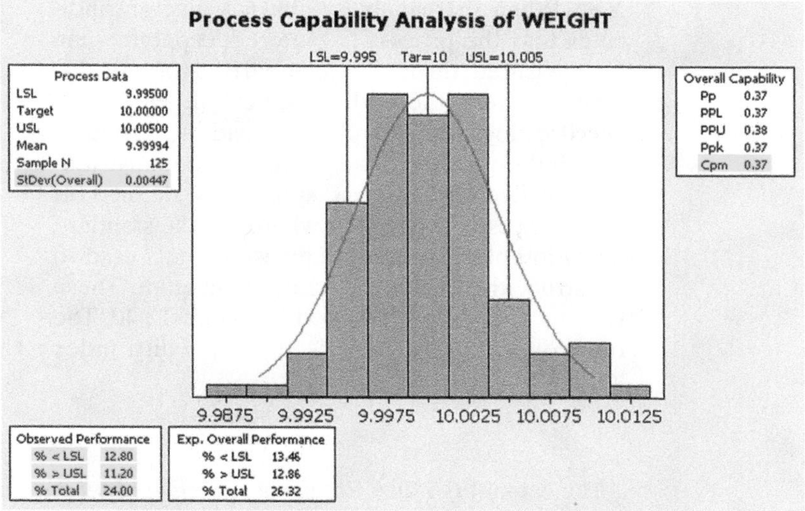

Figure 13.39
Minitab capability analysis diagram for the paint-filling process

Most quality-management professionals and statisticians agree that the capability analysis diagram is the best way to describe the performance of an in-control process. However, many companies have found it useful to have a numerical measure of capability. The ability to summarize capability in a single number has the advantages of convenience, simplicity, and ease of communication. However, it also has the major disadvantage of potentially misleading those who use it. Just as when you characterize a data set by its mean and ignore its variation, the information you provide to your audience is incomplete and may adversely affect their actions and decisions. (A more thorough discussion about the dangers of numerical measures of capability is presented later in this section.)

There are several different approaches to quantifying capability. We will briefly describe two of them. The first (and most direct) consists of counting the number of items that fall outside the specification limits in the capability analysis diagram and reporting the percentage of such items in the sample. The original data set or a graphical technique that displays the individual measurements—such as a stem-and-leaf display or a dot plot—can be used to obtain the needed count. Or, you can use the capability analysis option of a statistical software package.

The desired information for the paint data is provided in the lower-left corner of the Minitab printout, Figure 13.39. You can see that 24% of the 125 paint cans fall outside the specification limits (12.8% below 9.995 and 11.2% above 10.005). Thus, 24% of the 125 cans in the sample (i.e., 30 cans) are unacceptable.

When this percentage is used to characterize the capability of the process, the implication is that over time, if this process remains in control, roughly 24% of the paint cans will be unacceptable. Remember, however, that this percentage is an estimate—a sample statistic, not a known parameter. It is based on a sample of size 125 and is subject to both sampling error and measurement error. We discussed such percentages and proportions in detail in Chapter 6.

If it is known that the process follows approximately a normal distribution, as is often the case, a similar approach to quantifying process capability can be used. In this case, the mean and standard deviation of the sample of measurements used to construct the capability analysis diagram can be taken as estimates of the mean and standard deviation of the process. Then, the fraction of items that would fall outside the specification limits can be found by solving for the associated area under the normal curve, as we did in Chapter 4. As we said above, if you use this percentage to characterize process capability, remember that it is an estimate only and is subject to sampling error.

The second approach to measuring capability is to construct a **capability index.** Several such indexes have been developed. We will describe one used for stable processes that are centered on the target value—the C_p **index.***

*For off-center processes, its sister index, C_{pk}, is used. Consult the chapter references for a description of C_{pk}.

When the capability analysis diagram indicates that the process is centered, capability can be measured through a comparison of the distance between the USL and the LSL, called the **specification spread,** and the spread of the output distribution. The spread of the output distribution—called the **process spread**—is defined as 6σ and is estimated by $6s$, where s is the standard deviation of the sample of measurements used to construct the capability analysis diagram. These two distances are illustrated in Figure 13.40. The ratio of these distances is the capability index known as C_p.

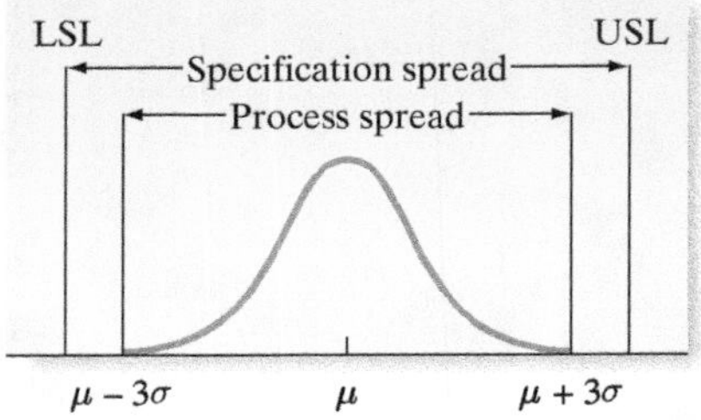

Figure 13.40
Process spread versus specification spread

The **capability index** for a process *centered on the desired mean* is

$$C_p = \frac{\text{(Specification spread)}}{\text{(Process spread)}} = \frac{\text{(USL} - \text{LSL)}}{6\sigma}$$

where σ is estimated by s, the standard deviation of the sample of measurements used to construct the capability analysis diagram.

Interpretation of Capability Index, C_p

C_p summarizes the performance of a stable, centered process relative to the specification limits. It indicates the extent to which the output of the process falls within the specification limits.

1. If $C_p = 1$ (specification spread = process spread), process is capable.
2. If $C_p > 1$ (specification spread > process spread), process is capable.
3. If $C_p < 1$ (specification spread < process spread), process is not capable.

If the process follows a normal distribution,

$C_p = 1.00$ means about 2.7 units per 1,000 will be unacceptable.
$C_p = 1.33$ means about 63 units per million will be unacceptable.
$C_p = 1.67$ means about .6 units per million will be unacceptable.
$C_p = 2.00$ means about 2 units per billion will be unacceptable.

In manufacturing applications where the process follows a normal distribution (approximately), managers typically require a C_p of at least 1.33. With a C_p of 1.33, the process spread takes up only 75% of the specification spread, leaving a little wiggle room in case the process moves off-center.

Example 13.10

Finding and Interpreting C_p—Paint-Filling Process

Problem Let's return to the paint-filling process analyzed in Examples 13.6 and 13.8. Using 25 samples of size 5 (125 measurements), we constructed $\bar{x}$- and R-charts and concluded that the process was in a state of statistical control. The specification limits for the acceptable amount of paint fill per can are shown in the capability analysis diagram of Figure 13.39.

a. Is it appropriate to construct a capability index for this process?

b. Find C_p for this process and interpret its value.

Solution

a. Because the process is stable (under control), its output distribution can be characterized by the same probability distribution at any point in time (see Figure 13.12). Accordingly, it is appropriate to assess the performance of the process using that distribution and related performance measures such as C_p.

b. From the definition of capability index,

$$C_p = \frac{(\text{USL} - \text{LSL})}{6\sigma}$$

From the capability analysis diagram of Figure 13.39, we can see that the upper and lower specification limits are 10.005 pounds and 9.995 pounds, respectively. But what is σ? Because the output distribution will never be known exactly, neither will σ, the standard deviation of the output distribution. It must be estimated with s, the standard deviation of a large sample drawn from the process. In this case, we use the standard deviation of the 125 measurements used to construct the capability analysis diagram. This value, $s = .00447$, is highlighted in the upper left of the Minitab printout, Figure 13.39. Then

$$C_p = \frac{(10.005 - 9.995)}{6(.00447)} = \frac{.01}{.02682} = .373$$

(This value of C_p is highlighted in the upper right corner of Figure 13.39.) Because C_p is less than 1.0, the process is not capable. The process spread is wider than the specification spread.

Look Back The C_p statistic confirms the results shown on the capability analysis diagram (Figure 13.39), where 24% of the sampled cans were found to be unacceptable.

■ Now Work Exercise 13.58

For two reasons, great care should be exercised in using and interpreting C_p. First, like the sample standard deviation, s, used in its computation, C_p is a statistic and is subject to sampling error—that is, the value of C_p will change from sample to sample. Thus, unless you understand the magnitude of the sampling error, you should be cautious in comparing the C_p's of different processes. Second, C_p does not reflect the shape of the output distribution. Distributions with different shapes can have the same C_p value. Accordingly, C_p should not be used in isolation, but in conjunction with the capability analysis diagram.

If a capability analysis study indicates that an in-control process is not capable, as in the paint-filling example, it is usually variation, rather than off-centeredness, that is the culprit. Thus, capability is typically achieved or restored by seeking out and eliminating common causes of variation.

Exercises 13.49–13.64

Learning the Mechanics

13.49 Explain why it is inappropriate to conduct a capability analysis study for a process that is not in statistical control.

13.50 Explain the difference between *process spread* and *specification spread*.

13.51 Describe two different ways to assess the capability of a process.

13.52 Why is it recommended to use and interpret C_p in conjunction with a capability analysis diagram rather than in isolation?

13.53 For a process that is in control and follows a normal distribution, interpret each of the following C_p values:
a. 1.00 **b.** 1.33 **c.** .50 **d.** 2.00

13.54 Find the specification spread for each of the following:
a. USL = 19.65, LSL = 12.45
b. USL = .0010, LSL = .0008
c. USL = 1.43, LSL = 1.27
d. USL = 490, LSL = 486

13.55 Find (or estimate) the process spread for each of the following.
a. $\sigma = 21$ **b.** $\sigma = 5.2$
c. $s = 110.06$ **d.** $s = .0024$

13.56 Find the value of C_p for each of the following situations:

a. USL = 1.0065, LSL = 1.0035, $s = .0005$

b. USL = 22, LSL = 21, $s = .2$

c. USL = 875, LSL = 870, $s = .75$

Applying the Concepts—Basic

13.57 Upper specification limit of a process. An in-control, centered process that follows a normal distribution has a $C_p = 2.0$. How many standard deviations away from the process mean is the upper specification limit?

13.58 Capability of an in-control process. A process is in control with a normally distributed output distribution with mean 1,000 and standard deviation 100. The USL and LSL for the process are 1,020 and 980, respectively.

NW

a. Assuming no changes in the behavior of the process, what percentage of the output will be unacceptable?

b. Find and interpret the C_p value of the process.

13.59 Water use at a thermal power plant. Thermal power plants use demineralized (DM) water for steam generation. Since it is costly to replace, power plants must conserve the use of DM water. DM water consumption was monitored at a thermal power plant in India and the results published in *Total Quality Management* (Feb. 2009). Plant management set the target for DM water consumption at .5%, the upper specification limit at .7%, and the lower specification limit at .1%. Based on data collected for a sample of 182 flow meter measurements, the overall standard deviation of the process was .265%. Use this information to find the capability index for this process. Interpret the result.

Applying the Concepts—Intermediate

13.60 Cereal box filling process. Refer to the data on weights of cereal boxes, Exercise 13.16 (p. 13-31). Assume the specification limits for the weights are USL = 24.2 ounces and LSL = 23.8 ounces.

CEREAL

a. Assuming the process is under control, construct a capability analysis diagram for the process.

b. Is the process capable? Support your answer with a numerical measure of capability.

13.61 Military aircraft bolts. Refer to Exercise 13.20 (p. 13-32) and the data on lengths of bolts used in military aircraft. Management has specified the USL and LSL as 37 cm and 35 cm, respectively.

BOLTS

a. Assuming the process is in control, construct a capability analysis diagram for the process.

b. Find the percentage of bolts that fall outside the specification limits.

c. Find the capability index, C_p.

d. Is the process capable? Explain.

13.62 Bioreactor production of antibodies. Benchtop bioreactors are used to produce antibodies for anti-cancer drugs. Engineers calibrate bioreactors in order to maximize production. The *African Journal of Biotechnology* (Dec. 2011) published a study designed to achieve a high percentage of antibody production from a bioreactor. The variable of interest was the natural logarithm of the number of viable cells produced in a bioreactor run. Data were collected for a sample of four bioreactor runs every 6 hours for 20 consecutive time periods. These data (simulated from information provided in the article) are listed in the accompanying table. Engineers have specified the following for the bioreactor runs: target mean = 6.3, LSL = 5.9, and USL = 6.5. Run a complete capability analysis on the data. How would you categorize the performance of the process?

BIOREC

Time Period	Hour	Run1	Run2	Run3	Run4
1	0	5.83	5.90	5.91	5.93
2	6	5.98	5.94	5.97	5.84
3	12	5.99	5.98	5.99	5.98
4	18	6.09	6.04	5.93	6.02
5	24	6.20	6.30	6.30	6.20
6	30	6.04	6.08	6.23	6.15
7	36	6.19	6.13	6.13	6.29
8	42	6.37	6.27	6.27	6.27
9	48	6.56	6.46	6.36	6.26
10	54	6.36	6.36	6.16	6.16
11	60	6.36	6.37	6.37	6.27
12	66	6.27	6.27	6.27	6.17
13	72	6.26	6.26	6.26	6.16
14	78	6.29	6.46	6.16	6.26
15	84	6.26	6.16	6.25	6.15
16	90	6.35	6.45	6.25	6.53
17	96	6.16	6.16	6.55	6.56
18	102	6.24	6.23	6.24	6.24
19	108	6.15	6.16	6.15	6.15
20	114	6.30	6.52	6.13	6.48

13.63 New iron-making process. *Mining Engineering* (Oct. 2004) published a study of a new technology for producing high-quality iron nuggets directly from raw iron ore and coal. For one phase of the study, the percentage change in the carbon content of the produced nuggets was measured at 4-hour intervals for 33 consecutive intervals. The data for the 33 time intervals are listed in the table below. Specifications state that the carbon content should be within 3.42 ± 0.3 percent.

CARBON

Interval	Carbon Change (%)	Interval	Carbon Change (%)
1	3.25	18	3.55
2	3.30	19	3.48
3	3.23	20	3.42
4	3.00	21	3.40
5	3.51	22	3.50
6	3.60	23	3.45
7	3.65	24	3.75
8	3.50	25	3.52
9	3.40	26	3.10
10	3.35	27	3.25
11	3.48	28	3.78
12	3.50	29	3.70
13	3.25	30	3.50
14	3.60	31	3.40
15	3.55	32	3.45
16	3.60	33	3.30
17	2.90		

Source: "Tmk3-Application of a new ironmaking technology for the iron ore mining industry," by G. Hoffman and O. Tsuge, from MINING ENGINEERING, Volume 56(9). Copyright © 2004 by the Society for Mining, Metallurg, & Exploration. Reprinted with permission.

a. Construct a capability analysis diagram for the iron-making process.

b. Determine the proportion of carbon measurements that fall outside specifications.

c. Find the capability index for the process and interpret its value.

13.64 Lowering the thickness of an expensive blow-molded container. BLWMLD Refer to the *Quality* (Mar. 2009) study of a plant that produces a high-volume, blow-molded container, Exercise 13.33 (p. 13-40). Recall that the quality manager at the plant wants to lower the average thickness for the expensive layer of material and still meet specifications. Specification limits for individual thickness values are .10 to .30 millimeter.

a. Find the standard deviation of the process data.

b. Calculate the capability index, C_p, for the process and interpret the result.

c. Compare the LCL of the process (from Exercise 13.33) to the LSL. Does this imply that the average thickness of the material can be lowered and still meet specifications?

Chapter Notes

Key Terms

A zone 13-21
B zone 13-21
capability analysis 13-53
capability analysis diagram 13-54
capability index 13-55
causal chain 13-52
cause-and-effect diagram 13-51
centerline 13-7
common causes of variation 13-12
conform to specifications 13-17
control chart 13-6
control limits 13-13
C_p index 13-55
C zone 13-21
distribution of the process 13-9
in control 13-10
individuals chart 13-16
lower control limit 13-14
nonconforming 13-17
oscillating sequence 13-7
out of (statistical) control 13-10
output distribution of the process 13-9
pattern-analysis rules 13-22
p-chart 13-42
process 13-4
process spread 13-56
process variation 13-6
quality 13-3
random behavior 13-10
rare event 13-14
rational subgroups 13-20
R-chart 13-33
run chart 13-6
s-chart 13-33
special (assignable) causes of variation 13-12
specification limits 13-17
specification spread 13-56
stability 13-10
statistical control 13-10
statistical process control (SPC) 13-11
statistical thinking 13-6
system 13-4
3-sigma limits 13-14
total quality management 13-2
trial values 13-24
upper control limit 13-13
x-chart 13-16
$\bar{x}$-chart 13-17

Key Formulas

Control Chart	Centerline	Control Limits	A–B Boundary	B–C Boundary
$\bar{x}$-chart	$\bar{\bar{x}} = \dfrac{\sum_{i=1}^{k} \bar{x}_i}{k}$	$\bar{\bar{x}} \pm A_2\bar{R}$	$\bar{\bar{x}} \pm \frac{2}{3}(A_2\bar{R})$	$\bar{\bar{x}} \pm \frac{1}{3}(A_2\bar{R})$
			or $\bar{\bar{x}} \pm 2\dfrac{(\bar{R}/d_2)}{\sqrt{n}}$	or $\bar{\bar{x}} \pm \dfrac{(\bar{R}/d_2)}{\sqrt{n}}$
R-chart	$\bar{R} = \dfrac{\sum_{i=1}^{k} R_i}{k}$	$(\bar{R}D_3, \bar{R}D_4)$	$\bar{R} \pm 2d_3\left(\dfrac{\bar{R}}{d_2}\right)$	$\bar{R} \pm d_3\left(\dfrac{\bar{R}}{d_2}\right)$
p-chart	$\bar{p} = \dfrac{\text{Total number defectives}}{\text{Total number units sampled}}$	$\bar{p} \pm 3\sqrt{\dfrac{\bar{p}(1-\bar{p})}{n}}$	$\bar{p} \pm 2\sqrt{\dfrac{\bar{p}(1-\bar{p})}{n}}$	$\bar{p} \pm \sqrt{\dfrac{\bar{p}(1-\bar{p})}{n}}$

Key Symbols

LCL	Lower control limit
UCL	Upper control limit
$\bar{\bar{x}}$	Average of the sample means
$\bar{R}$	Average of the sample ranges
A_2	Constant obtained from Table IX in Appendix D
D_3	Constant obtained from Table IX in Appendix D
D_4	Constant obtained from Table IX in Appendix D
d_2	Constant obtained from Table IX in Appendix D
d_3	Constant obtained from Table IX in Appendix D
$\hat{p}$	Estimated number of defectives in sample
$\bar{p}$	Overall proportion of defective units in all *nk* samples
p_0	Estimated overall proportion of defectives for entire process
SPC	Statistical process control
USL	Upper specification limit
LSL	Lower specification limit
C_p	Capability index

Key Ideas

Total quality management (TQM)
Involves the management of quality in all phases of a business

Statistical process control (SPC)
The process of monitoring and eliminating variation to keep a process in control

In-control process
Has an output distribution that *does not change over time*

Out-of-control process
Has an output distribution that *changes over time*

Dimensions of Quality
1. Performance
2. Features
3. Reliability
4. Conformance
5. Durability
6. Serviceability
7. Aesthetics
8. Reputation and Image

Major Sources of Process Variation
1. People
2. Machines
3. Materials
4. Methods
5. Measurement
6. Environment

Causes of Variation
1. Common causes
2. Special (assignable) causes

Types of Control Charts
1. **$\bar{x}$-chart:** monitors the process mean
2. ***R*-chart:** monitors the process variation
3. ***p*-chart:** monitors the proportion of nonconforming items

Specification limits
Define acceptable values for an output variable
LSL = lower specification limit
USL = upper specification limit
(USL − LSL) = specification spread

Capability analysis
Determines if process is capable of satisfying its customers

Capability index (C_p)
Summarizes performance of a process relative to the specification limits

$$C_p = (\text{USL} - \text{LSL})/6\sigma$$

Pattern-analysis rules
Determine whether a process is in or out of control

Rational subgroups
Samples designed to make it more likely that process changes will occur between (rather than within) subgroups

Sample size for *p*-chart:

$$n > 9(1 - p_0)/p_0,$$

where p_0 estimates true proportion defective

Cause-and-effect diagram
Facilitates process diagnosis and documents causal factors in a process

Guide to Control Charts

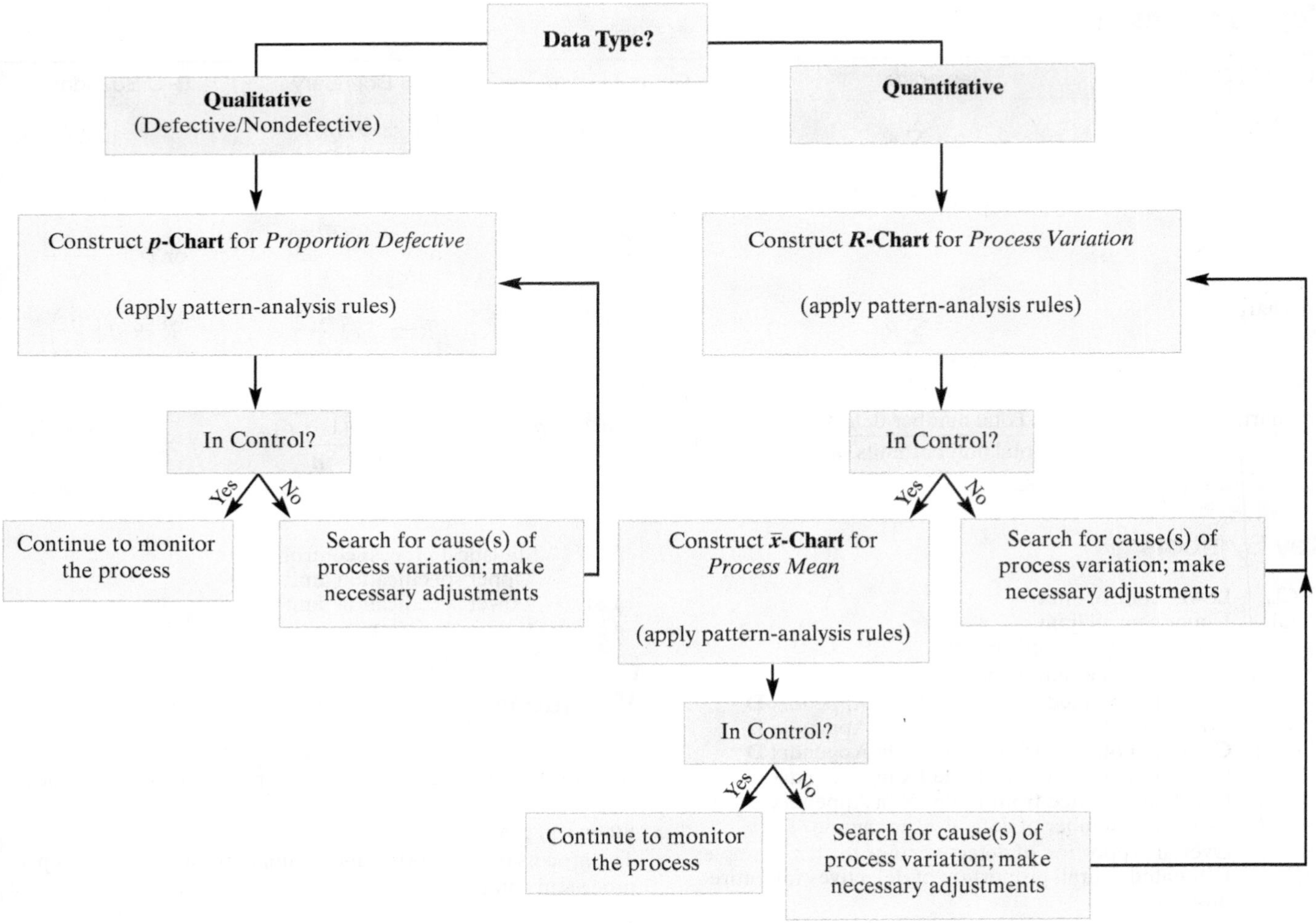

Supplementary Exercises 13.65–13.89

Learning the Mechanics

13.65 Define *quality* and list its important dimensions.

13.66 What is a process? Give an example of an organizational process.

13.67 What is a system? Give an example of a system with which you are familiar and describe its inputs, outputs, and transformation process.

13.68 Describe the six major sources of process variation.

13.69 Suppose all the output of a process over the last year was measured and found to be within the specification limits required by customers of the process. Should you worry about whether the process is in statistical control? Explain.

13.70 Select a problem, event, or condition whose cause or causes you would like to diagnose. Construct a cause-and-effect diagram that would facilitate your diagnosis.

13.71 In estimating a population mean μ using a sample mean $\bar{x}$, why is it likely that $\bar{x} \neq \mu$? Construct a cause-and-effect diagram for the effect $\bar{x} \neq \mu$.

13.72 Construct a cause-and-effect diagram to help explain why customer waiting time at the drive-in window of a fast-food restaurant is variable.

13.73 Processes that are in control are predictable; out-of-control processes are not. Explain.

13.74 Compare and contrast special and common causes of variation.

13.75 Explain the difference between control limits and specification limits.

13.76 Should control charts be used to monitor a process that is both in control and capable? Why or why not?

13.77 Under what circumstances is it appropriate to use C_p to assess capability?

13.78 A process is under control and follows a normal distribution with mean 100 and standard deviation 10. In constructing a standard $\bar{x}$-chart for this process, the control limits are set 3 standard deviations from the mean—that is, $100 \pm 3(10/\sqrt{n})$. The probability of observing an $\bar{x}$ outside the control limits is $(.00135 + .00135) = .0027$. Suppose it is desired to construct a control chart that signals the presence of a potential special cause of variation for less extreme values of $\bar{x}$. How many standard deviations from the mean should the control limits be set such that the probability of the chart falsely indicating the presence of a special cause of variation is .10 rather than .0027?

Applying the Concepts—Basic

13.79 Weight of a product. Consider the time series data for the weight of a manufactured product shown in the next column.

TIMEWT

a. Construct a time series plot. Be sure to connect the points and add a centerline.

b. Which type of variation pattern in Figure 13.6 best describes the pattern revealed by your plot?

Order of Production	Weight (grams)	Order of Production	Weight (grams)
1	6.0	9	6.5
2	5.0	10	9.0
3	7.0	11	3.0
4	5.5	12	11.0
5	7.0	13	3.0
6	6.0	14	12.0
7	8.0	15	2.0
8	5.0		

13.80 Lengths of pencils. The length measurements of 20 consecutively produced pencils are recorded in the table below.

PENCIL

a. Construct a time series plot. Be sure to connect the plotted points and add a centerline.

b. Which type of variation pattern in Figure 13.6 best describes the pattern shown in your plot?

Order of Production	Length (inches)	Order of Production	Length (inches)
1	7.47	11	7.57
2	7.48	12	7.56
3	7.51	13	7.55
4	7.49	14	7.58
5	7.50	15	7.56
6	7.51	16	7.59
7	7.48	17	7.57
8	7.49	18	7.55
9	7.48	19	7.56
10	7.50	20	7.58

13.81 Applying pattern-analysis rules. Use the appropriate pattern-analysis rules to determine whether the process being monitored by the following control chart is under the influence of special causes of variation.

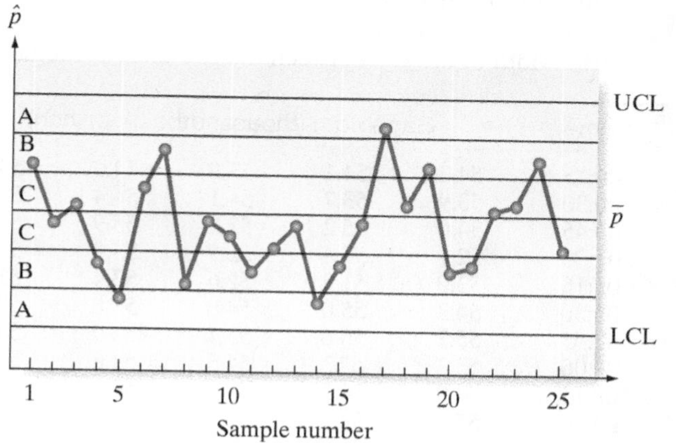

Applying the Concepts—Intermediate

13.82 Defective plastic mold. A company that manufactures plastic molded parts believes it is producing an unusually large number of defects. To investigate this suspicion, each shift drew seven random samples of 200 parts, visually inspected each part to determine whether it was defective, and tallied the primary type of defect present (Hart, 1992). These data are presented in the table at the top of the next page.

MOLD

Data for Exercise 13.82

			Type of Defect				
Sample	Shift	# of Defects	Crack	Burn	Dirt	Blister	Trim
1	1	4	1	1	1	0	1
2	1	6	2	1	0	2	1
3	1	11	1	2	3	3	2
4	1	12	2	2	2	3	3
5	1	5	0	1	0	2	2
6	1	10	1	3	2	2	2
7	1	8	0	3	1	1	3
8	2	16	2	0	8	2	4
9	2	17	3	2	8	2	2
10	2	20	0	3	11	3	3
11	2	28	3	2	17	2	4
12	2	20	0	0	16	4	0
13	2	20	1	1	18	0	0
14	2	17	2	2	13	0	0
15	3	13	3	2	5	1	2
16	3	10	0	3	4	2	1
17	3	11	2	2	3	2	2
18	3	7	0	3	2	2	0
19	3	6	1	2	0	1	2
20	3	8	1	1	2	3	1
21	3	9	1	2	2	2	2

a. From a statistical perspective, are the number of samples and the sample size of 200 adequate for constructing a *p*-chart for these data? Explain.
b. Construct a *p*-chart for this manufacturing process.
c. Should the control limits be used to monitor future process output? Explain.
d. Suggest a strategy for identifying the special causes of variation that may be present.

13.83 Robotics clamp gap width. University of Waterloo (Canada) statistician S. H. Steiner applied control chart methodology to the manufacturing of a horseshoe-shaped metal fastener called a *robotics clamp* (*Applied Statistics*, Vol. 47, 1998). Users of the clamp were concerned with the width of the gap between the two ends of the fastener.

CLAMP

Time	Gap Width (thousandths of an inch)				
00:15	54.2	54.1	53.9	54.0	53.8
00:30	53.9	53.7	54.1	54.4	55.1
00:45	54.0	55.2	53.1	55.9	54.5
01:00	52.1	53.4	52.9	53.0	52.7
01:15	53.0	51.9	52.6	53.4	51.7
01:30	54.2	55.0	54.0	53.8	53.6
01:45	55.2	56.6	53.1	52.9	54.0
02:00	53.3	57.2	54.5	51.6	54.3
02:15	54.9	56.3	55.2	56.1	54.0
02:30	55.7	53.1	52.9	56.3	55.4
02:45	55.2	51.0	56.3	55.6	54.2
03:00	54.2	54.2	55.8	53.8	52.1
03:15	55.7	57.5	55.4	54.0	53.1
03:30	53.7	56.9	54.0	55.1	54.2
03:45	54.1	53.9	54.0	54.6	54.8
04:00	53.5	56.1	55.1	55.0	54.0

Source: Based on "Grouped Data Exponentially Weighted Moving Average Control Charts" by Stefan H. Steiner from APPLIED STATISTICS-JOURNAL OF THE ROYAL STATISTICAL SOCIETY: SERIES C (APPLIED STATISTICS), Volume 47(2).

Their preferred target width was .054 inch. An optical measuring device was used to measure the gap width of the fastener during the manufacturing process. The manufacturer sampled five finished clamps every 15 minutes throughout its 16-hour daily production schedule and optically measured the gap. Data for 4 consecutive hours of production are presented in the accompanying table.

a. Construct an *R*-chart from these data.
b. Construct an $\bar{x}$-chart from these data.
c. Apply the pattern-analysis rules to the control charts. Does your analysis suggest that special causes of variation are present in the clamp manufacturing process? Which of the six rules led you to your conclusion?
d. Should the control limits be used to monitor future process output? Explain.

13.84 Package sorting time. AirExpress, an overnight mail service, is concerned about the operating efficiency of the package-sorting departments at its Toledo, Ohio, terminal. The company would like to monitor the time it takes for packages to be put in outgoing delivery bins from the time they are received. The sorting department operates 6 hours per day, from 6:00 P.M. to midnight. The company randomly sampled four packages during each hour of operation during 4 consecutive days. The time for each package to move through the system, in minutes, is given in the table on the next page.

TRNSIT

a. Construct an $\bar{x}$-chart from these data. For this chart to be meaningful, what assumption must be made about the variation of the process? Why?
b. What does the chart suggest about the stability of the package-sorting process? Explain.
c. Should the control limits be used to monitor future process output? Explain.

Data for Exercise 13.84

Sample	Transit Time (min.)			
1	31.9	33.4	37.8	26.2
2	29.1	24.3	33.2	36.7
3	30.3	31.1	26.3	34.1
4	39.6	29.4	31.4	37.7
5	27.4	29.7	36.5	33.3
6	32.7	32.9	40.1	29.7
7	30.7	36.9	26.8	34.0
8	28.4	24.1	29.6	30.9
9	30.5	35.5	36.1	27.4
10	27.8	29.6	29.0	34.1
11	34.0	30.1	35.9	28.8
12	25.5	26.3	34.8	30.0
13	24.6	29.9	31.8	37.9
14	30.6	36.0	40.2	30.8
15	29.7	33.2	34.9	27.6
16	24.1	26.8	32.7	29.0
17	29.4	31.6	35.2	27.6
18	31.1	33.0	29.6	35.2
19	27.0	29.0	35.1	25.1
20	36.6	32.4	28.7	27.9
21	33.0	27.1	26.2	35.1
22	33.2	41.2	30.7	31.6
23	26.7	35.2	39.7	31.5
24	30.5	36.8	27.9	28.6

13.85 Waiting times of airline passengers. Officials at Mountain Airlines are interested in monitoring the length of time customers must wait in line to check in at their airport counter in Reno, Nevada. To develop a control chart, five customers were sampled each day for 20 days. The data, in minutes, are presented in the table below.

CHECKN

Sample	Waiting Time (min.)				
1	3.2	6.7	1.3	8.4	2.2
2	5.0	4.1	7.9	8.1	.4
3	7.1	3.2	2.1	6.5	3.7
4	4.2	1.6	2.7	7.2	1.4
5	1.7	7.1	1.6	.9	1.8
6	4.7	5.5	1.6	3.9	4.0
7	6.2	2.0	1.2	.9	1.4
8	1.4	2.7	3.8	4.6	3.8
9	1.1	4.3	9.1	3.1	2.7
10	5.3	4.1	9.8	2.9	2.7
11	3.2	2.9	4.1	5.6	.8
12	2.4	4.3	6.7	1.9	4.8
13	8.8	5.3	6.6	1.0	4.5
14	3.7	3.6	2.0	2.7	5.9
15	1.0	1.9	6.5	3.3	4.7
16	7.0	4.0	4.9	4.4	4.7
17	5.5	7.1	2.1	.9	2.8
18	1.8	5.6	2.2	1.7	2.1
19	2.6	3.7	4.8	1.4	5.8
20	3.6	.8	5.1	4.7	6.3

a. Construct an *R*-chart from these data.
b. What does the *R*-chart suggest about the stability of the process? Explain.
c. Explain why the *R*-chart should be interpreted prior to the $\bar{x}$-chart.
d. Construct an $\bar{x}$-chart from these data.
e. What does the $\bar{x}$-chart suggest about the stability of the process? Explain.
f. Should the control limits for the *R*-chart and $\bar{x}$-chart be used to monitor future process output? Explain.

13.86 Waiting times of airline passengers (cont'd). Consider the airline check-in process described in Exercise 13.85.
a. Assume the process is under control and construct a capability analysis diagram for the process. Management has specified a USL of 5 minutes.
b. Is the process capable? Justify your answer.
c. If it is appropriate to estimate and interpret C_p for this process, do so. If it is not, explain why.
d. Why didn't management provide a LSL?

13.87 Credit histories with data-entry errors. A company called CRW runs credit checks for a large number of banks and insurance companies. Credit history information is typed into computer files by trained administrative assistants. The company is interested in monitoring the proportion of credit histories that contain one or more data-entry errors. Based on her experience with the data-entry operation, the director of the data processing unit believes that the proportion of histories with data-entry errors is about 6%. CRW audited 150 randomly selected credit histories each day for 20 days. The sample data are presented below.

CRW150

a. Use the sample size formula to show that a sample size of 150 is large enough to prevent the lower control limit of the *p*-chart they plan to construct from being negative.
b. Construct a *p*-chart for the data-entry process.
c. What does the chart indicate about the presence of special causes of variation? Explain.
d. Provide an example of a special cause of variation that could potentially affect this process. Do the same for a common cause of variation.
e. Should the control limits be used to monitor future credit histories produced by the data-entry operation? Explain.

Sample	Sample Size	Histories with Errors
1	150	9
2	150	11
3	150	12
4	150	8
5	150	10
6	150	6
7	150	13
8	150	9
9	150	11
10	150	5
11	150	7
12	150	6
13	150	12
14	150	10
15	150	11
16	150	7
17	150	6
18	150	12
19	150	14
20	150	10

13.88 Defects in graphite shafts. Over the last year, a company that manufactures golf clubs has received numerous complaints about the performance of its graphite shafts and has lost several market share percentage points. In response, the company decided to monitor its shaft production process to identify new opportunities to improve its product. The process involves pultrusion. A fabric is pulled through a thermosetting polymer bath and then through a long heated steel die. As it moves through the die, the shaft is

SHAFT1
SHAFT2

Shift Number	Number of Defective Shafts	Proportion of Defective Shafts
1	9	.05625
2	6	.03750
3	8	.05000
4	14	.08750
5	7	.04375
6	5	.03125
7	7	.04375
8	9	.05625
9	5	.03125
10	9	.05625
11	1	.00625
12	7	.04375
13	9	.05625
14	14	.08750
15	7	.04375
16	8	.05000
17	4	.02500
18	10	.06250
19	6	.03750
20	12	.07500
21	8	.05000
22	5	.03125
23	9	.05625
24	15	.09375
25	6	.03750
26	8	.05000
27	4	.02500
28	7	.04375
29	2	.01250
30	6	.03750
31	9	.05625
32	11	.06875
33	8	.05000
34	9	.05625
35	7	.04375
36	8	.05000

Source: CREATING QUALITY: CONCEPTS, SYSTEMS, STRATEGIES, AND TOOLS, by W. Kolarik. Copyright © 1995 by McGraw-Hill. Reprinted with permission.

cured. Finally, it is cut to the desired length. Defects that can occur during the process are internal voids, broken strands, gaps between successive layers, and microcracks caused by improper curing. The company's newly formed quality department sampled 10 consecutive shafts every 30 minutes, and nondestructive testing was used to seek out flaws in the shafts. The data from each 8-hour work shift were combined to form a shift sample of 160 shafts. Data on the proportion of defective shafts for 36 shift samples are presented in the table above.

a. Use the appropriate control chart to determine whether the process proportion remains stable over time.

b. Does your control chart indicate that both common and special causes of variation are present? Explain.

c. Data on the types of flaws identified are given in the table below. [*Note:* Each defective shaft may have more than one flaw.] To help diagnose the causes of variation in process output, construct a Pareto diagram for the types of shaft defects observed. Which are the "vital few"? The "trivial many"?

Type of Defect	Number of Defects
Internal voids	11
Broken strands	96
Gaps between layer	72
Microcracks	150

Critical Thinking—Challenge

13.89 Bayfield Mud Company case. In their text *Quantitative Analysis of Management* (2005), B. Render (Rollins College) and R. M. Stair (Florida State University) present the case of the Bayfield Mud Company. Bayfield supplies boxcars of 50-pound bags of mud treating agents to the Wet-Land Drilling Company. Mud treating agents are used to control the pH and other chemical properties of the cone during oil drilling operations. Wet-Land has complained to Bayfield that its most recent shipment of bags were underweight by about 5%. (The use of underweight bags may result in poor chemical control during drilling, which may hurt drilling efficiency, resulting in serious economic consequences.) Afraid of losing a long-time customer, Bayfield immediately began investigating their production process. Management suspected that the causes of the problem were the recently added third shift and the fact that all three shifts were under pressure to increase output to meet increasing demand for the product. Their quality-control staff began randomly sampling and weighing six bags of output each hour. The average weight of each sample over the last 3 days is recorded in the table below along with the weight of the heaviest and lightest bags in each sample. Does it appear that management's suspicion about the third shift is correct? Explain?

MUDBAG

Data for Exercise 13.89

Time	Average Weight (pounds)	Lightest	Heaviest	Time	Average Weight (pounds)	Lightest	Heaviest
6:00 A.M.	49.6	48.7	50.7	1:00	49.0	46.4	50.0
7:00	50.2	49.1	51.2	2:00	49.0	46.0	50.6
8:00	50.6	49.6	51.4	3:00	49.8	48.2	50.8
9:00	50.8	50.2	51.8	4:00	50.3	49.2	52.7
10:00	49.9	49.2	52.3	5:00	51.4	50.0	55.3
11:00	50.3	48.6	51.7	6:00	51.6	49.2	54.7
12:00 P.M.	48.6	46.2	50.4	7:00	51.8	50.0	55.6

(*Continued*)

Data for Exercise 13.89 (continued)

Time	Average Weight (pounds)	Lightest	Heaviest	Time	Average Weight (pounds)	Lightest	Heaviest
8:00	51.0	48.6	53.2	8:00	49.8	49.0	52.4
9:00	50.5	49.4	52.4	9:00	50.3	49.4	51.7
10:00	49.2	46.1	50.7	10:00	50.2	49.6	51.8
11:00	49.0	46.3	50.8	11:00	50.0	49.0	52.3
12:00 A.M.	48.4	45.4	50.2	12:00 P.M.	50.0	48.8	52.4
1:00 A.M.	47.6	44.3	49.7	1:00	50.1	49.4	53.6
2:00	47.4	44.1	49.6	2:00	49.7	48.6	51.0
3:00	48.2	45.2	49.0	3:00	48.4	47.2	51.7
4:00	48.0	45.5	49.1	4:00	47.2	45.3	50.9
5:00	48.4	47.1	49.6	5:00	46.8	44.1	49.0
6:00	48.6	47.4	52.0	6:00	46.8	41.0	51.2
7:00	50.0	49.2	52.2	7:00	50.0	46.2	51.7
8:00	47.4	44.0	48.7	1:00 P.M.	48.9	47.6	51.2
9:00	47.0	44.2	48.9	2:00	49.8	48.4	51.0
10:00	47.2	46.6	50.2	3:00	49.8	48.8	50.8
11:00	48.6	47.0	50.0	4:00	50.0	49.1	50.6
12:00 A.M.	49.8	48.2	50.4	5:00	47.8	45.2	51.2
1:00	49.6	48.4	51.7	6:00	46.4	44.0	49.7
2:00	50.0	49.0	52.2	7:00	46.4	44.4	50.0
3:00	50.0	49.2	50.0	8:00	47.2	46.6	48.9
4:00	47.2	46.3	50.5	9:00	48.4	47.2	49.5
5:00	47.0	44.1	49.7	10:00	49.2	48.1	50.7
6:00	48.4	45.0	49.0	11:00	48.4	47.0	50.8
7:00	48.8	44.8	49.7	12:00 A.M.	47.2	46.4	49.2
8:00	49.6	48.0	51.8	1:00	47.4	46.8	49.0
9:00	50.0	48.1	52.7	2:00	48.8	47.2	51.4
10:00	51.0	48.1	55.2	3:00	49.6	49.0	50.6
11:00	50.4	49.5	54.1	4:00	51.0	50.5	51.5
12:00 P.M.	50.0	48.7	50.9	5:00	50.5	50.0	51.9

Source: QUANTITATIVE ANALYSIS FOR MANAGEMENT, 6th ed., by Jerry Kinard and Brian Kinard. Copyright © 1997 by Prentice Hall, Upper Saddle River, NJ. Reprinted with permission of the author.

Activity 13.1 *Quality Control*: Consistency

In some businesses, such as the food service industry, the consistency of a product contributes greatly to customer satisfaction. When a customer orders a particular menu item on a regular basis, he or she expects to receive a product that has approximately the same taste and appearance each time. The challenge for a national chain is not only to have a single worker be consistent but also to have thousands of workers nationwide produce the same menu item with little variation in taste and appearance.

1. The quality of some products, such as coffee and french fries, deteriorates quickly as the finished product is waiting to be purchased. Visit a coffee house or fast-food restaurant and ask specific questions about steps taken to guarantee a fresh product. If a customer complains that a product has been sitting too long, how have the employees been instructed to respond? Is there a policy regarding how many complaints must be received before a product is thrown out and a new batch made?
2. Visit a popular national chain restaurant and ask about measures taken to ensure consistency of portion size, flavor, and attractiveness of menu items among restaurants in the chain. Be sure to ask about vendors who supply the components of a dish. Does the chain allow for regional variations in the menu? If so, to what degree? Does the national chain have a system in place to check for consistency? If so, how does it work?
3. Did either of the establishments you visited indicate the use of statistical methods in checking for quality? If so, what were the methods? Identify at least one way each of the two places you visited could use control charts to track the quality of a product.

References

Alwan, L. C., & Roberts, H. V. "Time-series modeling for statistical process control," *Journal of Business and Economic Statistics,* 1988, Vol. 6, pp. 87–95.

Banks, J. *Principles of quality Control.* New York: Wiley, 1989.

Checkland, P. *Systems Thinking, Systems Practice.* New York: Wiley, 1999.

Deming, W. E. *Out of the Crisis.* Cambridge, Mass.: MIT Center for Advanced Engineering Study, 1986.

DeVor, R. E., Chang, T., & Southerland, J. W. *Statistical Quality Design and Control*, 2nd ed. Upper Saddle River, N.J.: Prentice Hall, 2007.

Duncan, A. J. *Quality Control and Industrial Statistics*, 5th ed. Homewood, Ill.: Irwin, 1986.

Feigenbaum, A. V. *Total Quality Control,* 4th ed. New York: McGraw-Hill, 2004.

Garvin, D. A. *Managing Quality*. New York: Free Press/Macmillan, 1988.

Gitlow, H., Gitlow, S., Oppenheim, A., & Oppenheim, R. *Quality Management: Tools and Methods for Improvement,* 3rd ed. Homewood, Ill.: Irwin, 2004.

Grant, E. L., & Leavenworth, R. S. *Statistical Quality Control,* 7th ed. New York: McGraw-Hill, 2000.

Gryna, F. M., Jr., Chua, R., & Defeo, *J. Juran's Quality Planning and Analysis for Enterprise Quality,* 5th ed. New York: McGraw-Hill, 2005.

Hart, M. K. "Quality tools for improvement," *Production and Inventory Management Journal,* First Quarter 1992, Vol. 33, No. 1, p. 59.

Ishikawa, K. *Guide to Quality Control,* 2nd ed. White Plains, N.Y.: Kraus International Publications, 1986.

Joiner, B. L., & Goudard, M. A. "Variation, management, and W. Edwards Deming," *Quality Process,* Dec. 1990, pp. 29–37.

Kane, V. E. *Defect Prevention*. New York: Marcel Dekker, 1989.

Latzko, W. J. *Quality and Productivity for Bankers and Financial Managers*. New York: Marcel Dekker, 1986.

Moen, R. D., Nolan, T. W., & Provost, L. P. *Improving Quality through Planned Experimentation*. New York: McGraw-Hill, 1991.

Montgomery, D. C. *Introduction to Statistical Quality Control,* 6th ed. New York: Wiley, 2009.

Nelson, L. "The Shewhart control chart—Tests for special causes," *Journal of Quality Technology,* Oct. 1984, Vol. 16, No. 4, pp. 237–239.

Roberts, H. V. *Data Analysis for Managers,* 2nd ed. Redwood City, Calif.: Scientific Press, 1991.

Rosander, A. C. *Applications of Quality Control in the Service Industries*. New York: Marcel Dekker, 1985.

Rummler, G. A., & Brache, A. P. *Improving Performance: How to Manage the White Space on the Organization Chart,* 2nd ed. San Francisco: Jossey-Bass, 1995.

Ryan, T. P. *Statistical Methods for Quality Improvement,* 3rd ed. New York: Wiley, 2011.

Statistical Quality Control Handbook. Indianapolis, Ind.: AT&T Technologies, Select Code 700-444 (inquiries: 800-432-6600); originally published by Western Electric Company, 1956.

Wadsworth, H. M., Stephens, K. S., & Godfrey, A. B. *Modern Methods for Quality Control and Improvement,* 2nd ed. New York: Wiley, 2001.

Walton, M. *The Deming Management Method*. New York: Dodd, Mead, & Company, 1986.

Wheeler, D. J., & Chambers, D. S. *Understanding Statistical Process Control,* 2nd ed. Knoxville, Tenn.: Statistical Process Controls, Inc., 1992.

USING TECHNOLOGY Technology images shown here are taken from SPSS Statistics Professional 20.0, Minitab 16, XLSTAT for Pearson, and Excel 2010.

SPSS: Control Charts

Step 1 Access the SPSS spreadsheet file that contains the quality data.

Step 2 Click on the "Analyze" button on the SPSS menu bar and then click on "Quality Control" and "Control Charts," as shown in Figure 13.S.1.

Figure 13.S.1 SPSS menu options for control charts

Step 3 On the resulting dialog box (shown in Figure 13.S.2), select the type of control chart you want to produce (*x*-bar, *R*- or *p*-chart) and whether the cases (rows) on the spreadsheet represent individual quality measurements ("Cases are units") or the subgroups ("Cases are subgroups") and then click the "Define" button.

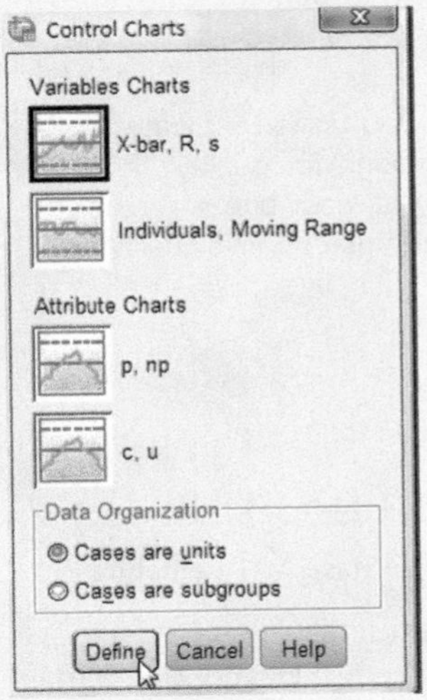

Figure 13.S.2 SPSS control charts selection box

Step 4a If you selected an *x*-bar or *R*-chart where cases are units, the dialog box shown in Figure 13.S.3 will appear. Make the appropriate selections (process variables and subgroup variable). (As an option, you can conduct a capability analysis by clicking the "Statistics" button and making the appropriate menu selections [specification limits, target value, and C_p statistic].)

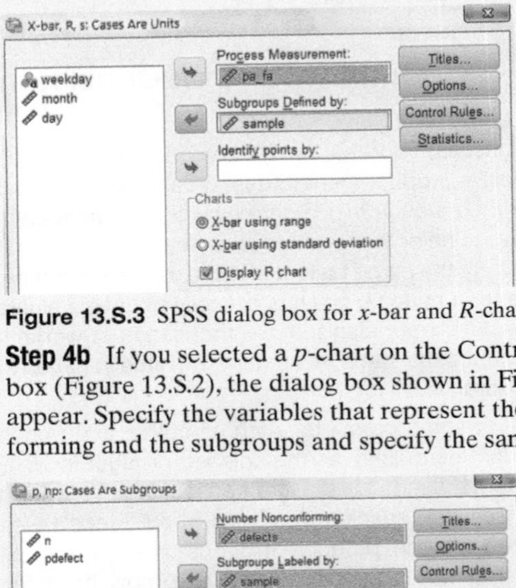

Figure 13.S.3 SPSS dialog box for *x*-bar and *R*-charts

Step 4b If you selected a *p*-chart on the Control Charts dialog box (Figure 13.S.2), the dialog box shown in Figure 13.S.4 will appear. Specify the variables that represent the number nonconforming and the subgroups and specify the sample size.

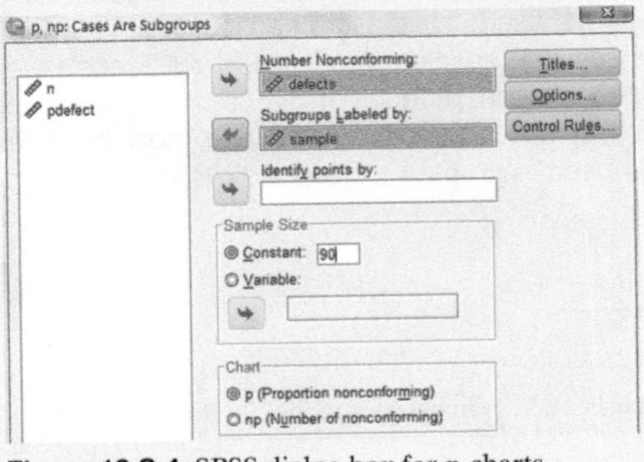

Figure 13.S.4 SPSS dialog box for *p*-charts

Step 5 Click "OK" to view the SPSS control chart.

Minitab: Control Charts

$\bar{x}$- or R-Chart

Step 1 Access the Minitab worksheet file that contains the quality data.

Step 2 Click on the "Stat" button on the Minitab menu bar and then click on "Control Charts," "Variables Charts for Subgroups," and either "Xbar" or "R," as shown in Figure 13.M.1. The resulting dialog box is shown in Figure 13.M.2.

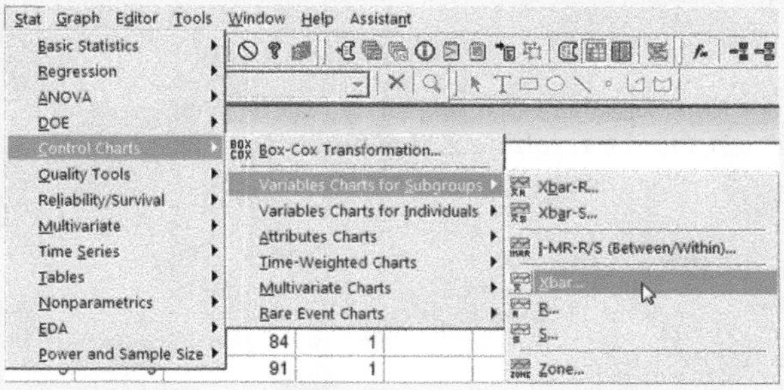

Figure 13.M.1 Minitab menu options for control charts

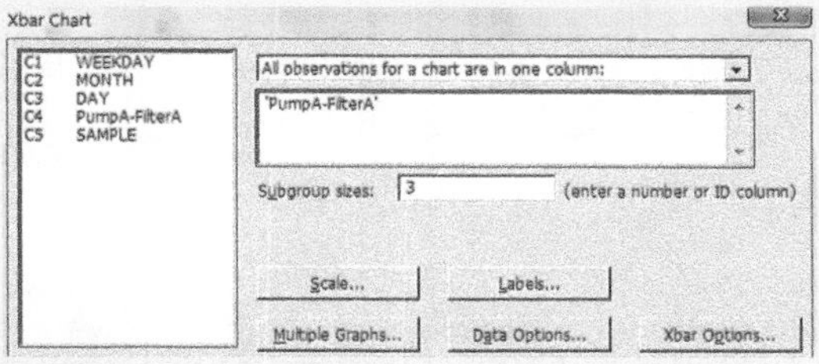

Figure 13.M.2 Minitab dialog box for x-bar chart

Step 3 If each row on the worksheet represents an individual quality measurement, then specify "All observations for a chart are in one column:" (as shown in Figure 13.M.2.) Enter the quality variable in the next box and specify the subgroup size.

If each row on the worksheet represents a subgroup, with columns representing the sample measurements, then specify "Observations for a subgroup are in one row of columns:" Enter the columns with the sample measurements in the next box.

Step 4 If you want Minitab to apply the pattern-analysis rules to the plotted points on the graph, click the "Xbar (or R) Options" button, click "Tests," and check the rules you want apply. Click "OK" to return to the Control Charts dialog box.

Step 5 Click "OK" to produce the Minitab control chart.

p-Chart

Step 1 Click on the "Stat" button on the Minitab menu bar and then click on "Control Charts" and "Attributes Charts" (see Figure 13.M.1).

Step 2 On the resulting menu, select "P." The resulting dialog box appears similar to the one shown in Figure 13.M.3.

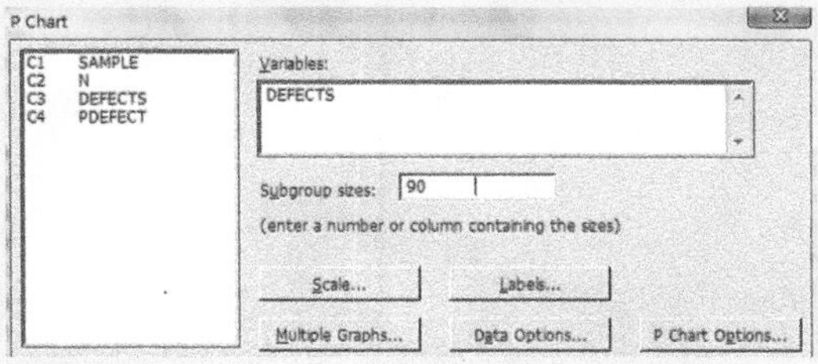

Figure 13.M.3 Minitab dialog box for p-chart

Step 3 Specify the variable that represents the number of nonconforming items and specify the subgroup (sample) size.

Step 4 If you want Minitab to apply the pattern-analysis rules to the plotted points on the graph, click the "P Chart Options" button, click "Tests," and check the rules you want to apply. Click "OK" to return to the Control Charts dialog box.

Step 5 Click "OK" to produce the Minitab control chart.

Capability Analysis Diagram

Step 1 Click on the "Stat" button on the Minitab menu bar and then click on "Quality Tools," "Capability Analysis," and "Normal," as shown in Figure 13.M.4. The resulting dialog box appears similar to the one shown in Figure 13.M.5.

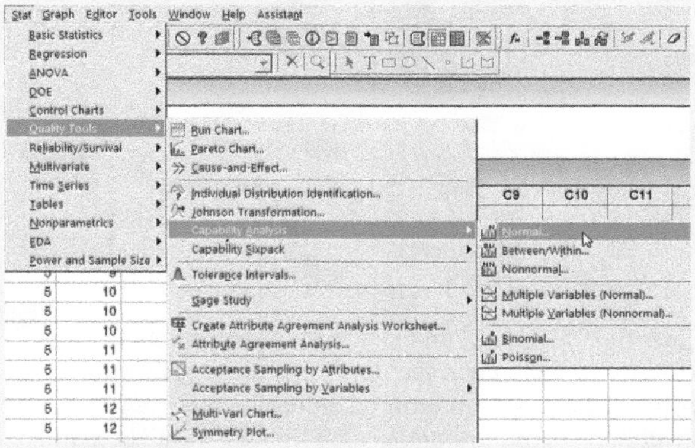

Figure 13.M.4 Minitab menu options for capability analysis

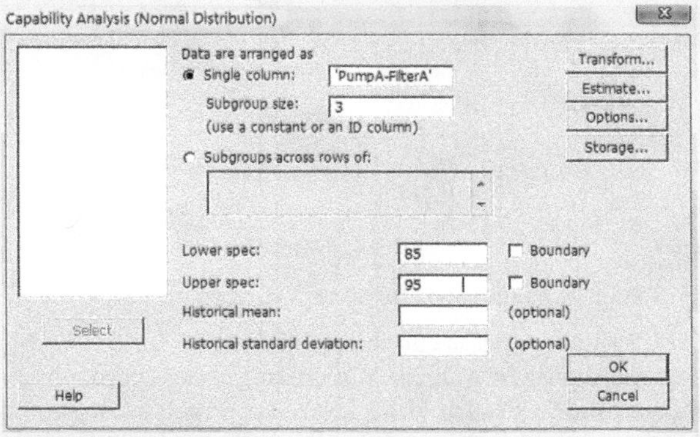

Figure 13.M.5 Minitab dialog box for capability analysis

Step 2 Specify the quality variable of interest, subgroup size, and lower and upper specification limits on the menu screen.

Step 3 Click the "Options" button to specify the type of statistics (e.g., Cp and percents outside specification limits) to be displayed on the graph.

Step 4 Click "OK" to produce the Minitab capability analysis diagram.

Excel/XLSTAT: Control Charts

Step 1 Within XLSTAT, open the Excel spreadsheet containing the control chart data.

Step 2 Click the "XLSTAT" button on the Excel main menu bar, select "SPC," then click either "Subgroup charts" (for an $\bar{x}$-chart or R-chart) or "Attribute charts" (for a p-chart), as shown in Figure 13.E.1.

Figure 13.E.1 XLSTAT menu options for control charts

Step 3 On the resulting dialog box, select the chart type (e.g., "X-bar chart"), as shown in Figure 13.E.2.

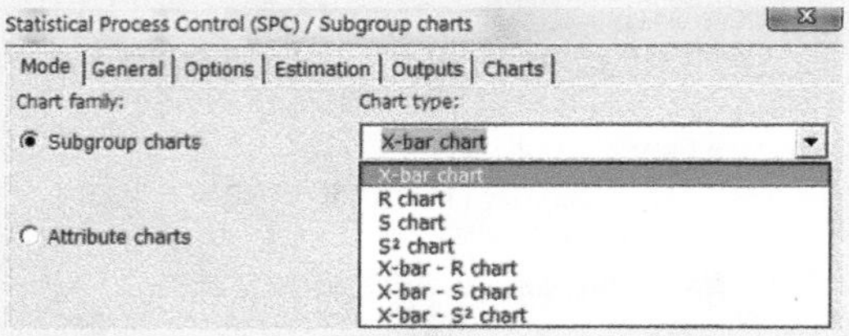

Figure 13.E.2 XLSTAT dialog box for statistical process control

Step 4 Click the "General" tab. When the resulting dialog box appears (Figure 13.E.3), click the appropriate "Data format" option (either data in one column or multiple columns), then specify the columns containing the data in the "Data" box and the column containing the subgroups in the "Groups" box.

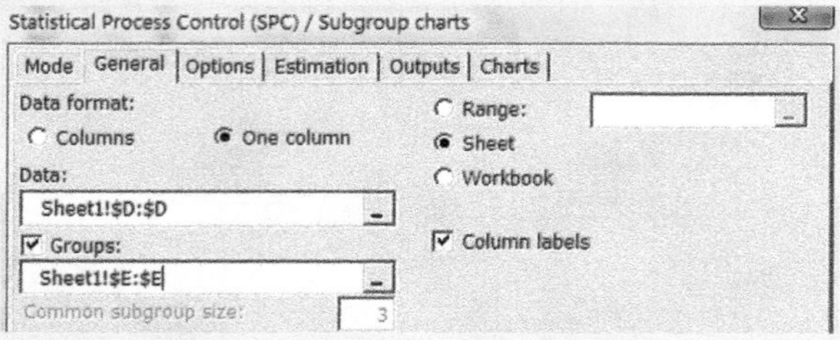

Figure 13.E.3 XLSTAT dialog box for control charts data

Step 5 To determine process capability, click the "Options" tab. On the resulting dialog box check "Calculate process capabilities," then enter the values for USL, LSL, and target, as shown in Figure 13.E.4.

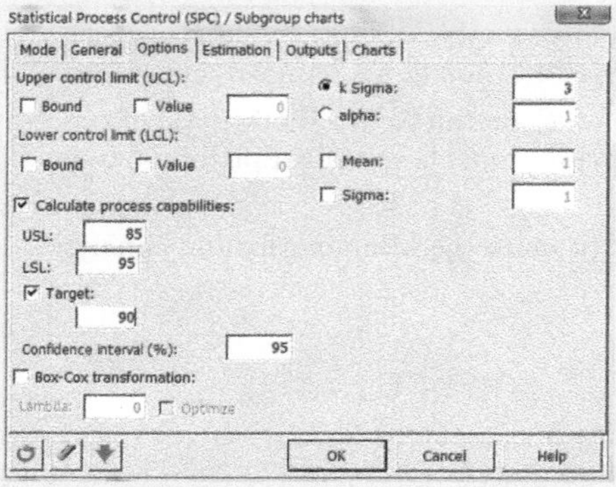

Figure 13.E.4 XLSTAT dialog box for process capability

Step 6 To choose how the upper and lower control limits will be calculated, click the "Estimation" tab. On the resulting dialog box check the method for estimating the process standard deviation (e.g., using R bar), as shown in Figure 13.E.5.

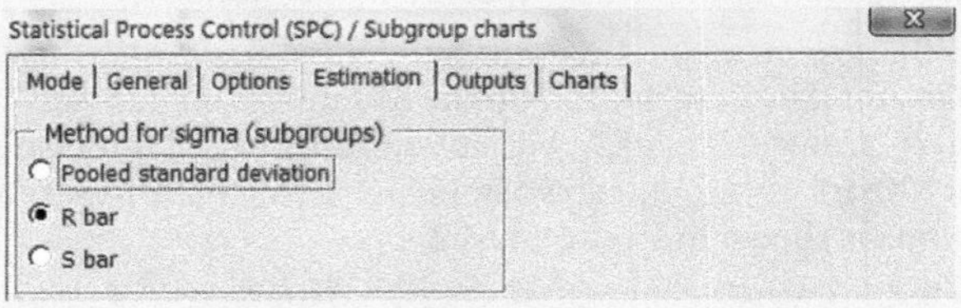

Figure 13.E.5 XLSTAT dialog box for process capability

Step 7 To add A–B and B–C boundaries for the chart, click the "Outputs" tab. On the resulting dialog box check "Display zones (A, B, and C)," as shown in Figure 13.E.6.

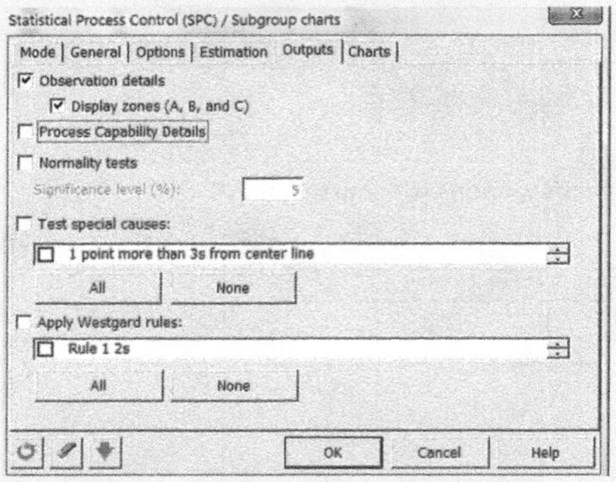

Figure 13.E.6 XLSTAT dialog box for process capability

Step 8 Click "OK," then "Continue" to display the control chart and additional results.

TI-84 Graphing Calculator: Control Charts

Control charts are not available with the TI-84 graphing calculator.

The Gasket Manufacturing Case

The Problem

A Midwestern manufacturer of gaskets for automotive and off-road vehicle applications was suddenly and unexpectedly notified by a major customer—a U.S. auto manufacturer—that they had significantly tightened the specification limits on the overall thickness of a hard gasket used in their automotive engines. Although the current specification limits were by and large being met by the gasket manufacturer, their product did not come close to meeting the new specification.

The gasket manufacturer's first reaction was to negotiate with the customer to obtain a relaxation of the new specification. When these efforts failed, the customer-supplier relationship became somewhat strained. The gasket manufacturer's next thought was that if they waited long enough, the automotive company would eventually be forced to loosen the requirements and purchase the existing product. However, as time went on, it became clear that this was not going to happen and that some positive steps would have to be taken to improve the quality of their gaskets. But what should be done? And by whom?

The Product

Figure C5.1 shows the product in question, a hard gasket. A hard gasket is composed of two outer layers of soft gasket material and an inner layer consisting of a perforated piece of sheet metal. These three pieces are assembled, and some blanking and punching operations follow, after which metal rings are installed around the inside of the cylinder bore clearance holes and the entire outside periphery of the gasket. The quality characteristic of interest in this case is the assembly thickness.

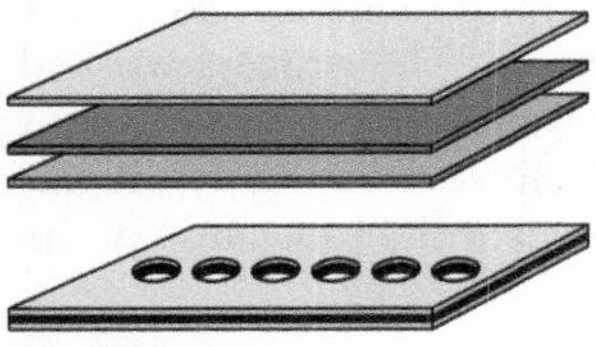

Figure C5.1
A hard gasket for automotive applications

The Process

An initial study by the staff engineers revealed that the variation in the thickness of soft gasket material—the two outer layers of the hard gasket—was large and undoubtedly responsible for much of the total variability in the final product. Figure C5.2 shows the roll mill process that fabricates the sheets of soft gasket material from which the two outer layers of the hard gasket are made. To manufacture a sheet of soft gasket material, an operator adds raw material, in a soft pelletlike form, to the gap—called the *knip*—between the two rolls. The larger roll rotates about its axis with no lateral movement; the smaller roll rotates and moves back and forth laterally to change the size of the knip. As the operator adds more and more material to the knip, the sheet is formed around the larger roll. When the smaller roll reaches a preset destination (i.e., final gap/sheet thickness), a bell rings and a red light goes on, telling the operator to stop adding raw material. The operator stops the rolls and cuts the sheet horizontally along the larger roll so that it may be pulled off the roll. The finished sheet, called a *pull*, is pulled onto a table where the operator checks its thickness with a micrometer. The operator can adjust the final gap if he or she believes that the sheets are coming out too

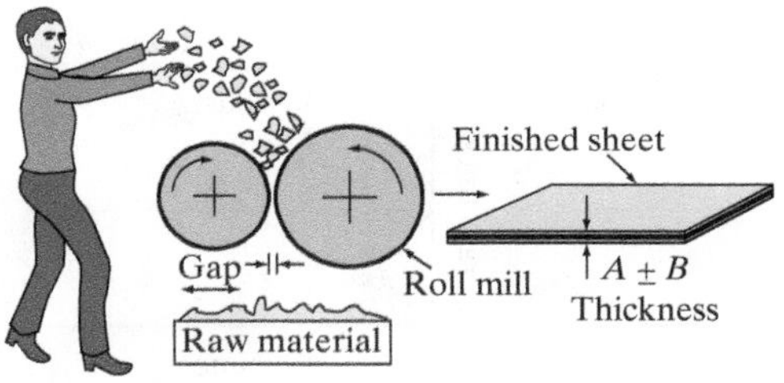

Figure C5.2
Roll mill for the manufacture of soft gasket material

thick or too thin relative to the prescribed nominal value (i.e., the target thickness).

Process Operation

Investigation revealed that the operator runs the process in the following way. After each sheet is made, the operator measures the thickness with a micrometer. The thickness values for three consecutive sheets are averaged, and the average is plotted on a piece of graph paper that, at the start of the shift, has only a solid horizontal line drawn on it to indicate the target thickness value for the particular soft gasket sheet the operator is making. Periodically, the operator reviews these evolving data and makes a decision as to whether or not the process mean—the sheet thickness—needs to be adjusted. This can be accomplished by stopping the machine, loosening some clamps on the small roll, and jogging the small roll laterally in or out by a few thousandths of an inch—whatever the operator feels is needed. The clamps are tightened, the gap is checked with a taper gauge, and if adjusted properly, the operator begins to make sheets again. Typically, this adjustment process takes 10 to 15 minutes. The questions of when to make such adjustments and how much to change the roll gap for each adjustment are completely at the operator's discretion, based on the evolving plot of thickness averages.

Figure C5.3 shows a series of plots that detail the history of one particular work shift over which the operator made several process adjustments. (These data come from the same shift that the staff engineers used to collect data for a process capability study that is described later.) Figure C5.3a shows the process data after the first 12 sheets have been made—four averages of three successive sheet thicknesses. At this point, the operator judged that the data were telling her that the process was running below the target, so she stopped the process and made an adjustment to slightly increase the final roll gap. She then proceeded to make more sheets. Figure C5.3b shows the state of the process somewhat later. Now it appeared to the operator that the sheets were coming out too thick, so she stopped and made another adjustment. As shown in Figure Figure C5.3c, the process seemed to run well for a while, but then an average somewhat below the target led the operator to believe that another adjustment was necessary. Figures C5.3d and C5.3e show points in time where other adjustments were made.

Figure C5.3f shows the complete history of the shift. A total of 24 × 3, or 72, sheets were made during this shift. When asked, the operator indicated that the history of this shift was quite typical of what happens on a day-to-day basis.

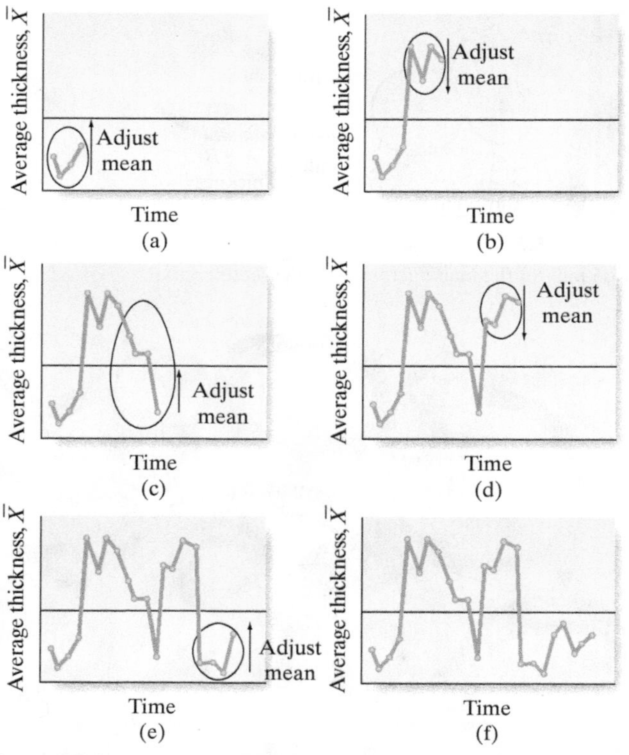

Figure C5.3
Process adjustment history over one shift

The Company's Stop-Gap Solution

While the staff engineers were studying the problem to formulate an appropriate action plan, something had to be done to make it possible to deliver hard gaskets within the new specification limits. Management decided to increase product inspection and, in particular, to grade each piece of material according to thickness so that the wide variation in thickness could be balanced out at the assembly process. Extra inspectors were used to grade each piece of soft gasket material. Sheets of the same thickness were shipped in separate bundles on pallets to a sister plant for assembly. Thick and thin sheets were selected as needed to make a hard gasket that met the specification. The process worked pretty well, and there was some discussion about making it permanent. However, some felt it was too costly and did not get at the root cause of the problem.

The Engineering Department's Analysis

Meanwhile, the staff engineers in the company were continuing to study the problem and came to the conclusion that the existing roll mill process equipment for making the soft gasket sheets simply was not capable of meeting the new specifications. This conclusion was reached as a result of an examination of production data and scrap logs over the past several months. They had researched some new equipment that had a track record for very good sheet-to-sheet consistency and had decided to write a proposal to replace the existing roll mills with this new equipment.

Table C5.1	Measurements of Sheet Thickness				
Sheet	**w (in.)**	**Sheet**	**w (in.)**	**Sheet**	**w (in.)**
1	0.0440	25	0.0464	49	0.0427
2	0.0446	26	0.0457	50	0.0437
3	0.0437	27	0.0447	51	0.0445
4	0.0438	28	0.0451	52	0.0431
5	0.0425	29	0.0447	53	0.0448
6	0.0443	30	0.0457	54	0.0429
7	0.0453	31	0.0456	55	0.0425
8	0.0428	32	0.0455	56	0.0442
9	0.0433	33	0.0445	57	0.0432
10	0.0451	34	0.0448	58	0.0429
11	0.0441	35	0.0423	59	0.0447
12	0.0434	36	0.0442	60	0.0450
13	0.0459	37	0.0459	61	0.0443
14	0.0466	38	0.0468	62	0.0441
15	0.0476	39	0.0452	63	0.0450
16	0.0449	40	0.0456	64	0.0443
17	0.0471	41	0.0471	65	0.0423
18	0.0451	42	0.0450	66	0.0447
19	0.0472	43	0.0472	67	0.0429
20	0.0477	44	0.0465	68	0.0427
21	0.0452	45	0.0461	69	0.0464
22	0.0457	46	0.0462	70	0.0448
23	0.0459	47	0.0463	71	0.0451
24	0.0472	48	0.0471	72	0.0428

Data Set: GASKET

To strengthen the proposal, their boss asked them to include data that demonstrated the poor capability of the existing equipment. The engineers, confident that the equipment was not capable, selected what they thought was the best operator and the best roll mill (the plant has several roll mill lines) and took careful measurements of the thickness of each sheet made on an 8-hour shift. During that shift, a total of 72 sheets/pulls were made. This was considered quite acceptable because the work standard for the process is 70 sheets per shift. The measurements of the sheet thickness (in the order of manufacture) for the 72 sheets are given in Table C5.1. The engineers set out to use these data to conduct a process capability study.

Relying on a statistical methods course that one of the engineers had in college 10 years ago, the group decided to construct a frequency distribution from the data and use it to estimate the percentage of the measurements that fell within the specification limits. Their histogram is shown in Figure C5.4. Also shown in the figure are the upper and lower specification values. The purple and red shaded parts of the histogram represent the amount of the product that lies outside of the specification limits. It is immediately apparent from the histogram that a large proportion of the output does not meet the customer's needs. Eight of the 72 sheets fall outside the specification limits. Therefore, in terms of percent conforming to specifications, the engineers estimated the process capability to be 88.8%. This was clearly unacceptable. This analysis confirmed the engineers' low opinion of the roll mill process equipment. They included it in their proposal and sent their recommendation to replace the equipment to the president's office.

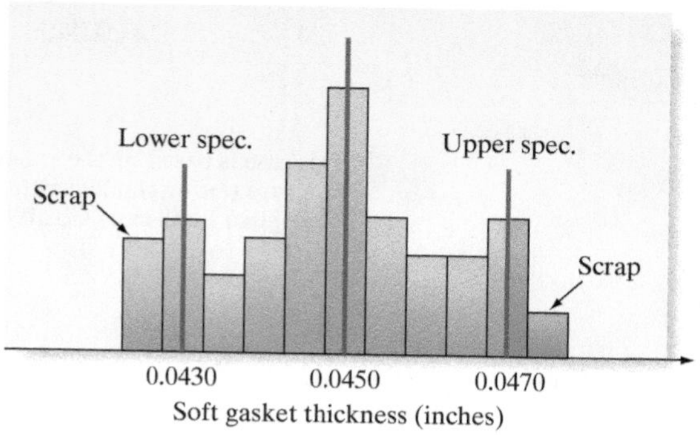

Figure C5.4
Histogram of data from process capability study

Your Assignment

You have been hired as an external consultant by the company's president, Marilyn Carlson. She would like you to critique the engineers' analysis, conclusion, and recommendations.

Suspecting that the engineers' work may be flawed, President Carlson would also like you to conduct your own study and make your own recommendations concerning how to resolve the company's problem. She would like you to use the data reported in Table C5.1 along with the data in Table C5.2, which she ordered be collected for you. These data were collected in the same manner as the data in Table C5.1. However, they were collected during a period of time when the roll mill operator was instructed *not* to adjust the sheet thickness. In your analysis, if you choose to construct control charts, use the same three-measurement subgrouping that the operators use.

Prepare an in-depth written report for the president that responds to her requests. It should begin with an executive summary and include whatever tables and figures are needed to support your analysis and recommendations. [The data file for this case is named **GASKET.** The file contains three variables: sheet number, sheet thickness, and a code for operator adjustments (A) or no adjustments (N).]

Table C5.2 Measurements of Sheet Thickness for a Shift Run with No Operator Adjustment

Sheet	Thickness (in.)	Sheet	Thickness (in.)	Sheet	Thickness (in.)
1	0.0445	25	0.0443	49	0.0445
2	0.0455	26	0.0450	50	0.0471
3	0.0457	27	0.0441	51	0.0465
4	0.0435	28	0.0449	52	0.0438
5	0.0453	29	0.0448	53	0.0445
6	0.0450	30	0.0467	54	0.0472
7	0.0438	31	0.0465	55	0.0453
8	0.0459	32	0.0449	56	0.0444
9	0.0428	33	0.0448	57	0.0451
10	0.0449	34	0.0461	58	0.0455
11	0.0449	35	0.0439	59	0.0435
12	0.0467	36	0.0452	60	0.0443
13	0.0433	37	0.0443	61	0.0440
14	0.0461	38	0.0434	62	0.0438
15	0.0451	39	0.0454	63	0.0444
16	0.0455	40	0.0456	64	0.0444
17	0.0454	41	0.0459	65	0.0450
18	0.0461	42	0.0452	66	0.0467
19	0.0455	43	0.0447	67	0.0445
20	0.0458	44	0.0442	68	0.0447
21	0.0445	45	0.0457	69	0.0461
22	0.0445	46	0.0454	70	0.0450
23	0.0451	47	0.0445	71	0.0463
24	0.0436	48	0.0451	72	0.0456

Data Set: GASKET

This case is based on the experiences of an actual company whose identity is disguised for confidentiality reasons. The case was originally written by DeVor, Chang, and Southerland (*Statistical Quality Design and Control* [New York: Macmillan Publishing Co., 1992], pp. 298–329) and has been adapted to focus on the material presented in Chapter 13.

Appendix A: Summation Notation

Denote the measurements of a quantitative data set as follows: $x_1, x_2, x_3, \ldots, x_n$, where x_1 is the first measurement in the data set, x_2 is the second measurement in the data set, x_3 is the third measurement in the data set, . . . , and x_n is the nth (and last) measurement in the data set. Thus, if we have five measurements in a set of data, we will write x_1, x_2, x_3, x_4, x_5 to represent the measurements. If the actual numbers are 5, 3, 8, 5, and 4, we have $x_1 = 5$, $x_2 = 3$, $x_3 = 8$, $x_4 = 5$, and $x_5 = 4$.

Most of the formulas used in this text require a summation of numbers. For example, one sum is the sum of all the measurements in the data set, or $x_1 + x_2 + x_3 + \cdots + x_n$. To shorten the notation, we use the symbol Σ for the summation–that is, $x_1 + x_2 + x_3 + \cdots + x_n = \sum_{i=1}^{n} x_i$. Verbally translate $\sum_{i=1}^{n} x_i$ as follows: "The sum of the measurements, whose typical member is x_i, beginning with the member x_1 and ending with the member x_n."

Suppose, as in our earlier example, that $x_1 = 5$, $x_2 = 3$, $x_3 = 8$, $x_4 = 5$, and $x_5 = 4$. Then the sum of the five measurements, denoted $\sum_{i=1}^{n} x_i$, is obtained as follows:

$$\begin{aligned}\sum_{i=1}^{5} x_i &= x_1 + x_2 + x_3 + x_4 + x_5 \\ &= 5 + 3 + 8 + 5 + 4 = 25\end{aligned}$$

Another important calculation requires that we square each measurement and then sum the squares. The notation for this sum is $\sum_{i=1}^{n} x_i^2$. For the preceding five measurements, we have

$$\begin{aligned}\sum_{i=1}^{5} x_i^2 &= x_1^2 + x_2^2 + x_3^2 + x_4^2 + x_5^2 \\ &= 5^2 + 3^2 + 8^2 + 5^2 + 4^2 \\ &= 25 + 9 + 64 + 25 + 16 = 139\end{aligned}$$

In general, the symbol following the summation sign represents the variable (or function of the variable) that is to be summed.

The Meaning of Summation Notation $\sum_{i=1}^{n} x_i$

Sum the measurements on the variable that appears to the right of the summation symbol, beginning with the 1st measurement and ending with the nth measurement.

Example A.1

Finding a Sum

Problem A sample data set contains the following six measurements: 5, 1, 3, 0, 2, 1. Find

$$\sum_{i=1}^{n} x_i$$

Solution For these data, the sample size $n = 6$. The measurements are denoted $x_1 = 5$, $x_2 = 1$, $x_3 = 3$, $x_4 = 0$, $x_5 = 2$, and $x_6 = 5$. Then

$$\sum_{i=1}^{n} x_i = x_1 + x_2 + x_3 + x_4 + x_5 + x_6 = 5 + 1 + 3 + 0 + 2 + 1 = 12$$

Example A.2

Finding a Sum of Squares

Problem Refer to Example A.1. Find

$$\sum_{i=1}^{n} x_i^2$$

Solution Now we desire the sum of squares of the six measurements.

$$\sum_{i=1}^{n} x_i^2 = x_1^2 + x_2^2 + x_3^2 + x_4^2 + x_5^2 + x_6^2 = 5^2 + 1^2 + 3^2 + 0^2 + 2^2 + 1^2$$
$$= 25 + 1 + 9 + 0 + 4 + 1 = 40$$

Example A.3

Finding a Sum of Differences

Problem Refer to Example A.1. Find

$$\sum_{i=1}^{n} (x_i - 2)$$

Solution Here, we subtract 2 from each measurement, then sum the six differences.

$$\sum_{i=1}^{n} (x_i - 2) = (x_1 - 2) + (x_2 - 2) + (x_3 - 2) + (x_4 - 2) + (x_5 - 2) + (x_6 - 2)$$
$$= (5 - 2) + (1 - 2) + (3 - 2) + (0 - 2) + (2 - 2) + (1 - 2)$$
$$= 3 + (-1) + 1 + (-2) + 0 + (-1) = 0$$

Appendix B: Basic Counting Rules

Sample points associated with many experiments have identical characteristics. If you can develop a counting rule to count the number of sample points, it can be used to aid in the solution of many probability problems. For example, many experiments involve sampling n elements from a population of N. Then, as explained in Section 3.1, we can use the formula

$$\binom{N}{n} = \frac{N!}{n!(N-n)!}$$

to find the number of different samples of n elements that could be selected from the total of N elements. This gives the number of sample points for the experiment.

Here, we give you a few useful counting rules. You should learn the characteristics of the situation to which each rule applies. Then, when working a probability problem, carefully examine the experiment to see whether you can use one of the rules.

Learning how to decide whether a particular counting rule applies to an experiment takes patience and practice. If you want to develop this skill, try to use the rules to solve some of the exercises in Chapter 3. Proofs of the rules below can be found in the text by W. Feller listed in the references to Chapter 3.

Multiplicative Rule

You have k sets of different elements, n_1 in the first set, n_2 in the second set,..., and n_k in the kth set. Suppose you want to form a sample of k elements by *taking one element from each of the* k *sets*. The number of different samples that can be formed is the product

$$n_1 \cdot n_2 \cdot n_3 \cdot \cdots \cdot n_k$$

Example B.1

Applying the Multiplicative Rule

Problem A product can be shipped by four airlines, and each airline can ship via three different routes. How many distinct ways exist to ship the product?

Solution A method of shipment corresponds to a pairing of one airline and one route. Therefore, $k = 2$, the number of airlines is $n_1 = 4$, the number of routes is $n_2 = 3$, and the number of ways to ship the product is

$$n_1 \cdot n_2 = (4)(3) = 12$$

Look Back How the multiplicative rule works can be seen by using a tree diagram, introduced in Section 3.6. The airline choice is shown by three branching lines in Figure B.1.

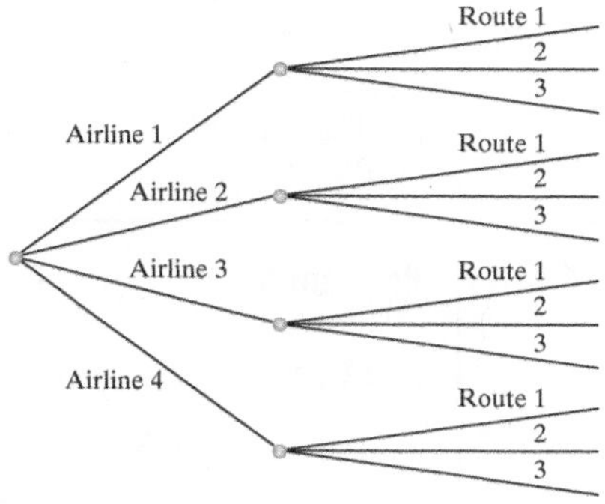

Figure B.1
Tree diagram for airline example

Example B.2

Applying the Multiplicative Rule

Problem You have 20 candidates for three different executive positions, E_1, E_2, and E_3. How many different ways could you fill the positions?

Solution For this example, there are $k = 3$ sets of elements:

Set 1: The candidates available to fill position E_1
Set 2: The candidates remaining (after filling E_1) that are available to fill E_2
Set 3: The candidates remaining (after filling E_1 and E_2) that are available to fill E_3

The numbers of elements in the sets are $n_1 = 20$, $n_2 = 19$, and $n_3 = 18$. Thus, the number of different ways to fill the three positions is

$$n_1 \cdot n_2 \cdot n_3 = (20)(19)(18) = 6{,}480$$

Partitions Rule

You have a *single* set of N distinctly different elements, and you want to partition it into k sets, the first set containing n_1 elements, the second containing n_2 elements,..., and the kth containing n_k elements. The number of different partitions is

$$\frac{N!}{n_1!n_2! \cdot \cdots \cdot n_k!} \quad \text{where } n_1 + n_2 + n_3 + \cdots + n_k = N$$

Example B.3

Applying the Partitions Rule

Problem You have 12 construction workers available for 3 job sites. Suppose you want to assign 3 workers to job 1, 4 to job 2, and 5 to job 3. How many different ways could you make this assignment?

Solution For this example, $k = 3$ (corresponding to the $k = 3$ job sites), $N = 12$, and $n_1 = 3$, $n_2 = 4$, $n_3 = 5$. Then the number of different ways to assign the workers to the job sites is

$$\frac{N!}{n_1!n_2!n_3!} = \frac{12!}{3!4!5!} = \frac{12 \cdot 11 \cdot 10 \cdot \cdots \cdot 3 \cdot 2 \cdot 1}{(3 \cdot 2 \cdot 1)(4 \cdot 3 \cdot 2 \cdot 1)(5 \cdot 4 \cdot 3 \cdot 2 \cdot 1)} = 27{,}720$$

Combinations Rule

The combinations rule given in Chapter 3 is a special case ($k = 2$) of the partitions rule—that is, sampling is equivalent to partitioning a set of N elements into $k = 2$ groups: elements that appear in the sample and those that do not. Let $n_1 = n$, the number of elements in the sample, and $n_2 = N - n$, the number of elements remaining. Then the number of different samples of n elements that can be selected from N is

$$\frac{N!}{n_1!n_2!} = \frac{N!}{n!(N-n)!} = \binom{N}{n}$$

This formula was given in Section 3.1.

Example B.4

Applying the Combinations Rule

Problem How many samples of 4 firefighters can be selected from a group of 10?

Solution We have $N = 10$ and $n = 4$; then

$$\binom{N}{n} = \binom{10}{4} = \frac{10!}{4!6!} = \frac{10 \cdot 9 \cdot 8 \cdot \cdots \cdot 3 \cdot 2 \cdot 1}{(4 \cdot 3 \cdot 2 \cdot 1)(6 \cdot 5 \cdot \cdots \cdot 2 \cdot 1)} = 210$$

Permutations Rule

The permutations rule is a generalization of the combinations rule where the order of the elements selected from the sample is important. (It can also be viewed as a special cases of the multiplicative rule.) A particular order is called a *permutation*. The number of different permutations of n elements that can be selected from a population of N elements is

$$\frac{N!}{(N-n)!} = N(N-1)(N-2)\cdots(N-n+1)$$

Example B.5

Applying the Permutations Rule

Problem There are three different entrances to a burning building. A fire captain must select three firefighters to enter the building, one for each entrance. The first firefighter selected will enter through the front door, the second through the back door, and the third one through a hole in the roof. How many permutations of three firefighters can be selected from a crew of 10 firefighters?

Solution Here we have $N = 10$ and $n = 3$. Since the order of selection is important, we apply the permutations rule:

$$\frac{N!}{(N-n)!} = \frac{10!}{(10-3)!} = \frac{10!}{7!} = \frac{10\cdot9\cdot8\cdot7\cdot6\cdot5\cdot4\cdot3\cdot2\cdot1}{7\cdot6\cdot5\cdot4\cdot3\cdot2\cdot1} = 10\cdot9\cdot8 = 720$$

Appendix C: Calculation Formulas for Analysis of Variance

C.1 Formulas for the Calculations in the Completely Randomized Design

$$\text{CM} = \text{Correction for mean}$$

$$= \frac{(\text{Total of all observations})^2}{\text{Total number of observations}} = \frac{\left(\sum_{i=1}^{n} y_i\right)^2}{n}$$

$$\text{SS(Total)} = \text{Total sum of squares}$$

$$= (\text{Sum of squares of all observations}) - \text{CM} = \sum_{i=1}^{n} y_i^2 - \text{CM}$$

$$\text{SST} = \text{Sum of squares for treatments}$$

$$= \begin{pmatrix} \text{Sum of squares of treatment totals with} \\ \text{each square divided by the number of} \\ \text{observations for that treatment} \end{pmatrix} - \text{CM}$$

$$= \frac{T_1^2}{n_1} + \frac{T_2^2}{n_2} + \cdots + \frac{T_k^2}{n_k} - \text{CM}$$

$$\text{SSE} = \text{Sum of squares for error} = \text{SS(Total)} - \text{SST}$$

$$\text{MST} = \text{Mean square for treatments} = \frac{\text{SST}}{k - 1}$$

$$\text{MSE} = \text{Mean square for error} = \frac{\text{SSE}}{n - k}$$

$$F = \text{Test statistic} = \frac{\text{MST}}{\text{MSE}}$$

where

n = Total number of observations
k = Number of treatments
T_i = Total for treatment i ($i = 1, 2, \ldots, k$)

C.2 Formulas for the Calculations in the Randomized Block Design

$$\text{CM} = \text{Correction for mean} = \frac{(\text{Total of all observations})^2}{\text{Total number of observations}} = \frac{\left(\sum y_i\right)^2}{n}$$

$$\text{SS(Total)} = \text{Total sum of squares} = (\text{Sum of squares of all observations}) - \text{CM} = \sum y_i^2 - \text{CM}$$

$$\text{SST} = \text{Sum of squares for treatments} = \begin{pmatrix} \text{Sum of squares of treatment totals with} \\ \text{each square divided by } b\text{, the number of} \\ \text{observations for that treatment} \end{pmatrix} - \text{CM} = \frac{T_1^2}{b} + \frac{T_2^2}{b} + \cdots + \frac{T_p^2}{b} - \text{CM}$$

$$\text{SST} = \text{Sum of squares for blocks} = \begin{pmatrix} \text{Sum of squares of block totals with} \\ \text{each square divided by } k\text{, the number} \\ \text{of observations in that block} \end{pmatrix} - \text{CM} = \frac{B_1^2}{k} + \frac{B_2^2}{k} + \cdots + \frac{B_b^2}{k} - \text{CM}$$

$$\text{SSE} = \text{Sum of squares for error} = \text{SS(Total)} - \text{SST} - \text{SSB}$$

$$\text{MST} = \text{Mean square for treatments} = \frac{\text{SST}}{k-1}$$

$$\text{MSB} = \text{Mean square for blocks} = \frac{\text{SSB}}{b-1}$$

$$\text{MSE} = \text{Mean square for error} = \frac{\text{SSE}}{n-k-b+1}$$

$$F = \text{Test statistic} = \frac{\text{MST}}{\text{MSE}}$$

where

n = Total number of observations

b = Number of blocks

k = Number of treatments

T_i = Total for treatment i ($i = 1, 2, \ldots, k$)

B_i = Total for block i ($i = 1, 2, \ldots, b$)

C.3 Formulas for the Calculations for a Two-Factor Factorial Experiment

$$\text{CM} = \text{Correction for mean}$$

$$= \frac{(\text{Total of all } n \text{ measurements})^2}{n} = \frac{\left(\sum_{i=1}^{n} y_i\right)^2}{n}$$

$$\text{SS(Total)} = \text{Total sum of squares}$$

$$= (\text{Sum of squares of all } n \text{ measurements}) - \text{CM} = \sum_{i=1}^{n} y_i^2 - \text{CM}$$

$$\text{SS}(A) = \text{Sum of squares for main effects, factor } A$$

$$= \left(\begin{array}{c}\text{Sum of squares of the totals } A_1, A_2, \ldots, A_a \\ \text{divided by the number of measurements} \\ \text{in a single total, namely } br\end{array}\right) - \text{CM}$$

$$= \frac{\sum_{i=1}^{a} A_i^2}{br} - \text{CM}$$

$$\text{SS}(B) = \text{Sum of squares for main effects, factor } B$$

$$= \left(\begin{array}{c}\text{Sum of squares of the totals } B_1, B_2, \ldots, B_b \\ \text{divided by the number of measurements} \\ \text{in a single total, namely } ar\end{array}\right) - \text{CM}$$

$$= \frac{\sum_{i=1}^{b} B_i^2}{ar} - \text{CM}$$

$$\text{SS}(AB) = \text{Sum of squares for } AB \text{ interaction}$$

$$= \left(\begin{array}{c}\text{Sum of squares of the cell totals} \\ AB_{11}, AB_{12}, \ldots, AB_{ab} \text{ divided by} \\ \text{the number of measurements} \\ \text{in a single total, namely } r\end{array}\right) - \text{SS}(A) - \text{SS}(B) - \text{CM}$$

$$= \frac{\sum_{j=1}^{b}\sum_{i=1}^{a} AB_{ij}^2}{r} - \text{SS}(A) - \text{SS}(B) - \text{CM}$$

where

a = Number of levels of factor A

b = Number of levels of factor B

r = Number of replicates (observations per treatment)

A_i = Total for level i of factor A $(i = 1, 2, \ldots, a)$

B_j = Total for level j of factor B $(j = 1, 2, \ldots, b)$

AB_{ij} = Total for treatment (i, j), i.e., for ith level of factor A and jth level of factor B

C.4 Tukey's Multiple Comparisons Procedure (Equal Sample Sizes)

Step 1 Select the desired experimentwise error rate, α

Step 2 Calculate

$$\omega = q_\alpha(k, v)\frac{s}{\sqrt{n_t}}$$

where

k = Number of sample means (i.e., number of treatments)

$s = \sqrt{\text{MSE}}$

v = Number of degress of freedom associated with MSE

n_t = Number of observations in each of the k samples (i.e., number of observations per treatment)

$q_\alpha(k, v)$ = Critical value of the Studentized range (Table XV in Appendix D)

Step 3 Calculate and rank the k sample means.

Step 4 Place a bar over those pairs of treatment means that differ by less than ω. A pair of treatments not connected by an overbar (i.e., differing by more than ω) implies a difference in the corresponding population means.

Note: The confidence level associated with all inferences drawn from the analysis is $(1 - \alpha)$.

C.5 Bonferroni Multiple Comparisons Procedure (Pairwise Comparisons)

Step 1 Calculate for each treatment pair (i, j)

$$B_{ij} = t_{\alpha/(2c)}s\sqrt{\frac{1}{n_i} + \frac{1}{n_j}}$$

where

k = Number of sample (treatment) means in the experiment

c = Number of pairwise comparisons

[*Note:* If all pairwise comparisons are to be made, then $c = k(k - 1)/2$]

$s = \sqrt{\text{MSE}}$

v = Number of degrees of freedom associated with MSE

n_i = Number of observations in sample for treatment i

n_j = Number of observations in sample for treatment j

$t_{\alpha/(2c)}$ = Critical value of t distribution with v df and tail area $\alpha/(2c)$ (Table III in Appendix D)

Step 2 Rank the sample means and place a bar over any treatment pair (i, j) whose sample means differ by less than B_{ij}. Any pair of means not connected by an overbar implies a difference in the corresponding population means.

Note: The level of confidence associated with all inferences drawn from the analysis is at least $(1 - \alpha)$.

C.6 Scheffé's Multiple Comparisons Procedure (Pairwise Comparisons)

Step 1 Calculate Scheffé's critical difference for each pair of treatments (i, j):

$$S_{ij} = \sqrt{(k - 1)(F_\alpha)(\text{MSE})\left(\frac{1}{n_1} + \frac{1}{n_j}\right)}$$

where

k = Number of sample (treatment) means

MSE = Mean squared error

n_i = Number of observations in sample for treatment i

n_j = Number of observations in sample for treatment j

F_α = Critical value of F-distribution with $k - 1$ numerator df and v denominator df (Tables V, VI, VII, and VIII in Appendix D)

v = Number of degrees of freedom associated with MSE

Step 2 Rank the k sample means and place a bar over any treatment pair (i, j) that differs by less than S_{ij}. Any pair of sample means not connected by an overbar implies a difference in the corresponding population means.

Appendix D: Tables

Table I Binomial Probabilities

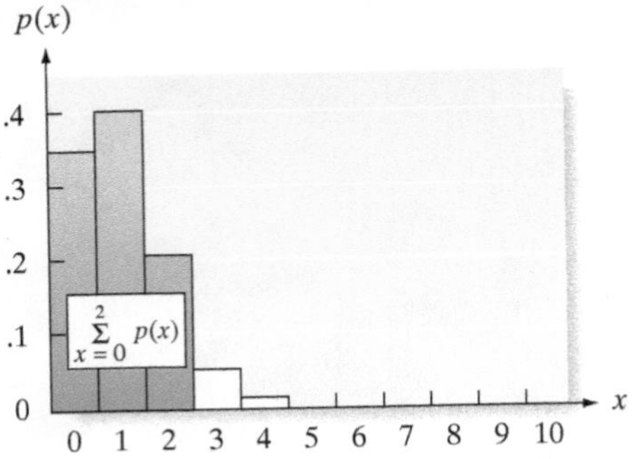

Tabulated values are $\sum_{x=0}^{k} p(x)$. *(Computations are rounded at the third decimal place.)*

a. $n = 5$

k \ p	.01	.05	.10	.20	.30	.40	.50	.60	.70	.80	.90	.95	.99
0	.951	.774	.590	.328	.168	.078	.031	.010	.002	.000	.000	.000	.000
1	.999	.977	.919	.737	.528	.337	.188	.087	.031	.007	.000	.000	.000
2	1.000	.999	.991	.942	.837	.683	.500	.317	.163	.058	.009	.001	.000
3	1.000	1.000	1.000	.993	.969	.913	.812	.663	.472	.263	.081	.023	.001
4	1.000	1.000	1.000	1.000	.998	.990	.969	.922	.832	.672	.410	.226	.049

b. $n = 6$

k \ p	.01	.05	.10	.20	.30	.40	.50	.60	.70	.80	.90	.95	.99
0	.941	.735	.531	.262	.118	.047	.016	.004	.001	.000	.000	.000	.000
1	.999	.967	.886	.655	.420	.233	.109	.041	.011	.002	.000	.000	.000
2	1.000	.998	.984	.901	.744	.544	.344	.179	.070	.017	.001	.000	.000
3	1.000	1.000	.999	.983	.930	.821	.656	.456	.256	.099	.016	.002	.000
4	1.000	1.000	1.000	.998	.989	.959	.891	.767	.580	.345	.114	.033	.001
5	1.000	1.000	1.000	1.000	.999	.996	.984	.953	.882	.738	.469	.265	.059

c. $n = 7$

k \ p	.01	.05	.10	.20	.30	.40	.50	.60	.70	.80	.90	.95	.99
0	.932	.698	.478	.210	.082	.028	.008	.002	.000	.000	.000	.000	.000
1	.998	.956	.850	.577	.329	.159	.063	.019	.004	.000	.000	.000	.000
2	1.000	.996	.974	.852	.647	.420	.227	.096	.029	.005	.000	.000	.000
3	1.000	1.000	.997	.967	.874	.710	.500	.290	.126	.033	.003	.000	.000
4	1.000	1.000	1.000	.995	.971	.904	.773	.580	.353	.148	.026	.004	.000
5	1.000	1.000	1.000	1.000	.996	.981	.937	.841	.671	.423	.150	.044	.002
6	1.000	1.000	1.000	1.000	1.000	.998	.992	.972	.918	.790	.522	.302	.068

d. $n = 8$

k \ p	.01	.05	.10	.20	.30	.40	.50	.60	.70	.80	.90	.95	.99
0	.923	.663	.430	.168	.058	.017	.004	.001	.000	.000	.000	.000	.000
1	.997	.943	.813	.503	.255	.106	.035	.009	.001	.000	.000	.000	.000
2	1.000	.994	.962	.797	.552	.315	.145	.050	.011	.001	.000	.000	.000
3	1.000	1.000	.995	.944	.806	.594	.363	.174	.058	.010	.000	.000	.000
4	1.000	1.000	1.000	.990	.942	.826	.637	.406	.194	.056	.005	.000	.000
5	1.000	1.000	1.000	.999	.989	.950	.855	.685	.448	.203	.038	.006	.000
6	1.000	1.000	1.000	1.000	.999	.991	.965	.894	.745	.497	.187	.057	.003
7	1.000	1.000	1.000	1.000	1.000	.999	.996	.983	.942	.832	.570	.337	.077

(continued)

Table I *(continued)*

e. $n = 9$

k \ p	.01	.05	.10	.20	.30	.40	.50	.60	.70	.80	.90	.95	.99
0	.914	.630	.387	.134	.040	.010	.002	.000	.000	.000	.000	.000	.000
1	.997	.929	.775	.436	.196	.071	.020	.004	.000	.000	.000	.000	.000
2	1.000	.992	.947	.738	.463	.232	.090	.025	.004	.000	.000	.000	.000
3	1.000	.999	.992	.914	.730	.483	.254	.099	.025	.003	.000	.000	.000
4	1.000	1.000	.999	.980	.901	.733	.500	.267	.099	.020	.001	.000	.000
5	1.000	1.000	1.000	.997	.975	.901	.746	.517	.270	.086	.008	.001	.000
6	1.000	1.000	1.000	1.000	.996	.975	.910	.768	.537	.262	.053	.008	.000
7	1.000	1.000	1.000	1.000	1.000	.996	.980	.929	.804	.564	.225	.071	.003
8	1.000	1.000	1.000	1.000	1.000	1.000	.998	.990	.960	.866	.613	.370	.086

f. $n = 10$

k \ p	.01	.05	.10	.20	.30	.40	.50	.60	.70	.80	.90	.95	.99
0	.904	.599	.349	.107	.028	.006	.001	.000	.000	.000	.000	.000	.000
1	.996	.914	.736	.376	.149	.046	.011	.002	.000	.000	.000	.000	.000
2	1.000	.988	.930	.678	.383	.167	.055	.012	.002	.000	.000	.000	.000
3	1.000	.999	.987	.879	.650	.382	.172	.055	.011	.001	.000	.000	.000
4	1.000	1.000	.998	.967	.850	.633	.377	.166	.047	.006	.000	.000	.000
5	1.000	1.000	1.000	.994	.953	.834	.623	.367	.150	.033	.002	.000	.000
6	1.000	1.000	1.000	.999	.989	.945	.828	.618	.350	.121	.013	.001	.000
7	1.000	1.000	1.000	1.000	.998	.988	.945	.833	.617	.322	.070	.012	.000
8	1.000	1.000	1.000	1.000	1.000	.998	.989	.954	.851	.624	.264	.086	.004
9	1.000	1.000	1.000	1.000	1.000	1.000	.999	.994	.972	.893	.651	.401	.096

g. $n = 15$

k \ p	.01	.05	.10	.20	.30	.40	.50	.60	.70	.80	.90	.95	.99
0	.860	.463	.206	.035	.005	.000	.000	.000	.000	.000	.000	.000	.000
1	.990	.829	.549	.167	.035	.005	.000	.000	.000	.000	.000	.000	.000
2	1.000	.964	.816	.398	.127	.027	.004	.000	.000	.000	.000	.000	.000
3	1.000	.995	.944	.648	.297	.091	.018	.002	.000	.000	.000	.000	.000
4	1.000	.999	.987	.838	.515	.217	.059	.009	.001	.000	.000	.000	.000
5	1.000	1.000	.998	.939	.722	.403	.151	.034	.004	.000	.000	.000	.000
6	1.000	1.000	1.000	.982	.869	.610	.304	.095	.015	.001	.000	.000	.000
7	1.000	1.000	1.000	.996	.950	.787	.500	.213	.050	.004	.000	.000	.000
8	1.000	1.000	1.000	.999	.985	.905	.696	.390	.131	.018	.000	.000	.000
9	1.000	1.000	1.000	1.000	.996	.966	.849	.597	.278	.061	.002	.000	.000
10	1.000	1.000	1.000	1.000	.999	.991	.941	.783	.485	.164	.013	.001	.000
11	1.000	1.000	1.000	1.000	1.000	.998	.982	.909	.703	.352	.056	.005	.000
12	1.000	1.000	1.000	1.000	1.000	1.000	.996	.973	.873	.602	.184	.036	.000
13	1.000	1.000	1.000	1.000	1.000	1.000	1.000	.995	.965	.833	.451	.171	.010
14	1.000	1.000	1.000	1.000	1.000	1.000	1.000	1.000	.995	.965	.794	.537	.140

(continued)

Table I *(continued)*

h. $n = 20$

k \ p	.01	.05	.10	.20	.30	.40	.50	.60	.70	.80	.90	.95	.99
0	.818	.358	.122	.012	.001	.000	.000	.000	.000	.000	.000	.000	.000
1	.983	.736	.392	.069	.008	.001	.000	.000	.000	.000	.000	.000	.000
2	.999	.925	.677	.206	.035	.004	.000	.000	.000	.000	.000	.000	.000
3	1.000	.984	.867	.411	.107	.016	.001	.000	.000	.000	.000	.000	.000
4	1.000	.997	.957	.630	.238	.051	.006	.000	.000	.000	.000	.000	.000
5	1.000	1.000	.989	.804	.416	.126	.021	.002	.000	.000	.000	.000	.000
6	1.000	1.000	.998	.913	.608	.250	.058	.006	.000	.000	.000	.000	.000
7	1.000	1.000	1.000	.968	.772	.416	.132	.021	.001	.000	.000	.000	.000
8	1.000	1.000	1.000	.990	.887	.596	.252	.057	.005	.000	.000	.000	.000
9	1.000	1.000	1.000	.997	.952	.755	.412	.128	.017	.001	.000	.000	.000
10	1.000	1.000	1.000	.999	.983	.872	.588	.245	.048	.003	.000	.000	.000
11	1.000	1.000	1.000	1.000	.995	.943	.748	.404	.113	.010	.000	.000	.000
12	1.000	1.000	1.000	1.000	.999	.979	.868	.584	.228	.032	.000	.000	.000
13	1.000	1.000	1.000	1.000	1.000	.994	.942	.750	.392	.087	.002	.000	.000
14	1.000	1.000	1.000	1.000	1.000	.998	.979	.874	.584	.196	.011	.000	.000
15	1.000	1.000	1.000	1.000	1.000	1.000	.994	.949	.762	.370	.043	.003	.000
16	1.000	1.000	1.000	1.000	1.000	1.000	.999	.984	.893	.589	.133	.016	.000
17	1.000	1.000	1.000	1.000	1.000	1.000	1.000	.996	.965	.794	.323	.075	.001
18	1.000	1.000	1.000	1.000	1.000	1.000	1.000	.999	.992	.931	.608	.264	.017
19	1.000	1.000	1.000	1.000	1.000	1.000	1.000	1.000	.999	.988	.878	.642	.182

i. $n = 25$

k \ p	.01	.05	.10	.20	.30	.40	.50	.60	.70	.80	.90	.95	.99
0	.778	.277	.072	.004	.000	.000	.000	.000	.000	.000	.000	.000	.000
1	.974	.642	.271	.027	.002	.000	.000	.000	.000	.000	.000	.000	.000
2	.998	.873	.537	.098	.009	.000	.000	.000	.000	.000	.000	.000	.000
3	1.000	.966	.764	.234	.033	.002	.000	.000	.000	.000	.000	.000	.000
4	1.000	.993	.902	.421	.090	.009	.000	.000	.000	.000	.000	.000	.000
5	1.000	.999	.967	.617	.193	.029	.002	.000	.000	.000	.000	.000	.000
6	1.000	1.000	.991	.780	.341	.074	.007	.000	.000	.000	.000	.000	.000
7	1.000	1.000	.998	.891	.512	.154	.022	.001	.000	.000	.000	.000	.000
8	1.000	1.000	1.000	.953	.677	.274	.054	.004	.000	.000	.000	.000	.000
9	1.000	1.000	1.000	.983	.811	.425	.115	.013	.000	.000	.000	.000	.000
10	1.000	1.000	1.000	.994	.902	.586	.212	.034	.002	.000	.000	.000	.000
11	1.000	1.000	1.000	.998	.956	.732	.345	.078	.006	.000	.000	.000	.000
12	1.000	1.000	1.000	1.000	.983	.846	.500	.154	.017	.000	.000	.000	.000
13	1.000	1.000	1.000	1.000	.994	.922	.655	.268	.044	.002	.000	.000	.000
14	1.000	1.000	1.000	1.000	.998	.966	.788	.414	.098	.006	.000	.000	.000
15	1.000	1.000	1.000	1.000	1.000	.987	.885	.575	.189	.017	.000	.000	.000
16	1.000	1.000	1.000	1.000	1.000	.996	.946	.726	.323	.047	.000	.000	.000
17	1.000	1.000	1.000	1.000	1.000	.999	.978	.846	.488	.109	.002	.000	.000
18	1.000	1.000	1.000	1.000	1.000	1.000	.993	.926	.659	.220	.009	.000	.000
19	1.000	1.000	1.000	1.000	1.000	1.000	.998	.971	.807	.383	.033	.001	.000
20	1.000	1.000	1.000	1.000	1.000	1.000	1.000	.991	.910	.579	.098	.007	.000
21	1.000	1.000	1.000	1.000	1.000	1.000	1.000	.998	.967	.766	.236	.034	.000
22	1.000	1.000	1.000	1.000	1.000	1.000	1.000	1.000	.991	.902	.463	.127	.002
23	1.000	1.000	1.000	1.000	1.000	1.000	1.000	1.000	.998	.973	.729	.358	.026
24	1.000	1.000	1.000	1.000	1.000	1.000	1.000	1.000	1.000	.996	.928	.723	.222

Table II Normal Curve Areas

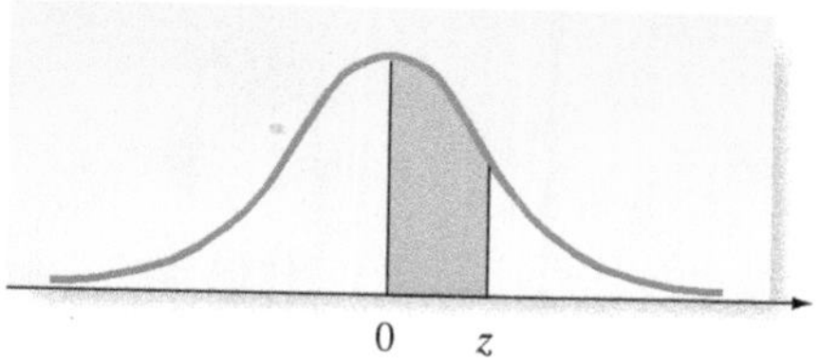

z	.00	.01	.02	.03	.04	.05	.06	.07	.08	.09
.0	.0000	.0040	.0080	.0120	.0160	.0199	.0239	.0279	.0319	.0359
.1	.0398	.0438	.0478	.0517	.0557	.0596	.0636	.0675	.0714	.0753
.2	.0793	.0832	.0871	.0910	.0948	.0987	.1026	.1064	.1103	.1141
.3	.1179	.1217	.1255	.1293	.1331	.1368	.1406	.1443	.1480	.1517
.4	.1554	.1591	.1628	.1664	.1700	.1736	.1772	.1808	.1844	.1879
.5	.1915	.1950	.1985	.2019	.2054	.2088	.2123	.2157	.2190	.2224
.6	.2257	.2291	.2324	.2357	.2389	.2422	.2454	.2486	.2517	.2549
.7	.2580	.2611	.2642	.2673	.2704	.2734	.2764	.2794	.2823	.2852
.8	.2881	.2910	.2939	.2967	.2995	.3023	.3051	.3078	.3106	.3133
.9	.3159	.3186	.3212	.3238	.3264	.3289	.3315	.3340	.3365	.3389
1.0	.3413	.3438	.3461	.3485	.3508	.3531	.3554	.3577	.3599	.3621
1.1	.3643	.3665	.3686	.3708	.3729	.3749	.3770	.3790	.3810	.3830
1.2	.3849	.3869	.3888	.3907	.3925	.3944	.3962	.3980	.3997	.4015
1.3	.4032	.4049	.4066	.4082	.4099	.4115	.4131	.4147	.4162	.4177
1.4	.4192	.4207	.4222	.4236	.4251	.4265	.4279	.4292	.4306	.4319
1.5	.4332	.4345	.4357	.4370	.4382	.4394	.4406	.4418	.4429	.4441
1.6	.4452	.4463	.4474	.4484	.4495	.4505	.4515	.4525	.4535	.4545
1.7	.4554	.4564	.4573	.4582	.4591	.4599	.4608	.4616	.4625	.4633
1.8	.4641	.4649	.4656	.4664	.4671	.4678	.4686	.4693	.4699	.4706
1.9	.4713	.4719	.4726	.4732	.4738	.4744	.4750	.4756	.4761	.4767
2.0	.4772	.4778	.4783	.4788	.4793	.4798	.4803	.4808	.4812	.4817
2.1	.4821	.4826	.4830	.4834	.4838	.4842	.4846	.4850	.4854	.4857
2.2	.4861	.4864	.4868	.4871	.4875	.4878	.4881	.4884	.4887	.4890
2.3	.4893	.4896	.4898	.4901	.4904	.4906	.4909	.4911	.4913	.4916
2.4	.4918	.4920	.4922	.4925	.4927	.4929	.4931	.4932	.4934	.4936
2.5	.4938	.4940	.4941	.4943	.4945	.4946	.4948	.4949	.4951	.4952
2.6	.4953	.4955	.4956	.4957	.4959	.4960	.4961	.4962	.4963	.4964
2.7	.4965	.4966	.4967	.4968	.4969	.4970	.4971	.4972	.4973	.4974
2.8	.4974	.4975	.4976	.4977	.4977	.4978	.4979	.4979	.4980	.4981
2.9	.4981	.4982	.4982	.4983	.4984	.4984	.4985	.4985	.4986	.4986
3.0	.4987	.4987	.4987	.4988	.4988	.4989	.4989	.4989	.4990	.4990
3.1	.49903	.49906	.49910	.49913	.49916	.49918	.49921	.49924	.49926	.48829
3.2	.49931	.49934	.49936	.49938	.49940	.49942	.49944	.49946	.49948	.49950
3.3	.49952	.49953	.49955	.49957	.49958	.49960	.49961	.49962	.49964	.49965
3.4	.49966	.49968	.49969	.49970	.49971	.49972	.49973	.49974	.49975	.49976
3.5	.49977	.49978	.49978	.49979	.49980	.49981	.49981	.49982	.49983	.49983
3.6	.49984	.49985	.49985	.49986	.49986	.49987	.49987	.49988	.49988	.49989
3.7	.49989	.49990	.49990	.49990	.49991	.49991	.49992	.49992	.49992	.49992
3.8	.49993	.49993	.49993	.49994	.49994	.49994	.49994	.49995	.49995	.49995
3.9	.49995	.49995	.49996	.49996	.49996	.49996	.49996	.49996	.49997	.49997

Source: Abridged from Table I of A. Hald. *Statistical Tables and Formulas* (New York: Wiley), 1952. Reproduced by permission of A. Hald.

Table III Critical Values of t

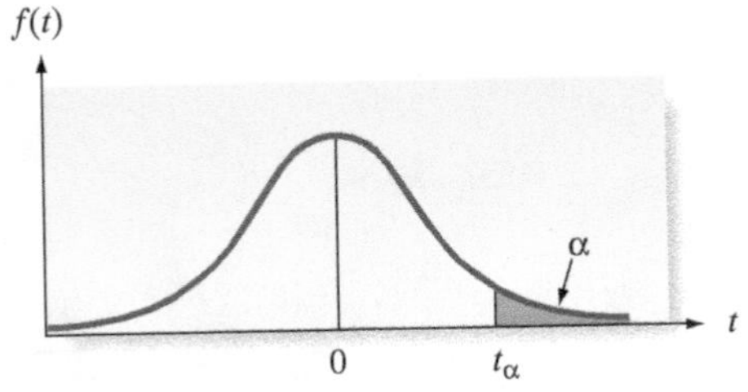

Degrees of Freedom	$t_{.100}$	$t_{.050}$	$t_{.025}$	$t_{.010}$	$t_{.005}$	$t_{.001}$	$t_{.0005}$
1	3.078	6.314	12.706	31.821	63.657	318.31	636.62
2	1.886	2.920	4.303	6.965	9.925	22.326	31.598
3	1.638	2.353	3.182	4.541	5.841	10.213	12.924
4	1.533	2.132	2.776	3.747	4.604	7.173	8.610
5	1.476	2.015	2.571	3.365	4.032	5.893	6.869
6	1.440	1.943	2.447	3.143	3.707	5.208	5.959
7	1.415	1.895	2.365	2.998	3.499	4.785	5.408
8	1.397	1.860	2.306	2.896	3.355	4.501	5.041
9	1.383	1.833	2.262	2.821	3.250	4.297	4.781
10	1.372	1.812	2.228	2.764	3.169	4.144	4.587
11	1.363	1.796	2.201	2.718	3.106	4.025	4.437
12	1.356	1.782	2.179	2.681	3.055	3.930	4.318
13	1.350	1.771	2.160	2.650	3.012	3.852	4.221
14	1.345	1.761	2.145	2.624	2.977	3.787	4.140
15	1.341	1.753	2.131	2.602	2.947	3.733	4.073
16	1.337	1.746	2.120	2.583	2.921	3.686	4.015
17	1.333	1.740	2.110	2.567	2.898	3.646	3.965
18	1.330	1.734	2.101	2.552	2.878	3.610	3.922
19	1.328	1.729	2.093	2.539	2.861	3.579	3.883
20	1.325	1.725	2.086	2.528	2.845	3.552	3.850
21	1.323	1.721	2.080	2.518	2.831	3.527	3.819
22	1.321	1.717	2.074	2.508	2.819	3.505	3.792
23	1.319	1.714	2.069	2.500	2.807	3.485	3.767
24	1.318	1.711	2.064	2.492	2.797	3.467	3.745
25	1.316	1.708	2.060	2.485	2.787	3.450	3.725
26	1.315	1.706	2.056	2.479	2.779	3.435	3.707
27	1.314	1.703	2.052	2.473	2.771	3.421	3.690
28	1.313	1.701	2.048	2.467	2.763	3.408	3.674
29	1.311	1.699	2.045	2.462	2.756	3.396	3.659
30	1.310	1.697	2.042	2.457	2.750	3.385	3.646
40	1.303	1.684	2.021	2.423	2.704	3.307	3.551
50	1.299	1.676	2.009	2.403	2.678	3.261	3.496
60	1.296	1.671	2.000	2.390	2.660	3.232	3.460
70	1.294	1.667	1.994	2.381	2.648	3.211	3.435
80	1.292	1.664	1.990	2.374	2.639	3.195	3.416
90	1.291	1.662	1.987	2.369	2.632	3.183	3.402
100	1.290	1.660	1.984	2.364	2.629	3.174	3.390
120	1.289	1.658	1.980	2.358	2.617	3.160	3.373
150	1.287	1.655	1.976	2.351	2.609	3.145	3.357
∞	1.282	1.645	1.960	2.326	2.576	3.090	3.291

Source: This table is reproduced with the kind permission of the Trustees of Biometrika from E. S. Pearson and H. O. Hartley (eds.). *The Biometrika Tables for Statisticians*, Vol. 1, 3rd ed., Biometrika, 1966.

Table IV Critical Values of χ^2

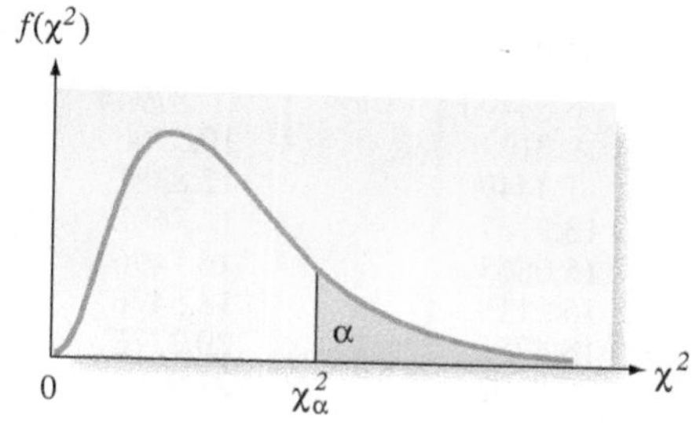

Degrees of Freedom	$\chi^2_{.995}$	$\chi^2_{.990}$	$\chi^2_{.975}$	$\chi^2_{.950}$	$\chi^2_{.900}$
1	.0000393	.0001571	.0009821	.0039321	.0157908
2	.0100251	.0201007	.0506356	.102587	.210720
3	.0717212	.114832	.215795	.351846	.584375
4	.206990	.297110	.484419	.710721	1.063623
5	.411740	.554300	.831211	1.145476	1.61031
6	.675727	.872085	1.237347	1.63539	2.20413
7	.989265	1.239043	1.68987	2.16735	2.83311
8	1.344419	1.646482	2.17973	2.73264	3.48954
9	1.734926	2.087912	2.70039	3.32511	4.16816
10	2.15585	2.55821	3.24697	3.94030	4.86518
11	2.60321	3.05347	3.81575	4.57481	5.57779
12	3.07382	3.57056	4.40379	5.22603	6.30380
13	3.56503	4.10691	5.00874	5.89186	7.04150
14	4.07468	4.66043	5.62872	6.57063	7.78953
15	4.60094	5.22935	6.26214	7.26094	8.54675
16	5.14224	5.81221	6.90766	7.96164	9.31223
17	5.69724	6.40776	7.56418	8.67176	10.0852
18	6.26481	7.01491	8.23075	9.39046	10.8649
19	6.84398	7.63273	8.90655	10.1170	11.6509
20	7.43386	8.26040	9.59083	10.8508	12.4426
21	8.03366	8.89720	10.28293	11.5913	13.2396
22	8.64272	9.54249	10.9823	12.3380	14.0415
23	9.26042	10.19567	11.6885	13.0905	14.8479
24	9.88623	10.8564	12.4011	13.8484	15.6587
25	10.5197	11.5240	13.1197	14.6114	16.4734
26	11.1603	12.1981	13.8439	15.3791	17.2919
27	11.8076	12.8786	14.5733	16.1513	18.1138
28	12.4613	13.5648	15.3079	16.9279	18.9392
29	13.1211	14.2565	16.0471	17.7083	19.7677
30	13.7867	14.9535	16.7908	18.4926	20.5992
40	20.7065	22.1643	24.4331	26.5093	29.0505
50	27.9907	29.7067	32.3574	34.7642	37.6886
60	35.5346	37.4848	40.4817	43.1879	46.4589
70	43.2752	45.4418	48.7576	51.7393	55.3290
80	51.1720	53.5400	57.1532	60.3915	64.2778
90	59.1963	61.7541	65.6466	69.1260	73.2912
100	67.3276	70.0648	74.2219	77.9295	82.3581
150	109.142	112.668	117.985	122.692	128.275
200	152.241	156.432	162.728	168.279	174.835
300	240.663	245.972	253.912	260.878	269.068
400	330.903	337.155	346.482	354.641	364.207
500	422.303	429.388	439.936	449.147	459.926

(continued)

Table IV *(continued)*

Degrees of Freedom	$\chi^2_{.100}$	$\chi^2_{.050}$	$\chi^2_{.025}$	$\chi^2_{.010}$	$\chi^2_{.005}$
1	2.70554	3.84146	5.02389	6.63490	7.87944
2	4.60517	5.99147	7.37776	9.21034	10.5966
3	6.25139	7.81473	9.34840	11.3449	12.8381
4	7.77944	9.48773	11.1433	13.2767	14.8602
5	9.23635	11.0705	12.8325	15.0863	16.7496
6	10.6446	12.5916	14.4494	16.8119	18.5476
7	12.0170	14.0671	16.0128	18.4753	20.2777
8	13.3616	15.5073	17.5346	20.0902	21.9550
9	14.6837	16.9190	19.0228	21.6660	23.5893
10	15.9871	18.3070	20.4831	23.2093	25.1882
11	17.2750	19.6751	21.9200	24.7250	26.7569
12	18.5494	21.0261	23.3367	26.2170	28.2995
13	19.8119	22.3621	24.7356	27.6883	29.8194
14	21.0642	23.6848	26.1190	29.1413	31.3193
15	22.3072	24.9958	27.4884	30.5779	32.8013
16	23.5418	26.2962	28.8454	31.9999	34.2672
17	24.7690	27.5871	30.1910	33.4087	35.7185
18	25.9894	28.8693	31.5264	34.8053	37.1564
19	27.2036	30.1435	32.8523	36.1908	38.5822
20	28.4120	31.4104	34.1696	37.5662	39.9968
21	29.6151	32.6705	35.4789	38.9321	41.4010
22	30.8133	33.9244	36.7807	40.2894	42.7956
23	32.0069	35.1725	38.0757	41.6384	44.1813
24	33.1963	36.4151	39.3641	42.9798	45.5585
25	34.3816	37.6525	40.6465	44.3141	46.9278
26	35.5631	38.8852	41.9232	45.6417	48.2899
27	36.7412	40.1133	43.1944	46.9630	49.6449
28	37.9159	41.3372	44.4607	48.2782	50.9933
29	39.0875	42.5569	45.7222	49.5879	52.3356
30	40.2560	43.7729	46.9792	50.8922	53.6720
40	51.8050	55.7585	59.3417	63.6907	66.7659
50	63.1671	67.5048	71.4202	76.1539	79.4900
60	74.3970	79.0819	83.2976	88.3794	91.9517
70	85.5271	90.5312	95.0231	100.425	104.215
80	96.5782	101.879	106.629	112.329	116.321
90	107.565	113.145	118.136	124.116	128.299
100	118.498	124.342	129.561	135.807	140.169
150	172.578	179.581	185.800	193.208	198.360
200	226.021	233.994	241.058	249.445	255.264
300	331.789	341.395	349.874	359.906	366.844
400	436.649	447.632	457.305	468.724	476.606
500	540.930	553.127	563.852	576.493	585.207

Source: From Thompson, C. M. "Tables of the percentage points of the χ^2-distribution," *Biometrika*, 1941, 32, 188–189. Reproduced by permission of the *Biometrika* Trustees.

Table V Percentage Points of the F-Distribution, $\alpha = .10$

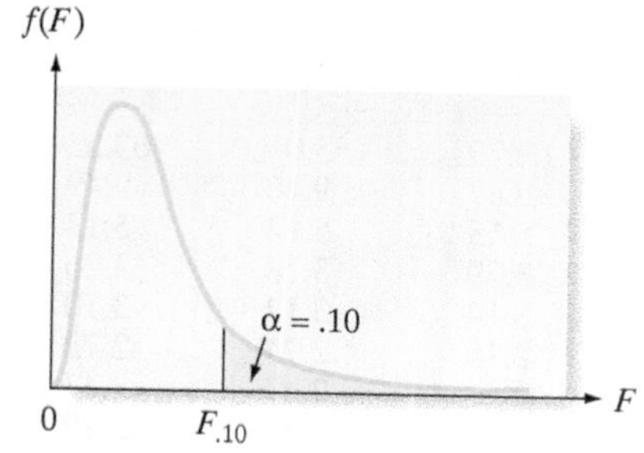

ν_2 \ ν_1	Numerator Degrees of Freedom								
Denominator Degrees of Freedom	1	2	3	4	5	6	7	8	9
1	39.86	49.50	53.59	55.83	57.24	58.20	58.91	59.44	59.86
2	8.53	9.00	9.16	9.24	9.29	9.33	9.35	9.37	9.38
3	5.54	5.46	5.39	5.34	5.31	5.28	5.27	5.25	5.24
4	4.54	4.32	4.19	4.11	4.05	4.01	3.98	3.95	3.94
5	4.06	3.78	3.62	3.52	3.45	3.40	3.37	3.34	3.32
6	3.78	3.46	3.29	3.18	3.11	3.05	3.01	2.98	2.96
7	3.59	3.26	3.07	2.96	2.88	2.83	2.78	2.75	2.72
8	3.46	3.11	2.92	2.81	2.73	2.67	2.62	2.59	2.56
9	3.36	3.01	2.81	2.69	2.61	2.55	2.51	2.47	2.44
10	3.29	2.92	2.73	2.61	2.52	2.46	2.41	2.38	2.35
11	3.23	2.86	2.66	2.54	2.45	2.39	2.34	2.30	2.27
12	3.18	2.81	2.61	2.48	2.39	2.33	2.28	2.24	2.21
13	3.14	2.76	2.56	2.43	2.35	2.28	2.23	2.20	2.16
14	3.10	2.73	2.52	2.39	2.31	2.24	2.19	2.15	2.12
15	3.07	2.70	2.49	2.36	2.27	2.21	2.16	2.12	2.09
16	3.05	2.67	2.46	2.33	2.24	2.18	2.13	2.09	2.06
17	3.03	2.64	2.44	2.31	2.22	2.15	2.10	2.06	2.03
18	3.01	2.62	2.42	2.29	2.20	2.13	2.08	2.04	2.00
19	2.99	2.61	2.40	2.27	2.18	2.11	2.06	2.02	1.98
20	2.97	2.59	2.38	2.25	2.16	2.09	2.04	2.00	1.96
21	2.96	2.57	2.36	2.23	2.14	2.08	2.02	1.98	1.95
22	2.95	2.56	2.35	2.22	2.13	2.06	2.01	1.97	1.93
23	2.94	2.55	2.34	2.21	2.11	2.05	1.99	1.95	1.92
24	2.93	2.54	2.33	2.19	2.10	2.04	1.98	1.94	1.91
25	2.92	2.53	2.32	2.18	2.09	2.02	1.97	1.93	1.89
26	2.91	2.52	2.31	2.17	2.08	2.01	1.96	1.92	1.88
27	2.90	2.51	2.30	2.17	2.07	2.00	1.95	1.91	1.87
28	2.89	2.50	2.29	2.16	2.06	2.00	1.94	1.90	1.87
29	2.89	2.50	2.28	2.15	2.06	1.99	1.93	1.89	1.86
30	2.88	2.49	2.28	2.14	2.05	1.98	1.93	1.88	1.85
40	2.84	2.44	2.23	2.09	2.00	1.93	1.87	1.83	1.79
60	2.79	2.39	2.18	2.04	1.95	1.87	1.82	1.77	1.74
120	2.75	2.35	2.13	1.99	1.90	1.82	1.77	1.72	1.68
∞	2.71	2.30	2.08	1.94	1.85	1.77	1.72	1.67	1.63

(continued)

Table V *(continued)*

ν_2 \ ν_1 (Denominator Degrees of Freedom \ Numerator Degrees of Freedom)	10	12	15	20	24	30	40	60	120	∞
1	60.19	60.71	61.22	61.74	62.00	62.26	62.53	62.79	63.06	63.33
2	9.39	9.41	9.42	9.44	9.45	9.46	9.47	9.47	9.48	9.49
3	5.23	5.22	5.20	5.18	5.18	5.17	5.16	5.15	5.14	5.13
4	3.92	3.90	3.87	3.84	3.83	3.82	3.80	3.79	3.78	3.76
5	3.30	3.27	3.24	3.21	3.19	3.17	3.16	3.14	3.12	3.10
6	2.94	2.90	2.87	2.84	2.82	2.80	2.78	2.76	2.74	2.72
7	2.70	2.67	2.63	2.59	2.58	2.56	2.54	2.51	2.49	2.47
8	2.54	2.50	2.46	2.42	2.40	2.38	2.36	2.34	2.32	2.29
9	2.42	2.38	2.34	2.30	2.28	2.25	2.23	2.21	2.18	2.16
10	2.32	2.28	2.24	2.20	2.18	2.16	2.13	2.11	2.08	2.06
11	2.25	2.21	2.17	2.12	2.10	2.08	2.05	2.03	2.00	1.97
12	2.19	2.15	2.10	2.06	2.04	2.01	1.99	1.96	1.93	1.90
13	2.14	2.10	2.05	2.01	1.98	1.96	1.93	1.90	1.88	1.85
14	2.10	2.05	2.01	1.96	1.94	1.91	1.89	1.86	1.83	1.80
15	2.06	2.02	1.97	1.92	1.90	1.87	1.85	1.82	1.79	1.76
16	2.03	1.99	1.94	1.89	1.87	1.84	1.81	1.78	1.75	1.72
17	2.00	1.96	1.91	1.86	1.84	1.81	1.78	1.75	1.72	1.69
18	1.98	1.93	1.89	1.84	1.81	1.78	1.75	1.72	1.69	1.66
19	1.96	1.91	1.86	1.81	1.79	1.76	1.73	1.70	1.67	1.63
20	1.94	1.89	1.84	1.79	1.77	1.74	1.71	1.68	1.64	1.61
21	1.92	1.87	1.83	1.78	1.75	1.72	1.69	1.66	1.62	1.59
22	1.90	1.86	1.81	1.76	1.73	1.70	1.67	1.64	1.60	1.57
23	1.89	1.84	1.80	1.74	1.72	1.69	1.66	1.62	1.59	1.55
24	1.88	1.83	1.78	1.73	1.70	1.67	1.64	1.61	1.57	1.53
25	1.87	1.82	1.77	1.72	1.69	1.66	1.63	1.59	1.56	1.52
26	1.86	1.81	1.76	1.71	1.68	1.65	1.61	1.58	1.54	1.50
27	1.85	1.80	1.75	1.70	1.67	1.64	1.60	1.57	1.53	1.49
28	1.84	1.79	1.74	1.69	1.66	1.63	1.59	1.56	1.52	1.48
29	1.83	1.78	1.73	1.68	1.65	1.62	1.58	1.55	1.51	1.47
30	1.82	1.77	1.72	1.67	1.64	1.61	1.57	1.54	1.50	1.46
40	1.76	1.71	1.66	1.61	1.57	1.54	1.51	1.47	1.42	1.38
60	1.71	1.66	1.60	1.54	1.51	1.48	1.44	1.40	1.35	1.29
120	1.65	1.60	1.55	1.48	1.45	1.41	1.37	1.32	1.26	1.19
∞	1.60	1.55	1.49	1.42	1.38	1.34	1.30	1.24	1.17	1.00

Source: From Merrington, M., & Thompson, C. M. "Tables of percentage points of the inverted beta (F)-distribution," *Biometrika*, 1943, 33, 73–88. Reproduced by permission of the *Biometrika* Trustees.

Table VI Percentage Points of the F-Distribution, $\alpha = .05$

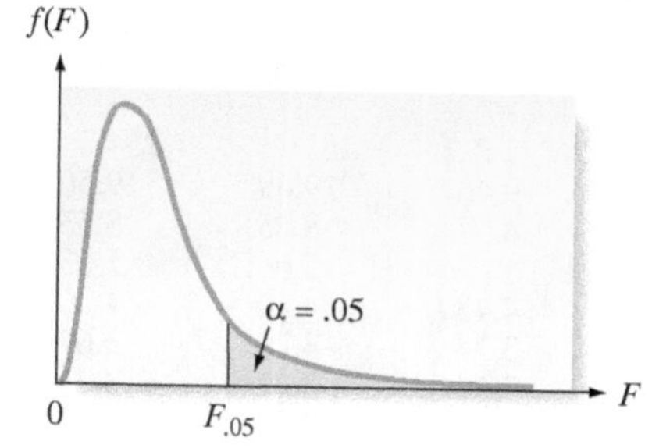

ν_2 \ ν_1	Numerator Degrees of Freedom								
Denominator Degrees of Freedom	1	2	3	4	5	6	7	8	9
1	161.4	199.5	215.7	224.6	230.2	234.0	236.8	238.9	240.5
2	18.51	19.00	19.16	19.25	19.30	19.33	19.35	19.37	19.38
3	10.13	9.55	9.28	9.12	9.01	8.94	8.89	8.85	8.81
4	7.71	6.94	6.59	6.39	6.26	6.16	6.09	6.04	6.00
5	6.61	5.79	5.41	5.19	5.05	4.95	4.88	4.82	4.77
6	5.99	5.14	4.76	4.53	4.39	4.28	4.21	4.15	4.10
7	5.59	4.74	4.35	4.12	3.97	3.87	3.79	3.73	3.68
8	5.32	4.46	4.07	3.84	3.69	3.58	3.50	3.44	3.39
9	5.12	4.26	3.86	3.63	3.48	3.37	3.29	3.23	3.18
10	4.96	4.10	3.71	3.48	3.33	3.22	3.14	3.07	3.02
11	4.84	3.98	3.59	3.36	3.20	3.09	3.01	2.95	2.90
12	4.75	3.89	3.49	3.26	3.11	3.00	2.91	2.85	2.80
13	4.67	3.81	3.41	3.18	3.03	2.92	2.83	2.77	2.71
14	4.60	3.74	3.34	3.11	2.96	2.85	2.76	2.70	2.65
15	4.54	3.68	3.29	3.06	2.90	2.79	2.71	2.64	2.59
16	4.49	3.63	3.24	3.01	2.85	2.74	2.66	2.59	2.54
17	4.45	3.59	3.20	2.96	2.81	2.70	2.61	2.55	2.49
18	4.41	3.55	3.16	2.93	2.77	2.66	2.58	2.51	2.46
19	4.38	3.52	3.13	2.90	2.74	2.63	2.54	2.48	2.42
20	4.35	3.49	3.10	2.87	2.71	2.60	2.51	2.45	2.39
21	4.32	3.47	3.07	2.84	2.68	2.57	2.49	2.42	2.37
22	4.30	3.44	3.05	2.82	2.66	2.55	2.46	2.40	2.34
23	4.28	3.42	3.03	2.80	2.64	2.53	2.44	2.37	2.32
24	4.26	3.40	3.01	2.78	2.62	2.51	2.42	2.36	2.30
25	4.24	3.39	2.99	2.76	2.60	2.49	2.40	2.34	2.28
26	4.23	3.37	2.98	2.74	2.59	2.47	2.39	2.32	2.77
27	4.21	3.35	2.96	2.73	2.57	2.46	2.37	2.31	2.25
28	4.20	3.34	2.95	2.71	2.56	2.45	2.36	2.29	2.24
29	4.18	3.33	2.93	2.70	2.55	2.43	2.35	2.28	2.22
30	4.17	3.32	2.92	2.69	2.53	2.42	2.33	2.27	2.21
40	4.08	3.23	2.84	2.61	2.45	2.34	2.25	2.18	2.12
60	4.00	3.15	2.76	2.53	2.37	2.25	2.17	2.10	2.04
120	3.92	3.07	2.68	2.45	2.29	2.17	2.09	2.02	1.96
∞	3.84	3.00	2.60	2.37	2.21	2.10	2.01	1.94	1.88

(continued)

Table VI *(continued)*

ν_2 \ ν_1	Numerator Degrees of Freedom									
	10	12	15	20	24	30	40	60	120	∞
1	241.9	243.9	245.9	248.0	249.1	250.1	251.1	252.2	253.3	254.3
2	19.40	19.41	19.43	19.45	19.45	19.46	19.47	19.48	19.49	19.50
3	8.79	8.74	8.70	8.66	8.64	8.62	8.59	8.57	8.55	8.53
4	5.96	5.91	5.86	5.80	5.77	5.75	5.72	5.69	5.66	5.63
5	4.74	4.68	4.62	4.56	4.53	4.50	4.46	4.43	4.40	4.36
6	4.06	4.00	3.94	3.87	3.84	3.81	3.77	3.74	3.70	3.67
7	3.64	3.57	3.51	3.44	3.41	3.38	3.34	3.30	3.27	3.23
8	3.35	3.28	3.22	3.15	3.12	3.08	3.04	3.01	2.97	2.93
9	3.14	3.07	3.01	2.94	2.90	2.86	2.83	2.79	2.75	2.71
10	2.98	2.91	2.85	2.77	2.74	2.70	2.66	2.62	2.58	2.54
11	2.85	2.79	2.72	2.65	2.61	2.57	2.53	2.49	2.45	2.40
12	2.75	2.69	2.62	2.54	2.51	2.47	2.43	2.38	2.34	2.30
13	2.67	2.60	2.53	2.46	2.42	2.38	2.34	2.30	2.25	2.21
14	2.60	2.53	2.46	2.39	2.35	2.31	2.27	2.22	2.18	2.13
15	2.54	2.48	2.40	2.33	2.29	2.25	2.20	2.16	2.11	2.07
16	2.49	2.42	2.35	2.28	2.24	2.19	2.15	2.11	2.06	2.01
17	2.45	2.38	2.31	2.23	2.19	2.15	2.10	2.06	2.01	1.96
18	2.41	2.34	2.27	2.19	2.15	2.11	2.06	2.02	1.97	1.92
19	2.38	2.31	2.23	2.16	2.11	2.07	2.03	1.98	1.93	1.88
20	2.35	2.28	2.20	2.12	2.08	2.04	1.99	1.95	1.90	1.84
21	2.32	2.25	2.18	2.10	2.05	2.01	1.96	1.92	1.87	1.81
22	2.30	2.23	2.15	2.07	2.03	1.98	1.94	1.89	1.84	1.78
23	2.27	2.20	2.13	2.05	2.01	1.96	1.91	1.86	1.81	1.76
24	2.25	2.18	2.11	2.03	1.98	1.94	1.89	1.84	1.79	1.73
25	2.24	2.16	2.09	2.01	1.96	1.92	1.87	1.82	1.77	1.71
26	2.22	2.15	2.07	1.99	1.95	1.90	1.85	1.80	1.75	1.69
27	2.20	2.13	2.06	1.97	1.93	1.88	1.84	1.79	1.73	1.67
28	2.19	2.12	2.04	1.96	1.91	1.87	1.82	1.77	1.71	1.65
29	2.18	2.10	2.03	1.94	1.90	1.85	1.81	1.75	1.70	1.64
30	2.16	2.09	2.01	1.93	1.89	1.84	1.79	1.74	1.68	1.62
40	2.08	2.00	1.92	1.84	1.79	1.74	1.69	1.64	1.58	1.51
60	1.99	1.92	1.84	1.75	1.70	1.65	1.59	1.53	1.47	1.39
120	1.91	1.83	1.75	1.66	1.61	1.55	1.50	1.43	1.35	1.25
∞	1.83	1.75	1.67	1.57	1.52	1.46	1.39	1.32	1.22	1.00

Denominator Degrees of Freedom

Source: From Merrington, M., & Thompson, C. M. "Tables of percentage points of the inverted beta (*F*)-distribution," *Biometrika*, 1943, 33, 73–88. Reproduced by permission of the *Biometrika* Trustees.

Table VII Percentage Points of the F-Distribution, $\alpha = .025$

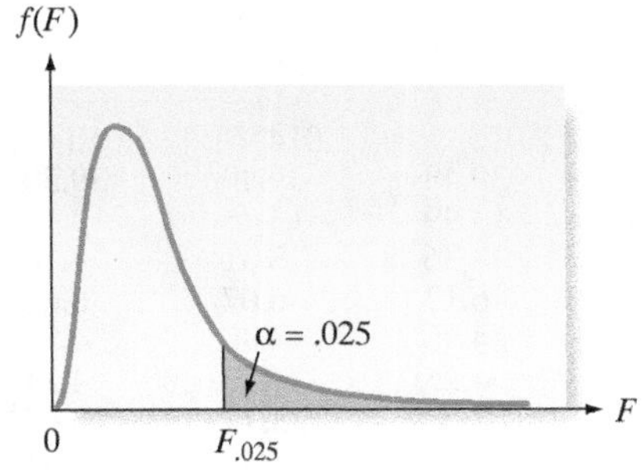

ν_2 \ ν_1	Numerator Degrees of Freedom								
Denominator Degrees of Freedom	**1**	**2**	**3**	**4**	**5**	**6**	**7**	**8**	**9**
1	647.8	799.5	864.2	899.6	921.8	937.1	948.2	956.7	963.3
2	38.51	39.00	39.17	39.25	39.30	39.33	39.36	39.37	39.39
3	17.44	16.04	15.44	15.10	14.88	14.73	14.62	14.54	14.47
4	12.22	10.65	9.98	9.60	9.36	9.20	9.07	8.98	8.90
5	10.01	8.43	7.76	7.39	7.15	6.98	6.85	6.76	6.68
6	8.81	7.26	6.60	6.23	5.99	5.82	5.70	5.60	5.52
7	8.07	6.54	5.89	5.52	5.29	5.12	4.99	4.90	4.82
8	7.57	6.06	5.42	5.05	4.82	4.65	4.53	4.43	4.36
9	7.21	5.71	5.08	4.72	4.48	4.32	4.20	4.10	4.03
10	6.94	5.46	4.83	4.47	4.24	4.07	3.95	3.85	3.78
11	6.72	5.26	4.63	4.28	4.04	3.88	3.76	3.66	3.59
12	6.55	5.10	4.47	4.12	3.89	3.73	3.61	3.51	3.44
13	6.41	4.97	4.35	4.00	3.77	3.60	3.48	3.39	3.31
14	6.30	4.86	4.24	3.89	3.66	3.50	3.38	3.29	3.21
15	6.20	4.77	4.15	3.80	3.58	3.41	3.29	3.20	3.12
16	6.12	4.69	4.08	3.73	3.50	3.34	3.22	3.12	3.05
17	6.04	4.62	4.01	3.66	3.44	3.28	3.16	3.06	2.98
18	5.98	4.56	3.95	3.61	3.38	3.22	3.10	3.01	2.93
19	5.92	4.51	3.90	3.56	3.33	3.17	3.05	2.96	2.88
20	5.87	4.46	3.86	3.51	3.29	3.13	3.01	2.91	2.84
21	5.83	4.42	3.82	3.48	3.25	3.09	2.97	2.87	2.80
22	5.79	4.38	3.78	3.44	3.22	3.05	2.93	2.84	2.76
23	5.75	4.35	3.75	3.41	3.18	3.02	2.90	2.81	2.73
24	5.72	4.32	3.72	3.38	3.15	2.99	2.87	2.78	2.70
25	5.69	4.29	3.69	3.35	3.13	2.97	2.85	2.75	2.68
26	5.66	4.27	3.67	3.33	3.10	2.94	2.82	2.73	2.65
27	5.63	4.24	3.65	3.31	3.08	2.92	2.80	2.71	2.63
28	5.61	4.22	3.63	3.29	3.06	2.90	2.78	2.69	2.61
29	5.59	4.20	3.61	3.27	3.04	2.88	2.76	2.67	2.59
30	5.57	4.18	3.59	3.25	3.03	2.87	2.75	2.65	2.57
40	5.42	4.05	3.46	3.13	2.90	2.74	2.62	2.53	2.45
60	5.29	3.93	3.34	3.01	2.79	2.63	2.51	2.41	2.33
120	5.15	3.80	3.23	2.89	2.67	2.52	2.39	2.30	2.22
∞	5.02	3.69	3.12	2.79	2.57	2.41	2.29	2.19	2.11

(continued)

Table VII *(continued)*

ν_2 \ ν_1 (Denominator Degrees of Freedom \ Numerator Degrees of Freedom)	10	12	15	20	24	30	40	60	120	∞
1	968.6	976.7	984.9	993.1	997.2	1,001	1,006	1,010	1,014	1,018
2	39.40	39.41	39.43	39.45	39.46	39.46	39.47	39.48	39.49	39.50
3	14.42	14.34	14.25	14.17	14.12	14.08	14.04	13.99	13.95	13.90
4	8.84	8.75	8.66	8.56	8.51	8.46	8.41	8.36	8.31	8.26
5	6.62	6.52	6.43	6.33	6.28	6.23	6.18	6.12	6.07	6.02
6	5.46	5.37	5.27	5.17	5.12	5.07	5.01	4.96	4.90	4.85
7	4.76	4.67	4.57	4.47	4.42	4.36	4.31	4.25	4.20	4.14
8	4.30	4.20	4.10	4.00	3.95	3.89	3.84	3.78	3.73	3.67
9	3.96	3.87	3.77	3.67	3.61	3.56	3.51	3.45	3.39	3.33
10	3.72	3.62	3.52	3.42	3.37	3.31	3.26	3.20	3.14	3.08
11	3.53	3.43	3.33	3.23	3.17	3.12	3.06	3.00	2.94	2.88
12	3.37	3.28	3.18	3.07	3.02	2.96	2.91	2.85	2.79	2.72
13	3.25	3.15	3.05	2.95	2.89	2.84	2.78	2.72	2.66	2.60
14	3.15	3.05	2.95	2.84	2.79	2.73	2.67	2.61	2.55	2.49
15	3.06	2.96	2.86	2.76	2.70	2.64	2.59	2.52	2.46	2.40
16	2.99	2.89	2.79	2.68	2.63	2.57	2.51	2.45	2.38	2.32
17	2.92	2.82	2.72	2.62	2.56	2.50	2.44	2.38	2.32	2.25
18	2.87	2.77	2.67	2.56	2.50	2.44	2.38	2.32	2.26	2.19
19	2.82	2.72	2.62	2.51	2.45	2.39	2.33	2.27	2.20	2.13
20	2.77	2.68	2.57	2.46	2.41	2.35	2.29	2.22	2.16	2.09
21	2.73	2.64	2.53	2.42	2.37	2.31	2.25	2.18	2.11	2.04
22	2.70	2.60	2.50	2.39	2.33	2.27	2.21	2.14	2.08	2.00
23	2.67	2.57	2.47	2.36	2.30	2.24	2.18	2.11	2.04	1.97
24	2.64	2.54	2.44	2.33	2.27	2.21	2.15	2.08	2.01	1.94
25	2.61	2.51	2.41	2.30	2.24	2.18	2.12	2.05	1.98	1.91
26	2.59	2.49	2.39	2.28	2.22	2.16	2.09	2.03	1.95	1.88
27	2.57	2.47	2.36	2.25	2.19	2.13	2.07	2.00	1.93	1.85
28	2.55	2.45	2.34	2.23	2.17	2.11	2.05	1.98	1.91	1.83
29	2.53	2.43	2.32	2.21	2.15	2.09	2.03	1.96	1.89	1.81
30	2.51	2.41	2.31	2.20	2.14	2.07	2.01	1.94	1.87	1.79
40	2.39	2.29	2.18	2.07	2.01	1.94	1.88	1.80	1.72	1.64
60	2.27	2.17	2.06	1.94	1.88	1.82	1.74	1.67	1.58	1.48
120	2.16	2.05	1.94	1.82	1.76	1.69	1.61	1.53	1.43	1.31
∞	2.05	1.94	1.83	1.71	1.64	1.57	1.48	1.39	1.27	1.00

Source: From Merrington, M., & Thompson, C. M. "Tables of percentage points of the inverted beta (F)-distribution," *Biometrika*, 1943, 33, 73–88. Reproduced by permission of the *Biometrika* Trustees.

Table VIII Percentage Points of the *F*-Distribution, $\alpha = .01$

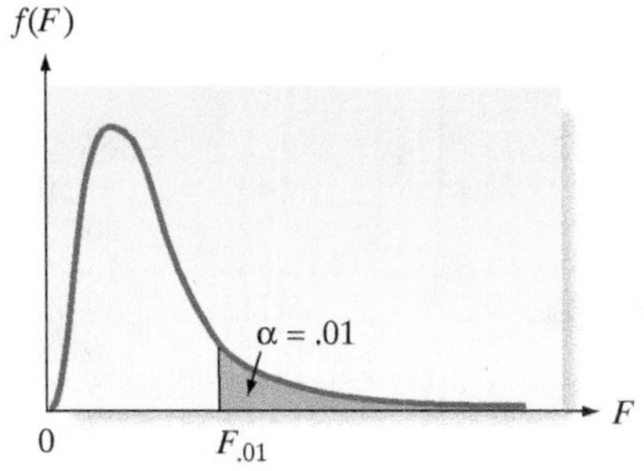

ν_2 \ ν_1 (Numerator Degrees of Freedom)	1	2	3	4	5	6	7	8	9
1	4,052	4,999.5	5,403	5,625	5,764	5,859	5,928	5,982	6,022
2	98.50	99.00	99.17	99.25	99.30	99.33	99.36	99.37	99.39
3	34.12	30.82	29.46	28.71	28.24	27.91	27.67	27.49	27.35
4	21.20	18.00	16.69	15.98	15.52	15.21	14.98	14.80	14.66
5	16.26	13.27	12.06	11.39	10.97	10.67	10.46	10.29	10.16
6	13.75	10.92	9.78	9.15	8.75	8.47	8.26	8.10	7.98
7	12.25	9.55	8.45	7.85	7.46	7.19	6.99	6.84	6.72
8	11.26	8.65	7.59	7.01	6.63	6.37	6.18	6.03	5.91
9	10.56	8.02	6.99	6.42	6.06	5.80	5.61	5.47	5.35
10	10.04	7.56	6.55	5.99	5.64	5.39	5.20	5.06	4.94
11	9.65	7.21	6.22	5.67	5.32	5.07	4.89	4.74	4.63
12	9.33	6.93	5.95	5.41	5.06	4.82	4.64	4.50	4.39
13	9.07	6.70	5.74	5.21	4.86	4.62	4.44	4.30	4.19
14	8.86	6.51	5.56	5.04	4.69	4.46	4.28	4.14	4.03
15	8.68	6.36	5.42	4.89	4.56	4.32	4.14	4.00	3.89
16	8.53	6.23	5.29	4.77	4.44	4.20	4.03	3.89	3.78
17	8.40	6.11	5.18	4.67	4.34	4.10	3.93	3.79	3.68
18	8.29	6.01	5.09	4.58	4.25	4.01	3.84	3.71	3.60
19	8.18	5.93	5.01	4.50	4.17	3.94	3.77	3.63	3.52
20	8.10	5.85	4.94	4.43	4.10	3.87	3.70	3.56	3.46
21	8.02	5.78	4.87	4.37	4.04	3.81	3.64	3.51	3.40
22	7.95	5.72	4.82	4.31	3.99	3.76	3.59	3.45	3.35
23	7.88	5.66	4.76	4.26	3.94	3.71	3.54	3.41	3.30
24	7.82	5.61	4.72	4.22	3.90	3.67	3.50	3.36	3.26
25	7.77	5.57	4.68	4.18	3.85	3.63	3.46	3.32	3.22
26	7.72	5.53	4.64	4.14	3.82	3.59	3.42	3.29	3.18
27	7.68	5.49	4.60	4.11	3.78	3.56	3.39	3.26	3.15
28	7.64	5.45	4.57	4.07	3.75	3.53	3.36	3.23	3.12
29	7.60	5.42	4.54	4.04	3.73	3.50	3.33	3.20	3.09
30	7.56	5.39	4.51	4.02	3.70	3.47	3.30	3.17	3.07
40	7.31	5.18	4.31	3.83	3.51	3.29	3.12	2.99	2.89
60	7.08	4.98	4.13	3.65	3.34	3.12	2.95	2.82	2.72
120	6.85	4.79	3.95	3.48	3.17	2.96	2.79	2.66	2.56
∞	6.63	4.61	3.78	3.32	3.02	2.80	2.64	2.51	2.41

(ν_2: Denominator Degrees of Freedom)

(continued)

Table VIII *(continued)*

ν_1 / ν_2 (Denominator Degrees of Freedom)	Numerator Degrees of Freedom									
	10	12	15	20	24	30	40	60	120	∞
1	6,056	6,106	6,157	6,209	6,235	6,261	6,287	6,313	6,339	6,366
2	99.40	99.42	99.43	99.45	99.46	99.47	99.47	99.48	99.49	99.50
3	27.23	27.05	26.87	26.69	26.60	26.50	26.41	26.32	26.22	26.13
4	14.55	14.37	14.20	14.02	13.93	13.84	13.75	13.65	13.56	13.46
5	10.05	9.89	9.72	9.55	9.47	9.38	9.29	9.20	9.11	9.02
6	7.87	7.72	7.56	7.40	7.31	7.23	7.14	7.06	6.97	6.88
7	6.62	6.47	6.31	6.16	6.07	5.99	5.91	5.82	5.74	5.65
8	5.81	5.67	5.52	5.36	5.28	5.20	5.12	5.03	4.95	4.86
9	5.26	5.11	4.96	4.81	4.73	4.65	4.57	4.48	4.40	4.31
10	4.85	4.71	4.56	4.41	4.33	4.25	4.17	4.08	4.00	3.91
11	4.54	4.40	4.25	4.10	4.02	3.94	3.86	3.78	3.69	3.60
12	4.30	4.16	4.01	3.86	3.78	3.70	3.62	3.54	3.45	3.36
13	4.10	3.96	3.82	3.66	3.59	3.51	3.43	3.34	3.25	3.17
14	3.94	3.80	3.66	3.51	3.43	3.35	3.27	3.18	3.09	3.00
15	3.80	3.67	3.52	3.37	3.29	3.21	3.13	3.05	2.96	2.87
16	3.69	3.55	3.41	3.26	3.18	3.10	3.02	2.93	2.84	2.75
17	3.59	3.46	3.31	3.16	3.08	3.00	2.92	2.83	2.75	2.65
18	3.51	3.37	3.23	3.08	3.00	2.92	2.84	2.75	2.66	2.57
19	3.43	3.30	3.15	3.00	2.92	2.84	2.76	2.67	2.58	2.49
20	3.37	3.23	3.09	2.94	2.86	2.78	2.69	2.61	2.52	2.42
21	3.31	3.17	3.03	2.88	2.80	2.72	2.64	2.55	2.46	2.36
22	3.26	3.12	2.98	2.83	2.75	2.67	2.58	2.50	2.40	2.31
23	3.21	3.07	2.93	2.78	2.70	2.62	2.54	2.45	2.35	2.26
24	3.17	3.03	2.89	2.74	2.66	2.58	2.49	2.40	2.31	2.21
25	3.13	2.99	2.85	2.70	2.62	2.54	2.45	2.36	2.27	2.17
26	3.09	2.96	2.81	2.66	2.58	2.50	2.42	2.33	2.23	2.13
27	3.06	2.93	2.78	2.63	2.55	2.47	2.38	2.29	2.20	2.10
28	3.03	2.90	2.75	2.60	2.52	2.44	2.35	2.26	2.17	2.06
29	3.00	2.87	2.73	2.57	2.49	2.41	2.33	2.23	2.14	2.03
30	2.98	2.84	2.70	2.55	2.47	2.39	2.30	2.21	2.11	2.01
40	2.80	2.66	2.52	2.37	2.29	2.20	2.11	2.02	1.92	1.80
60	2.63	2.50	2.35	2.20	2.12	2.03	1.94	1.84	1.73	1.60
120	2.47	2.34	2.19	2.03	1.95	1.86	1.76	1.66	1.53	1.38
∞	2.32	2.18	2.04	1.88	1.79	1.70	1.59	1.47	1.32	1.00

Source: From Merrington, M., & Thompson, C. M. "Tables of percentage points of the inverted beta (F)-distribution," *Biometrika*, 1943, 33, 73–88. Reproduced by permission of the *Biometrika* Trustees.

Table IX Control Chart Constants

Number of Observations in Subgroup, n	A_2	d_2	d_3	D_3	D_4
2	1.880	1.128	.853	.000	3.267
3	1.023	1.693	.888	.000	2.574
4	.729	2.059	.880	.000	2.282
5	.577	2.326	.864	.000	2.114
6	.483	2.534	.848	.000	2.004
7	.419	2.704	.833	.076	1.924
8	.373	2.847	.820	.136	1.864
9	.337	2.970	.808	.184	1.816
10	.308	3.078	.797	.223	1.777
11	.285	3.173	.787	.256	1.744
12	.266	3.258	.778	.283	1.717
13	.249	3.336	.770	.307	1.693
14	.235	3.407	.762	.328	1.672
15	.223	3.472	.755	.347	1.653
16	.212	3.532	.749	.363	1.637
17	.203	3.588	.743	.378	1.622
18	.194	3.640	.738	.391	1.608
19	.187	3.689	.733	.403	1.597
20	.180	3.735	.729	.415	1.585
21	.173	3.778	.724	.425	1.575
22	.167	3.819	.720	.434	1.566
23	.162	3.858	.716	.443	1.557
24	.157	3.895	.712	.451	1.548
25	.153	3.931	.709	.459	1.541

Source: ASTM Manual on the Presentation of Data and Control Chart Analysis, Philadelphia, PA: American Society for Testing Materials, pp. 134–136, 1976.

Table X **Critical Values for the Durbin-Watson *d*-Statistic, $\alpha = .05$**

	$k = 1$		$k = 2$		$k = 3$		$k = 4$		$k = 5$	
n	d_L	d_U	d_L	d_U	d_L	d_U	d_L	d_U	d_L	d_U
15	1.08	1.36	.95	1.54	.82	1.75	.69	1.97	.56	2.21
16	1.10	1.37	.98	1.54	.86	1.73	.74	1.93	.62	2.15
17	1.13	1.38	1.02	1.54	.90	1.71	.78	1.90	.67	2.10
18	1.16	1.39	1.05	1.53	.93	1.69	.92	1.87	.71	2.06
19	1.18	1.40	1.08	1.53	.97	1.68	.86	1.85	.75	2.02
20	1.20	1.41	1.10	1.54	1.00	1.68	.90	1.83	.79	1.99
21	1.22	1.42	1.13	1.54	1.03	1.67	.93	1.81	.83	1.96
22	1.24	1.43	1.15	1.54	1.05	1.66	.96	1.80	.96	1.94
23	1.26	1.44	1.17	1.54	1.08	1.66	.99	1.79	.90	1.92
24	1.27	1.45	1.19	1.55	1.10	1.66	1.01	1.78	.93	1.90
25	1.29	1.45	1.21	1.55	1.12	1.66	1.04	1.77	.95	1.89
26	1.30	1.46	1.22	1.55	1.14	1.65	1.06	1.76	.98	1.88
27	1.32	1.47	1.24	1.56	1.16	1.65	1.08	1.76	1.01	1.86
28	1.33	1.48	1.26	1.56	1.18	1.65	1.10	1.75	1.03	1.85
29	1.34	1.48	1.27	1.56	1.20	1.65	1.12	1.74	1.05	1.84
30	1.35	1.49	1.28	1.57	1.21	1.65	1.14	1.74	1.07	1.83
31	1.36	1.50	1.30	1.57	1.23	1.65	1.16	1.74	1.09	1.83
32	1.37	1.50	1.31	1.57	1.24	1.65	1.18	1.73	1.11	1.82
33	1.38	1.51	1.32	1.58	1.26	1.65	1.19	1.73	1.13	1.81
34	1.39	1.51	1.33	1.58	1.27	1.65	1.21	1.73	1.15	1.81
35	1.40	1.52	1.34	1.58	1.28	1.65	1.22	1.73	1.16	1.80
36	1.41	1.52	1.35	1.59	1.29	1.65	1.24	1.73	1.18	1.80
37	1.42	1.53	1.36	1.59	1.31	1.66	1.25	1.72	1.19	1.80
38	1.43	1.54	1.37	1.59	1.32	1.66	1.26	1.72	1.21	1.79
39	1.43	1.54	1.38	1.60	1.33	1.66	1.27	1.72	1.22	1.79
40	1.44	1.54	1.39	1.60	1.34	1.66	1.29	1.72	1.23	1.79
45	1.48	1.57	1.43	1.62	1.38	1.67	1.34	1.72	1.29	1.78
50	1.50	1.59	1.46	1.63	1.42	1.67	1.38	1.72	1.34	1.77
55	1.53	1.60	1.49	1.64	1.45	1.68	1.41	1.72	1.38	1.77
60	1.55	1.62	1.51	1.65	1.48	1.69	1.44	1.73	1.41	1.77
65	1.57	1.63	1.54	1.66	1.50	1.70	1.47	1.73	1.44	1.77
70	1.58	1.64	1.55	1.67	1.52	1.70	1.49	1.74	1.46	1.77
75	1.60	1.65	1.57	1.68	1.54	1.71	1.51	1.74	1.49	1.77
80	1.61	1.66	1.59	1.69	1.56	1.72	1.53	1.74	1.51	1.77
85	1.62	1.67	1.60	1.70	1.57	1.72	1.55	1.75	1.52	1.77
90	1.63	1.68	1.61	1.70	1.59	1.73	1.57	1.75	1.54	1.78
95	1.64	1.69	1.62	1.71	1.60	1.73	1.58	1.75	1.56	1.78
100	1.65	1.69	1.63	1.72	1.61	1.74	1.59	1.76	1.57	1.78

Source: From Durbin, J., & Watson, G. S. "Testing for serial correlation in least squares regression, II," *Biometrika*, 1951, 30, 159–178. Reproduced by permission of the *Biometrika* Trustees.

Table XI Critical Values for the Durbin-Watson d-Statistic, $\alpha = .01$

n	$k = 1$		$k = 2$		$k = 3$		$k = 4$		$k = 5$	
	d_L	d_U	d_L	d_U	d_L	d_U	d_L	d_U	d_L	d_U
15	.81	1.07	.70	1.25	.59	1.46	.49	1.70	.39	1.96
16	.84	1.09	.74	1.25	.63	1.44	.53	1.66	.44	1.90
17	.87	1.10	.77	1.25	.67	1.43	.57	1.3	.48	1.85
18	.90	1.12	.80	1.26	.71	1.42	.61	1.60	.52	1.80
19	.93	1.13	.83	1.26	.74	1.41	.65	1.58	.56	1.77
20	.95	1.15	.86	1.27	.77	1.41	.68	1.57	.60	1.74
21	.97	1.16	.89	1.27	.80	1.41	.72	1.55	.63	1.71
22	1.00	1.17	.91	1.28	.83	1.40	.75	1.54	.66	1.69
23	1.02	1.19	.94	1.29	.86	1.40	.77	1.53	.70	1.67
24	1.04	1.20	.96	1.30	.88	1.41	.80	1.53	.72	1.66
25	1.05	1.21	.98	1.30	.90	1.41	.83	1.52	.75	1.65
26	1.07	1.22	1.00	1.31	.93	1.41	.85	1.52	.78	1.64
27	1.09	1.23	1.02	1.32	.95	1.41	.88	1.51	.81	1.63
28	1.10	1.24	1.04	1.32	.97	1.41	.90	1.51	.83	1.62
29	1.12	1.25	1.05	1.33	.99	1.42	.92	1.51	.85	1.61
30	1.13	1.26	1.07	1.34	1.01	1.42	.94	1.51	.88	1.61
31	1.15	1.27	1.08	1.34	1.02	1.42	.96	1.51	.90	1.60
32	1.16	1.28	1.10	1.35	1.04	1.43	.98	1.51	.92	1.60
33	1.17	1.29	1.11	1.36	1.05	1.43	1.00	1.51	.94	1.59
34	1.18	1.30	1.13	1.36	1.07	1.43	1.01	1.51	.95	1.59
35	1.19	1.31	1.14	1.27	1.08	1.44	1.03	1.51	.97	1.59
36	1.21	1.32	1.15	1.38	1.10	1.44	1.04	1.51	.99	1.59
37	1.22	1.32	1.16	1.38	1.11	1.45	1.06	1.51	1.00	1.59
38	1.23	1.33	1.18	1.39	1.12	1.45	1.07	1.52	1.02	1.58
39	1.24	1.34	1.19	1.39	1.14	1.45	1.09	1.52	1.03	1.58
40	1.25	1.34	1.20	1.40	1.15	1.46	1.10	1.52	1.05	1.58
45	1.29	1.38	1.24	1.42	1.20	1.48	1.16	1.53	1.11	1.58
50	1.32	1.40	1.28	1.45	1.24	1.49	1.20	1.54	1.16	1.59
55	1.36	1.43	1.32	1.47	1.28	1.51	1.25	1.55	1.21	1.59
60	1.38	1.45	1.35	1.48	1.32	1.52	1.28	1.56	1.25	1.60
65	1.41	1.47	1.38	1.50	1.35	1.53	1.31	1.57	1.28	1.61
70	1.43	1.49	1.40	1.52	1.37	1.55	1.34	1.58	1.31	1.61
75	1.45	1.50	1.42	1.53	1.39	1.56	1.37	1.59	1.34	1.62
80	1.47	1.52	1.44	1.54	1.42	1.57	1.39	1.60	1.36	1.62
85	1.48	1.53	1.46	1.55	1.43	1.58	1.41	1.60	1.39	1.63
90	1.50	1.54	1.47	1.56	1.45	1.59	1.43	1.61	1.41	1.64
95	1.51	1.55	1.49	1.57	1.47	1.60	1.45	1.62	1.42	1.64
100	1.52	1.56	1.50	1.58	1.48	1.60	1.46	1.63	1.44	1.65

Source: From Durbin, J., & Watson, G. S. "Testing for serial correlation in least squares regression, II," *Biometrika*, 1951, 30, 159–178. Reproduced by permission of the *Biometrika* Trustees.

Table XII Critical Values of T_L and T_U for the Wilcoxon Rank Sum Test: Independent Samples

Test statistic is the rank sum associated with the smaller sample (if equal sample sizes, either rank sum can be used).

a. $\alpha = .025$ one-tailed; $\alpha = .05$ two-tailed

n_2 \ n_1	3		4		5		6		7		8		9		10	
	T_L	T_U	T_L	T_U	T_L	T_U	T_L	T_U	T_L	T_U	T_L	T_U	T_L	T_U	T_L	T_U
3	5	16	6	18	6	21	7	23	7	26	8	28	8	31	9	33
4	6	18	11	25	12	28	12	32	13	35	14	38	15	41	16	44
5	6	21	12	28	18	37	19	41	20	45	21	49	22	53	24	56
6	7	23	12	32	19	41	26	52	28	56	29	61	31	65	32	70
7	7	26	13	35	20	45	28	56	37	68	39	73	41	78	43	83
8	8	28	14	38	21	49	29	61	39	73	49	87	51	93	54	98
9	8	31	15	41	22	53	31	65	41	78	51	93	63	108	66	114
10	9	33	16	44	24	56	32	70	43	83	54	98	66	114	79	131

b. $\alpha = .05$ one-tailed; $\alpha = .10$ two-tailed

n_2 \ n_1	3		4		5		6		7		8		9		10	
	T_L	T_U	T_L	T_U	T_L	T_U	T_L	T_U	T_L	T_U	T_L	T_U	T_L	T_U	T_L	T_U
3	6	15	7	17	7	20	8	22	9	24	9	27	10	29	11	31
4	7	17	12	24	13	27	14	30	15	33	16	36	17	39	18	42
5	7	20	13	27	19	36	20	40	22	43	24	46	25	50	26	54
6	8	22	14	30	20	40	28	50	30	54	32	58	33	63	35	67
7	9	24	15	33	22	43	30	54	39	66	41	71	43	76	46	80
8	9	27	16	36	24	46	32	58	41	71	52	84	54	90	57	95
9	10	29	17	39	25	50	33	63	43	76	54	90	66	105	69	111
10	11	31	18	42	26	54	35	67	46	80	57	95	69	111	83	127

Source: From Wilcoxon, F., & Wilcox, R. A. "Some rapid approximate statistical procedures," 1964, 20–23. Courtesy of Lederle Laboratories Division of American Cyanamid Company, Madison, NJ.

Table XIII Critical Values of T_0 in the Wilcoxon Paired Difference Signed Rank Test

One-Tailed	Two-Tailed						
		$n = 5$	$n = 6$	$n = 7$	$n = 8$	$n = 9$	$n = 10$
$\alpha = .05$	$\alpha = .10$	1	2	4	6	8	11
$\alpha = .025$	$\alpha = .05$		1	2	4	6	8
$\alpha = .01$	$\alpha = .02$			0	2	3	5
$\alpha = .005$	$\alpha = .01$				0	2	3
		$n = 11$	$n = 12$	$n = 13$	$n = 14$	$n = 15$	$n = 16$
$\alpha = .05$	$\alpha = .10$	14	17	21	26	30	36
$\alpha = .025$	$\alpha = .05$	11	14	17	21	25	30
$\alpha = .01$	$\alpha = .02$	7	10	13	16	20	24
$\alpha = .005$	$\alpha = .01$	5	7	10	13	16	19
		$n = 17$	$n = 18$	$n = 19$	$n = 20$	$n = 21$	$n = 22$
$\alpha = .05$	$\alpha = .10$	41	47	54	60	68	75
$\alpha = .025$	$\alpha = .05$	35	40	46	52	59	66
$\alpha = .01$	$\alpha = .02$	28	33	38	43	49	56
$\alpha = .005$	$\alpha = .01$	23	28	32	37	43	49
		$n = 23$	$n = 24$	$n = 25$	$n = 26$	$n = 27$	$n = 28$
$\alpha = .05$	$\alpha = .10$	83	92	101	110	120	130
$\alpha = .025$	$\alpha = .05$	73	81	90	98	107	117
$\alpha = .01$	$\alpha = .02$	62	69	77	85	93	102
$\alpha = .005$	$\alpha = .01$	55	61	68	76	84	92
		$n = 29$	$n = 30$	$n = 31$	$n = 32$	$n = 33$	$n = 34$
$\alpha = .05$	$\alpha = .10$	141	152	163	175	188	201
$\alpha = .025$	$\alpha = .05$	127	137	148	159	171	183
$\alpha = .01$	$\alpha = .02$	111	120	130	141	151	162
$\alpha = .005$	$\alpha = .01$	100	109	118	128	138	149
		$n = 35$	$n = 36$	$n = 37$	$n = 38$	$n = 39$	
$\alpha = .05$	$\alpha = .10$	214	228	242	256	271	
$\alpha = .025$	$\alpha = .05$	195	208	222	235	250	
$\alpha = .01$	$\alpha = .02$	174	186	198	211	224	
$\alpha = .005$	$\alpha = .01$	160	171	183	195	208	
		$n = 40$	$n = 41$	$n = 42$	$n = 43$	$n = 44$	$n = 45$
$\alpha = .05$	$\alpha = .10$	287	303	319	336	353	371
$\alpha = .025$	$\alpha = .05$	264	279	295	311	327	344
$\alpha = .01$	$\alpha = .02$	238	252	267	281	297	313
$\alpha = .005$	$\alpha = .01$	221	234	248	262	277	292
		$n = 46$	$n = 47$	$n = 48$	$n = 49$	$n = 50$	
$\alpha = .05$	$\alpha = .10$	389	408	427	446	466	
$\alpha = .025$	$\alpha = .05$	361	379	397	415	434	
$\alpha = .01$	$\alpha = .02$	329	345	362	380	398	
$\alpha = .005$	$\alpha = .01$	307	323	339	356	373	

Source: From Wilcoxon, F., & Wilcox, R. A. "Some rapid approximate statistical procedures," 1964, p. 28. Courtesy of Lederle Laboratories Division of American Cyanamid Company, Madison, NJ.

Table XIV Critical Values of Spearman's Rank Correlation Coefficient

The values correspond to a one-tailed test of H_0: $p = 0$. The value should be doubled for two-tailed tests.

n	$\alpha = .05$	$\alpha = .025$	$\alpha = .01$	$\alpha = .005$	n	$\alpha = .05$	$\alpha = .025$	$\alpha = .01$	$\alpha = .005$
5	.900	–	–	–	18	.399	.476	.564	.625
6	.829	.886	.943	–	19	.388	.462	.549	.608
7	.714	.786	.893	–	20	.377	.450	.534	.591
8	.643	.738	.833	.881	21	.368	.438	.521	.576
9	.600	.683	.783	.833	22	.359	.428	.508	.562
10	.564	.648	.745	.794	23	.351	.418	.496	.549
11	.523	.623	.736	.818	24	.343	.409	.485	.537
12	.497	.591	.703	.780	25	.336	.400	.475	.526
13	.475	.566	.673	.745	26	.329	.392	.465	.515
14	.457	.545	.646	.716	27	.323	.385	.456	.505
15	.441	.525	.623	.689	28	.317	.377	.448	.496
16	.425	.507	.601	.666	29	.311	.370	.440	.487
17	.412	.490	.582	.645	30	.305	.364	.432	.478

Source: From Olds, E. G. "Distribution of sums of squares of rank differences for small samples," *Annals of Mathematical Statistics*, 1938, 9. Reproduced with the permission of the editor, *Annals of Mathematical Statistics*.

Table XV Critical Values of the Studentized Range, $\alpha = .05$

ν \ k	2	3	4	5	6	7	8	9	10	11
1	17.97	26.98	32.82	37.08	40.41	43.12	45.40	47.36	49.07	50.59
2	6.08	8.33	9.80	10.88	11.74	12.44	13.03	13.54	13.99	14.39
3	4.50	5.91	6.82	7.50	8.04	8.48	8.85	9.18	9.46	9.72
4	3.93	5.04	5.76	6.29	6.71	7.05	7.35	7.60	7.83	8.03
5	3.64	4.60	5.22	5.67	6.03	6.33	6.58	6.80	6.99	7.17
6	3.46	4.34	4.90	5.30	5.63	5.90	6.12	6.32	6.49	6.65
7	3.34	4.16	4.68	5.06	5.36	5.61	5.82	6.00	6.16	6.30
8	3.26	4.04	4.53	4.89	5.17	5.40	5.60	5.77	5.92	6.05
9	3.20	3.95	4.41	4.76	5.02	5.24	5.43	5.59	5.74	5.87
10	3.15	3.88	4.33	4.65	4.91	5.12	5.30	5.46	5.60	5.72
11	3.11	3.82	4.26	4.57	4.82	5.03	5.20	5.35	5.49	5.61
12	3.08	3.77	4.20	4.51	4.75	4.95	5.12	5.27	5.39	5.51
13	3.06	3.73	4.15	4.45	4.69	4.88	5.05	5.19	5.32	5.43
14	3.03	3.70	4.11	4.41	4.64	4.83	4.99	5.13	5.25	5.36
15	3.01	3.67	4.08	4.37	4.60	4.78	4.94	5.08	5.20	5.31
16	3.00	3.65	4.05	4.33	4.56	4.74	4.90	5.03	5.15	5.26
17	2.98	3.63	4.02	4.30	4.52	4.70	4.86	4.99	5.11	5.21
18	2.97	3.61	4.00	4.28	4.49	4.67	4.82	4.96	5.07	5.17
19	2.96	3.59	3.98	4.25	4.47	4.65	4.79	4.92	5.04	5.14
20	2.95	3.58	3.96	4.23	4.45	4.62	4.77	4.90	5.01	5.11
24	2.92	3.53	3.90	4.17	4.37	4.54	4.68	4.81	4.92	5.01
30	2.89	3.49	3.85	4.10	4.30	4.46	4.60	4.72	4.82	4.92
40	2.86	3.44	3.79	4.04	4.23	4.39	4.52	4.63	4.73	4.82
60	2.83	3.40	3.74	3.98	4.16	4.31	4.44	4.55	4.65	4.73
120	2.80	3.36	3.68	3.92	4.10	4.24	4.36	4.47	4.56	4.64
∞	2.77	3.31	3.63	3.86	4.03	4.17	4.29	4.39	4.47	4.55

ν \ k	12	13	14	15	16	17	18	19	20
1	51.96	53.20	54.33	55.36	56.32	57.22	58.04	58.83	59.56
2	14.75	15.08	15.38	15.65	15.91	16.14	16.37	16.57	16.77
3	9.95	10.15	10.35	10.52	10.69	10.84	10.98	11.11	11.24
4	8.21	8.37	8.52	8.66	8.79	8.91	9.03	9.13	9.23
5	7.32	7.47	7.60	7.72	7.83	7.93	8.03	8.12	8.21
6	6.79	6.92	7.03	7.14	7.24	7.34	7.43	7.51	7.59
7	6.43	6.55	6.66	6.76	6.85	6.94	7.02	7.10	7.17
8	6.18	6.29	6.39	6.48	6.57	6.65	6.73	6.80	6.87
9	5.98	6.09	6.19	6.28	6.36	6.44	6.51	6.58	6.64
10	5.83	5.93	6.03	6.11	6.19	6.27	6.34	6.40	6.47
11	5.71	5.81	5.90	5.98	6.06	6.13	6.20	6.27	6.33
12	5.61	5.71	5.80	5.88	5.95	6.02	6.09	6.15	6.21
13	5.53	5.63	5.71	5.79	5.86	5.93	5.99	6.05	6.11
14	5.46	5.55	5.64	5.71	5.79	5.85	5.91	5.97	6.03
15	5.40	5.49	5.57	5.65	5.72	5.78	5.85	5.90	5.96
16	5.35	5.44	5.52	5.59	5.66	5.73	5.79	5.84	5.90
17	5.31	5.39	5.47	5.54	5.61	5.67	5.73	5.79	5.84
18	5.27	5.35	5.43	5.50	5.57	5.63	5.69	5.74	5.79
19	5.23	5.31	5.39	5.46	5.53	5.59	5.65	5.70	5.75
20	5.20	5.28	5.36	5.43	5.49	5.55	5.61	5.66	5.71
24	5.10	5.18	5.25	5.32	5.38	5.44	5.49	5.55	5.59
30	5.00	5.08	5.15	5.21	5.27	5.33	5.38	5.43	5.47
40	4.90	4.98	5.04	5.11	5.16	5.22	5.27	5.31	5.36
60	4.81	4.88	4.94	5.00	5.06	5.11	5.15	5.20	5.24
120	4.71	4.78	4.84	4.90	4.95	5.00	5.04	5.09	5.13
∞	4.62	4.68	4.74	4.80	4.85	4.89	4.93	4.97	5.01

Source: Biometrika Tables for Statisticians, Vol. I, 3rd ed., edited by E. S. Pearson and H. O. Hartley (Cambridge University Press, 1996). Reproduced by permission of Professor E. S. Pearson and the *Biometrika* Trustees.

Answers to Selected Exercises

Chapter 11

11.3 $\beta_1 = \frac{1}{3}, \beta_0 = \frac{14}{3}, y = \frac{14}{3} + (1/3)x$ **11.9** No **11.11 a.** $\Sigma(y - \hat{y}) = 0.02$, SSE = 1.2204 **c.** SSE = 108.00 **11.13 b.** Negative linear relationship **c.** 8.54, −.994 **11.15 a.** $y = \beta_0 + \beta_1 x + \varepsilon$ **b.** $\hat{y} = -97.41 + 1.19x$ **c.** No practical interpretation **d.** For every 1-point increase in 2001 Math SAT score, estimate 2011 Math SAT score to increase 1.19 points **11.17 a.** $\hat{y} = 7.21 + 35.92x$ **b.** y-intercept: no practical interpretation; slope: for each unit change in surface area to volume, estimate drug release rate to increase by 35.92 **c.** 25.17 **d.** Not reliable; $x = .50$ is outside range **11.19 a.** $\hat{y} = -14.14 + .63x$ **b.** For each additional 1 million births, estimate number of software millionaire birthdays to increase by .63 **c.** 7.83 **d.** $\hat{y} = 2.72 + .31x$ **e.** For each additional CEO birthday, estimate number of software millionaire birthdays to increase by .63 **f.** 5.79 **11.21 a.** $E(y) = \beta_0 + \beta_1 x$ **b.** $\hat{y} = 250.14 - .629x$ **c.** No practical interpretation **d.** For every 1-yard increase in driving distance, driving accuracy to decrease .629% **e.** Slope **11.23** $7.88 million **11.27** Plot b **11.29 a.** .3475 **b.** 1.179 **11.31 a.** .2 **b.** About 95% of the observed payoffs fall within .4 unit of their predicted values **11.33 a.** 2.01 **b.** About 95% of the observed release rates fall within 4% of their predicted values **11.35 a.** SSE = 44.16, $s^2 = 11.04, s = 3.32$ **b.** SSE = 9.69, $s^2 = 2.42, s = 1.56$ **c.** x = CEO birthdays **11.37 a.** SSE = 1.017, $s^2 = .0462, s = .215$ **c.** About 95% of the observed sweetness index values fall within .43 units of their predicted values **11.39 a.** $s = 5.37$; about 95% of the observed FCAT-Math scores fall within 10.74 points of their predicted values **b.** $s = 3.42$; about 95% of the observed FCAT-Reading scores fall within 6.84 points of their predicted values **c.** Reading score **11.41 a.** 95% CI:31 ± 1.13; 90% CI:31 ± .92 **b.** 95% CI:64 ± 4.28; 90% CI:64 ± 3.53 **c.** 95% CI: − 8.4 ± .67; 90% CI:−8.4 ± .55 **11.43** 80% CI:.82 ± .33; 98% CI: .82 ± .76 **11.45 a.** $H_0: \beta_1 = 0, H_a: \beta_1 > 0$ **b.** Reject H_0, p-value ≈ 0 **c.** (1.09, 1.29) **11.47 a.** Positive **b.** (−1.18, 1.72) **c.** Insufficient evidence of a linear relationship **11.49** (30.17, 41.67); 90% confident that for each additional unit increase in surface area to volume, the increase in the drug release rate is between 30.17 and 41.67 **11.51 a.** (−.048, 1.304) **b.** (.179, .434) **c.** No; yes **11.53 a.** $H_0: \beta_1 = 0, H_a: \beta_1 < 0$ **b.** $t = -13.23$, p-value ≈ 0 **c.** Reject H_0 **11.55** No, $t = .66$ **11.57 a.** Yes, $p\text{-value} = \frac{.008}{2} = .004$ **b.** Possible outlier **c.** $p\text{-value} = \frac{.332}{2} = .166$, do not reject H_0 **11.59 a.** Positive **b.** Negative **c.** 0 slope **d.** Positive or negative **11.61 a.** .944 **b.** .802 **11.63 a.** 18% of sample variation in points scored is explained by the linear relationship with yards from goal line **b.** −.424; negative **11.65 a.** $E(y) = \beta_0 + \beta_1 x$ **b.** Moderately strong positive linear relationship between RMP and SET ratings **c.** Positive **d.** Reject $H_0: \rho = 0$ **e.** .4624 **11.67 a.** Strong positive linear relationship between number of females in managerial positions and number of females with college degree **b.** Very weak positive linear relationship between number of females in managerial positions and number of female HS graduates with no college **c.** Moderately strong positive linear relationship between number of males in managerial positions and number of males with college degree **d.** Moderate positive linear relationship between number of males in managerial positions and number of male HS graduates with no college **11.69 a.** .624; 62.4% of sample variation in software millionaire birthdays is explained by the linear relationship with number of U.S. births **b.** .917; 91.7% of sample variation in software millionaire birthdays is explained by the linear relationship with number of CEO births **c.** Yes **11.71** $r^2 = .2286, r = -.478$ **11.73** $r = .243, r^2 = .059$ **11.75** Yes, reject $H_0: \rho = 0$ for all occupations; no **11.77 c.** 4.64 ± 1.12 **d.** 2.28 ± .63; −.41 ± 1.17 **11.79 a.** $\hat{y} = 1.375 + .875x$ **c.** 1.5 **d.** .1875 **e.** (3.23, 3.89) **f.** (3.81, 5.94) **11.81 a.** (4783, 6792) **b.** (2643, 8933) **11.83** For run = 1:90% confident that mean sweetness index of all runs with pectin value of 220 falls between 5.65 and 5.84 **11.85 a.** (5.44, 15.32) **b.** Narrower **11.87 a.** (2.955, 4.066); 99% confident that the mean mass of all spills with elapsed time of 15 minutes is between 2.995 and 4.066 **b.** (1.02, 6.00); 99% confident that the actual mass of a single spill with elapsed time of 15 minutes is between 1.02 and 6.0 **c.** Prediction interval for y; yes **11.89 a.** Yes, $t = -5.91$; negative **b.** (.656, 2.829) **c.** (1.467, 2.018) **11.91** $\hat{y} = -32.35 + 4.82x$; $t = 16.60$, p-value = 0, reject H_0; $r^2 = .69$ **11.93** $\hat{y} = 62.449 - .34673x$; $t = -12.56$, p-value = 0, reject H_0; $r^2 = .07$ **11.95 a.** $\hat{y} = 37.08 - 1.6x$ **c.** 57.2 **d.** 4.4 **e.** −1.6 ± .5 **f.** 13.08 ± 6.93 **g.** 13.08 ± 7.86 **11.97 a.** Moderately strong positive linear relationship between skill level and goal-setting ability **b.** Reject H_0 at $\alpha = .01$ **c.** .49 **11.99 b.** $\hat{y} = 569.58 - .0019x$ **e.** Range of x: $15,100 to $70,000 **f.** $t = -.82$, do not reject H_0 **11.101 a.** $E(y) = \beta_0 + \beta_1 x$ **b.** $\hat{y} = -2{,}298.4 + 11{,}598.9x$ **c.** No practical interpretation **d.** (11,146.1, 12,051.7) **e.** 1,117.6 **f.** $H_0: \beta_1 = 0, H_a: \beta_1 > 0$ **g.** p-value < .0001 **h.** .8925 **i.** .9447 **j.** (1,297.6, 5,704.6) **k.** (3,362.5, 3,639.7) **11.103 b.** $\hat{y} = 44.13 + .237x$ **c.** 19.40 **d.** Possibly **e.** $t = 1.27$, do not reject H_0 **f.** (−.16, .63) **g.** 57.143 ± 34.818 **h.** $x = 110$ outside range **i.** $\bar{x} = 44.1579$ **11.105 a.** Increasing trend **b.** Positive **c.** Support; $t = 4.60$, reject H_0 **11.107 c.** $r_1 = .965, r_2 = .996$ **d.** Yes **11.109 a.** Yes, $t = -4.37$ **11.111** Machine-hours: $t = 3.30, p = .008$, reject H_0, $r^2 = .521$; labor-hours: $t = 1.43, p = .183$, do not reject H_0, $r^2 = .170$

Chapter 12

12.1 a. $E(y) = \beta_0 + \beta_1 x_1 + \beta_2 x_2$ **b.** $E(y) = \beta_0 + \beta_1 x_1 + \beta_2 x_2 + \beta_3 x_3 + \beta_4 x_4$ **c.** $E(y) = \beta_0 + \beta_1 x_1 + \beta_2 x_2 + \beta_3 x_3 + \beta_4 x_4 + \beta_5 x_5$ **12.3 a.** $t = 1.45$, do not reject H_0 **b.** $t = 3.21$, reject H_0 **12.5** $n - (k + 1)$ **12.7 a.** Yes, $s = .117$ **b.** Yes, $F = 55.2$ **12.9 a.** $93,002 **b.** $98,774 **c.** 32% of sample variation in salary is explained by the model **d.** 95% confident that for each additional year of experience, mean salary will increase between $2,700 to $3,200, holding PhD status and manager status constant **e.** 95% confident that mean salary of PhDs will be $11,500 to $22,300 higher than salaries for non-PhDs, holding years of experience and manager status constant **f.** 95% confident that mean salary of managers will be $7,600 to $14,600 higher than salaries for nonmanagers, holding years of experience and PhD status constant **12.11 a.** $F = 4.74$, p-value < .01, reject H_0 **b.** 13% of sample variation in Mach score can be explained by the model **c.** No **12.13 a.** $\hat{y} = 1.81231 + 0.10875x_1 + 0.00017x_2$ **c.** (.027, .190) **d.** (.00009, .00025) **e.** $\hat{y} = 1.20785 + 0.06343x_1 + 0.00056x_2$; (.016, .111); (.00024, .00088) **12.15 a.** $E(y) = \beta_0 + \beta_1 x_1 + \beta_2 x_2 + \beta_3 x_3 + \beta_4 x_4$

b. Reject H_0 **c.** Yes **d.** H_0: $\beta_1 = \beta_2 = \beta_3 = \beta_4 = 0$ **e.** $F > 3.37$ **f.** Thrill: reject H_0; Change: do not reject H_0; Surprise: do not reject H_0 **12.17 a.** $\hat{y} = 14.0107 - 2.1865x_1 - .04794x_2 - .3223x_3 + .493x_4$ **c.** Yes, $F = 40.85$ **d.** R_a^2 **e.** $t = -2.25$, reject H_0 **f.** (.24, .74) **12.19 a.** $E(y) = \beta_0 + \beta_1x_1 + \beta_2x_2 + \beta_3x_3 + \beta_4x_4 + \beta_5x_5$ **b.** $\hat{y} = 13{,}614.5 + 0.0888x_1 - 9.201x_2 + 14.394x_3 + 0.35x_4 - 0.848x_5$ **d.** 458.83 **e.** $F = 147.3$, $p < .001$, reject H_0 **f.** .917 **g.** Yes, $t = -6.14$ **12.21 b.** $F = 5.11$, reject H_0 **12.23 a.** Model 1: $t = 2.58$, reject H_0: $\beta_1 = 0$; Model 2: $t = 3.32$, reject H_0: $\beta_1 = 0$, $t = 6.47$, reject H_0: $\beta_2 = 0$, $t = -4.77$, reject H_0: $\beta_3 = 0$, $t = 0.24$, do not reject H_0: $\beta_4 = 0$; Model 3: $t = 3.21$, reject H_0: $\beta_1 = 0$, $t = 5.24$, reject H_0: $\beta_2 = 0$, $t = -4.00$, reject H_0: $\beta_3 = 0$, $t = 2.28$, reject H_0: $\beta_4 = 0$, $t = .014$, do not reject H_0: $\beta_5 = 0$ **c.** Model 2 **12.25 a.** 3.78 **b.** 4.68 **12.27 a.** 95% confident that mean desire is between 13.42 and 14.31 for all females with a self-esteem of 24, body satisfaction of 3, and impression of reality TV of 4 **b.** 95% confident that mean desire is between 8.79 and 10.89 for all males with a self-esteem of 22, body satisfaction of 9, and impression of reality TV of 4 **12.29 a.** (11,599.6, 13,665.5) **b.** (12,157.9, 13,107.1) **c.** Yes **12.31 a.** $\hat{y} = 130.22 + .169x_1 + .0259x_2 - 1.1115x_3$ **b.** $F = 100.06$, reject H_0 **c.** (−5.76,198.85) **12.33 a.** $\hat{y} = -3783 + .00875x_1 + 1.93x_2 + 3444x_3 + 2093x_4$ **b.** $F = 72.11$, reject H_0 **c.** (1,449, 2,424) **12.35 c.** Interaction is present **12.37 a.** $\hat{y} = -2.55 + 3.82x_1 + 2.63x_2 - 1.29x_1x_2$ **b.** Twisted plane **c.** $x_2 = 1$: $\hat{y} = .08 + 2.53x_1$; $x_2 = 3$: $\hat{y} = 5.34 - .05x_1$; $x_2 = 5$: $\hat{y} = 10.6 - 2.63x_1$ **e.** H_0: $\beta_3 = 0$ vs. H_a: $\beta_3 \neq 0$ **f.** $t = -8.06$, reject H_0 **12.39 a.** $E(y) = \beta_0 + \beta_1x_1 + \beta_2x_2 + \beta_3x_1x_2$ **b.** $(\beta_1 + 2.5\beta_3)$ **c.** $(\beta_1 + 5\beta_3)$ **d.** $(\beta_2 + 100\beta_3)$ **e.** H_0: $\beta_3 = 0$ **12.41 a.** $E(y) = \beta_0 + \beta_1x_1 + \beta_2x_2 + \beta_3x_1x_2$ **b.** $\beta_3 < 0$ **12.43 a.** $\hat{y} = 11.779 - 1.972x_1 + .585x_4 - .553x_1x_4$ **b.** 9.97 **c.** $F = 45.1$, reject H_0 **d.** .439 **e.** 2.35 **f.** $t = -2.00$, reject H_0 **12.45 a.** $E(y) = \beta_0 + \beta_1x_1 + \beta_2x_2 + \beta_3x_3 + \beta_4x_1x_3 + \beta_5x_2x_3$ **b.** $\hat{y} = 10{,}769 - 1{,}288x_1 + 218.8x_2 - 1{,}550.1x_3 - 10.99x_1x_3 + 19.99x_2x_3$ **c.** $t = -.93$, do not reject H_0 **d.** $t = 1.78$, do not reject H_0 **12.47 b.** $\hat{y} = .906 - .023x_1 + .305x_2 + .275x_5 - .003x_1x_2 + .002x_1x_5$; yes **12.49 a.** $E(y) = \beta_0 + \beta_1x + \beta_2x^2$ **b.** $E(y) = \beta_0 + \beta_1x_1 + \beta_2x_2 + \beta_3x_1x_2 + \beta_4x_1^2 + \beta_5x_2^2$ **c.** $E(y) = \beta_0 + \beta_1x_1 + \beta_2x_2 + \beta_3x_3 + \beta_4x_1x_2 + \beta_5x_1x_3 + \beta_6x_2x_3 + \beta_7x_1^2 + \beta_8x_2^2 + \beta_9x_3^2$ **12.51 a.** Yes, $F = 85.94$ **b.** H_0: $\beta_2 = 0$ vs. H_a: $\beta_2 > 0$ **c.** H_0: $\beta_2 = 0$ vs. H_a: $\beta_2 < 0$ **12.53 a.** Yes, $F = 25.93$ **b.** $t = -10.74$, reject H_0 **c.** $t = .60$, do not reject H_0 **12.55 b.** 22.6% of the sample variation in points scored is explained by the quadratic model **c.** No **d.** H_0: $\beta_2 = 0$ **12.57 b.** First-order model; first-order model; second-order model **12.59 a.** $E(y) = \beta_0 + \beta_1x_1 + \beta_2x_2 + \beta_3x_1x_2 + \beta_4x_1^2 + \beta_5x_2^2$ **b.** 14% of sample variation in attitude toward improving efficiency can be explained by the model **c.** Downward curvature in the relationship between attitude and congruence **d.** Evidence of interaction **12.61 a.** $E(y) = \beta_0 + \beta_1x$ **b.** $E(y) = \beta_0 + \beta_1x + \beta_2x^2$ **c.** Quadratic model **d.** $F = 57.75$, overall model is statistically useful; $t = 3.98$, sufficient evidence of curvature **e.** Quadratic model **12.63 a.** Curvilinear **b.** $\hat{y} = 154{,}243 - 1{,}908.9x + 5.93x^2$ **c.** $t = 5.66$, reject H_0 **12.65 b.** Possibly **c.** $\hat{y} = 2{,}802.4 + 122.95x$ **d.** $\hat{y} = 4{,}944.2 - 183.03x + 7.46x^2$ **e.** $t = 3.38$, reject H_0: $\beta_2 = 0$; 2nd-order **12.67** $E(y) = \beta_0 + \beta_1x_1 + \beta_2x_2$, where x_1 = {1 level 1, 0 if not}, x_2 = {1 level 2, 0 if not}; $\beta_0 = \mu_3$, $\beta_1 = \mu_1 - \mu_3$, $\beta_2 = \mu_2 - \mu_3$ **12.69 a.** Level 1: 10.2; Level 2: 6.2; Level 3: 22.2; Level 4: 12.2 **b.** H_0: $\beta_1 = \beta_2 = \beta_3 = 0$ **12.71 a.** Method: x_1 = {1 manual, 0 if automated}; Soil: x_2 = {1 if clay, 0 if not}, x_3 = {1 if gravel, 0 if not}; Slope: x_4 = {1 if East, 0 if not}, x_5 = {1 if South, 0 if not}, x_6 = {1 if West, 0 if not}, x_7 = {1 if Southeast, 0 if not} **b.** $E(y) = \beta_0 + \beta_1x_1$ **c.** $E(y) = \beta_0 + \beta_1x_2 + \beta_2x_3$ **d.** $E(y) = \beta_0 + \beta_1x_4 + \beta_2x_5 + \beta_3x_6 + \beta_4x_7$ **12.73 a.** $E(y) = \beta_0 + \beta_1x$, x = {1 if developer, 0 if not} **b.** $E(y) = \beta_0 + \beta_1x_1 + \beta_2x_2$, x_1 = {1 if low, 0 if not}, x_2 = {1 if medium, 0 if not} **c.** $E(y) = \beta_0 + \beta_1x$, x = {1 if fixed price, 0 if not} **d.** $E(y) = \beta_0 + \beta_1x_1 + \beta_2x_2$, x_1 = {1 if time-of-delivery, 0 if not}, x_2 = {1 if cost, 0 if not} **12.75 a.** x_1 = {1 if blond Caucasian, 0 if not}, x_2 = {1 if brunette Caucasian, 0 if not} **b.** $E(y) = \beta_0 + \beta_1x_1 + \beta_2x_2$ **c.** $\beta_0 + \beta_1$ **d.** β_1 **e.** $\beta_0 > 0$; $\beta_1 > 0$; $\beta_2 \approx 0$ **f.** Yes **12.77 a.** x_1 = {1 if large/private, 0 if not}, x_2 = {1 if small/public, 0 if not}, x_3 = {1 if small/private, 0 if not} **b.** $E(y) = \beta_0 + \beta_1x_1 + \beta_2x_2 + \beta_3x_3$ **c.** Differences in mean likelihood of reporting sustainability policies among the four groups **d.** x_1 = {1 if small, 0 if large}, x_2 = {1 if private, 0 if public} **e.** $E(y) = \beta_0 + \beta_1x_1 + \beta_2x_2$ **f.** Large/public: β_0; large/private: $\beta_0 + \beta_2$; small/public: $\beta_0 + \beta_1$; small/private: $\beta_0 + \beta_1 + \beta_2$ **g.** Public: $\mu_S - \mu_L = \beta_1$; private: $\mu_S - \mu_L = \beta_1$ **h.** $E(y) = \beta_0 + \beta_1x_1 + \beta_2x_2 + \beta_3x_1x_2$ **i.** Large/public: β_0; large/private: $\beta_0 + \beta_2$; small/public: $\beta_0 + \beta_1$; small/private: $\beta_0 + \beta_1 + \beta_2 + \beta_3$ **j.** Public: $\mu_S - \mu_L = \beta_1$; private: $\mu_S - \mu_L = \beta_1 + \beta_3$ **12.79 a.** $E(y) = \beta_0 + \beta_1x$, where x = {1 if Lotion/Cream, 0 if not} **b.** $\hat{y} = .7775 + .1092x$ **c.** H_0: $\beta_1 = 0$ **d.** $t = .24$, do not reject H_0 **e.** $\hat{y} = 7.56 - 1.65x$; $t = -.46$, do not reject H_0 **12.81 a.** $E(y) = \beta_0 + \beta_1x_1 + \beta_2x_2$, x_1 = {1 if group V, 0 if not}, x_2 = {1 if group S, 0 if not} **b.** $\hat{y} = 3.1667 - 1.0833x_1 - 1.4537x_2$ **c.** $F = 20.45$, reject H_0 **12.83 a.** $E(y) = \beta_0 + \beta_1x_1 + \beta_2x_1^2$ **b.** $E(y) = \beta_0 + \beta_1x_1 + \beta_2x_1^2 + \beta_3x_2 + \beta_4x_3$, where x_2 and x_3 are dummy variables **c.** add terms: $\beta_5x_1x_2 + \beta_6x_1x_3 + \beta_7x_1^2x_2 + \beta_8x_1^2x_3$ **d.** $\beta_5 = \beta_6 = \beta_7 = \beta_8 = 0$ **e.** $\beta_2 = \beta_5 = \beta_6 = \beta_7 = \beta_8 = 0$ **f.** $\beta_3 = \beta_4 = \beta_5 = \beta_6 = \beta_7 = \beta_8 = 0$ **12.85 a.** $\hat{y} = 48.8 - 3.4x_1 + .07x_1^2$; $\hat{y} = 46.44 + .3x_1 + .05x_1^2$; $\hat{y} = 41.3 - .7x_1 + .03x_1^2$ **12.87 a.** .58 **b.** .03 **12.89 a.** Model is statistically useful; reject H_0: $\beta_1 = \beta_2 = \cdots = \beta_{12} = 0$ **b.** No significant impact; do not reject H_0: $\beta_1 = 0$ **c.** Positive impact; reject H_0: $\beta_3 = 0$ **d.** $E(y) = \beta_0 + \beta_1x_3 + \beta_2x_5 + \beta_3x_6 + \cdots + \beta_9x_{12} + \beta_{10}x_3x_5 + \beta_{11}x_3x_6 + \cdots + \beta_{17}x_3x_{12}$ **12.91 a.** x_2 = {1 if low, 0 if not}, x_3 = {1 if neutral, 0 if not} **b.** $E(y) = \beta_0 + \beta_1x_1 + \beta_2x_2 + \beta_3x_3$ **c.** $E(y) = \beta_0 + \beta_1x_1 + \beta_2x_2 + \beta_3x_3 + \beta_4x_1x_2 + \beta_5x_1x_3$ **d.** Part c **12.93 a.** x_1 = {1 if channel catfish, 0 if not}, x_2 = {1 if largemouth bass, 0 if not} **b.** $E(y) = \beta_0 + \beta_1x_1 + \beta_2x_2 + \beta_3x_3$, where x_3 = weight **c.** $E(y) = \beta_0 + \beta_1x_1 + \beta_2x_2 + \beta_3x_3 + \beta_4x_1x_3 + \beta_5x_2x_3$ **d.** $\hat{y} = 3.1 + 26.5x_1 - 4.1x_2 + 0.0037x_3$ **f.** $\hat{y} = 3.5 + 25.6x_1 - 3.47x_2 + 0.0034x_3 + 0.0008x_1x_3 - .0013x_2x_3$ **g.** .0042 **12.95 a.** $E(y) = \beta_0 + \beta_1x_1 + \beta_2x_1^2 + \beta_3x_2 + \beta_4x_3 + \beta_5x_4 + \beta_6x_1x_2 + \beta_7x_1x_3 + \beta_8x_1x_4 + \beta_9x_1^2x_2 + \beta_{10}x_1^2x_3 + \beta_{11}x_1^2x_4$, where x_1 = sales volume and $x_2 - x_4$ are dummy variables for region **b.** $E(y) = (\beta_0 + \beta_5) + (\beta_1 + \beta_8)x_1 + (\beta_2 + \beta_{11})x_1^2$ **c.** $E(y) = (\beta_0 + \beta_3) + (\beta_1 + \beta_6)x_1 + (\beta_2 + \beta_9)x_1^2$ **d.** β_3 through β_{11} **e.** Yes, $F = 8.21$, $p = .000$ **12.97** a and b, a and d, a and e, b and c, b and d, b and e, c and e, d and e **12.99 a.** 5; 3 **b.** H_0: $\beta_3 = \beta_4 = 0$ **c.** $F = .38$, do not reject H_0 **12.101 a.** H_0: $\beta_4 = \beta_5 = 0$ **b.** Complete model: $E(y) = \beta_0 + \beta_1x_1 + \beta_2x_2 + \beta_3x_1x_2 + \beta_4x_2^2 + \beta_5x_1x_2^2$; reduced model: $E(y) = \beta_0 + \beta_1x_1 + \beta_2x_2 + \beta_3x_1x_2$ **c.** H_0: $\beta_3 = \beta_5 = 0$ **d.** Complete model: $E(y) = \beta_0 + \beta_1x_1 + \beta_2x_2 + \beta_3x_1x_2 + \beta_4x_2^2 + \beta_5x_1x_2^2$; reduced model: $E(y) = \beta_0 + \beta_1x_1 + \beta_2x_2 + \beta_4x_2^2$ **e.** H_0: $\beta_1 = \beta_3 = \beta_5 = 0$ **f.** Complete model: $E(y) = \beta_0 + \beta_1x_1 + \beta_2x_2 + \beta_3x_1x_2 + \beta_4x_2^2 + \beta_5x_1x_2^2$; reduced model: $E(y) = \beta_0 + \beta_2x_2 + \beta_4x_2^2$ **12.103 a.** $E(y) = \beta_0 + \beta_1x_1 + \beta_2x_2 + \beta_3x_1x_2 + \beta_4x_1^2 + \beta_5x_2^2$ **b.** H_0: $\beta_4 = \beta_5 = 0$ **c.** Complete model: $E(y) = \beta_0 + \beta_1x_1 + \beta_2x_2 + \beta_3x_1x_2 + \beta_4x_1^2 + \beta_5x_2^2$; reduced model: $E(y) = \beta_0 + \beta_1x_1 + \beta_2x_2 + \beta_3x_1x_2$ **d.** $SSE_R = 25{,}310{,}639$, $SSE_C = 19{,}370{,}350$, $MSE_C = 317{,}547$ **e.** $F = 9.35$ **f.** $F > 2.39$ **g.** reject H_0 **12.105 a.** $E(y) = \beta_0 + \beta_1x_1 + \beta_2x_2 + \beta_3x_3 + \beta_4x_4 + \beta_5x_1x_4 + \beta_6x_2x_4 + \beta_7x_3x_4$ **b.** $F = 24.40$, reject H_0 **c.** H_0: $\beta_5 = \beta_6 = \beta_7 = 0$ **d.** $F = 1.74$, do not reject H_0 **12.107 a.** Positive **c.** $E(y) = \beta_0 + \beta_1x_1 + \beta_2x_1^2 + \beta_3x_2 + \beta_4x_1x_2 + \beta_5x_1^2x_2$ **e.** H_0: $\beta_4 = \beta_5 = 0$ **f.** $F = .83$, do not reject H_0 **12.109 a.** $E(y) = \beta_0 + \beta_1x_1 + \beta_2x_2 + \beta_3x_3$ **b.** Add terms: $\beta_4x_1x_2 + \beta_5x_1x_3$ **c.** AL: β_1; TDS-3A: $\beta_1 + \beta_4$; FE: $\beta_1 + \beta_5$ **d.** Test H_0: $\beta_4 = \beta_5 = 0$ using a nested model F-test **12.111 a.** x_2 **b.** Yes **c.** Fit all models of the form $E(y) = \beta_0 + \beta_1x_2 + \beta_2x_i$

12.113 a. 7; $E(y) = \beta_0 + \beta_1 x_i$ **b.** 6; $E(y) = \beta_0 + \beta_1 x_1 + \beta_2 x_i$ **c.** 5; $E(y) = \beta_0 + \beta_1 x_1 + \beta_2 x_2 + \beta_3 x_i$ **12.115 a.** 11 **b.** 10 **d.** No interactions or squared terms; inflated Type I error rate **e.** $E(y) = \beta_0 + \beta_1(\text{AMAP}) + \beta_2(\text{NDF}) + \beta_3(\text{AMAP})(\text{NDF}) + \beta_4(\text{AMAP})^2 + \beta_5(\text{NDF})^2$ **f.** Test H_0: $\beta_3 = \beta_4 = \beta_5 = 0$ **12.117 a.** 11 **b.** 10 **c.** 1 **d.** $E(y) = \beta_0 + \beta_1 x_{11} + \beta_2 x_4 + \beta_3 x_2 + \beta_4 x_7 + \beta_5 x_{10} + \beta_6 x_1 + \beta_7 x_9 + \beta_8 x_3$ **e.** 67.7% of sample variation in overall satisfaction can be explained by the model **f.** No interactions or squared terms in model; high probability of making at least one Type I error **12.119** Yes **12.121 a.** 2,234 **b.** No **c.** Yes, $z = 5.32$ **12.123 a.** No **b.** No **c.** Yes **d.** Possibly **12.125** Multicollinearity **12.127 a.** Satisfied **b.** Violated **c.** Some outliers **d.** Violated **e.** No **12.129 a.** $\hat{y} = 30{,}856 - 191.57x$ **b.** -1162.07 **c.** Yes, curvilinear trend **d.** Yes **12.131** Nonconstant error variance **12.133** Confidence interval **12.135 a.** $\hat{y} = 90.1 - 1.836x_1 + .285x_2$ **b.** .916 **c.** Yes, $F = 64.91$ **d.** $t = -5.01$, reject H_0 **e.** 10.68 **12.137** $E(y) = \beta_0 + \beta_1 x_1 + \beta_2 x_2 + \beta_3 x_3$, where $x_1 = \{1 \text{ if level 2, 0 otherwise}\}$, $x_2 = \{1 \text{ if level 3, 0 otherwise}\}$, $x_3 = \{1 \text{ if level 4, 0 otherwise}\}$ **12.141** No degrees of freedom for error **12.143 a.** Confidence interval for $(\mu_1 - \mu_2)$ **b.** $E(y) = \beta_0 + \beta_1 x$, $x = \{1 \text{ if public college, 0 if private college}\}$ **12.145 a.** Type of extractor is qualitative; size is quantitative **b.** $E(y) = \beta_0 + \beta_1 x_1 + \beta_2 x_2$, where x_1 = diameter of orange, $x_2 = \{1 \text{ if brand B, 0 if not}\}$ **c.** $E(y) = \beta_0 + \beta_1 x_1 + \beta_2 x_2 + \beta_3 x_1 x_2$ **e.** H_0: $\beta_3 = 0$ **12.147** x_4 and x_5 **12.149 a.** β_0: no practical interpretation; β_1: for every 1-unit increase in proportion of block with low-density areas, estimate density to increase 2.006 units; β_2: for every 1-unit increase in proportion of block with high-density areas, estimate density to increase 5.006 units **b.** 68.6% of sample variation in population density can be explained by the model **c.** H_0: $\beta_1 = \beta_2 = 0$ **d.** $F = 133.3$ **e.** reject H_0 **12.151** Importance and Support are correlated at .6991; no **12.153 a.** $E(y) = \beta_0 + \beta_1 x_1 + \beta_2 x_2$, where $x_2 = \{1 \text{ if intervention group, 0 if control group}\}$ **b.** Slope $= \beta_1$ **c.** $E(y) = \beta_0 + \beta_1 x_1 + \beta_2 x_2 + \beta_3 x_1 x_2$ **d.** Intervention slope $= (\beta_1 + \beta_3)$; control slope $= \beta_1$ **12.155 a.** Possibly **b.** Yes **c.** No **12.157 b.** $E(y) = \beta_0 + \beta_1 x_1 + \beta_2 x_1^2 + \beta_3 x_2 + \beta_4 x_1 x_2 + \beta_5 x_1^2 x_2$, where $x_2 = \{1 \text{ if 1-35W, 0 if not}\}$ **c.** Yes, $F = 457.73$ **d.** Assumptions satisfied **12.159 a.** $E(y) = \beta_0 + \beta_1 x_1 + \beta_2 x_2 + \beta_3 x_3$, where $x_1 = \{1 \text{ if VH, 0 otherwise}\}$, $x_2 = \{1 \text{ if H, 0 otherwise}\}$, $x_3 = \{1 \text{ if M, 0 otherwise}\}$ **b.** No **c.** $\hat{y} = 10.2 + .5x_1 + 2.02x_2 + .683x_3$ **d.** Yes, $F = 63.09$ **12.161 b.** Yes, $F = 16.10$ **c.** Yes, $t = 2.5$ **d.** 945 **12.163 a.** $E(y) = \beta_0 + \beta_1 x_1 + \beta_2 x_6 + \beta_3 x_7$, where $x_6 = \{1 \text{ if good, 0 otherwise}\}$, $x_7 = \{1 \text{ if fair, 0 otherwise}\}$ **c.** Excellent: $\hat{y} = 188{,}875 + 15{,}617x_1$; good: $\hat{y} = 85{,}829 + 15{,}617x_1$; fair: $\hat{y} = 36{,}388 + 15{,}617x_1$ **e.** Yes, $F = 8.43$ **f.** (x_1 and x_3), (x_1 and x_5), (x_3 and x_5) highly correlated **g.** Assumptions satisfied **12.165 a.** H_0: $\beta_1 = \beta_2 = \beta_3 = \beta_4 = \beta_5 = 0$ **b.** $F = 18.24$, reject H_0 **c.** H_0: $\beta_3 = \beta_4 = \beta_5 = 0$ **d.** $F = 8.46$, reject H_0 **e.** Second-order model **12.167 a.** 78% of sample variation in price is explained by the model **b.** $F = 1{,}693.55$, reject H_0 **c.** \$2,234 **d.** \$9 **e.** $-\$252$ **f.** yes, $t = 2.39$ **12.169** $\hat{y} = -11.5 + 0.189x_1 + 0.159x_2 - 0.00114x_1^2 - 0.000871x_2^2$

Chapter 13

13.7 Out of control **13.9 a.** 1.023 **b.** 0.308 **c.** 0.167 **13.11 b.** $\bar{\bar{x}} = 20.11625$, $\bar{R} = 3.31$ **c.** UCL = 22.529, LCL = 17.703 **d.** Upper A–B: 21.725, Lower A–B: 18.507, Upper B–C: 20.920, Lower B–C: 19.312 **e.** Yes **13.13 a.** 70 **b.** 32.5 **c.** UCL = 80.01, LCL = 59.99 **d.** Yes **f.** Yes **13.15 a.** UCL = .9175, LCL = .4291, Upper A–B: .8361, Lower A–B: .5105, Upper B–C: .7547, Lower B–C: .5919 **b.** Out of control **c.** No **13.17 c.** 15.1 **c.** No **d.** No **e.** Yes **13.19 a.** $\bar{x} = 13.05$, Upper A–B: 13.55, Lower A–B: 12.55, Upper B–C: 13.3, Lower B–C: 12.8 **b.** Out of control **c.** Under-reporting likely **13.21 a.** $\bar{\bar{x}} = 100.08$, $\bar{R} = .8065$, UCL = 100.91, LCL = 99.26, Upper A–B: 100.63, Lower A–B: 99.53, Upper B–C: 100.36, Lower B–C: 99.81; in control **b.** $\bar{\bar{x}} = 100.09$, $\bar{R} = .75$, UCL = 100.86, LCL = 99.33, Upper A–B: 100.61, Lower A–B: 99.58, Upper B–C: 100.35, Lower B–C: 99.84; out of control **13.25 a.** UCL = 16.802 **b.** Upper A–B: 13.853, Lower A–B: 2.043, Upper B–C: 10.900, Lower B–C: 4.996 **c.** In control **13.27** R-chart: $\bar{R} = 4.03$, UCL = 7.754, LCL = 0.306, Upper A–B: 6.513, Lower A–B: 1.547, Upper B–C: 5.271, Lower B–C: 2.789, in control; $\bar{x}$-chart: $\bar{\bar{x}} = 21.728$, UCL = 23.417, LCL = 20.039, Upper A–B: 22.854, Lower A–B: 20.602, Upper B–C: 22.291, Lower B–C: 21.165, out of control **13.29 a.** 32.5 **b.** UCL = 57.75, LCL = 7.259 **c.** Yes **e.** Out of control **13.31 a.** UCL = .7645 **b.** Process in control **c.** Yes **d.** 6 **13.33 a.** $\bar{R} = .0238$, UCL = .0778, LCL = 0, Upper A–B: .0598, Lower A–B: .0122, Upper B–C: .0418, Lower B–C: .0058; in control **b.** $\bar{\bar{x}} = .2214$, UCL = .2661, LCL = .1767, Upper A–B: .2512, Lower A–B: .1916, Upper B–C: .2363, Lower B–C: .2065; in control **c.** In control; .2214 **13.35 a.** $\bar{R} = .8065$, UCL = 2.076; yes **b.** $\bar{R} = .75$, UCL = 1.931; out of control **13.37** Proportion **13.39** 104 **13.41 a.** $\bar{p} = .0575$, UCL = .1145, LCL = .0005, Upper A–B: .0955, Lower A–B: .0195, Upper B–C: .0765, Lower B–C: .0385 **d.** No **e.** No **13.43 a.** Postoperative complication **b.** Months **c.** .10 **e.** UCL = .191, LCL = .009, Upper A–B: .161, Lower A–B: .039, Upper B–C: .130, Lower B–C: .070 **g.** Out of control **13.45 a.** $\bar{p} = .04$, UCL = .099, LCL = 0, Upper A–B: .079, Lower A–B: .001, Upper B–C: .060, Lower B–C: .020 **b.** No **c.** No **13.47** $\bar{p} = .06$, UCL = .092, LCL = .028, Upper A–B: .081, Lower A–B: .039, Upper B–C: .071, Lower B–C: .049; out of control **13.55 a.** 126 **b.** 31.2 **c.** 660.36 **d.** .0144 **13.57** 6σ **13.59** .377 **13.61 b.** .51 **c.** 3.9967 **d.** Yes **13.63 a.** LSL = 3.12, USL = 3.72 **b.** .152 **c.** $C_p = .505$ **13.69** Yes **13.79 a.** $\bar{x} = 6.4$ **b.** increasing variance **13.81** Out of control (Rule 2) **13.83 a.** $\bar{R} = 2.76$, UCL = 5.83 **b.** $\bar{\bar{x}} = 54.26$, UCL = 55.85, LCL = 52.67 **c.** Mean chart out of control **d.** No **13.85 a.** $\bar{R} = 5.455$, UCL = 11.532, Upper A–B: 9.508, Lower A–B: 1.402, Upper B–C: 7.481, Lower B–C: 3.429 **b.** In control **d.** $\bar{\bar{x}} = 3.867$, UCL = 7.013, LCL = .721, Upper A–B: 5.965, Lower A–B: 1.769, Upper B–C: 4.916, Lower B–C: 2.818 **e.** In control **f.** Yes **13.87 a.** $n > 141$ **b.** $\bar{p} = .063$, UCL = .123, LCL = .003, Upper A–B: .103, Lower A–B: .023, Upper B–C: .083, Lower B–C: .043 **c.** Out of control **e.** No **13.89** No

Index

Credits

Photos

Chapter 11

pp. 601, 612, 627, 637, 645 JustASC/Shutterstock; **p. 608** Scott Leigh/iStockphoto

Chapter 12

pp. 666, 687, 735, 752 Fotosav/Shutterstock; **p. 669** David Stockman/iStockphoto; **p. 674** Tina Fineberg/AP Images; **p. 698** LeahKat/Shutterstock; **p. 709** Marie C. Fields/Shutterstock; **p. 741** Harry Hu/iStockphoto; **p. 778** Roberto A. Sanchez/iStockphoto

Chapter 13

pp. 13-1, 13-27, 13-38 Losevsky Photo and Video/Shutterstock; **p. 13-24** GWImages/Shutterstock; **p. 13-45** Stephen Mahar/Shutterstock; **p. 13-69** WithGod/Shutterstock

Technology Images

Normal Curve Areas

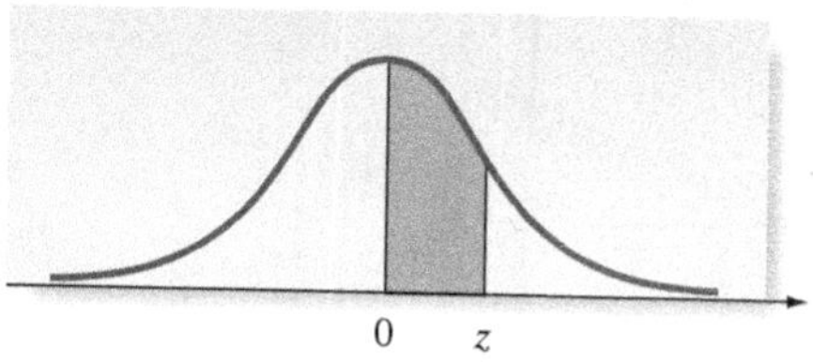

z	.00	.01	.02	.03	.04	.05	.06	.07	.08	.09
.0	.0000	.0040	.0080	.0120	.0160	.0199	.0239	.0279	.0319	.0359
.1	.0398	.0438	.0478	.0517	.0557	.0596	.0636	.0675	.0714	.0753
.2	.0793	.0832	.0871	.0910	.0948	.0987	.1026	.1064	.1103	.1141
.3	.1179	.1217	.1255	.1293	.1331	.1368	.1406	.1443	.1480	.1517
.4	.1554	.1591	.1628	.1664	.1700	.1736	.1772	.1808	.1844	.1879
.5	.1915	.1950	.1985	.2019	.2054	.2088	.2123	.2157	.2190	.2224
.6	.2257	.2291	.2324	.2357	.2389	.2422	.2454	.2486	.2517	.2549
.7	.2580	.2611	.2642	.2673	.2704	.2734	.2764	.2794	.2823	.2852
.8	.2881	.2910	.2939	.2967	.2995	.3023	.3051	.3078	.3106	.3133
.9	.3159	.3186	.3212	.3238	.3264	.3289	.3315	.3340	.3365	.3389
1.0	.3413	.3438	.3461	.3485	.3508	.3531	.3554	.3577	.3599	.3621
1.1	.3643	.3665	.3686	.3708	.3729	.3749	.3770	.3790	.3810	.3830
1.2	.3849	.3869	.3888	.3907	.3925	.3944	.3962	.3980	.3997	.4015
1.3	.4032	.4049	.4066	.4082	.4099	.4115	.4131	.4147	.4162	.4177
1.4	.4192	.4207	.4222	.4236	.4251	.4265	.4279	.4292	.4306	.4319
1.5	.4332	.4345	.4357	.4370	.4382	.4394	.4406	.4418	.4429	.4441
1.6	.4452	.4463	.4474	.4484	.4495	.4505	.4515	.4525	.4535	.4545
1.7	.4554	.4564	.4573	.4582	.4591	.4599	.4608	.4616	.4625	.4633
1.8	.4641	.4649	.4656	.4664	.4671	.4678	.4686	.4693	.4699	.4706
1.9	.4713	.4719	.4726	.4732	.4738	.4744	.4750	.4756	.4761	.4767
2.0	.4772	.4778	.4783	.4788	.4793	.4798	.4803	.4808	.4812	.4817
2.1	.4821	.4826	.4830	.4834	.4838	.4842	.4846	.4850	.4854	.4857
2.2	.4861	.4864	.4868	.4871	.4875	.4878	.4881	.4884	.4887	.4890
2.3	.4893	.4896	.4898	.4901	.4904	.4906	.4909	.4911	.4913	.4916
2.4	.4918	.4920	.4922	.4925	.4927	.4929	.4931	.4932	.4934	.4936
2.5	.4938	.4940	.4941	.4943	.4945	.4946	.4948	.4949	.4951	.4952
2.6	.4953	.4955	.4956	.4957	.4959	.4960	.4961	.4962	.4963	.4964
2.7	.4965	.4966	.4967	.4968	.4969	.4970	.4971	.4972	.4973	.4974
2.8	.4974	.4975	.4976	.4977	.4977	.4978	.4979	.4979	.4980	.4981
2.9	.4981	.4982	.4982	.4983	.4984	.4984	.4985	.4985	.4986	.4986
3.0	.4987	.4987	.4987	.4988	.4988	.4989	.4989	.4989	.4990	.4990
3.1	.49903	.49906	.49910	.49913	.49916	.49918	.49921	.49924	.49926	.48829
3.2	.49931	.49934	.49936	.49938	.49940	.49942	.49944	.49946	.49948	.49950
3.3	.49952	.49953	.49955	.49957	.49958	.49960	.49961	.49962	.49964	.49965
3.4	.49966	.49968	.49969	.49970	.49971	.49972	.49973	.49974	.49975	.49976
3.5	.49977	.49978	.49978	.49979	.49980	.49981	.49981	.49982	.49983	.49983
3.6	.49984	.49985	.49985	.49986	.49986	.49987	.49987	.49988	.49988	.49989
3.7	.49989	.49990	.49990	.49990	.49991	.49991	.49992	.49992	.49992	.49992
3.8	.49993	.49993	.49993	.49994	.49994	.49994	.49994	.49995	.49995	.49995
3.9	.49995	.49995	.49996	.49996	.49996	.49996	.49996	.49996	.49997	.49997

Source: Abridged from Table I of A. Hald. *Statistical Tables and Formulas* (New York: Wiley), 1952. Reproduced by permission of A. Hald.

Critical Values of *t*

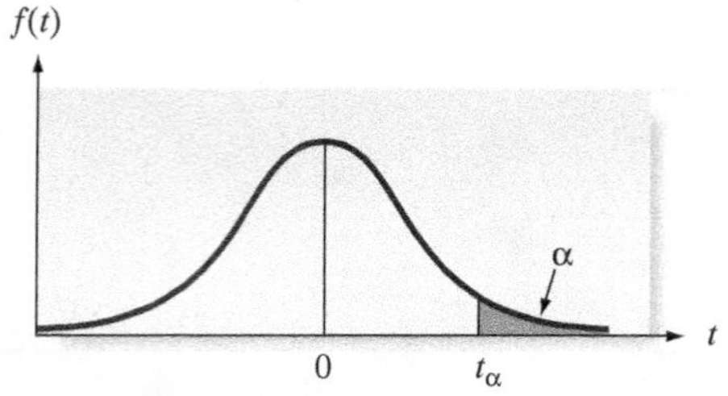

Degrees of Freedom	$t_{.100}$	$t_{.050}$	$t_{.025}$	$t_{.010}$	$t_{.005}$	$t_{.001}$	$t_{.0005}$
1	3.078	6.314	12.706	31.821	63.657	318.31	636.62
2	1.886	2.920	4.303	6.965	9.925	22.326	31.598
3	1.638	2.353	3.182	4.541	5.841	10.213	12.924
4	1.533	2.132	2.776	3.747	4.604	7.173	8.610
5	1.476	2.015	2.571	3.365	4.032	5.893	6.869
6	1.440	1.943	2.447	3.143	3.707	5.208	5.959
7	1.415	1.895	2.365	2.998	3.499	4.785	5.408
8	1.397	1.860	2.306	2.896	3.355	4.501	5.041
9	1.383	1.833	2.262	2.821	3.250	4.297	4.781
10	1.372	1.812	2.228	2.764	3.169	4.144	4.587
11	1.363	1.796	2.201	2.718	3.106	4.025	4.437
12	1.356	1.782	2.179	2.681	3.055	3.930	4.318
13	1.350	1.771	2.160	2.650	3.012	3.852	4.221
14	1.345	1.761	2.145	2.624	2.977	3.787	4.140
15	1.341	1.753	2.131	2.602	2.947	3.733	4.073
16	1.337	1.746	2.120	2.583	2.921	3.686	4.015
17	1.333	1.740	2.110	2.567	2.898	3.646	3.965
18	1.330	1.734	2.101	2.552	2.878	3.610	3.922
19	1.328	1.729	2.093	2.539	2.861	3.579	3.883
20	1.325	1.725	2.086	2.528	2.845	3.552	3.850
21	1.323	1.721	2.080	2.518	2.831	3.527	3.819
22	1.321	1.717	2.074	2.508	2.819	3.505	3.792
23	1.319	1.714	2.069	2.500	2.807	3.485	3.767
24	1.318	1.711	2.064	2.492	2.797	3.467	3.745
25	1.316	1.708	2.060	2.485	2.787	3.450	3.725
26	1.315	1.706	2.056	2.479	2.779	3.435	3.707
27	1.314	1.703	2.052	2.473	2.771	3.421	3.690
28	1.313	1.701	2.048	2.467	2.763	3.408	3.674
29	1.311	1.699	2.045	2.462	2.756	3.396	3.659
30	1.310	1.697	2.042	2.457	2.750	3.385	3.646
40	1.303	1.684	2.021	2.423	2.704	3.307	3.551
50	1.299	1.676	2.009	2.403	2.678	3.261	3.496
60	1.296	1.671	2.000	2.390	2.660	3.232	3.460
70	1.294	1.667	1.994	2.381	2.648	3.211	3.435
80	1.292	1.664	1.990	2.374	2.639	3.195	3.416
90	1.291	1.662	1.987	2.369	2.632	3.183	3.402
100	1.290	1.660	1.984	2.364	2.629	3.174	3.390
120	1.289	1.658	1.980	2.358	2.617	3.160	3.373
150	1.287	1.655	1.976	2.351	2.609	3.145	3.357
∞	1.282	1.645	1.960	2.326	2.576	3.090	3.291

Source: This table is reproduced with the kind permission of the Trustees of Biometrika from E. S. Pearson and H. O. Hartley (eds.). *The Biometrika Tables for Statisticians*,. Vol. 1, 3rd ed., Biometrika, 1966.

Selected Formulas

CHAPTER 2

Relative Frequency = (frequency)/n

$$\bar{x} = \frac{\Sigma x}{n}$$

$$s^2 = \frac{\Sigma(x - \bar{x})^2}{n - 1} = \frac{\Sigma x^2 - \frac{(\Sigma x)^2}{n}}{n - 1}$$

$$s = \sqrt{s^2}$$

$$z = \frac{x - \mu}{\sigma} = \frac{x - \bar{x}}{s}$$

Chebyshev = At least $\left(1 - \frac{1}{k^2}\right)100\%$

$\text{IQR} = Q_U - Q_L$

CHAPTER 3

$P(A^c) = 1 - P(A)$

$P(A \cup B) = P(A) + P(B) - P(A \cap B)$

$= P(A) + P(B)$ if A and B mutually exclusive

$P(A \cap B) = P(A|B) \cdot P(B) = P(B|A) \cdot P(A)$

$= P(A) \cdot P(B)$ if A and B independent

$$P(A|B) = \frac{P(A \cap B)}{P(B)}$$

$$\binom{N}{n} = \frac{N!}{n!(N - n)!}$$

Bayes's: $P(S_i|A) =$

$$\frac{P(S_i)P(A|S_i)}{P(S_1)P(A|S_1) + P(S_2)P(A|S_2) + \cdots + P(S_k)P(A|S_k)}$$

CHAPTER 6

CI for μ: $\bar{x} \pm (z_{\alpha/2})\sigma/\sqrt{n}$ (large n)

$\bar{x} \pm (t_{\alpha/2})s/\sqrt{n}$ (small n, σ unknown)

CI for p: $\hat{p} \pm z_{\alpha/2}\sqrt{\frac{\hat{p}\hat{q}}{n}}$

Estimating μ: $n = (z_{\alpha/2})^2(\sigma^2)/(\text{SE})^2$

Estimating p: $n = (z_{\alpha/2})^2(pq)/(\text{SE})^2$

CI for σ^2: $= \frac{(n - 1)s^2}{\chi^2_{\alpha/2}} < \sigma^2 < \frac{(n - 1)s^2}{\chi^2_{1-\alpha/2}}$

CHAPTER 4

Key Formulas

Random Variable	Prob. Dist'n	Mean	Variance
General Discrete:	Table, formula, or graph for $p(x)$	$\sum_{\text{all } x} x \cdot p(x)$	$\sum_{\text{all } x} (x - \mu)^2 \cdot p(x)$
Binomial:	$p(x) = \binom{n}{x} p^x q^{n-x}$ $x = 0, 1, 2, \ldots, n$	np	npq
Poisson:	$p(x) = \frac{\lambda^x e^{-\lambda}}{x!}$ $x = 0, 1, 2, \ldots$	λ	λ
Uniform:	$f(x) = 1/(d - c)$ $(c \le x \le d)$	$(c + d)/2$	$(d - c)^2/12$
Normal:	$f(x) = \frac{1}{\sigma\sqrt{2\pi}} e^{-\frac{1}{2}[(x-\mu)/\sigma]^2}$	μ	σ^2
Standard Normal:	$f(z) = \frac{1}{\sqrt{2\pi}} e^{-\frac{1}{2}(z)^2}$ $z = (x - \mu)/\sigma$	$\mu = 0$	$\sigma^2 = 1$

CHAPTER 5

Sample Mean (large n):	Approx. normal,	$\mu_{\bar{x}} = \mu$	$\sigma^2_{\bar{x}} = \sigma^2/n$

CHAPTER 7

Test for μ: $z = \dfrac{\bar{x} - \mu}{\sigma/\sqrt{n}}$ (large n)

$t = \dfrac{\bar{x} - \mu}{s/\sqrt{n}}$ (small n, σ unknown)

Test for p: $z = \dfrac{\hat{p} - p_0}{\sqrt{p_0 q_0/n}}$

Test for σ^2: $\chi^2 = (n - 1)s^2/(\sigma_0)^2$

CHAPTER 8

CI for $\mu_1 - \mu_2$:

$$(\bar{x}_1 - \bar{x}_2) \pm z_{\alpha/2}\sqrt{\frac{\sigma_1^2}{n_1} + \frac{\sigma_2^2}{n_2}} \quad \text{(large } n_1 \text{ and } n_2\text{)}$$

Test for $\mu_1 - \mu_2$:

$$z = \frac{(\bar{x}_1 - \bar{x}_2) - (\mu_1 - \mu_2)}{\sqrt{\dfrac{\sigma_1^2}{n_1} + \dfrac{\sigma_2^2}{n_2}}} \quad \text{(large } n_1 \text{ and } n_2\text{)}$$

$$s_p^2 = \frac{(n_1 - 1)s_1^2 + (n_2 - 1)s_2^2}{n_1 + n_2 - 2}$$

CI for $\mu_1 - \mu_2$:

$$(\bar{x}_1 - \bar{x}_2) \pm t_{\alpha/2}\sqrt{s_p^2\left(\frac{1}{n_1} + \frac{1}{n_2}\right)} \quad \text{(small } n_1 \text{ and/or } n_2\text{)}$$

Test for $\mu_1 - \mu_2$:

$$t = \frac{(\bar{x}_1 - \bar{x}_2) - (\mu_1 - \mu_2)}{\sqrt{s_p^2\left(\dfrac{1}{n_1} + \dfrac{1}{n_2}\right)}} \quad \text{(small } n_1 \text{ and/or } n_2\text{)}$$

CI for μ_d: $\bar{x}_d \pm t_{\alpha/2}\dfrac{s_d}{\sqrt{n}}$

Test for μ_d: $t = \dfrac{\bar{x}_d - \mu_d}{s_d/\sqrt{n}}$

CI for $p_1 - p_2$: $(\hat{p}_1 - \hat{p}_2) \pm z_{\alpha/2}\sqrt{\dfrac{\hat{p}_1\hat{q}_1}{n_1} + \dfrac{\hat{p}_2\hat{q}_2}{n_2}}$

Test for $p_1 - p_2$: $z = \dfrac{(\hat{p}_1 - \hat{p}_2) - (p_1 - p_2)}{\sqrt{\hat{p}\hat{q}\left(\dfrac{1}{n_1} + \dfrac{1}{n_2}\right)}}$

$$\hat{p} = \frac{x_1 + x_2}{n_1 + n_2}$$

Test for (σ_1^2/σ_2^2): $F = (s_1^2/s_2^2)$

Estimating $\mu_1 - \mu_2$: $n_1 = n_2 = (z_{\alpha/2})^2(\sigma_1^2 + \sigma_2^2)/(\text{ME})^2$

Estimating $p_1 - p_2$: $n_1 = n_2 = (z_{\alpha/2})^2(p_1q_1 + p_2q_2)/(\text{ME})^2$

CHAPTER 9

ANOVA Test for completely randomized design:
$F = \text{MST/MSE}$

ANOVA Test for randomized block design:
$F = \text{MST/MSE}$

ANOVA Test for factorial design interaction:
$F = \text{MS(A} \times \text{B)/MSE}$

Pairwise comparisons: $c = k(k - 1)/2$

CHAPTER 10

Multinomial test: $\chi^2 = \Sigma \dfrac{(n_i - E_i)^2}{E_i}$

$E_i = n(p_{i0})$

Contingency table test: $\chi^2 = \Sigma \dfrac{(n_{ij} - E_{ij})^2}{E_{ij}}$

$$E_{ij} = \frac{R_i C_j}{n}$$

CHAPTER 11

$$\text{SS}_{xx} = \Sigma(x - \bar{x})^2 = \Sigma x^2 - \frac{(\Sigma x)^2}{n}$$

$$\text{SS}_{yy} = \Sigma(y - \bar{y})^2 = \Sigma y^2 - \frac{(\Sigma y)^2}{n}$$

$$\text{SS}_{xy} = \Sigma(x - \bar{x})(y - \bar{y}) = \Sigma xy - \frac{(\Sigma x)(\Sigma y)}{n}$$

$$\hat{y} = \hat{\beta}_0 + \hat{\beta}_1 x$$

$$\hat{\beta}_1 = \frac{SS_{xy}}{SS_{xx}}$$

$$\hat{\beta}_1 = \bar{y} - \hat{\beta}_1\bar{x}$$

$$r = \frac{\text{SS}_{xy}}{\sqrt{\text{SS}_{xx}}\sqrt{\text{SS}_{yy}}}$$

(Continued on previous page)